2
DOG FACTS

DOG FACTS

THE PET PARENT'S A-to-Z HOME CARE ENCYCLOPEDIA

Puppy to Adult, Disease & Prevention, Dog Training

Veterinary Care, First Aid, Holistic Medicine

AMY SHOJAI

FURRY MUSE PUBLICATIONS

DOG FACTS

A Furry Muse Book
Published by Furry Muse Publications
Hard Cover Edition
978-1-944423-86-5

http://www.SHOJAI.com

PUBLISHER'S NOTE
Every effort has been made to ensure that the information contained in this book is complete and accurate. However, neither the publisher nor the author is engaged in rendering professional advice or services to the individual reader. The ideas, procedures, and suggestions contained in this book are not intended as a substitute for consulting with your pet's physician. All matters regarding your pet's health require medical supervision. Neither the author nor the publisher shall be liable or responsible for any loss or damage allegedly arising from any information or suggestion in this book. While the author has made every effort to provide accurate product names and contact information neither the publisher nor the author assumes any responsibility for errors, or for changes that occur after publications.

Hard Cover Edition:
November 2017
10 9 8 7 6 5 4 3 2 1

For all the cats and dogs
Who have touched my soul—

And for one special
Furry Muse
Who started it all.

Still missing you.

6
DOG FACTS

CONTENTS

ACKNOWLEDGEMENTS

This book would not have happened without an incredible support team of friends, family and accomplished colleagues and veterinary experts. In particular, I must thank my fellow dog lovers in the Dog Writers Association of America, who have offered me both professional support and friendship along the way.

DOG FACTS is the result of 25+ years of researching, loving, and writing about these unique creatures that share our hearts—and our pillows.

After more than 30 books (and counting), I'm even more grateful today for passionate dog parents. Without you, there would be no reason for my work. Wags and purrs to my Triple-A Team (Amy's Audacious Allies) for all your help sharing the word about all my books. Youse guyz rock!

I am grateful to all the cats and dogs I've met over the years who have shared my heart. Nineteen-year-old Seren-Kitty, nine-year-old Magical-Dawg and the newcomer Karma-Kat inspire me daily. Thanks be to ALL the dogs: those who live in our past, our present, and our future. I hope this book helps you wag from puppyhood throughout your golden years.

I never would have been a pet lover, a reader and now a writer if not for my fantastic parents who instilled in me a love of the written word, and never looked askance when I preferred animals to dolls. And of course, my deepest thanks to my husband Mahmoud, who continues to support my writing passion, even when he doesn't always understand it.

I love hearing from you! Please drop me a line at my blog http://AmyShojai.com or my website http://www.shojai.com where you can subscribe to my PET PEEVES newsletter (and maybe win some pet books!). Follow me on twitter @amyshojai and like me on Facebook: http://www.facebook.com/amyshojai.cabc

Amy Shojai

10 
DOG FACTS

The author has taken great pains to compile the most up-to-date information currently available for dog lovers on the care of their dog; however, veterinary medicine is constantly improving. Please consult with your veterinarian on a regular basis to provide the best care for your dog.

DOG FACTS

ABSCESS Abscess refers to the body's attempt to wall off infection. The fight against infection results in an accumulation of white blood cells and other blood components, commonly called pus. This liquid collects in a fleshy pocket beneath the skin, which swells and becomes very painful. The swelling is called an abscess.

Almost anything, like a bite wound, splinter, or even an insect sting, can result in an abscess if the surface of the skin is penetrated. When the skin surface heals over the wound, bacteria is sealed inside, the body's immune system is activated, and a pocket of infection may form.

ABSCESS

SYMPTOMS: Painful skin swelling or draining sore; fever; lethargy; loss of appetite
FIRST AID: Moist warm compresses applied to sore; cleaning sore with damp cloths; supportive nutrition
VET CARE: Surgical lancing and draining; usually antibiotics
PREVENTION: Neuter/spay dogs; prevent roaming with fenced yards; provide regular anal gland and dental care

Signs of abscess include a soft swelling and/or draining of purulent material at the site, pain, fever above 102.5 degrees, lethargy, loss of appetite and reluctance to move the affected area. Bite wounds that plant infectious organisms deep into the tissue are prime causes of abscesses; they commonly are found in the head and neck region but may appear anywhere on the body. Abscesses can also result from chewing an inappropriate object which splinters.

Dogs also can suffer from abscessed teeth (see PERIODONTAL DISEASE). Head and neck abscesses typically cause one side of the neck to swell, and your dog may drool and refuse food. Dogs also commonly suffer from anal gland abscesses, in which the area surrounding the rectum becomes red, swollen and tender (see ANAL GLAND).

The diagnosis of an abscess is generally made from the signs. If your dog has a heavy coat, the injury may be hidden from view and the problem not noticed until the dog is in pain and flinches from your touch, or the abscess begins to drain. As the injury swells with pus, the skin stretches and becomes thin until it ultimately ruptures. The smelly fluid is white-to-greenish with tinges of blood, and may soak the surrounding fur.

Abscesses should be treated as soon as they're noticed to prevent further damage to the surrounding area. The infection can spread until nearby tissue dies, muscle or nerves are damaged, and/or the resulting massive wound is difficult to heal.

First aid can help speed the healing, but not all dogs will allow you to treat them at home because abscesses can be very tender. You can help draw out the infection when the abscess is soft and swollen but hasn't yet begun to drain. Apply wet hot compresses (hot as you can stand), and apply to the area for two to five times daily for five minutes on and five minutes off until it cools. Once the sore opens and begins to drain, keep the area clean by rinsing with lukewarm water. You may need to soak this first with a wet compress if the discharge has dried in the fur.

In most cases, the abscess is so painful your dog must be anesthetized before the veterinarian can treat him. The fur around the swelling is clipped, and the area disinfected with a surgical scrub solution like betadine. Then the wound is lanced, the infection drained, and the abscess is flushed with a solution like peroxide and water. Antibiotics are often prescribed as well.

When the abscess is very deep or intrusive, a drain or "wick" may be surgically stitched into place to keep the area draining as the surface skin heals, and prevent the abscess from recurring. When the surgical site is within reach of the dog's teeth, a collar restraint prevents the dog from bothering the healing wound (see ELIZABETHAN COLLAR).

If an abscess ruptures on its own, and if your dog will allow you, use a 50/50 solution of hydrogen peroxide and water to clean the area. When the wound is shallow, simply keep the area clean over the course of a week by flushing the area with this solution once or twice a day until it heals. Usually, though, it's best to have your veterinarian evaluate the sore.

Prevent abscesses by reducing your dog's chances of injury. Neutering or spaying your dog will diminish aggression and subsequent bite wounds. Supervise chew objects, and make sure only safe alternatives are offered. Good dental hygiene and routine care of anal glands help reduce the chance of abscesses in these areas.

ACANTHOSIS NIGRICANS This unusual disease in its primary form most commonly affects Dachshunds, and literally means "thickened black skin." Typically, Dachshunds develop the disease prior to age two. However, it is commonly seen as a secondary disorder in any age or breed dog (see ATOPY, CHRONIC DERMATITIS, HYPOTHYROIDISM, and CUSHING'S DISEASE) and can be managed by removing the underlying cause and providing topical therapy.

Primary disease is recognized as the skin of the dog's armpits and groin darken to black, and a greasy rancid discharge forms which is often accompanied by a bacterial skin infection. The disease slowly spreads to affect more and more of the body until it may encompass the legs, chest, abdomen, and lower back.

The cause of the primary form is unknown, and there is no specific treatment. Diagnosis is based on clinical signs, and sometimes a skin biopsy in which a sample is removed and examined microscopically.

ACANTHOSIS NIGRICANS

SYMPTOMS: Thickened, blackened skin and greasy rancid skin discharge beginning at groin and armpits, spreading over body
HOME CARE: Seborrhea shampoos
VET CARE: Same as home care, also antibiotics for skin infection; sometimes cortisone to soothe irritation
PREVENTION: None

Current management aims at keeping the dog as comfortable as possible by using canine seborrhea shampoos that remove bacteria and excess oil. Oral antibiotics are helpful when infection is present, and sometimes cortisone preparations may soothe skin irritation. Oral corticosteroids and vitamin E may be effective. Ask your veterinarian for a recommendation.

There is no way to predict or prevent the condition. However, it is recommended that dogs suffering from the disease not be bred, to prevent them passing the condition on to puppies in the event that it is inheritable.

ACNE

Canine acne results from the plugging of hair follicles, and is common in adolescent dogs, particularly short-coated breeds like Doberman Pinschers, Great Danes and Boxers.

The cause of canine acne is thought to be similar to the condition that arises in human adolescents. The sensitivity of the sebaceous glands and hair follicles is increased by sexual hormones that are present at puberty, between the ages of five to twelve months. An increased production of sebum, the oily material that helps lubricate the skin and hair coat, may promote inflammation of these areas and resulting skin problems.

The diagnosis is based on clinical signs. Acne primarily affects the skin of the dog's chin, and sometimes lips and muzzle. Signs primarily are unsightly blackheads, pimples, and crusty sores. There is rarely any itchiness involved. Most dogs, like most humans, outgrow the problem. The condition is primarily a cosmetic concern.

Canine acne rarely requires treatment, and usually resolves on its own. A few cases may continue into adulthood, though. Just keeping the affected area clean by applying a warm wet compress and sponging with water once or twice a day will help the area heal.

Holistic veterinarians recommend applying a tincture (or tea) of the herb calendula on a cotton ball, used as a compress for five minutes each day to help speed healing. Crab apple flower essence often is recommended to stop infection when given in a dose of four drops, about four times a day (see FLOWER ESSENCE).

When crusty sores persist, medicated ointments and shampoos or antibiotics available from your veterinarian may help. Use peroxide diluted half and half in water, or an antibacterial soap like pHisoHex twice a day to cleanse the area, then apply an antibacterial ointment recommended by your veterinarian. Products containing benzoyl peroxide have a flushing action that help keep the follicles clean, and are quite effective. Check with your veterinarian for a safe recommendation.

ACNE

SYMPTOMS: Blackheads and pimples on chin; red or swollen skin; itchiness or pain
HOME CARE: Apply damp heat to chin; cleanse twice daily with plain water or cleansers like benzoyl peroxide-type solutions
HOLISTIC HELP: Crab Apple flower essence; calendula tincture; tea
VET CARE: Clipping fur; cleansing; antibiotics
PREVENTION: Most dogs outgrow the condition; feed from stainless steel rather than plastic food bowls

ACUPUNCTURE

ACUPUNCTURE Acupuncture inserts needles into the skin, and is a bioenergetic therapy based on the traditional Chinese medicine (TCM) system of life energy. Acupuncture is considered a holistic therapy but has become a mainstay of many traditional veterinary practices. Therapies similar to acupuncture may have arisen 7000 years ago in India, and have been used for at least 3000 years in China.

Life energy, or Qi, is said to flow along invisible pathways that communicate with specific organs or tissues throughout the body. TCM views all illness as an imbalance of the flow of Qi. Acupuncture seeks to cure disease by correcting the imbalance of Qi by pressure-stimulation of acupoints that fall along the pathways, or meridians, using needles.

To many people, talk of meridians sounds like magic, and science is still trying to explain how the acupoints and meridians really work. A Spanish study in humans that injected radioactive tracers at acupoints found that they traveled along similar pathways to the traditional meridians. The paths may be invisible, but they are there. Acupoints also appear to have lower electrical resistance than other areas of the body. Some studies indicate the meridians' energy flow may be a system of information transmission through neurochemicals. That's similar to the mechanism that carries thought processes from the brain throughout the body. Other theories propose a bioelectrical system independent of the nerves, which may be similar in concept to a computer software program that provides an internal operating system that's never seen.

Acupressure points for Older Dogs

LI4 Pain point for the front, fore arm, shoulder neck and mouth, Benefits pain in all parts, of the body, balances gastrointestinal system and strengthens the immune system. **Located in the due claw.**

LU9- Strengthens arteries and assist with deficient energy. Alleviates pain in the chest, cough and asthma. Reduces shoulder, elbow pain and arthritis in the metacarpals. **Found in the crease on the inside foreleg at the wrist.**

BL11- Strengthens bones and benefits joints. Helps to regulate the lungs and chest. Is used to relieve arthritis and various joint problems and deformity, neck, and spin pain, stiffness. **Found on spin between shoulder blades**

BL23- the Kidney is a vital origin for older dogs, it is important to keep the kidney functioning and tonifed. Benefits arthritis Lower back pain, paralysis of the pelvic limb and local swelling of the hock**, Found just lateral to the spine parallel to the last rib.**
St 36-, tonifies, and strengthens spleen, lung, kidney and stomach. Drains pathogenic influences, Benefits allergies and generalized weakness, fatigued extremities, builds immune system, indigestion, diarrhea and constipation, consumptive disorder, hypertension, seizures, and shock. (Do not use if pregnant but can benefit difficult labor) **located in the lateral portion of the cranial tibia muscle. Regulates**

KI3- Tonifies Kidneys and benefits lower back, and stifle. Helps to expel stones, and is good for brain/ mind function. Found **in the pocket on the inside leg just below the hock**

Bl60 Aspirin point, reduce pain thought the body. Opposite of KI3

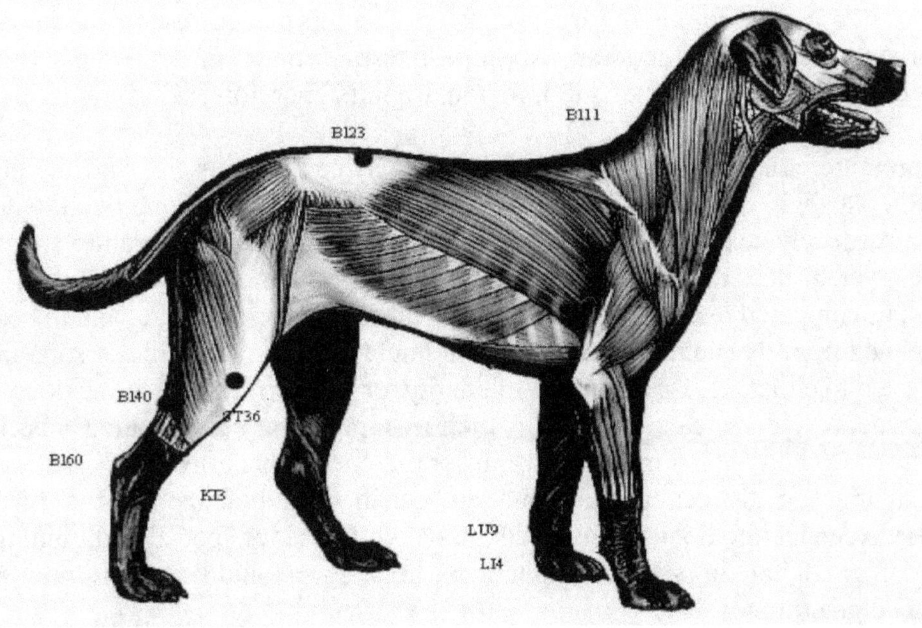

DOG FACTS

Although the mechanism remains a mystery, even conventional medicine recognizes that stimulation of acupoints works. The National Institute of Health (NIH) has funded many studies in humans that point to relief of pain, nausea, addiction, and asthma, and the World Health Organization lists a variety of human health conditions that may benefit from these therapies. And in 1996, the American Veterinary Medical Association endorsed acupuncture, calling it an "integral part of veterinary medicine."

Fewer studies have been performed in animals, but the benefits appear to be similar. The stimulation of these points will actually release neurochemicals or endorphins in the brain that cause pain relief. Conditions in pets such as arthritis, reproductive disorders, back and musculoskeletal problems, skin conditions like allergies, pain relief, and neurological disorders such as epilepsy have been shown to benefit from this therapy.

Veterinarians follow a kind of body map developed by the Chinese thousands of years ago that locates the meridians and the point positions. Acupuncture points in the horse date back to around the same time as those for people because the horse was considered valuable property, and was so important to keep healthy. Many of the points in humans or horse also work in other animals, though, and over the years veterinarians have mapped dog and cat acupoints by transposing human and horse points to the dog and cat.

There are 14 meridians and 361 traditional acupoints; many of the points are duplicated in mirror images on either side of the body. Additional points may not be located directly on a meridian. The meridians and points have traditional Chinese names, but in the United States and Europe most commonly are designated by letters that correspond to the meridian's ruling organ (i.e., L=lung meridian, LI=large intestine meridian, ST=stomach meridian) along with a location number of the individual point. Therefore, ST25 refers to the 25th point on the stomach meridian.

Acupressure points are found in depressions between the muscles and the bones, and will feel like a slight dip in the tissue. They are almost never on a bone like the elbow, but will be immediately next to it. Some specialists say they can feel temperature changes at the acupoints which alert them to problems. A warm point indicates an area of an acute blockage, as compared to a cold point where it's more of a chronic state, and the energy has been depleted from that area. The acupoint is stimulated with the needle or sometimes gold balls inserted to either release an excess of energy, or to return energy to the point.

Pet owners of course cannot "needle" their own pets. But acupressure (pressing firmly in recommended body positions) may also offer therapeutic benefits.

Veterinarians study acupuncture and are certified to practice by the International Veterinary Acupuncture Society. Some also travel to China for specialized training. If your veterinarian is not able to provide acupuncture, he or she should be able to refer you to an experienced practitioner.

ADDISON'S DISEASE This is technically referred to as hypoadrenocorticism. Addison's Disease is a malfunction of part of the endocrine system. The condition is named for the 19th-century English doctor who first described it in humans.

Endocrine glands include the pituitary gland, thyroid, pancreas, and adrenal glands as well as others located throughout the body. Each gland secretes specific hormones directly into the bloodstream which help regulate various body functions.

Addison's Disease results when the adrenal glands, located adjacent to the kidneys, fail to produce enough of the hormones cortisone and aldosterone. These hormones help regulate the blood concentrations of the electrolytes sodium, chloride, calcium and potassium, and without regulation, the dog becomes very sick.

The cause of the disease is not known, but it is suspected that most cases result from a malfunction of the immune system. There is no one breed more prone than another, but most cases of Addison's Disease affect young to middle aged female dogs four to five years old or younger.

ADDISON'S DISEASE

SYMPTOMS: Loss of appetite; weakness; vomiting; slow heart rate; diarrhea leading to dehydration; sometimes increased thirst and urination; eventually shock, coma and death
HOME CARE: None
VET CARE: Address shock with fluid therapy; replace hormones
PREVENTION: None; once diagnosed, monthly injections or daily oral hormone replacement; reduce dog's stress levels; daily prednisone helpful during stressful times

Initially, signs of illness are subtle, and may only become apparent when the dog suffers some stressful event, such as boarding. Intermittent loss of appetite, weakness and vomiting, and increased thirst and urination are early symptoms.

As the adrenal glands become more and more damaged, the dog suffers severe illness even without a stressful event. Vomiting worsens and diarrhea and dehydration develop with dogs typically suffering a severe weight loss. In some cases, the dog's skin may become dark. Without prompt treatment, the dog will go into shock, then coma, and ultimately will die.

The diagnosis is made by testing the blood for telltale signs of electrolyte abnormalities and hormone imbalance. Dogs in crises require fluid therapy and replacement of the hormones.

Because the cause isn't known, there is no way to predict which dogs may be affected or prevent the disease from developing. A properly treated dog can lead a happy, relatively normal life, but maintenance therapy is required for the remainder of the dog's life. Monthly injections or daily oral medications supply your dog with the necessary hormones.

ADMINISTER MEDICATION All dog owners will eventually need to medicate their dog. The task may be simple or problematic, depending on the size and temperament of your individual pet.

But almost all treatments, from topically applied ointments and salves to oral medications like pills or liquids, and even injections can be given at home, once you learn how. And in many instances, treating your dog at home may be easier on him--and you--than the stress of a ride to the veterinarian's office.

Whether your dog is big, small or in between, it's beneficial to enlist an extra pair of hands for medicating. That way, one person can restrain and comfort the dog while the other performs the treatment.

Wrapping a small to medium-size dog in a blanket or towel may help restrict his movements enough for you to treat without a second person's help. For those confident owners who have established a trusting relationship with their dogs, restraints may not be necessary.

TOPICAL TREATMENTS: Dogs usually accept skin medications without restraints, unless the area is very sore. When the area being treated is within licking range, though, care must be taken that the dog does not clean off the medication. Some medicines may taste bad and keep your dog from licking, but don't count on that deterring a determined canine. After applying the lotion or cream, engage your dog in a favorite game or keep him quiet for 15 minutes or so until the medication is dry or absorbed. Other times, it may be necessary to apply a restraint to keep your dog from bothering the wound (see ELIZABETHAN COLLAR).

Ear medicating also usually requires minimal restraint, unless the ears are very tender. Have your dog lie down on his side so the opening of the affected ear is directed at the ceiling. Then grasp the external ear flap with one hand, and drip in the medication. Avoid sticking anything inside the sore ears; gravity will ensure the treatment gets deep inside the ear. You may gently massage the outside of the ear base to help evenly spread the medication (see EAR MITES). Ask your dog to turn over, and repeat the procedure on the other ear.

When medicating eyes, take care you do not touch the dog's eye with the applicator. A second pair of hands may be necessary to steady your dog's head so that his movement doesn't inadvertently injure him. Liquids can be easily dripped into the affected eye by first placing one hand beneath the dog's chin and tipping his face toward the ceiling. Ointments are squeezed into the cupped tissue of the lower eyelid, or into the corner of the dog's eye. Once applied, gently close the eyelid to spread the medicine over the surface of the eye.

ORAL TREATMENTS: Swallowed, or oral medications, may be liquid, paste, or pill forms. Liquids and pastes come in squeeze bottles, or are applied with eye droppers or syringes that make medicating the dog quite simple. Generally, they are flavored as well, so that your dog willingly accepts them. Tip back your dog's head, insert the applicator in the corner of his mouth, and squirt the medication into his cheek. Hold his mouth closed, keeping his head tipped up, and stroke his throat until you see he swallows.

Pilling a dog involves opening his mouth, placing the capsule or tablet on the back of the tongue, closing his mouth and inducing him to swallow. Generally, dogs are easy to pill, particularly large dogs that have handle-shaped muzzles. If you have the least doubt about your ability to pill your dog, enlist an extra pair of hands to open his mouth while you insert the pill. Try the blanket wrap on small dogs, or kneel on the floor with the dog between your legs facing out, so he can't squirm away.

Most dogs have incredible jaw strength that makes it difficult to lever the mouth open against their will. Rather, your job is to induce the dog to open wide on his own. Place the palm of one hand over the dog's muzzle so that the thumb on one side and middle finger on the other fit be-hind the upper canine (long) tooth on each side. Tilt the dog's head back so he's looking at the ceiling. Gently press the dog's lips against his teeth to encourage him to open his mouth. Or, simply slip one finger inside your dog's mouth, and press on the roof of his mouth and he'll open wide. Then use your other hand to push the pill to the back of his tongue, quickly close his mouth, and stroke his throat until he swallows.

A pill syringe available at most pet supply stores works well for some owners who don't want to risk putting their fingers in the dog's mouth. Your veterinarian can demonstrate its safe use so you won't hurt the back of your dog's throat.

Hiding medication in treats works very well with dogs, who tend to gulp food whole. Check with your veterinarian first, though, because some drugs should not be mixed with certain foods. Use a hunk of cheese, a dab of peanut butter, or anything you're sure the dog will eat in one swallow. Mixing medicine in the whole bowl of food isn't recommended, because the dog may not be properly medicated if he doesn't eat it all at once.

Unless the medication is a time-release treatment that's supposed to dissolve slowly, the pill can be crushed and mixed into a strong-tasting treat. Use the bowl of a spoon to powder the pill and combine with a mouthful of canned food. If you're hiding medication in treats, be sure to offer them before meals to ensure every bit is eaten.

Following any treatment, reward your dog with positive attention. Give him lots of praise and play his favorite game so that he associates the activity with good things for him. That should help make the next session run even more smoothly.

ADOPTION, OF DOG BY HUMAN Adoption refers to the act of actively accepting another being into your life. By adopting your dog, you acknowledge responsibility for the life, health, and welfare of that dog.

Finding a dog to adopt is easy. Newspaper advertisements are glutted with give-away animals, and worthy candidates abound at animal welfare organizations. Often, a friend or acquaintance has available an adoptable dog, or you may be taken by the adorable stray that appears in your yard. Many people prefer a specific canine size, type, or personality to better fit their lifestyle, and more than four hundred distinct canine breeds are available. Professional breeding kennels produce puppies according to standards defined by various dog associations (see APPENDIX A, DOG BREEDS/ASSOCIATIONS); however, purebred registered animals, particularly those that are relatively uncommon, are typically more costly because of the expense involved in producing healthy animals of a particular type.

A number of difficulties can be avoided by adopting a healthy dog. The dejected stray down the block, though, may steal your heart. Although adopting a needy waif can be rewarding, such animals often require expensive veterinary care to get them healthy. You also run the risk of exposing your other pets to illness (see QUARANTINE).

The healthy dog's fur is clean and shiny, without bald patches or red, scaly skin. Eyes, nose, and ears are free of discharge, and the dog's bottom is clean without sign of diarrhea. A veterinary exam is always advisable to rule out hidden problems. Reputable shelters or kennels may provide preliminary health care prior to adoption, such as basic first vaccinations or discount spaying or neutering. Some offer limited guarantees on the health of the animal.

Adoption should not be a whim; it is not a temporary arrangement, but is for the lifetime of the dog. We do not give back the human children we adopt when the "cute" stage passes or when they become inconvenient to have around; neither should a dog be a disposable commodity. At its best, adoption is a joyful yet serious act undertaken only after careful consideration.

ADOPTION, OF PUPPIES (OR OTHERS) BY DOG Some dogs exhibit nurturing behavior toward other animals and seem to "adopt" puppies or others that are not their own. The behavior most often occurs when a female dog is still nursing, and is hormonally ready to nurse and care for another animal's offspring. In kennel situations, if a litter for some reason is not accepted by the mother, the breeder may induce a "foster mom-dog" to take on the challenge by making the strange puppies smell like the foster-mom's babies. Other times, dogs take on the responsibility without persuasion. Dogs have been known to nurse and raise kittens, puppies, and even rabbits or other species.

Dogs that have given birth often retain mothering urges even after being spayed, and some dogs that have never given birth—even male dogs—enjoy interaction with youngsters so much they take fostering responsibility very seriously.

In most instances, dogs that adopt other puppies or animals have enjoyed positive interspecies experiences during their impressionable weeks of life (see PUPPY/SOCIALIZATION).

AFFECTION Dogs have well-known reputations as loyal, loving companions—the quintessential "man's best friend," and deservedly so. Dogs are naturally social creatures that thrive on interaction.

Dogs communicate their moods, emotions, and desires in a variety of ways, from obvious to subtle. Although affection should be reciprocal, our dogs are unique in that many offer us blind adoration, whether we deserve it or not. It is the rare dog who is indifferent to people, although mistreatment and/or poor breeding can warp the canine personality into a dysfunctional animal. Dogs are also individuals, with a wide range of personalities.

Dogs show their affection toward other dogs—and even cats or other pets—by sleeping together and licking or nuzzling each other. Simply sharing space can be a subtle sign of affection between dogs. Affectionate dogs may share toys or food, and enjoy playing together.

Dogs often show affection to humans in the same ways. They beg for attention by crawling into your lap, sleeping next to you, and licking your face and hands. Dogs exuberantly invite owners to play, and want you to share your food. They want contact with you, and may sleep across your feet or lean against your leg. Some dogs actually learn to "grin" to show their happiness.

Often, animal experts are reluctant to say any creature experiences the same emotions as people. Obviously, we can't know for certain what our dogs are feeling. But from every indication, dogs are every bit as devoted to us as we are to them.

AGGRESSION

Aggression is the forceful reaction of a dog that feels threatened. Aggression can be normal behavior under certain circumstances. Dogs are naturally protective, and will often defend their territory (including owners) from any perceived threat. But when aggression becomes unreasonable or uncontrollable, the aggressive dog is a danger to everyone, including himself.

Contrary to popular belief, dog aggression is not the same as viciousness. By definition, viciousness results from a desire to inflict pain on another, and that's a human trait pets don't have. Aggression is simply a component of dog behavior, and is normal within the appropriate context. Aggression is resolved once the animal (1) launches an attack, (2) turns tail and runs, or (3) displays a subordinate position—cries "uncle."

Dogs that are in pain or ill often become short-tempered and exhibit aggressive behavior when the owner unknowingly touches a sore place. If your usually easy-going dog suddenly growls, snaps or bites for no apparent reason, have him examined by a veterinarian.

It doesn't matter if your dog is the retiring, shy type, or a confident macho canine, any dog may become aggressive given the right circumstances. Growls, snarls, barks, and bites are your dog's way to control the situation.

Heredity plays a large role in how aggressive your dog may be. Certain breeds tolerate close contact with other dogs or strange people better than others. Much of this inbred aggression is our own fault, since for hundreds of years individual breeds have been developed to promote these traits. Also, owners may consciously—or unconsciously—

encourage aggressive behavior during puppyhood because they want a "guard dog." But what may be cute and manageable in a ten pound puppy becomes dangerous when the adult weighs 60 pounds or more.

Aggression can be categorized by the cause, or trigger, that prompts the behavior. Poor behavior can result from fear or anxiety, overly-enthusiastic play, misplaced predatory behavior, excessive dominance, or a combination of these or others. Physical punishment won't work, and will likely make the aggressive behavior even worse. Once aggression is a problem, the trigger must be identified so that a treatment specific to that cause can be initiated.

The first step in categorizing aggression is to examine the context and body language involved. Once the type of aggression has been classified, a treatment program can be designed for the individual animal.

Dominance Aggression Ninety percent of these pets are male dogs that develop the behavior by age 18 to 36 months, which corresponds with canine social maturity. Testosterone makes dogs react more intensely, and more quickly, for a longer period of time. When the dominant aggressive dog is female, the behavior tends to develop during puppyhood. The hallmark of dominance aggression is that it gets worse with punishment. It may be hereditary. Dominance aggressive behavior includes guarding food and possessions (toys or other objects), and redirected aggression.

Redirected Aggression This behavior happens in response to a verbal or physical correction or thwarting of a desire, where the victim was not part of the trigger. For instance, the dog can't reach to bite the mailman, so he bites the owner instead.

Fear Aggression Dogs tends to bark, growl or snarl while backing up, shake or tremble during or after the display, bite from behind and then run, or cower and look for escape. Heredity plays a large role in shyness and aggression, particularly in certain breeds of dogs. Shyness is an important component of aggression because many animals bite out of fear. Using commercial products that mimic the "no-fear" pheromones that mother dogs produce during nursing may be of help. Many cases of canine aggression are neurochemically related to anxiety, and may benefit from antianxiety drugs. Generally, these drugs are used for only a short time, along with behavior modification techniques, and are not intended for indefinite use.

Interdog Aggression This is related to social standing and usually affects male-male or female-female interactions. Dogs challenge each other with stares, shoulder or hip bumps and shoves, mounting behavior, or blocking access to food, play, or attention. Older or weaker pets often are victimized. Neutering decreases interdog aggression in about two-thirds of the cases.

Territorial Aggression Dogs protect property (house, car) by barking, growling, snarling, and biting no matter who is present. Aggression is made worse by boundary confinement (fence, chain, etc.). The aggression goes away when there's no territory to defend, but these dogs typically identify new territory quickly. Treatment includes modifying the environment, behavior modification, and sometimes drugs.

Predatory Aggression in dogs is extremely dangerous. These dogs silently stalk smaller animals or infants and/or stare at them silently and drool. They may track and stalk bicyclists or skateboarders. High-pitched sounds, uncoordinated movements as an infant might make, or sudden silences (as happens with prey animals) may provoke an attack.

Many of the terrier breeds have a highly developed predatory instinct similar to cats. They enjoy games of chase and pounce, and this can be dangerous for smaller pets in the household. Households with terriers should avoid keeping other pets like rabbits, ferrets, smaller cats or dogs that tend to be prime targets for such breeds.

Play Aggression looks similar to predatory aggression but begins as a game. This is more typical of youngsters who have not yet learned to inhibit their bite and may attack your ankles as you walk by. Remember, it may be endearing when your dog is a five-pound puppy, but grappling your hands and feet is painful when the dog reaches adulthood. Don't allow your hands or feet to be targets--ever. Playing rough games of wrestling with your puppy encourages him to be aggressive as an adult.

Protective Aggression is unique to dogs. These animals protect owners from other people or dogs. Quick moves or embraces may stimulate the aggression. Protective aggressive dogs are not aggressive in the absence of their owners.

Idiopathic Aggression is also exclusive to dogs. This is an atypical, toggle- switch aggression with no known trigger. Most affected dogs are one to three years old, and the behavior often is misdiagnosed as dominant aggression.

In many cases, aggression can be greatly reduced by neutering be-fore the dog reaches sexual maturity. In addition, proper socialization during puppyhood prepares your pet for dealing with life without resorting to aggression (see PUPPY/SOCIALIZATION).

Holistic veterinarians may recommend specialized massage techniques such as TTouch to help counter some types of aggression. Aromatherapy, using bergamot essential oil, is said to help very wild or fractious pets. You can try placing a couple of drops of the oil on a bandana for the dog to wear around his neck.

Another type of aggression, commonly referred to as "rage syndrome," is a rare pathological disorder. An abnormality of the brain causes seizure-like episodes of inexplicable rage in which the dog may attack anything--living or not--within sight with little or no provocation. The rage disappears as suddenly as it appears. Certain breeds are associated with this condition, in particular Springer Spaniels. Bull Terriers and Cocker Spaniels also are implicated. The dog's history along with a neurological examination is required to diagnose the problem. Behavior modification techniques that work with other aggression problems are ineffective in rage syndrome, but some types of seizure medications like Phenobarbital help some dogs. Cures are impossible, and sadly, in cases where the dog presents a danger, euthanasia is the only option.

For your safety and that of others, familiarize yourself to the signs of aggression (see COMMUNICATION) so that you can avoid provoking an aggressive dog to attack. Above all, do not hesitate to seek professional help. In many cases, an aggressive dog is an accident waiting to happen; if your dog's actions makes you fear for your own safety or others, his aggression is best diagnosed and treated by a professional animal behaviorist or therapist. Some dogs benefit from psychoactive drug therapy (see APPENDIX B, VETERINARY RESOURCES).

ALLERGY Allergy is an over-reaction of the dog's immune system. Antibodies are specialized cells of the immune system that protect the body from foreign invaders, such as viruses and bacteria. Specific white blood cells such as eosinophils also play a role in the development of allergies. But sometimes these protective cells mis-recognize harmless substances like dust, mold or pollen as dangerous, and attack. The heightened response to these substances, called allergens, results in the allergy symptoms your dog suffers.

Dogs theoretically can develop allergies to anything, just like their human owners. To develop an allergy, the dog must have been exposed to it in the past; this primes, or sensitizes, the body's immune system to overreact. In other words, a dog that has never been exposed to fleas will not suffer a reaction on first contact, but may develop an allergic response with subsequent exposure. A tendency to develop some allergies is inherited, and so are more common in certain breeds.

Although people typically suffer from "hay fever" that makes them sneeze, eyes itch and nose run, allergic dogs usually develop itchy skin diseases. Effective treatment requires eliminating the allergen that causes the reaction (see ANAPHYLAXIS).

FLEA ALLERGY

SYMPTOMS: Seasonal itchiness, especially of rear back and tail area; hair loss; scabby skin; visible fleas, or pepperlike debris on skin
HOME CARE: Treat dog and home or outside environment for fleas
VET CARE: Sometimes steroids to reduce inflammation or itchiness; veterinary-prescribed treatments
PREVENTION: Avoid fleas

DOG FACTS

Flea allergy is the most common allergy affecting dogs, with some surveys estimating 40 percent of the dog population affected. Allergic dogs develop skin disease when they react to a protein in flea saliva, and it may only take one bite to provoke all-over itching.

Signs are seasonal, which typically are the warm summer months of flea sea-son but can be year around in some parts of the country. The most common sign is extreme itchiness on the rear half of the dog, particularly the area on the back immediately above the tail.

Flea control is essential for dogs suffering from flea allergic dermatitis. There are many products available to safely eliminate fleas on your dog and his environment.

ATOPY

SYMPTOMS: Front-half itching; face rubbing; foot licking; armpit scratching; neck and chest itchiness
HOME CARE: Keep dog's coat and environment clean
HOLISTIC HELP: Calendula ointment; Echinacea; vitamin C and E supplements; EFA supplements; flower essence remedies; bathe with oatmeal products
VET CARE: Skin testing; allergy shots; sometimes dietary supplements of EFAs
PREVENTION: Avoid dust, pollens, or whatever causes the problem

Ten to fifteen percent of the dog population is allergic to something they breathe from the environment, making inhalant allergy, or atopy, the second most common allergy in dogs. Atopy can develop in any dog, but does have a genetic component. Breeds most commonly affected include the small terriers, especially the West Highland White Terrier, as well as Boxers, Dalmatians, Golden Retrievers, English and Irish Setters, Lhasa Apsos, Miniature Schnauzers, and Shar-Peis. Most signs first develop when the dog is between one to three years old.

Some surveys indicate that nearly half of all flea-allergic dogs also suffer from atopy. This allergy is the equivalent to human "hay fever" with dogs reacting to the same things owners do. Pollen, mold, fungi and even the house dust mite make people cough, wheeze and have difficulty breathing, but atopic dogs more typically suffer itchiness on the front half of their body. This includes recurrent ear infection (see OTITIS), face rubbing, foot licking, armpit scratching, and neck and chest scratching. Atopy, like flea allergy, may also be seasonal.

To get rid of the allergen, you must first know what's causing the problem, and that can be hard to determine. Although blood tests are available, they aren't considered reliable by most veterinarians and re-searchers. Instead, intradermal skin testing helps diagnose atopy. Suspect allergens are injected into the shaved skin of the sedated dog. In five to 15 minutes, positive reactions become swollen, red and elevated, while negative reactions fade away.

Dogs may react to a single or multiple allergens, but even when you know your dog reacts to house dust, it's nearly impossible to eliminate exposure.

Totally eliminating exposure to environmental allergens is impossible with dogs that typically are indoor/outdoor pets. After all, an owner can't vacuum the yard, or filter the air. But reducing indoor exposure can be helpful, and cleanliness is key. Reservoirs that attract and capture allergenic substances should be reduced or eliminated; trade rough surfaces like carpeting and upholstery for linoleum or wooden floors and smooth fabrics that are easier to keep clean. Water filters on a vacuum help scrub particles from the air; avoid brooming, which tends to float allergens rather than capture them. High Efficiency Particulate Air (HEPA) filter systems can be helpful, too.

Other treatments may help relieve your dog's symptoms, even if eliminating exposure is impossible. Dogs are furry dust mops and carry allergens with them, so bathing or just rinsing off the coat helps enormously. Use plain water, or an oatmeal-type shampoo product, which is has natural anti-itch properties. The webbing of the dog's toes in the footpads can absorb allergens like grass pollen, so rinsing off the dog's feet after outdoor excursions may relieve some symptoms.

Veterinary prescribed antihistamines relieve the symptoms in some dogs, and cortisone-containing drugs can help reduce itching. Some dogs benefit from dietary supplements of the essential fatty acids that help promote healthy skin and fur. The proper combination of these compounds appears to reduce the inflammatory skin response that results from atopy.

Holistic veterinarians recommend using calendula ointment two or three times a day to sooth the itchy areas. The herb Echinacea can help the immune system work more efficiently, particularly when given before allergies start in early spring. Vitamins C and E have both been shown to have anti-inflammatory effects. Holistic vets suggest dogs under 15 pounds can take 250 milligrams of vitamin C a day during allergy season, while heavier dogs do better on 500 to 1000 milligrams a day. Giving too much will cause diarrhea, so err on the side of caution. For vitamin E, you can give 50 international units (IU) once daily during allergy season to pets under 10 pounds, and give 200 IU to dogs weighing from 10 to 40 pounds, and 400 IU for dogs over 40 pounds. It's best to give with food, to prevent upset tummies.

Hypo-sensitization, or immunotherapy, may also help certain dogs. The treatment is a gradual process in which the dog's resistance to allergens is enhanced by exposing him to gradually increasing amounts of the substances. After skin tests determine the culprits, the dog is "vaccinated" with minute amounts of the allergens in the hopes that resistance to them will build and reduce the dog's sensitivity and resulting symptoms. Because improvement from immunotherapy is slow, injections are usually continued for at least a year. Maintenance injections may be required for life.

FOOD ALLERGY

SYMPTOMS: Intense all-over itching all year long; rarely, vomiting or diarrhea
HOME CARE: Feed appropriate diet
VET CARE: Elimination diet to diagnose; sometimes a therapeutic vet-prescribed diet
PREVENTION: Avoid problem foods once identified

Depending on who you consult, canine food allergies are considered both common and rare. Some surveys estimate up to ten percent of all dogs are affected by food sensitivity of one kind or another. These animals react to one or more ingredients in their diet. Protein like beef, milk, corn, wheat, or eggs in commercial pet foods are typical culprits. However, diagnosis is difficult and may be complicated by other allergies.

If the pancreas doesn't work right, the dog can't digest protein completely. In this case, exposure to large quantities of undigested protein can cause an allergy. Some dog breeds are more prone to pancreatic insufficiency, and as a result are more likely to develop food sensitivities. Finally, food allergies may develop if the immune system over-responds. Some dogs seem to inherit a suppresser-function that malfunctions. Size of the protein particles doesn’t matter, and the bowel can be perfectly healthy, but the immune system over-reacts and mounts an inappropriate response to protein.

The typical food-allergic dog is two years old or older, and suffers intense all-over itchiness that occurs year round. Canine food allergy less often results in vomiting or diarrhea. There may be an increased risk in West Highland White Terriers, Miniature Schnauzers, Golden Retrievers, and Shar-Peis. However, any dog can develop the condition at any age, even as early as six months old.

As in other allergies, avoiding the allergen--the food ingredient(s)--relieves the symptoms. A 10-to-12-week-long veterinarian supervised elimination diet diagnoses food allergy and identifies the culprits. The FDA says diets labeled to control allergies can only be prescribed and distributed by veterinarians, and there are several on the market.

Food allergies tend to develop only after the pet has been exposed to the protein, be that corn or beef or lamb. Therefore, veterinarians identify the problem proteins by feeding the pet unique ingredients he’s never eaten before. Diagnostic diets that contain novel ingredients like rabbit and potato, or kangaroo and rice, are available by prescription and must be used under veterinary supervision. Once the symptoms go away, suspect proteins are added back to the diet one by one to see which prompts a relapse. Once identified, the trigger ingredient can be avoided by choosing foods that don’t contain it.

Such a "hypoallergenic diet" minimizes allergic reactions. Since every pet is different, there is no such thing as a one-size-fits-all hypoallergenic diet. There’s nothing about lamb or alligator or kangaroo that’s hypoallergenic—they just are novel.

Unfortunately, the novelty may wear off once the food is fed routinely. If that pet has any of those predisposing factors like a pancreatic insufficiency, an inflammatory bowel disorder, or a problem with its suppresser function, it may be only a matter of time before he develops a sensitivity to the new protein. Complicating matters even further, veterinarians fear running out of novel proteins.

But understandably, some owners are reluctant to put their pet through the tedious diagnosis process of an elimination diet that still may not pinpoint the problem. Therapeutic diets from your veterinarian are typically higher cost, and this may also be a factor. Some food-allergic dogs do well when fed lamb and rice-based commercial diets, as long as they haven't previously eaten these ingredients. Just remember that lamb and rice-based diets often contain other ingredients, which may still cause your dog to react. And over time, dogs may become allergic to any unique ingredient.

Diets using hydrolyzed proteins may offer help for some dogs. Basically, the proteins are split into tiny pieces and concentrated. The immune system reacts to complete or large pieces of proteins. It doesn’t recognize the protein fractions and so has no allergic response. There are several hydrolyzed protein diets for pets now available.

CONTACT ALLERGY is relatively uncommon in dogs, probably because of their protective fur covering. When it occurs, the reaction is similar to what people experience when exposed to poison ivy. The reaction may happen hours after contact, or it may take weeks of repeated exposure before symptoms develop. Signs include itchy bumps, reddened skin, weepy sores and/or crust, blisters or pustules at the place of contact, and thinning coat or hair loss. Signs of contact allergy may be mis-diagnosed (see ATOPY, RINGWORM, or SEBORRHEA).

Typical sites of contact allergy skin disease are the sparsely furred areas of the body like the feet, abdomen, muzzle and chin, groin, testicles and the hocks and stifles which are the areas of the legs that contact the ground when your dog reclines. Left untreated, the area of first contact may spread and involve more of the body, because the dog will scratch and further damage the skin. Potentially, any substance could result in a contact allergy, but the most common culprits are household products like detergents and soaps, insecticides like flea powders or collars, plastic or rubber dishes or toys, and the dyes typically found in indoor/outdoor carpets. Diagnosis is based primarily on incriminating signs, and identifying and removing the allergen will resolve the problem. Cortisone-type medications prescribed by your veterinarian help control the itching and keep your dog from further damaging himself until the lesions heal.

Allergies cannot be cured, and avoiding the allergy source is the only way to control the symptoms. To complicate matters, multiple allergies make identification of the culprit(s) nearly impossible.

Dogs are often sensitive to more than one thing, and allergies tend to be cumulative. For instance, if your dog is allergic to both fleas and to pollen, they individually may not cause him problems, but the combination of the two pushes him over his allergy threshold so that he itches. Every allergic dog has an individual "itch" threshold, which is the amount of allergen necessary to provoke signs of disease.

This is actually good news, for although eliminating all allergens may be impossible, simply reducing the amount of exposure may substantially relieve your dog's symptoms. In other words, get rid of the fleas, and your dog may be able to handle exposure to house dust without scratching.

There can be many causes for itchy skin, and only a veterinarian can diagnose canine allergy. Identifying the allergen(s) and treating the signs should be a joint venture between you and your veterinarian, to best serve the health of your dog.

AMPUTATION

Amputation is the surgical removal of part of the body, most usually an extremity like a leg or the tail. Amputation may be required when there is nerve damaged from traumatic injury like frostbite or fracture which renders the tail or limb useless. Some dog breeds are "tail-beaters," so happy that they wag their tails against objects and repeatedly injure themselves. Slow-healing invasive infections can destroy muscle tissue and threaten the integrity of the rest of the body. And cancer may be impossible to cure. When the body becomes irreversibly damaged, amputation removes the injured or diseased portion and allows the rest of the body to remain healthy.

Once healed, otherwise healthy dogs are rarely slowed down by the loss of a leg or tail, and typically the cosmetic effect bothers owners more than their dog. Further, dogs which have suffered discomfort from the injury often rebound quickly once the pain–along with the limb–have been removed. Three-legged dogs navigate surprisingly well, often able to run and even jump (see DOCKING and CROPPING).

ANAL GLAND All dogs have two anal glands, or sacs, located beneath the skin at about eight and four o'clock on either side of the rectum. The pea-size glands are similar to a skunk's scent organs, but in the dog's case are used primarily for identification rather than protection. They give the dog's feces an individual scent. Dogs sniff each other's tail regions when the meet as a way of "reading" each other's scent-name.

The glands secrete a liquid or sometimes creamy brown to yellow substance, and are usually expressed whenever the dog passes a stool. They may also be expressed when the dog suddenly contracts the anal sphincter, the circular muscle that controls the rectum. The contraction may occur when your dog is frightened or stressed, and can result in a strong odor.

Most dogs don't require help with anal gland maintenance. But others have overactive sacs that can cause an odor problem, and these dogs need help keeping the glands expressed. Smaller breeds most typically develop impacted anal glands if the sacs fail to empty normally. This can be due to soft stools that don't supply enough pressure to empty the sacs, be due to overactive glands, or to smaller-than-normal gland openings. Anal gland problems in dogs may be related to allergies, too, so address these issues if your dog is also scratching a lot and paw-licking (see ALLERGY).

The secretions become pasty and thick when not regularly expressed, and simply plug the normal exit. Signs of a problem include your dog licking herself excessively, and/or giving off an offensive odor.

Left untreated, impacted anal glands can become painfully infected. The area on one or both sides of the rectum will swell. Your dog may lick herself to relieve the discomfort, or scoot on her bottom—sit down and pull herself forward while dragging her anal region against the floor—to try to clear the blockage. When infected, the secretions from the glands will contain blood or pus. In severe cases, an abscess may develop at the site, characterized by a soft red to purple hairless swelling on one or both sides of the rectum (see ABSCESS).

The treatment in all instances is manual expression of the anal glands. Your veterinarian or groomer can perform this service for your dog, especially if the dog is very tender. Improper manipulations of the glands can force the matter deeper into the tissue, causing further problems, so it's best to ask your veterinarian or groomer for a demonstration if you'd like to care for your dog in the future.

ANAL GLAND PROBLEMS

SYMPTOMS: Excessive licking of anal area; scooting; strong odor; bloody or puslike discharge; soft, red to purple swelling beside the rectum
HOME CARE: Wet warm cloths applied for fifteen minutes several times daily
HOLISTIC HELP: Add fiber to diet; treat with homeopathic Silica
VET CARE: Express contents of glands; apply antibiotic ointment into gland opening; sometimes oral antibiotics; surgical lancing removal of the infected gland
PREVENTION: None; if this is a chronic problem, routine emptying of the glands by owner or groomer

Here's how it's done. Wear gloves for the procedure, then lift your dog's tail and find the sacs on each side of the anus. They'll feel a bit like small marbles beneath the skin. With your thumb and forefinger on the skin at each side of the gland, gently push in and upward, and squeeze as you would to express a pimple. Use a damp cloth to wipe away the smelly discharge as the sac empties.

When the glands are infected, they'll need to be expressed every week and an antibiotic infused directly into the sac itself. Ointments like Panalog work well; the tip of the tube is inserted into the sac opening, and the gland filled with the medicine. Usually it's best if your veterinarian applies the medication into the anal gland. An oral antibiotic administered at home may also be prescribed. Warm wet compresses applied to the infected area for fifteen minutes two or three times daily will help the infection resolve more quickly.

Holistic vets recommend adding fiber to the diet, which absorbs larger amount of water and causes stools to get larger. The larger stools put more pressure on anal sacs during elimination, so they empty normally. Try offering dogs under 15 pounds about one-eighth cup of minced veggies each day, mixed into the regular food. Dogs that weigh 15 to 50 pounds can have from one-fourth to one-half cup, and dogs over 50 pounds can have as much as two cups a day. Run broccoli and carrots through the blender with no-salt chicken broth to make it more palatable.

The homeopathic remedy Silica is said to help anal sacs empty normally. You can give two or three drops, or three to five pellets of Silica 6C twice a day for three days to see if it helps.

Abscesses require surgical lancing so that the infection inside can be flushed out and drained away. The incision is left open so that the wound will heal from the inside out. The opening should be rinsed daily with a 50/50 solution of hydrogen peroxide and water, and the dog typically is also given an oral antibiotic.

In most cases, the abscess heals without complications. Dogs that suffer recurrences of impaction or infection require that the owner, veterinarian or groomer empty the anal glands on a regular basis, at least once a week. In some instances, surgical removal of the problem glands may be necessary.

ANAPHYLAXIS

SYMPTOMS: Salivation; drooling; difficulty breathing; uncontrolled urination; incoordination; vomiting; collapse
HOME CARE: EMERGENCY, SEE VET IMMEDIATELY!
VET CARE: Intravenous administration of epinephrine (adrenaline) and oxygen therapy
PREVENTION: Avoid medicating dog without vet advice; prevent insect bites or stings

ANAPHYLAXIS An anaphylactic response refers to an extremely rare but potentially lethal allergic reaction. It can result from any substance, but most commonly is associated with reactions to medicine such as penicillin or a vaccination, or to insect bites and stings.

The immune system overreacts to the offending substances and responds by flooding the body with immune components like histamine that are supposed to neutralize the offender. Instead, the histamine causes intense inflammation both locally and throughout the body, with itchiness appearing on the head and face (sometimes in hives), and constriction of the respiratory system. Quite simply, the affected dog can't breathe. Severe anaphylactic reactions can kill a dog within minutes.

Signs of reaction include excessive salivation and drooling, difficulty breathing, uncontrollable urination, incoordination, vomiting, and collapse. This is an emergency situation that needs immediate veterinary attention. The treatment of choice is administration of intravenous epinephrine (adrenaline), glucocorticoids, and fluid therapy along with oxygen therapy (see INSECT BITES/STINGS).

ANEMIA

SYMPTOMS: Depression; increased sleep; anorexia; weakness; weight loss; rapid pulse or breathing; pale gums or tongue; fainting spells during exercise
HOME CARE: Nutritional support; needs veterinary care
VET CARE: Blood transfusion; treatment for underlying cause; other medication as needed
PREVENTION: Flea and tick treatment; regular fecal exams and deworming as needed

ANEMIA Anemia is a disorder of the blood in which there is a lower than normal number of red blood cells. Anemia is the most common blood disorder in dogs, and can affect any dog of any age or breed. However, because puppies have less blood volume to begin with, anemia in these youngsters can become serious much more quickly.

There are a number of underlying causes, but in general, the signs are the same. The most typical causes are blood loss from traumatic injury; blood-sucking parasites like fleas; or a bone marrow disorder, often caused by chronic kidney disease that interferes with making new red blood cells.

Dogs suffering from anemia usually act depressed, lose their appetite and sleep a great deal, show an overall weakness, and may lose weight. Severe anemia may cause pulse and respiration rate to increase, and dogs may suffer a heart murmur (see ARRHYTHMIA). Excessive exercise can cause the anemic dog to faint. Such dogs appear pale, which is most easily seen in the normally pink mucus membranes like the gums.

Red cells in the dog live only about 110 to 120 days. They are constantly being replaced by the bone marrow as the old ones die, so the number of red cells remain relatively fixed. **Regenerative anemia** results when the bone marrow still creates new red cells, but can't keep up with their loss or destruction. **Autoimmune hemolytic anemia** (AIHA) can occur if your dog's immune system mis-recognizes red cells as foreign. When this happens, the body attacks and destroys its own red blood cells, a process referred to as hemolysis. The cause usually cannot be determined, but many cases are thought to be associated with exposure to certain drugs or viruses, diseases like cancer, lupus erythematosus, or blood parasite diseases like babesiosis and ehrlichiosis. Some dogs may inherit an enzyme defect that shortens the lifespan of red cells. Feeding onions can also result in AIHA. And in certain instances, newborn puppies may suffer a hemolytic reaction when their mother's protective immunity, which is passed to them through her milk, attacks the puppies' red cells (see BLOOD, IMMUNE SYSTEM, and VACCINATIONS).

Dogs may also suffer anemia from bleeding disorders resulting from clotting defects in the blood. Clotting problems are most often associated with poisons like rat bait, but may also result from diseases like hemophilia and Von Willebrand's Disease.

When the bone marrow stops making red cells, **non-regenerative anemia** results. These kinds of anemia can be caused by chronic diseases, tumors, and infections that suppress the bone marrow function. Toxins, poisons, and drugs may also cause suppression of the bone marrow, as can kidney disease. When the kidneys malfunction, they're unable to produce enough of the hormone erythropoietin, which prompts the bone marrow to produce red cells.

The best way to prevent anemia is to protect your dog from blood-sucking parasites like fleas, ticks and hookworms. Keeping your dog confined in a fenced yard or under leash control will help prevent traumatic injuries from encounters with cars.

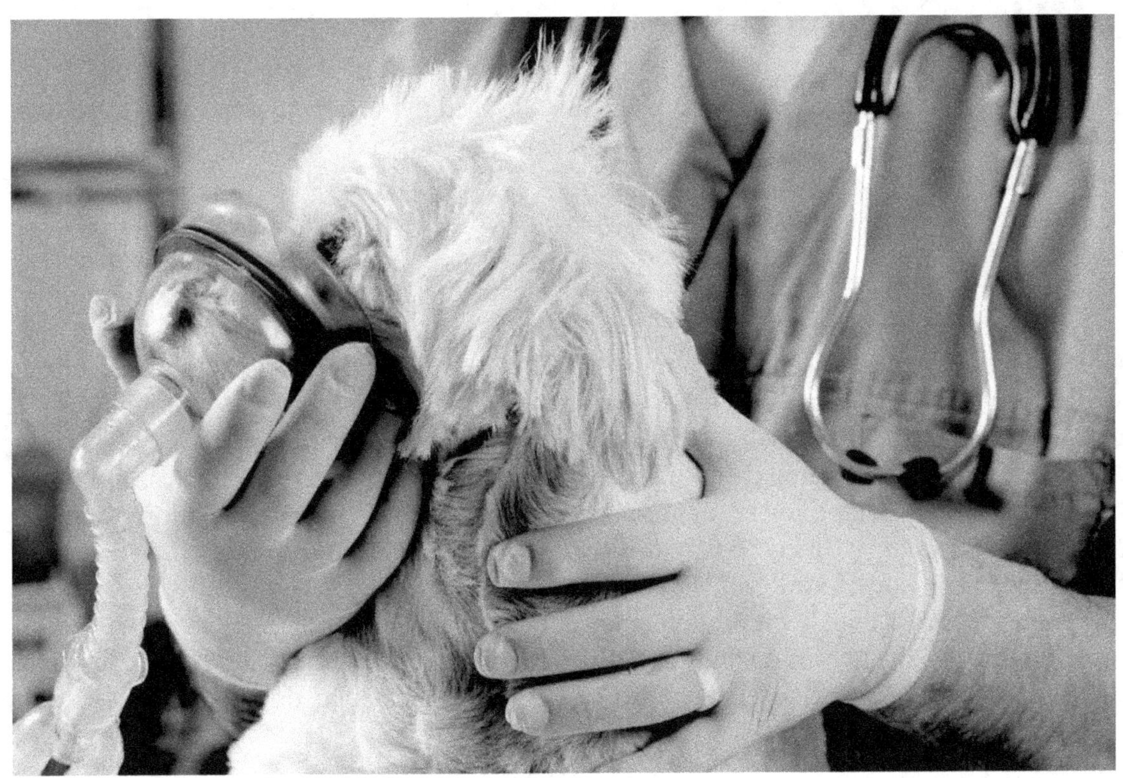

ANESTHETIC Drugs used to block the sensation of touch, pressure, and/or pain are referred to as anesthetics, or anesthesia. These drugs may or may not cause a loss of consciousness, and are used to prevent pain or stress during surgical or traumatic procedures. We can't explain to our dogs what is happening or ask them to hold still, and anesthesia is an important veterinary tool used to immobilize your dog during treatment.

Anesthetic drug doses are determined by your dog's weight. Some dog breeds like Afghan Hounds, Whippets and others seem to have a low tolerance for these drugs, and may require less anesthetic than other breeds of the same size. Even dogs of the same breed and size may react differently to anesthetics. For that reason, such drugs should only be given under veterinary supervision. Often, they are given in repeated small doses until the desired effect is attained.

When treatment is isolated to the skin surface, a local anesthetic like xylocaine may be used, which only blocks feeling on a small area and allows the dog to remain conscious. Local anesthetics can be applied to the skin as an ointment, spray or cream, or may be injected into surrounding tissue. Sedatives and tranquilizers affect the whole dog, acting to calm him down but not put him to sleep, and may be used to make your dog easier to handle. Local anesthetics are appropriate for such problems as removing porcupine quills, but aren't suitable for major procedures like neutering.

For major surgeries, a general anesthetic is used to render the dog unconscious and prevent pain. Certain drugs have amnesiac properties so your dog won't remember any unpleasantness. Today, a wide array of general anesthetic agents are available and often are used in combination to reduce potential side effects. Both injectable drugs like Telazol and inhaled anesthetic gases like halothane and isoflurane are common. Inhalant anesthetic is usually delivered to the lungs through an endotracheal tube that carries the gas into the dog's lungs; sometimes a mask is used instead, and fits over the dog's face.

Anesthetics are eliminated from the body by the lungs, kidneys, and/or liver, and if any of these organs are compromised by disease, your dog may suffer complications from the drugs. Anesthetics also affect the way the heart works, and dogs with heart disease require special anesthetic consideration. Overall, modern veterinary anesthetics are very safe and quite effective. Even dogs with pre-existing problems can be anesthetized safely as long as the risk is known ahead of time and the proper precautions are taken. Screening tests prior to surgery determine what anesthetics are best for your particular dog, especially if he is very young, old or ill.

ANOREXIA

Anorexia refers to a dog losing her appetite. The condition may be abrupt in which your dog suddenly refuses to eat, or gradual where she eats less over the long term. Anorexia is the most common sign of illness in dogs, and often occurs in conjunction with fever. Your dog may also show signs of weight loss, depression, and sometimes vomiting.

Some finicky dogs develop preferences for certain foods, and refuse to eat anything else. When you give in and feed the desired ration, you've trained the dog how to get her own way (see FOOD).

Most often, though, dogs that refuse food are suffering from a physical or emotional problem. Stress can suppress your dog's appetite; being left at the kennel, or the loss of a beloved family member (human or another pet) can quell the dog's appetite. And refusing to eat can be an early sign of nearly any disease, including diabetes mellitus, liver disease, canine distemper, and canine parvovirus. Other times, periodontal disease may make the dog's mouth so sore, she refuses to eat. Even a respiratory infection that stops up the dog's nose can spoil her dinner by ruining her sense of smell and taste. Anorexia can make healthy dogs ill, and sick dogs even sicker. Good nutrition is necessary to fight disease and keep well dogs healthy, and there are only a few instances where withholding or reducing food intake is recommended. Obesity, or chronic diarrhea or vomiting may be examples.

In most instances, if your dog refuses to eat or her appetite is markedly reduced for longer than three or four days, consult with your veterinarian. The underlying cause for the anorexia must be identified, and the condition treated to resolve the problem.

At home, you can stimulate your dog to eat by making her food more palatable. Try adding warm water to dry foods to make a slurry. Spiking a regular ration with pureed chicken or beef baby food, yogurt or cottage cheese may tempt your dog's palate. A canned product with high meat/fat content is also a good alternative. Some dogs will eat if the owner hand-feeds.

Holistic vets suggest using aromatherapy to help jump-start the flagging appetite. Put one or two drops of the essential oils rose, or vetiver, on a bandana for the dog to wear, or on the pet's bedding. The homeopathic remedy Nux vomica as well as Lycopodium, also are helpful. Dogs can take three pellets of either remedy (potency of 6C or 12x) twice a day for no more than two days.

Medical marijuana (or cannabis) today is also available for pets, but must be formulated so that pets receive the medical benefits of the cannabis (hemp) plant while reducing potential toxic concentrations of the herb. Hemp can be used to decrease nausea and stimulate appetite. Ask your veterinarian if this supplement may benefit your pet.

In severe cases, the veterinarian may recommend drugs to help stimulate your dog's appetite. Other times, force-feeding may be recommended. Typically the diet is made into a paste that's syringe-fed to the dog (see ADMINISTER MEDICATION/ORAL TREATMENTS). In rare cases, the veterinarian may resort to placing a feeding tube directly into the stomach to force-feed the dog.

ANTIFREEZE

Antifreeze is one of the most frustrating poisons for dog owners, because pets willingly drink the sweet-tasting substance. Composed of ethylene glycol, the odorless, colorless fluid is used to protect cars from freezing temperatures. It's also used to remove rust, and is found in some color film processing solutions used in home darkrooms.

Antifreeze is deadly. About one half teaspoon per pound of dog is lethal. That means a ten pound dog could ingest as little as five teaspoons and be affected, while an average-size dog weighing forty-five pounds would need to drink less than half a cup. It's estimated that approximately 10,000 dogs each year are poisoned by antifreeze, and nearly 88 percent of pets that drink antifreeze die. All dogs are at risk, but those younger than three years old are affected most often, probably because of the curious nature of youth. Most poisonings take place during the fall, winter, and early spring when antifreeze is routinely used.

Your dog's survival depends on quick treatment, because the poison is rapidly absorbed into the system. Peak blood concentrations occur in dogs within one to three hours after ingestion, with initial signs appearing approximately one hour after poisoning. Dogs may die from kidney failure in as little as four to eight hours.

ANTIFREEZE

SYMPTOMS: Drunken behavior; excessive thirst; increased urination; diarrhea; vomiting; convulsions; loss of appetite; panting
FIRST AID: EMERGENCY! SEE VET IMMEDIATELY! induce vomiting; administer activated charcoal within two hours
VET CARE: Induce vomiting; pump stomach; treat with intravenous fluids and 100-proof alcohol, or with 4MP; provide supportive care
PREVENTION: Store out of dog's reach; use pet-safe products

From the blood, the poison enters the brain and spinal fluid causing neurologic signs, with the dog staggering as though he's drunk. Other signs include weakness, depression, loss of appetite, panting, and rapid heart rate. Convulsions, though rare, can also be a sign of poisoning. Although the substance is not particularly irritating to the gastrointestinal tract, sometimes the dog will suffer vomiting. One of the earliest signs is an increased thirst; as a result, urine output of approximately six times the norm has been observed in dogs within three hours of ingestion.

The more antifreeze that is passed in the urine early on, the better, because the substance is at first relatively harmless. But quite soon the ethylene glycol is processed by the body into oxalic acid, an extremely toxic substance used as a bleaching and cleaning agent that literally corrodes the urinary tract. It's not the antifreeze itself, but the oxalic acid that poisons the pet. Oxalic acid often also combines with calcium and forms crystals which block the flow of urine.

Your dog may seem to return to normal in about 12 to 18 hours, but then the depression will return although the intoxication goes away. Damage continues, sometimes over a week's time, with the kidney damage finally resulting in the dog ceasing to urinate. Coma and death are the end result of renal failure (see KIDNEY DISEASE).

If your dog is to survive, treatment must begin as soon as possible; treatment begun after 24 hours following poisoning offers only a slim chance of recovery. If you suspect your dog has swallowed antifreeze, see your veterinarian immediately.

If help is more than two hours away, though, and you've seen your dog drink antifreeze, making him vomit the poison can improve his chance of survival. Beyond this two-hour window, the poison will already be in his system and vomiting won't help. Don't induce vomiting if your dog acts depressed, is not fully conscious, or acts drunk.

To induce vomiting, first feed a small meal or offer a treat, so it's easier to make him throw up. Then give 3 percent hydrogen peroxide, about 1 to 2 teaspoons for every 10 pounds your pet weighs. Use an eyedropper, turkey baster or needleless syringe to squirt onto the back of the dog's tongue, and the foaming action and taste should prompt vomiting within five minutes. You can repeat the dose two or three times (five minutes between doses). Or you can use syrup of Ipecac instead, at a dose of 1 teaspoon for dogs up to 35 pounds, and up to 1 tablespoon for larger dogs. Ipecac syrup takes a little longer to work and the dosage should NOT be repeated (see ADMINISTERING MEDICATION, ORAL TREATMENT).

Administering activated charcoal (available from your drugstore) will also help improve your dog's chance of survival. After you've induced vomiting, or if you're unable to get him to vomit, give him the crushed tablets mixed with water. Charcoal binds the poison to prevent its absorption in the intestinal tract. Any first aid should be followed by a veterinarian's evaluation as soon as possible.

Your veterinarian's treatment is designed to prevent further absorption or metabolism of the poison, and to increase urination to get rid of it. Up to three hours following ingestion, the veterinarian will flush the dog's stomach with a saline/charcoal solution. Intravenous fluid therapy helps head off dehydration and also encourages your dog to urinate as much antifreeze as possible before it's changed into its more lethal form.

In the past, dogs were treated for antifreeze intoxication by administering 100 proof ethanol alcohol intravenously on a continuous basis for several days. By raising the dog's blood/alcohol content, the liver is forced to address the alcohol instead of changing the antifreeze to oxalic acid. Consequently, this gives the body time to pass the unchanged antifreeze through urination.

An antidote for antifreeze poisoning in dogs became commercially available in January 1997. It is expensive, but Fomepizole (4MP) given to the dog within the first 8 to 12 hours following ingestion can save the dog’s life. It is given in three intravenous doses to the dog at 12 hour intervals and prevents the liver from metabolizing the poison so that the dog's body eliminates the antifreeze naturally through urination.

When enough of the poison has already been changed, the kidneys will be damaged. People suffering from kidney failure benefit from dialysis machines, but this luxury is rarely available for our pets. However, peritoneal dialysis is effective, and consists of fluid being pumped into the abdominal cavity where it absorbs waste the damaged kidneys can't process, and then is drawn back out. It's hoped the procedure will offer the body time to heal the kidneys, so that normal function can return.

When damage to the kidneys is severe, it may be permanent; lesser damage may be reversible and the kidneys may return to normal or near normal function in three to four weeks. Aggressive supportive therapy (even ongoing veterinary hospitalization) may be necessary.

Today, antifreeze manufacturers throughout the United States may be required by law (or if not, may still voluntarily) add a bitter flavoring agent to their normally sweet-tasting products to make them less attractive to pets as well as kids. The nontoxic bittering agent, denatonium benzoate, commonly is used in dangerous liquids to deter tasting or drinking, as well as a prevention treatment for nail-biting in people. Pet owners will still need to remain vigilant, of course.

Prevent the possibility of antifreeze intoxication by keeping antifreeze out of your dog's reach. Garages and storage areas where antifreeze may be found should be off limits to your pets. Dispose of drained radiator fluid in a sealed container, and be sure to clean spills immediately. Alternative antifreeze products that use less-toxic chemicals such as propylene glycol are also available. Ask your veterinarian for a recommendation (see POISON).

AROMATHERAPY

Aromatherapy is a relatively new holistic modality that uses certain scents like medicines to affect the body on a biochemical level. The fragrant scents used in aromatherapy are absorbed by the mucus membranes in the nose, and go directly to the brain to cause the therapeutic effect. For instance, the scent of lavender oil causes temporary sedation and helps pets relax. Other types of aromatherapy can affect the blood pressure and heart rate, or impact the pet's emotional state by reducing fear or stress.

Essential oils used in aromatherapy are available from holistic veterinarians, health food stores, and online. These oils are derived from natural sources, although synthetic and less expensive products can be found. As with flower essences, you can purchase single or combination oil blends.

Not everything is known about effective doses or potential toxicities, so it is best to work directly with a holistic veterinarian before using aromatherapy with your pet. Some oils, like peppermint and pennyroyal, can be dangerous or even fatal when used on pets.

Once your veterinarian has recommended the appropriate essential oil for your pet's circumstances, they typically can be applied at home. The oils are very strong and can burn the skin at full strength, so typically are diluted half-and-half with vegetable oil. The diluted oil can be used either in a diffuser, or applied to the fur at the back of the pet's neck or inside tip of the ears, so the scent reaches him but he can't lick it off. Apply the scent to a neck bandana for dogs to wear.

Aromatherapy usually works very quickly, so is a short-term therapy. The effect also wears off quickly within four to six hours, but often, a single treatment is enough. Holistic veterinarians say it's fine to use veterinary approved aromatherapy up to three times a day for one or two days if there's not an immediate improvement, but after that, you should call the veterinarian.

ARRHYTHMIA The term arrhythmia refers to a heartbeat that is abnormal. The natural rhythm of the dog's heart is stimulated by electrical impulses. Changes in the impulse may result in increased heart rate (tachycardia,) decreased rhythm (bradycardia), or irregularity. Turbulence in the blood flow through the heart results in a distinctive sound referred to as a heart murmur.

Drugs, toxins, electrolyte or body acid/base imbalance resulting from severe vomiting or diarrhea, kidney stones and urinary blockage, and heart disease all are potential causes of arrhythmias. Drugs are available that help control and regulate the beat of the heart. However, the underlying cause must be addressed if the problem is to be resolved.

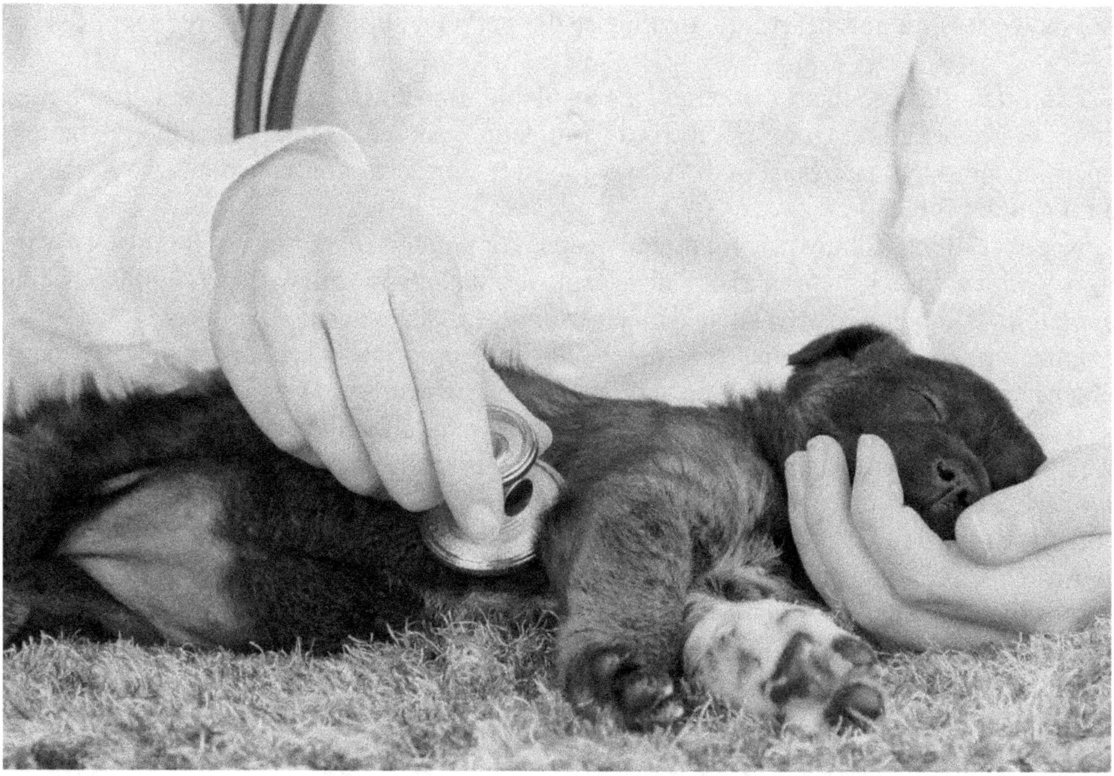

ARTHRITIS The term arthritis covers a vast array of joint disorders that are generally divided into two groups: inflammatory, and non-inflammatory. Inflammatory joint disease is characterized by pain and swelling in one or more joints, while non-inflammatory joint diseases are usually caused by degeneration of the joints and characterized by pain and stiffness.

The joints of the body are the "hinges" between two or more bones that allow movement by providing a smooth, lubricated surface composed of cartilage. The cartilage is coated with a lubricated fluid similar to plasma, and encased in a joint capsule. This firm yet somewhat spongy surface offers ten times less friction than any man- made ball bearing system. The fluid feeds the joint, and motion of the joint pumps fluid to the cartilage to maintain joint health and nutrition.

ARTHRITIS

SYMPTOMS: Stiff joints; endless circling before lying down; difficulty rising; lameness, especially in the morning; limping or holding up a leg; reluctance to move, particularly in cold weather; avoiding stairs; refusing to jump
HOME CARE: Massage; apply heat to painful areas; moderate exercise, especially swimming; veterinary-prescribed pain medication
HOLISTIC HELP: Nutraceuticals/supplements; chiropractic adjustment; acupuncture/acupressure; aromatherapy
VET CARE: Sometimes steroids to reduce pain; analgesic drugs; occasionally orthopedic surgery
PREVENTION: Prompt veterinary treatment of joint or bone injury; keep dogs slim

Joint disease occurs when the cartilage is injured through trauma, the function of the joint is compromised from bone, muscle, or ligament injury, or disease attacks the joint components. The resulting pain restricts movement, which in turn interferes with joint nutrition when the fluid distribution is curtailed. Consequently, a vicious cycle is born.

Joint disease is quite common in dogs. It's often associated with a lifetime of wear and tear on the joints, and large or heavy dogs tend to be affected most often because of the additional stress placed on their joints. The condition results in painful movement, and can develop in young dogs but usually doesn't become apparent until the dog reaches ten years old or older.

There are several kinds of arthritis. **Rheumatoid arthritis** affects the connective tissue throughout the body, and is considered rare in dogs. Most often it affects small or Toy breeds. The cause isn't known, but it's thought that the immune system may be involved.

Signs of rheumatoid arthritis in dogs include morning stiffness, lameness that may move from leg to leg, and swollen joints, especially the small ones of the legs. The dog may also exhibit swollen glands, with fever and depressed appetite. The condition is diagnosed with X-rays, analysis of joint fluid, and blood tests.

Autoimmune arthritis is a relatively rare group of diseases in which the immune system erroneously attacks the joints and causes the problem. The most common of these is idiopathic non-erosive arthritis; the cause isn't known, but it usually affects large breed young adult dogs, especially Doberman Pinschers and German Shepherd Dogs. Signs include loss of appetite, joint swelling and stiffness in one or more leg, and intermittent fever. Typically, treatment includes immune suppressing drugs and anti-inflammatory medications like corticosteroids (see LUPUS ERYTHEMATOSUS COMPLEX).

Dogs may also suffer from **septic arthritis** when bacteria infects the joint space. This can occur when a penetrating wound gives access to the area, or bacteria spreads from nearby bone infections or through the bloodstream. Infectious rickettsial diseases spread by ticks may cause septic arthritis due to the spirochete. Several weeks of oral or intravenous antibiotic therapy is the treatment of choice (see ROCKY MOUNTAIN SPOTTED FEVER, EHRLICHIOSIS, and LYME DISEASE.

The most common type of canine arthritis is **osteoarthritis** or **degenerative arthritis.** It's a chronic disease that occurs when simple wear and tear slowly destroys the thin layer of cartilage protecting the joint surface. The most common joints affected are the hips, elbows, and knees. Most cases affect older dogs, but the condition can develop at any age from injury to the bone, cartilage or ligaments, especially in large breed or heavy dogs. Dogs suffering hip dysplasia often suffer from arthritis. As the cartilage wears away, the area becomes inflamed and painful, which in turn causes even more cartilage damage. A vicious cycle of joint degeneration is born; once started, arthritis is a progressive disease that doesn't stop.

Dogs with osteoarthritis will suffer varying degrees of lameness or stiffness that is typically worse in the morning. The affected dog may limp, hold up the affected leg, or simply refuse to move. One of the most common causes of lameness—that is, limping or holding up a leg—is knee arthritis, which is almost always secondary to a torn cruciate ligament (see KNEE INJURY).

Myofascial pain syndrome is also a common finding in arthritic dogs. It results in trigger points, or taut bands of muscle that are tender to the touch and that can refer pain to other parts of the body. For instance, dogs with hip dysplasia may compensate by altering their gait to protect the sore area, which in turn can cause more pain. The syndrome is often misdiagnosed as tendonitis, joint degradation, muscle strain, or some other muscular disorder. It can be effectively treated with acupuncture.

Wet or cold weather aggravates the pain. Dogs may be reluctant to move, particularly after they've been resting. They may struggle to rise, and circle a long time before lying down. Jumping onto furniture or into cars, or navigating stairs can become a challenge. Moderate exercise is beneficial, and keeps the joints loose and warms up the muscles so that the pain lessens.

Diagnosis is based on X-rays that show characteristic changes in the bone. The space between the joints may narrow, new but abnormal bone may form in and around the joint, and destruction of the bone surface may be apparent. The veterinarian can also manipulate the joint by flexing the affected limb, and may detect a "grating" sensation. Usually the affected joint is warm to the touch, and sometimes swollen, which the veterinarian can detect by feeling, or palpating, the area.

Treatment of osteoarthritis is aimed at relieving the dog's pain, maintaining muscle tone, and preventing stiffness. Moderate exercise helps keep the joint limber, and promotes sound muscle which help to support the joint. It also keeps the dog fit and prevents weight gain, which can further stress diseased joints. Swimming is a particularly good exercise for arthritic dogs; however, be sure to warm and dry your dog thoroughly after swimming. Moderate exercise promotes the natural lubrication and nutrition of the joints.

Overweight arthritic dogs should be put on a reducing diet (see OBESITY). Intersperse daily exercise with frequent rest periods, and cut back on play if your dog becomes noticeably lame. Some dogs must be physically restrained from over-doing, since they'd rather put up with the pain than not join you for your jog or hunt.

NSAIDs—nonsteroidal anti-inflammatory drugs—are a class of medication that can be very helpful to arthritic dogs. They work by affecting the production of certain enzymes that are involved in joint inflammation and pain. Carprofen, trade name Rimadyl, works in a great many dogs. Rimadyl is a pill given twice a day.

Another drug called etodolac, brand name Etogesic, works in a similar way to Rimadyl, but some owners consider it more convenient since it's given only once a day. Dogs who have elevated liver enzymes and don't tolerate aspirin well could benefit from Etogesic.

Other drugs may be used less frequently because of potential side effects. Ketoprofen is a good analgesic but has more of a tendency to cause stomach ulcers than does Rimadyl. Peroxicam is another NSAID also used to treat certain cancers.

Currently there is no COX-II inhibitor drug approved for use in dogs, but human drugs can be very safe and effective if used correctly. The human products Celebrex and Vioxx may be prescribed for off-label use in dogs by your veterinarian.

DOG FACTS

Today, a variety of nutritional supplements are used like drugs to treat a wide range of health conditions. Also called "functional foods," these are substances intended to maintain or improve health beyond what ordinary nutrients in the food provide (see NUTRACEUTICALS).

Special "joint diets" are also available, and typically contain high levels of omega-3 fatty acids, alpha linoleic acid, carnitine, various antioxidants and glucosamine/chondroitin sulfate.

It's also possible to add appropriate supplements to your dog's diet. Glycosaminoglycan (GAG) and proteoglycan compounds help slow the progression of arthritis by protecting the joint cartilage. Chondroitin and glucosamine also have anti-inflammatory properties, and can reduce swelling, and that can help with the pain. These supplements are probably most effective in dogs that have only mild arthritis, and don't prevent arthritis but can slow the progression of the disease.

Medical marijuana (or cannabis) today is also available for pets, but must be formulated so that pets receive the medical benefits of the cannabis (hemp) plant while reducing potential toxic concentrations of the herb. Hemp can be used to control pain and inflammation. Ask your veterinarian if this supplement may benefit your pet.

Adequan has been FDA-approved as a disease-modifying osteoarthritis drug for dogs. It is similar to the oral glucosamine-type drugs, but when given by injection, the concentrated dose can have a more dramatic effect. It only works in about 50-60 percent of patients. It generally takes two or three injections before you notice any change.

Acupuncture is not a drug, but can act like one to relieve the pain of arthritis. It can be used along with other drug therapies. Laser therapy also offers a pain relief option for dogs.

In severe cases, surgery may be the best option. Hip, knee and elbow surgeries relieve the pain and provide mobility (see HIP DYSPLASIA).

Arthroscopy employs a flexible tube with fiber optics that permits the veterinarian to see the inside of the joint through tiny noninvasive incisions. A procedure called "wash out" has been shown to be very effective in people with arthritis, and is now being applied to arthritic dogs with the help of arthroscopy. Basically, the joint and tissue is debrided—scoured to remove damaged tissue and loose material—then washed clean. That not only gets rid of foreign matter, it also dilutes the biological chemicals that cause inflammation.

In some instances, in a process called arthrodesis, the painful joint can be eliminated entirely by fusing the two bones together. Arthrodesis can be performed in the knee, elbow, ankle, wrist or hock. It leaves the dog with a limp due to lost mobility, but eliminates the pain of the joint. With fusion of the hock, the wrist or ankle area, dogs do quite well. Mobility is more affected when they have arthrodesis of the knee or elbow.

Acupuncture can relieve the pain of arthritis and can be used with drugs, or nutraceuticals such as Cosequin. The insertion of needles in proscribed locations throughout the body prompts the release of natural painkillers called endorphins. Most dogs tolerate these needles quite well. Acupuncture is particularly helpful because it has no side effects.

The "aspirin" point (BL60) is located on the outside of the rear ankle. Use the tip of your finger to press this spot gently for about 60 seconds, once or twice a day, to help relieve pain.

Your veterinarian may recommend PEMF therapy, which stimulate the electrical and chemical processes in the tissues to relieve inflammation and pain. Devices may be designed for whole body treatment or targeted areas of the body. Some of these devices have successfully completed efficacy studies and are FDA-approved. Therapeutic products may be available in mats, wraps or other devices from your veterinarian or over the counter (see PULSED ELECTROMAGNETIC FIELD).

Massaging your dog can help relieve his aching joints and loosen tight muscles. Use gentle circular rubbing motions all over his body, from head to tail, and flex his joints to keep them limber. Try using hot water bottles, heating pads or circulating water blankets (buffered with layers of towels) on sore joints.

Age-related arthritis can't be prevented, but treating the signs early can keep your dog more comfortable. Provide accommodations such as ramps and steps to aid your dog's mobility.

Should your dog suffer a joint, bone, or ligament injury, prompt treatment will minimize the chance of developing arthritis down the road. Keeping your dog slim will reduce the stress and strain on his joints, and may slow down the effects of arthritis.

ARTIFICIAL INSEMINATION (AI)

AI is the procedure of breeding by collecting semen from a male and introducing it into the vagina of a female. Most commonly, AI is chosen when the dogs are unable to breed naturally. Reasons may include a great size difference between the pair, anatomical problems like a too narrow vagina or muscle weakness that interferes with the male mounting, inexperience or even antagonism between the pair, or inability to arrange transportation to bring the dogs together. The procedure is usually performed by a veterinarian, or an experienced professional breeder. Often, the owner's help is enlisted to hold and calm the dogs during the procedure.

If the resulting litter is to be registered, the registering body (for example, the AKC) has strict procedures to follow and forms to complete. According to the AKC, for fresh semen, both the sire and dam must be present during the extraction of the semen and the insemination of the bitch. For fresh extended semen, the person(s) who performed the semen extraction and insemination must complete forms of certification, and the sire must be AKC DNA certified. Specific forms and consents must be filled out to register a litter produced using frozen semen.

The semen is collected from the stud dog using an artificial vagina and a clear plastic tube. The presence of a female dog in heat may be necessary to give the male the proper signals. Once the semen is collected, the male dog is removed from the room. The semen is drawn from the tube into a sterile syringe, and then a catheter is attached to the syringe. AI should take place within 10 to 15 minutes for the semen to remain viable. If not possible to inseminate immediately, the semen can be chilled for up to 24 hours to preserve viability.

The catheter is fed into the bitch's vagina, and the semen delivered through the catheter. It's recommended that the bitch remain standing for ten to fifteen minutes following the procedure.

Should insemination need to be delayed beyond that, the semen should be frozen for future use. Semen is mixed with an extender that preserves it, and slowly frozen in liquid nitrogen, and this process requires veterinarians with the specialized equipment and training.

AI performed with fresh semen that's promptly inseminated mirrors natural breeding, but varies depending on the skill of the breeder. When using fresh semen that's been chilled, the success rate drops to 59 to 80 percent. Frozen semen placed in the vagina beside the cervix holds the lowest success rate (52 to 60 percent). However, it is a viable option in circumstances where normal breeding is not possible (see REPRODUCTION).

ARTIFICIAL RESPIRATION Artificial respiration is the procedure of supplying air to a dog that has stopped breathing.

Respiratory distress in dogs is characterized by gasping, panting, or slowed breathing. When your dog isn't receiving adequate oxygen, the gums in his mouth, rims of his eyes, and/or inside of his ears become pale or slightly blue. Sometimes, the dog will lose consciousness. Your dog may stop breathing due to the trauma of being hit by a car, or as a result of electrical shock, or drowning. A strong blow or penetrating chest wound can damage the lungs or tear the diaphragm, a muscle separating the abdomen from the chest cavity that normally works to expand the lungs. A swallowed object that becomes stuck and blocks the airways may also interfere with breathing.

If you can see the toy, bone or other object, you can attempt to remove it with tweezers, pliers or your fingers. However, leave string-type objects for your veterinarian to address; the other end may have a fishhook attached.

When unable to remove the object, lay your dog on his side, place the heel of your hand directly behind the last rib, and gently thrust upwards three or four times in quick succession. In many cases, this modified Heimlich maneuver will dislodge the obstruction; if it doesn't, get your dog immediate veterinary assistance.

When respiratory distress isn't due to obstruction, you must breathe for your dog until you can get him to a veterinarian. First, remove his collar. Then place your dog on his right side on a flat, firm surface; a table or kitchen counter works well for small dogs, while medium to larger dogs can be positioned on the floor. Pull the dog's tongue forward to keep it from blocking the airway, then gently close the mouth with his tongue extended outside. Extend your dog's neck forward from the body, keeping the chin slightly raised. Then place the flat of your hand on your dog's ribs, and press down sharply to express the old air from his system, then quickly release. When the diaphragm is intact, the lungs will fill with air naturally when you release the pressure.

If this recoil mechanism doesn't work, you must breathe air into your dog's lungs. The mouth-to-nose method is the most effective. Keep his tongue forward, then place both hands about your dog's muzzle to seal his lips so the air will not escape. Then place your lips over your dog's nose.

Blow two quick breaths just hard enough to move his sides, and watch to see if his chest expands. Blowing into his nose directs air to the lungs when the lips are properly sealed. For small pets, think of blowing up a paper bag—gently does it!—or you could over-inflate and damage the lungs. However, you'll need to blow pretty hard to expand the lungs of larger dogs.

Between breaths, pull your mouth away to let the air naturally escape before giving another breath. Continue rescue breathing at a rate of 15 to 20 breaths per minute until he starts breathing on his own, or you reach the veterinary clinic (see CARDIOPULMONARY RESUSCITATION).

ASPIRIN

Aspirin (acetylsalicylic acid) is a common pain reliever used by people, and sometimes used in veterinary medicine for dogs. Aspirin is commonly prescribed to relieve the discomfort of canine arthritis. However, your dog's body metabolizes, or breaks down, aspirin at a different rate that humans. That means the dosage for dogs is going to vary from people so always consult your veterinarian to be safe before giving aspirin. Also, use only buffered, or enteric coated aspirin products, or you risk stomach upset or worse.

Giving your dog too much aspirin, particularly the non-buffered type, may result in an ulcer, or bleeding of the stomach. Vomiting is the most frequent sign, with the digested blood making the vomitus look like old coffee grounds; occasionally, bright red fresh blood will be apparent. Over time, the dog will lose weight, and suffer anemia.

Diagnosis is made by using X-rays in conjunction with special dyes, or by visual examination of the gastrointestinal tract using a special instrument that's fed down the dog's throat (see ENDOSCOPE). Treatment includes discontinuing the aspirin, and prescribing ulcer medication similar to what is used in humans. Veterinary supervision is necessary.

ASPIRIN POISONING

SYMPTOMS: Vomiting blood that looks like old coffee grounds; weight loss; anemia; abdominal pain
HOME CARE: Stop giving the aspirin
VET CARE: Supportive care; sometimes ulcer-type medication
PREVENTION: Give medication only with your veterinarian's direction

ASTHMA

Asthma is a sudden narrowing of the airways that results in breathing distress. It's thought to be caused by inhalant allergy which triggers the bronchials—muscles and glandular structures surrounding the lower airways in the lungs—to constrict.

Asthma is considered to be very rare in dogs. Signs include audible wheezing, straining to breathe, coughing, and sometimes collapse from lack of oxygen. Treatment seeks to open the breathing passages, and reduce accompanying inflammation so the dog can breathe. Antihistamines are effective, and help dilate the airways, calm the inflammation, and their sedative effect acts to reduce the dog's excitability. In some instances, steroids may be helpful as well to reduce inflammation and the allergic reaction. Your veterinarian will prescribe the most appropriate medication for your dog's situation. Reducing house dust or other possible allergy triggers may help improve your dog's condition (see ALLERGY).

BABESIOSIS Babesiosis is a disease caused by a blood parasite, a protozoa belonging to the genus *Babesia* that's transmitted by ticks. There are more than 70 kinds of Babesia parasites that affect domestic and wild animals; most are both tick and host specific, which means they preferentially target certain ticks and animals.

Dogs are affected by *Babesia canis vogeli* and *Babesia gibsoni*. All dogs are susceptible, but more cases occur in the southern United States and South Africa where the tick vectors *Dermacentor variabilis* (the American dog tick) and *Rhipicephalus sanguineous* (the brown dog tick) are found. Puppies are most susceptible to B. canis disease than are adult dogs, but disease caused by *B. gibsoni* may kill dogs of any age.

BABESIOISIS

SYMPTOMS: Anemia; high fever; lethargy; loss of appetite; dark urine; jaundice; incoordination; teeth grinding; coma
HOME CARE: None
VET CARE: Antiprotozoal drugs; fluid therapy; blood transfusions
PREVENTION: Prevent ticks by using appropriate insecticides and/or promptly remove attached ticks

The parasite is passed to the host through tick saliva when the tick takes a blood meal. It also can be transmitted via contaminated blood or through bites, which may account for a relatively high prevalence in American Staffordshire and American Pit Bull Terriers. Once transmitted, the protozoa infects and destroys the red blood cells (see ANEMIA).

The dog's own body also destroys red cells when the immune system attacks the parasite. Dogs suffering from the disease may show sudden severe (acute) signs, a gradual onset of ongoing symptoms (chronic), or no signs at all. Ticks become infected by feeding on dogs already infected with the parasite. The disease results in severe anemia which can ultimately impact the liver, kidneys, and spleen. The first sign is fever that may reach as high as 107 degrees. The dog suffers from lethargy and/or loss of appetite. When severe anemia is present, the urine will turn dark due to leakage of hemoglobin (red blood cell pigment) into the urine; this is sometimes referred to as "red water." When the liver is involved, jaundice is apparent (yellow-tinge to light areas of skin), and when the central nervous system (CNS) is affected, the dog will exhibit incoordination, teeth grinding, and mania, followed by coma. Four to eight days following the first symptoms, the dog may die.

Diagnosis is made by finding the parasite in the blood during microscopic examination, or sometimes by testing the blood for antibodies against the parasite. The specific drug, dosage, and treatment depends on the goal of the treatment, which may range from alleviating signs, to eliminating or even preventing infection. Some of these drugs are so effective that one treatment will kill the parasite. The Companion Animal Parasite Council (CAPC) recommends that veterinarians treat babesiosis with either imidocarb diproprionate (large *Babesia* spp.) or a combination of atovaquone and azithromycin (*Babesia gibsoni*). Even with treatment, the infection can persist for the lifetime of the dog.

When treated before severe anemia or CNS signs become apparent, dogs usually recover without further supportive therapy. But fluid therapy, blood transfusions, or other measures may be required, particularly in late-stage disease.

Babesiosis can be prevented by protecting your dog against ticks and keeping dogs from fighting. In most cases, the tick must be attached to your dog for 24 to 48 hours before the parasite will be passed, so prompt removal of ticks will prevent transmission of the disease. Even better, modern ascaricidal preparations work to prevent ticks from ever attaching to your dog at all (see TICKS).

BAD BREATH

BAD BREATH Also referred to as halitosis, offensive mouth odor is not normal for your pet. Doggy breath may result from strong smelling canned foods for a short time following meals, but a persistent odor commonly indicates a health problem.

Dogs are susceptible to the same dental problems that people suffer, and are at even higher risk because they aren't able to care for their own teeth through brushing. The earliest sign of gum and tooth infections is bad breath.

Mouth odor can signal disease or even poisoning. Arsenic poisoning causes a strong garlic breath, and a symptom of late-stage diabetes is acetone breath that smells something like nail polish remover. Signs of kidney disease include mouth ulcers and ammonia-like mouth odor.

DOG FACTS

Your dog's pungent breath isn't something to sniff at, and cannot—should not—be masked with a mint. To resolve the issue, the cause must be diagnosed by your veterinarian. Usually, bad breath resulting from periodontal disease can be prevented with routine dental care.

BAD BREATH

SYMPTOMS: Mouth odor
HOME CARE: Offer "dental" treats and chews; brush teeth
VET CARE: Anesthesia and dentistry; sometimes antibiotics
PREVENTION: Routinely brush dog's teeth; regular veterinary dental care

BALANOPOSTHITIS Balanoposthitis is the inflammation and sometimes infection of the penis and/or its fleshy covering (prepuce). Mild cases are common in male dogs. Normally, there is either no discharge or only an occasional small amount of yellow-white secretion from the prepuce. An abnormal condition should be suspected anytime there is a discharge of pus from the opening.

Balanoposthitis may result from injury or from the intrusion of a foreign body that prompts overgrowth of the normal microorganisms. Dogs suffering severe cases can suffer sudden swelling and inflammation of the penis and prepuce, lots of discharge, and pain. Typically, the dog will engage in a great deal of licking of the area. Without treatment, an abscess can develop (see ABSCESS).

Treatment involves thoroughly cleaning the area with sterile saline solutions, along with administering antibiotic therapy. Medicated ointments are typically infused into the prepuce cavity over a two to four week period. Sometimes oral medication is also prescribed. Dogs that have suffered a bout of balanoposthitis often have recurrences of the problem, and owners should remain vigilant to catch problems early.

BALANOPOSTHITIS

SYMPTOMS: Yellow, yellow-green or bloody discharge from penis or prepuce; swelling; redness; pain with or without licking; fever; lethargy; anorexia
HOME CARE: Clean with sterile saline solutions; apply veterinary-prescribed medications
VET CARE: Same; also infusion of medicated solution and/or antibiotic ointments into prepuce; sometimes oral antibiotics
PREVENTION: None. When problem is chronic, keep area clean

BITCH A bitch is a female dog, specifically those of reproductive age. The term is considered derogatory when applied to anything other than dogs, but is both accurate and highly appropriate when used in the proper context. The word differentiates between male and female canines, particularly in professional circles, where the male is the *dog* and the female is the *bitch.*

BLADDER STONES

SYMPTOMS: Break in house training; dribbling urine; "posing" without production; bloody or strong-smelling urine; whining during urination; excessive licking of genitals; splay-legged posture during urination; splattery or weak urine stream
HOME CARE: None
VET CARE: Usually surgical removal; occasionally therapeutic diets to dissolve stone; antibiotics
PREVENTION: Low-dose antibiotics to reduce recurrence; encourage drinking of water, and moderate exercise; Dalmatians benefit from special diets and drug therapy

BLADDER STONES Also referred to as urolithiasis, the development of microscopic to egg-size mineral deposits, or stones, in the urinary tract is considered relatively common in dogs. When people suffer this problem, the stones typically develop in the kidneys, but the bladder is the more common location for dogs.

It's estimated that nearly three percent of dogs suffer from urolithiasis, with most cases occurring in two to ten year old animals; however, some dog breeds are predisposed to the condition. The Miniature Schnauzer, Dachshund, Dalmatian, Pug, Bulldog, Welsh Corgi, Basset Hound, Beagle and terrier breeds are at highest risk.

The stones are actually crystalline substances composed of various minerals found in the dog's urine. For stones to form, one or more of these minerals must be present in the urine. Also, the urine must remain a sufficient time in the urinary tract for crystals to precipitate. Finally, the urine must be a favorable pH for crystallization.

These three factors—and thus, stone formation—are influenced not only by genetics, but also by infection, diet, digestion, volume of urine, and frequency of urination. The causes of some types of stones are known, while others remain a mystery. For instance, urate stones are caused by metabolic problems, while struvite stones usually are associated with urinary tract infections.

Stone types are classified according to composition, and some breeds more typically suffer one type of stone over another. High-risk dog breeds most commonly suffer from struvite, while in non-high-risk breeds, the most common composition is cystine and to a lesser extent struvite. Other common compositions are oxalate stones, urate stones (most common in Dalmatians), and silicate stones (most common in German Shepherd Dogs), with a variety of other minerals occurring less frequently; however, any dog can develop any type of stone.

Knowing the stone composition is important, because treatment may be different depending on the type of stone. Some mineral compositions can be dissolved by feeding a special diet, but most large stones require surgical removal. The chemical composition of the stone often points to the cause, which when treated may help prevent recurrence of the problem.

Stones irritate the lining of the urinary tract, can cause cystitis, and in the most serious cases may block the passage of urine. Signs of bladder stones range from none to severe, and also may vary between male and female dogs because of anatomical distinctions. Signs are any one or combination of the following: a break in house-training, dribbling urine, spending lots of time "posing" in the yard with little result, bloody urine or urine with a strong ammonia smell, whining during urination, or excessively licking the genitals. Dogs of either sex may assume a strange splay-legged position when urination is painful. Partial obstruction may result in a weak, splattery stream of urine even when your pet shows no other signs of distress.

If crystals or stones cut off the passage of urine, life-threatening blockage occurs and is an emergency. Blockage more frequently is suffered by males, because of the narrower urethral passage. This is an excruciating situation for your pet, because with no place to go, the urine simply fills the bladder like a balloon, and eventually backs up into the kidneys. Blockage may develop suddenly, or over days or weeks. Even partial blockage causes severe damage which can result in renal failure (see KIDNEY DISEASE). But complete blockage can kill your dog within 72 hours, and requires immediate veterinary assistance.

The bladder must be emptied before it bursts; rupture causes peritonitis which dogs rarely survive. It's sometimes possible to pass a catheter through the dog's urethra past the blockage, or to flush the urolith back into the bladder; this is usually done with the dog anesthetized. Other times, a needle is inserted through the abdominal wall and into the bladder to drain the urine, a process called cystocentesis. The blockage may require surgical intervention.

Dogs often require supportive care, such as fluid therapy, particularly when dehydrated or depressed. Dogs require close monitoring for at least a week following relief of obstruction, to ensure it does not recur. Owners must remain vigilant for several weeks even after the dog is sent home.

Diagnosis of bladder stones is usually based on signs, X-rays, and/or palpation or "feeling" the bladder through the abdominal wall. The type of stone can usually be determined by considering the dog's breed, sex, diet, and the presence (or absence) of urinary tract infection and its cause.

Often, surgical removal of the stones is required, along with flushing the urinary tract of any remaining crystals. There are commercially available (by veterinary prescription) calculolytic diets that dissolve struvite and ammonium urate stones within two to twenty weeks, which may be appropriate in certain cases. Great care must be taken in using these diets, though, as oftentimes the stones are of mixed composition and not all of the stone will be dissolved—or, the stone may shrink to a size that allows it to pass into and block the urethra.

Depending on the type of stone, a mineral- and protein-restricted diet may help prevent recurrence. Also, the urine is analyzed and when infection is present, an appropriate therapy such as penicillin is instituted. A low-dose antibiotic medication may be prescribed thereafter as a preventative, because keeping the urinary tract free of bacteria will prevent future development of such "infection stones."

Dalmatians are the only breed that inconsistently metabolizes uric acid, which results in urate stones. Diet greatly influences the concentration of uric acid, as does a medication called allopurinol. The combination of using a modified prescription diet and the drug allopurinol is instrumental in controlling the formation of such stones in the Dalmatian.

If your dog is of a breed that is considered at high risk for bladder stones, remain vigilant to catch the earliest sign of distress. Encourage your dog to drink by keeping plenty of fresh water available, and promoting moderate exercise. Dietary and antibiotic therapy are not recommended as a preventative for dogs that have never before suffered an episode of urinary tract stones.

BLEEDING

Bleeding occurs whenever the integrity of the body's tissue is breached, and serves primarily to cleanse a wound. Bleeding results from cuts, abrasions and lacerations, and clotting factors in the blood help protect injuries during healing by forming a scab over the wound. A veterinarian should address any deep or gaping injury, whether accompanied by excessive bleeding or not.

Capillary bleeding from abrasions or scratches typically produces oozing wounds with negligible bleeding. Arterial bleeding results in a spurting flow of bright red blood that surges with each beat of the dog's heart. When a vein is cut, the blood is dark red and flows evenly.

Bleeding generally can be stopped by applying even, direct pressure to the wound. Cover the area with a clean cloth or gauze pad and press firmly for five to seven minutes, then check if the bleeding has stopped by carefully lifting the cloth. Continue the pressure until the bleeding subsides. Be careful moving the pad, as it may stick to the wound as the new scab forms. If this happens, simply place a fresh pad or cloth over the first.

When bleeding continues despite direct pressure, raising the injury above the heart level helps slow the bleeding by using gravity to reduce the blood pressure to the wound. It may help to apply indirect pressure to the arteries between your dog's heart and the injury. Find the pressure points inside each leg at the "arm pit" on front legs and the crotch where the hind legs connect to the torso. The underside of the tail base is another pressure point. With a cut vein, applying pressure below the injury stops bleeding.

When excessive bleeding continues despite your efforts, and if the injury is to a leg or tail, a tourniquet may be used when the life of the dog is at stake. Tourniquets are considered tools of last resort, however, because their improper use may damage the limb or tissue to the point that amputation becomes necessary.

Use a strip of cloth, gauze, or even one leg from a pair of panty hose to fashion your tourniquet. Be sure the material is at least one inch wide to reduce the risk of cutting your pet's skin. Circle the limb twice with the fabric, positioning the material about two inches from the wound. Tie the ends once, then securely knot a pencil or comparable object like a kitchen knife or wooden spoon above the first tie. Slowly turn the pencil to twist and tighten the material; stop as soon as bleeding slows to a trickle, and fasten the pencil in place. The pressure must be released every fifteen minutes for a brief period to allow circulation into the affected limb. Your dog should be seen by a veterinarian immediately.

Internal bleeding is more difficult to detect because bruises and swellings are often hidden beneath the fur (see HEMATOMA). Bleeding from the anus or mouth, blood in the urine, stool or vomit, or loss of consciousness may all be signs of internal bleeding. Bloody urine, feces, or bleeding from the mouth, ears, nose or eyes can also point to poisoning or advanced liver disease, and cystitis and bladder stones may result in bloody urine. Unless the injury is limited to a scratch or simple abrasion, any dog that is bleeding should see a veterinarian immediately.

BLINDNESS

Vision loss can be gradual, sudden, complete or partial. Dogs may become blind as a result of injury or more commonly, as the consequence of an eye disease (see CATARACTS, GLAUCOMA, and PROGRESSIVE RETINAL ATROPHY).

People often remain unaware that dogs have any vision problems at all, because they compensate so well. Loss of sight typically causes problems when they're in unfamiliar surroundings. But at home they know the lay of the house and have mapped it by sight, sound and scent; they remember each landmark. Owners may suddenly realize there's a problem if they rearrange the furniture, for example.

A classic sign of PRA is fear of the dark. Dogs do fine in the house, or in the yard during the day, but lose night vision first and become uncomfortable going outside at night. When blindness is due to cataracts, prompt surgery may restore some vision. But injuries or diseases that cause permanent damage can't be reversed. Blind dogs compensate by relying more on their other senses, and won't be nearly as concerned about the deficit as the owners.

BLINDNESS

SYMPTOMS: Bumping into furniture; reluctance to navigate stairs or jumps; clingy; snaps when touched unexpectedly; fearful to go outside at night; moves cautiously; pupil of eye stays dilated
HOME CARE: Keep environment the same; avoid startling dog
VET CARE: Appropriate diagnosis and/or treatment, if possible
PREVENTION: None

However, the animal's comfort level, safety, and emotional health should be addressed by making necessary accommodations. Keep all the furniture in one place, and don't move it around too much. Dogs memorize the pattern of the house. If the furniture is changed constantly they become a little anxious. It's vital to keep the food and water bowls, the bed, and favorite toys in the same spot, so your dog can always find his belongings.

Blind dogs become more dependent on you as a Seeing Eye person, and may become clingy and stand very close to you. Previously social dogs might become standoffish once their vision is gone. A blind dog can become nippy and bite when somebody surprises him. It's only fair to warn him, and protect others from an accidental nip. Try attaching bells to the collars of other pets in the home, so the blind dog can more easily find them. It may also help for you to wear a bell, or speak to announce your presence to avoid startling the dog.

Keeping the lights turned up and a nightlight on can be helpful for PRA dogs with fading vision. Protect him from injury, perhaps blocking off the basement stairs with a baby gate. Don't let anyone tell you that blind dogs must be put to sleep. A blind dog is still a very happy dog.

BLOAT (GASTRIC DILATATION-VOLVULUS)

Known more commonly as bloat, gastric dilatation-volvulus (GDV) is a little understood syndrome affecting up to 60,000 dogs each year. Gastric dilatation is the painful swelling of the stomach with gas and/or frothy material; volvulus is the rotation, or twisting, of the stomach. Bloat refers to one or both scenarios, and either can result in death.

When bloat occurs, the stomach contents cannot be expelled either by vomiting, burping, or by passing into the intestines. The stomach distention causes pressure on other internal organs, which results in shock. If the stomach twists, circulation is cut off and the stomach and spleen can die; the rotation also compresses a vein that returns blood to the heart, resulting in severe depression of normal blood circulation.

Slowed circulation increases the chance that bacteria may leak from the intestines into the bloodstream and cause infection. When both distention and twisting are present, multiple organ failure and death typically occur within hours as a result of the shock.

BLOAT

SYMPTOMS: Restless behavior; unproductive attempts to vomit or defecate; swollen, painful stomach; pale gums; irregular breathing; collapse
HOME CARE: EMERGENCY! SEE VET IMMEDIATELY!
VET CARE: Passage of stomach tube to vent gas; emergency surgery
PREVENTION: Gastropexy surgery to fix stomach in place

Dogs become restless from the discomfort within a few hours of eating. Typically they whine, lie down then get up, and pace in an effort to get comfortable. The dog may try to vomit or defecate without success. The stomach becomes swollen and painful, and signs of shock—pale gums, irregular or shallow breathing, rapid heartbeat—are soon followed by collapse. Bloat is a life-threatening emergency that requires immediate veterinary intervention if your dog is to survive.

All dogs can be affected, but purebred dogs are three times more likely to suffer bloat compared to mixed breed dogs. Breeds that have a narrow but deep chest have the greatest incidence of the condition. The deep, narrow-chest conformation of certain breeds may create a more acute angle at the junction of the esophagus with the stomach, and predispose them to accumulate gas in their stomach. Research from Europe suggests many affected dogs may have subtle swallowing abnormalities that interfere with their esophagus so they swallow more air or are less able to burp to rid themselves of trapped stomach gas.

Anxious, irritable, nervous, and aggressive characteristics seem to make the dog predisposed, with some research indicating nervous dogs have a twelve times higher risk than calm, happy dogs. One study indicated that incidence of the syndrome was lowest during morning hours, and increased throughout the day, peaking during late evening.

Great Danes have the highest incidence, with about a 40 percent chance they'll have an episode before they reach age seven. A recent survey estimated the lifetime risk of bloat at 24 percent for large breed (50 to 99 pounds) and 22 percent for giant breed dogs (over 99 pounds). The chances of bloat in large breed dogs increased dramatically at three years of age, compared to six months of age in giant breeds. Dogs that are underweight also have an increased risk, which may be an indication they already have problems with their gastrointestinal tract.

The symptoms presented in a high-risk dog breed are usually suggestive of the condition, but X-rays may be required to confirm the diagnosis. Treatment is aimed at relieving the pressure in the stomach by venting the gas and removing the solid contents. Simply passing a stomach tube down the throat and into the stomach will manage the distension problem, but a twisted stomach requires surgical correction—and an X-ray doesn't always offer a clear picture of the problem.

In corrective surgery, the abdomen is opened and the surgeon massages the juncture of esophagus and stomach so the tube can pass into and decompress the gas. Then the surgeon returns the stomach to a normal location, and addresses any damage to the stomach, spleen or other organs from blood loss.

Even when the stomach decompresses by stomach tube without surgery, gastropexy surgery is recommended to fix the stomach to the body wall so it can't twist. That prevents a recurrence of the condition in more than 90 percent of cases. It can be done at the same time as spay or neuter surgery, and laparoscopic surgery techniques can make the procedure much less invasive and reduce recovery time.

Dogs with gastric dilatation-volvulus that do not undergo a gastropexy have recurrence rates of more than 70 percent and mortality rates of 80 percent.

Although bloat can't be completely prevented, predisposing factors can be reduced, and should be taken into account particularly if your dog is a high-risk breed. Limiting water and exercise before and after meals, commonly recommended in the past, in fact did not reduce the incidence of bloat in more recent studies. Another recommendation—raising the food bowl—actually increased the risk of bloat by about 200 percent.

Avoid sudden changes in food, which can prompt gorging behavior. When a diet change is necessary, introduce it gradually over a seven to ten day period. Meal-feed your dog small quantities of food several times a day, rather than feeding all at once. And if there's food competition between your dogs, feed them in separate rooms to help slow gulpers and calm their anxiety over stolen food. Try mixing dry food with water to reduce your dog's urge to gulp water; this also increases the food volume, which may help slow fast eaters.

BLOOD is a liquid composed of a number of specialized cells, and serves as the body's transportation system. Plasma, the yellow liquid portion of the blood, ferries clotting agents, nutrients, immune components and waste products to their various destinations throughout the body. Plasma also transports the solid components of blood: the red cells, white cells, and platelets.

Red cells (erythrocytes) carry oxygen throughout the body. Hemoglobin is the oxygen-carrying pigment that gives these cells their red color. Platelets and specialized proteins make clotting possible, and serve to control and stop bleeding. Five kinds of white cells—neutrophils, monocytes, lymphocytes, eosinophils and basophils—are variously involved with the body's immune system. Along with antibodies, the white cells help identify and protect against viral or bacterial infection.

Blood components are the same in all dogs, no matter the breed, except in the racing Greyhound. Greyhounds have a much higher red cell volume than other breeds (60 in Greyhounds compared to 40 in all other dogs), probably because of the greater need for oxygen demanded by racing.

But just like people, there are important differences between individual dogs. Blood groups and types vary from dog to dog, and the differences are inherited.

Giving incompatible blood can have life- threatening consequences. Antigens, a kind of protein on the surface of blood cells, define a blood type. The immune system responds to a foreign antigen by producing antibodies against it. When the dog has very strong antibodies against the wrong blood type, they attack and destroy the foreign blood the same way they would a virus or bacteria.

Antigens on the surface of the blood cells define a blood type. Antigens are proteins, toxins or other substances to which the body responds by producing antibodies.

Previously, canine blood groups were identified with letters similarly to human blood types, but currently they're designated DEA (dog erythrocyte antigen) with a number that identifies each. This is important, because when a dog is injured or ill, a transfusion with whole blood or blood components may be necessary to save the dog's life. But giving the wrong type of blood can have dire consequences.

Thirteen different canine blood group systems have been identified, and dogs can be classified as positive or negative for each. The canine blood groups most commonly recognized are DEA-1.1, DEA-1.2, DEA-3, DEA-4, DEA-5, DEA-6, DEA-7 and DEA-8. When a dog has those specific antigens on its red cells, it's said to be positive for that particular group; if the red cells do not have a given antigen, then the dog is negative for that blood group.

Some blood types cause more dangerous reactions than others, and the DEA-1.1 group is the worst offender. DEA 1.1 negative dogs should get only DEA 1.1 negative blood, whereas DEA 1.1 positive dogs may get either DEA 1.1 positive or negative blood. An incompatible transfusion can result in both clumping and destruction of the red cells. Usually the reaction is immediate, but it may be delayed up to four days.

The dog's immune system doesn't seem to immediately recognize incompatible blood, but must be first exposed to incompatible blood before building antibodies against it. For that reason, most dogs can receive a transfusion from any other blood group the first time. After that, though, the immune system is "primed" to recognize the foreign blood and if it's given again, a life-threatening transfusion reaction can happen.

Blood incompatibility can cause problems in breeding situations, although it's considered much rarer in dogs than in cats. Called neonatal isoerythrolysis (NI), the condition results when the dam's blood is incompatible with that of her puppies. This can happen if she has pre-formed antibodies (considered rare), or if she's been sensitized by a previous transfusion. In either case, these antibodies will be in the mother dog's milk when she gives birth. By breeding a male dog with DEA-1.1 positive blood to a female dog with DEA-1.1 negative blood, resulting puppies that have their father's blood type are at risk; when they drink the mother dog's first milk (colostrum), antibodies it contains attack and destroy the puppy's red cells. Such puppies start out healthy, but become weaker and weaker, and usually die within the first week of life (see FADING PUPPY SYNDROME.

A hemolytic transfusion reaction happens when the red cells are attacked by the immune system, and broken down. In an acute reaction, the affected dog can show nearly immediate signs of distress; heartbeat and respiration slow, there's a loss of blood pressure, and the dog may uncontrollably vomit, defecate and/or urinate, and finally collapse. More commonly, the reaction is milder and develops over a period of hours as the transfusion is given. A delayed reaction is also possible, in which the dog tolerates the transfusion at first, then develops signs down the road when the body destroys the blood faster than it normally would.

Many times, a dog's first transfusion takes place under emergency circumstances to save the dog's life. If he's never before been transfused, it's likely he'll have no adverse reaction to the blood, even if it is incompatible. But it's advisable whenever possible—and always after your dog has been previously transfused—to identify the dog's blood type so that sensitization of your dog's blood and/or a possible life-threatening reaction can be avoided.

There are in-house test kits available for your veterinarian to screen for the most problematic blood types, and cross-matching can be done in your veterinarian's office. It won't determine the type, but will tell if the donor's blood is compatible with the recipient's--in other words, whether a transfusion reaction will occur or not. Cross-matching won't be helpful if the dog has never before been transfused, but is highly recommended in cases where the dog has received blood before. A drop of serum or plasma from the recipient dog is mixed with a drop of blood from the prospective donor dog; clumping indicates the blood is incompatible.

Certain blood types are more desirable for transfusion than others. Those that are the least antigenic--least likely to cause a reaction--are best. DEA-1.1 is often the donor blood type of choice, because it will not sensitize or cause a reaction in a DEA-1.1-negative dog; a large percentage of the dog population is this type and won't have a reaction. DEA-4-positive is also a good choice, because it causes little problem when there is a reaction, and about 98 percent of all dogs are positive for this blood type and would have no reaction.

Many veterinarians keep a dog on call that serves as a blood donor. Teaching hospitals at veterinary schools often operate their own animal blood banks, and commercial animal blood banks also make a variety of products available.

BOTULISM

Botulism is not an infection, but is an intoxication resulting in a usually fatal paralysis caused by ingestion of the toxin produced by the bacteria *Clostridium botulinum*. Thankfully, botulism intoxication is a rare condition.

The organism grows in decomposing animal tissue and sometimes plant material, and is probably found in the highest frequency in domesticated chickens and wild waterfowl like ducks. Dogs may contract the toxin from eating improperly canned food, raw meat, or rotting carcasses, or by wound contamination that results in the toxin being produced in the dog's damaged tissue. Dogs are comparatively resistant to ingested botulism.

The neurotoxin targets the nerve endings that control the muscles. Signs of botulism intoxication include vomiting or regurgitation, abdominal pain characterized by a "hunching" or arched back posture, dry mouth, and progressive weakness beginning in the hind legs that produces an odd hopping gait. Paralysis eventually spreads to include the whole body, and the dog typically has trouble seeing, and difficulty chewing and swallowing. Death usually results from respiratory and/or cardiac paralysis.

Diagnosis is difficult, because it's hard to find the toxin in the dog's blood, tissues, vomit or feces, or even in the suspect food. Most commonly, diagnosis is determined by suspect signs and eliminating other causes for the paralysis. Unlike some other paralytic diseases that have similar signs, botulism intoxication also affects muscles in the head.

An antitoxin is available for treatment when botulism is suspected, but is not terribly helpful unless administered very early in the disease. Antibiotic therapy offers little help, either. Treatment is almost exclusively supportive, aimed at relieving the dog's symptoms and keeping him alive until his own body can clear the toxin. It may take one to three weeks for full recovery.

Botulism intoxication is best prevented by keeping your dog from raiding the garbage, or from scavenging the remains of wildlife. Any wound should be promptly seen and attended by a veterinarian.

BOTULISM

SYMPTOMS: Vomiting or regurgitation; abdominal pain (hunching posture); dry mouth; progressive weakness; paralysis within 12-24 hours; difficulty chewing and swallowing
HOME CARE: None
VET CARE: Antitoxin early in the disease; supportive therapy to relieve symptoms
PREVENTION: Keep dog from scavenging garbage or dead animals; attend to wounds promptly

BREED Breed refers to a distinct type of dog having predictable physical and/or temperament characteristics that are consistently reproduced in that dog's offspring.

DOG FACTS

A dog of a particular breed has a known, traceable ancestry referred to as the pedigree. A "purebred" dog is one produced by mating a male and female dog of the same breed. Registering the litter produced from such a breeding authenticates breed status of those puppies by placing them on record in a dog registry association. There are over 400 distinct dog breeds recognized around the world; more than 100 are described in this book (see APPENDIX A, DOG ASSOCIATIONS AND DOG BREEDS AT A GLANCE).

Dogs have been associated with humans for at least 15,000 years, with recent genetic research pointing to as early as 100,000 years ago. Consequently, the form and function of dogs have been altered throughout history, and the domestication process has literally molded dogs into new forms.

"Natural" dog types like the Alaskan Malamute and Saluki appeared in nature. They have probably changed very little over the centuries; selective breeding by dog fanciers refined these breeds.

"Spontaneous mutations" are inexplicable deviations of nature that dog fanciers promoted and developed into new breeds. Mutations range from body shape and size, ear placement and tail carriage, to scenting and sighting ability, or even hair coat and color. Size mutation examples include the giantism (acromegaly) of mastiff-type breeds like the Great Dane and St. Bernard, or midgetism of toy breeds like the Toy Poodle which are simply miniature versions of larger breeds. Dwarfism (achondroplasia) results in shortened, somewhat curved leg bones of breeds like Dachshunds and Basset Hounds.

Hybrids are created by combining existing breeds to form new ones; however, most existing dog breeds are so ancient, that although it's likely many are hybrids, their origin is obscure. Many of the variety of breeds we know today have been around for 3000 years, or longer.

Despite the great variety in size and shape, all dogs are easily recognizable as canines. Dog breeds range in size from two to three pound to pony-size 200 pound plus canines. Mastiff-type breeds are larger and tend to be more heavily muscled and cobby (compact, short-bodied), while sighthound breeds like Greyhounds and Whippets are no less muscled but appear more lithe. There is a wide range between the two extremes.

Some of the earliest mutations had to do with the dog's coat, which today is found in a wide range of lengths, textures and colors. There are five basic coat types. "Long fur with undercoat" types include the Rough Collie and German Shepherd Dog; "silky coat" breeds include the Afghan Hound, Pekingese, setters and spaniels; "smooth coat" are the shorthaired dogs like Boxers, Chihuahuas and Rottweilers; "wiry" coats are found on most terriers and the Schnauzer; and the "non-shedding curly" type coat grows constantly but must be trimmed, and is sported by breeds like Poodles and the Bedlington Terrier.

DOG FACTS

Coat color offers a rainbow of hues: Westie white, Kerry Blue blue, Weimaraner silver, Scottie black, and a range of browns from light tan to Golden Retriever gold, Irish Setter red, and Labrador chocolate. Dogs in solid colors are referred to as "self-colored."

Pattern is equally diverse. Ticked refers to small isolated areas of black or colored hairs over a white ground color. Sable is produced by black-tipped hairs on a background of silver, gold, grey, fawn or brown. Brindle is a pattern of black tiger-like stripes on a lighter background (usually tan). Parti-color (also pied or piebald) refers to patches of two or more colors on the coat. Harlequin is patches of color (usually black or grey) on a white background.

Tricolor is a coat with three distinct colors, usually white, black and tan. Merle color pattern has dark blotches against a lighter background of the same color, while mottled pattern is characterized by round blotches of color on a lighter background. Points are the same color on the face, ears, legs and tail, and are usually white, black or tan. Grizzle is a mixture of black or red hairs with white (also called roan), and is often a bluish- to iron-gray color, or may be orange or lemon.

Mixed-breed dogs come in a variety of colors, shapes and sizes that rival any purebred. Also referred to as random-bred or mutt dogs, they are the result of unplanned breedings of various purebred or other mixed-breed dogs. They have no pedigree, are not often registered, but may superficially resemble a purebred; however, it is impossible to predict what their offspring will be like. They make wonderful pets, though, and are the dog type of choice for many households throughout the world.

BRONCHITIS

Characterized by bursts of dry, harsh, honking coughs, bronchitis is the inflammation of the large breathing tubes (bronchials) of the lungs. Chronic bronchitis is a common problem in older dogs, and is seen a great deal in small breed dogs like terriers, Poodles and Beagles.

Some cases of bronchitis are caused by allergy. Dogs suffering from allergic bronchitis frequently cough all year long. The cough may be prompted simply by massaging the dog's throat, or induced by excitement, exercise, tugging against the leash, or even drinking. As with most inhalant allergies, only rarely can the cause be identified (see ALLERGY).

The condition causes an increase in the production and accumulation of mucus in the airways. The thick sticky substance is very irritating and difficult to move. Dogs cough from the resulting inflammation, and also in an attempt to clear their lungs. Dogs aren't able to spit, so they often gag or retch at the end of a coughing spell.

In most cases, the cause of chronic bronchitis isn't known, and the dog is otherwise quite healthy. There currently is no evidence that viral or bacterial infections play any role in the condition.

Chronic bronchitis is diagnosed by the presence of an ongoing cough, and ruling out other causes (see KENNEL COUGH, HEARTWORM DISEASE, and CANCER). An examination of the airways and/or X-rays may confirm the diagnosis. When the culprit is an allergy, an analysis of a tracheal wash usually reveals no bacteria, but many eosinophils (white cells important to allergic response).

Even when chronic bronchitis is diagnosed, unless the coughing is severe, treatment may not be required. In fact, cough suppressant medications may actually exacerbate the problem by interfering with the mechanism that clears the mucus.

When the condition is considered severe, your veterinarian may prescribe long-term low doses of corticosteroid drugs to help control the inflammation. Expectorant medications are also helpful, which help break up mucus and other secretions and aid in coughing them up. Bronchodilator drugs that open the airways and help breathing seem to benefit some dogs.

There's no way to prevent chronic bronchitis from occurring. However, if the cause is due to allergy and the culprit can be identified, avoiding that allergen will help relieve the dog's symptoms.

BRUCELLOSIS

This canine venereal disease is caused by the bacterium *Brucella canis (B. canis)*, and causes a number of problems, including abortions. *B. canis* was first recognized in the mid-1960s, and is found in dogs all over the world. It's estimated that about one percent of pet dogs and five percent of strays are infected, but the incidence of disease varies depending on the geographic region.

Most cases of canine brucellosis are associated with dogs in kennel situations, because the close proximity aids in spreading the disease. Female dogs harbor the organism in the greatest concentration in the placenta and vaginal secretions, while male dogs pass the infection through their semen. Brucellosis is transmitted through sexual contact, or through ingestion of the bacteria from contact with contaminated surfaces. Infected bitches can infect kennel runs with their uterine discharges or aborted fetuses, which may potentially spread disease to other dogs.

Once the bacteria has been introduced either orally or sexually, the organism multiplies in the nearest lymph nodes--either the neck and head, or the groin region. The nodes may become slightly enlarged, but rarely are fever or other signs of illness seen. Occasionally, the dog may lose weight, appear fatigued, or seem to lose interest in mating. The organism then spills into the dog's bloodstream, and can maintain a presence for two years or longer. During this period, the bacteria infects the prostate and testicles of male dogs, and the pregnant female dog's placenta. Both male and female dogs can shed the bacteria in urine for at least three months after becoming infected.

The infection in the pregnant female results in abortion (usually after six to eight weeks into gestation), still-birth at or near term, or weak puppies that die within days of birth. Rarely will puppies survive, but when they do, they become carriers of the bacterium. Infected bitches usually abort puppies only during the pregnancy that initially follows infection. Sometimes, though, the disease also kills puppies in the second or even third pregnancy following infection.

BRUCELLOSIS

SYMPTOMS: Lymph node enlargement; weight loss; fatigue; loss of libido; abortion, stillbirth, fading puppies; swollen or wasting testicles; back pain; uveitis
HOME CARE: None
VET CARE: Antibiotic therapy
PREVENTION: Test dogs and remove positive animals from kennel/breeding situations; kennel dogs in separate runs

In male dogs, brucellosis results in infertility caused by inflammation and atrophy of the testicles. The testicles may swell, and then shrink and waste away as the sperm-producing tissue is destroyed.

Low sperm count, production of abnormal sperm, and/or sterility results. Some dogs develop back problems caused by inflammation of the discs in the lower back.

Dogs are diagnosed by testing a sample of their blood for the bacteria. There are several types of tests available, and the most accurate (blood culture) is also the most expensive, especially when a group of dogs must be screened. Another test screens the blood and measures the level of antibodies specific for the disease, which indicates the dog has been exposed to brucellosis. Therefore, a negative test is quite accurate—no antibodies means no exposure, and no disease—but a positive only means exposure has occurred, not necessarily that infection is present. A positive antibody test for brucellosis should be confirmed with a more specific test.

There is no vaccine available to prevent the disease. Several antibiotics will clear the bacteria from the dog's bloodstream. However, the organism "hides out" in the lymph nodes and other tissues of the body, and can re-infect the bloodstream once therapy is stopped.

Brucellosis is controlled by testing all dogs before introducing them into a kennel situation, and removing any dogs that carry the bacteria. Particularly in breeding situations, prior screening of both the male and female is essential to protect both dogs and any subsequent puppies that may be born. Kennels that keep dogs caged individually typically have a lower incidence of the disease.

There have been rare cases of humans contracting brucellosis, usually through contact with aborted puppies or laboratory exposure. It's not currently considered a common hazard to people, but when it does occur, people typically experience flu-like symptoms. Intermittent headache, fever, swollen lymph nodes, chills, muscle pain, and sore throat are some signs. Unlike the canine disease, antibiotics are very effective in eliminating *B. canis* infection in people (see ZOONOSIS).

BURNS

SYMPTOMS: Red skin; blistering, swelling, tender or painful area; charred tissue; fur easily pulls out
FIRST AID: Apply cool water with cloth; see vet as soon as possible
VET CARE: Cold compresses, salves, or ointments; surgical removal of dead tissue; sometimes fluid therapy or pain medication
PREVENTION: Prevent access to hazards; tape down electrical cords or paint with dog repellent; keep caustic solutions out of reach

BURNS A burn refers to injury resulting from exposure to fire, heat, caustic substances, electricity or radiation. Dogs can suffer burns from kitchen accidents involving spills of hot cooking oil or boiling water, from walking through fresh tar, chemical burns (see POISON), chewing electric cords (see ELECTRICAL SHOCK), over-exposure to the sun (see SUNBURN), and rarely direct contact with fire. Frostbite also resembles a burn injury.

The extent of damage depends on the intensity and length of exposure. A minor burn will cause the skin to turn red and sometimes blister or swell, and the area will be tender. Deeper burns char or turn the tissue white. Fur in the affected areas will become loose and easily pulled out.

Severe burns cause excruciating pain. They are usually accompanied by excessive loss of fluid, and shock. When 15 percent or more of the body surface is burned, the outlook is grim.

First aid involves relieving the pain and stopping further damage. Soak a towel in cool water and apply to the injured area to alleviate the pain. For superficial burns, clip away the surrounding fur, rinse gently with cool water, and blot dry with a clean soft cloth. A topical antibiotic like Neosporin will help prevent infection, and keep the area moist while it heals. You may need to employ a collar restraint to prevent the dog from licking the wound (see ELIZABETHAN COLLAR).

Moderate to severe burns should be addressed by your veterinarian. Even a superficial injury can be more serious than you think, because damage may be hidden by the hair coat.

To avoid burns, make the kitchen off-limits to your dog when you're cooking. When open flame is accessible, such as candles or fireplace, either confine the dog to a safe place or increase your vigilance to prevent accidents. Dog-proof your house by making electrical cords inaccessible or unattractive. Tape electrical cords out of the way, and/or apply a bad-tasting solution like Bitter Apple to deter persistent chewing. Supervise your dog's outdoor excursions to prevent him blundering into a sticky situation and getting into hot water--or tar.

CALLUS A callus is a hard thickened area of gray, hairless skin that forms as a protective barrier, usually on a pressure point above bone. Calluses can form anywhere on the body but typically develop on the elbow, usually as a result of the ongoing pressure of contact when the dog lies down. Small calluses aren't usually a concern, but they can develop into problems, particularly in dogs housed in kennels with cement floors.

Callus sores occur most frequently in large breed or heavy dogs. In addition to the elbows, they may develop on the underside of the forelegs, or the outside of the rear legs, thighs and buttocks. Draining pressure sores can develop at these sites if the irritation is not relieved. Infected sores are treated like an abscess.

Prevent problem calluses by padding your dog's sleeping areas, particularly concrete runs, with blankets, rugs, or foam rubber pads. This helps distribute the dog's weight more evenly, and alleviates the pressure on the callus.

CANCER The term cancer refers to an abnormal growth of cells that interfere with normal body functions. All body cells have a finite lifespan. When they die, cells are replaced through a process called mitosis in which a single cell splits into two cells identical to the parent cell. For reasons we don't fully understand, normal cells sometimes mutate during mitosis, producing fast-growing abnormal cells that act like parasites, invading and replacing healthy tissues. Considered a disease primarily of old age, the Veterinary Cancer Society says cancer is the leading cause of death in dogs (47 percent) over the age of ten.

Under ideal circumstances, the body's immune system recognizes these cells as foreign, and eliminates them before they can cause problems. But all too often, the body can't fight off the attack. Growths of abnormal cells, called tumors or neoplasms, are the result. Those that remain localized and relatively harmless are termed benign, while potentially deadly tumors are called malignant.

Malignant tumors can be confined to one area, but often they spread, or metastasize, throughout the body. The seriousness of a specific kind of cancer is determined by how malignant it is. The most treatable are considered low-grade cancers because although they reach a great size, they tend not to metastasize until relatively late in the disease. The most dangerous cancers are already spreading at the earliest stages, when the point of origination is still very small or even nearly undetectable. A malignant tumor becomes deadly when it interferes with normal body processes.

The exact cause of cancer remains a mystery, but we do know that cancer-causing agents, referred to as carcinogens, may increase the risk of developing certain kinds of disease. Cumulative exposure over a dog's lifetime may be why older dogs develop cancer more often.

Exposure to ultraviolet rays (sunlight) increases the risk of skin cancer. Certain components in foods may increase a dog's risk of cancer, or they may protect against it. The role diet plays in cancer is not yet fully understood. However, the relation between sexual hormones and some types of cancers has been well documented. The risk of mammary cancer in female dogs, and prostate and testicular cancer in male dogs can be reduced or even eliminated by neutering or spaying the dog. There also can be inherited tendencies, with certain breeds—or families/lines of dogs within a certain breed—being more prone to some cancers.

CANCER

SYMPTOMS: see **VETERINARY CANCER SOCIETY'S TOP 10 CANCER SIGNS**
HOME CARE: Maintain good nutrition; nursing care
HOLISTIC HELP: Vitamin supplements; nutraceuticals; herbal therapy; homeopathy
VET CARE: Surgery; chemotherapy; radiation
PREVENTION: Spay females before first heat cycle, neuter males before puberty; avoid sun exposure in light-colored dogs; remain alert to lumps and bumps

Early detection greatly improves your dog's prognosis and chance for successful treatment. Any lump or bump you find on your dog should be evaluated immediately by your veterinarian. However, symptoms of cancer are often similar to other illnesses or conditions. Most canine cancers are external, but a dog's fur can make lumps or sores difficult to detect. And when a cancer is internal, you may not notice anything is wrong until your dog becomes sick. Be vigilant for any physical and/or behavioral changes in your dog, and alert your veterinarian immediately.

Dogs can suffer from more kinds of cancer than any other domestic animal, including the same variety of cancers that people do. It's impossible to catalogue them all here. But the cancers people commonly suffer—cancer of the lungs, cervix, prostate, colon, and pancreas—are relatively uncommon in dogs. They often suffer from skin cancer, (the most common); breast cancer, which accounts for over half the cases; lymphoma, which ranks third with an incidence of 24 cases per 100,000 per year; followed by oral tumors, bone cancer, and testicular cancer.

Secondhand smoke can trigger a variety of diseases in dogs, with a higher likelihood in certain breeds. Short-nosed breeds like Pugs and Pit Bulls are twice as likely to contract lung cancer while longer-nosed breeds like Collies and German Shepherds are two-and-a-half times more likely to get nasal cancer. Cocker Spaniels, Boxers, and Retrievers are more prone to lymphoma than other breeds.

Several types of skin cancer affect dogs, and some studies estimate that up to 30 percent of canine cancers arise from the skin. The most common are sebaceous adenomas; thankfully, about 75 percent are benign. These tumors develop from the oil producing sebaceous glands, and are seen most commonly in Cocker Spaniels. They resemble a cauliflower, and are usually less than an inch in size; sometimes the skin surface ulcerates.

Mast cell tumors account for twelve to 21 percent of all canine skin cancers, and are common in Boxers and Boston Terriers. These tumors are usually less than an inch in size with a bumpy surface, and are found most often on the lower abdomen, hind legs, and prepuce. About 30 percent of mast cell tumors are malignant, and metastasize to other organs.

Squamous cell carcinoma is associated with over-exposure to sunlight (see SUNBURN). This skin cancer most frequently affects the belly of white dogs like Dalmatians and American Staffordshire Terriers, and the faces of white faced dogs, but can also appear on the feet and legs. It looks like a cauliflower, or like a grayish hard, flat non-healing ulcer. Although squamous cell carcinoma rarely spreads throughout the body, it is locally invasive and can be very damaging to the surrounding areas.

Mammary cancer accounts for 52 percent of all tumors in female dogs, and nearly half of the cases are malignant. Investigators at Michigan State University College of Veterinary Medicine are studying the molecular genetics of the disease, using known gene mutations in human breast cancer to offer a roadmap to find out more about the canine disease. Four genes in humans have been identified. BRCA1 and BRCA2 cause 40-45 percent of inherited forms in people, and mutations in TP53 and AT also contribute. Preliminary results from the two-year canine study indicate that a mutation of at least one of these genes plays an important role in canine mammary cancer as well.

Lymph gland cancers are also quite common in dogs, and are probably the third or fourth most common type of cancer accounting for perhaps seven percent of all canine cancers. Malignant lymphoma, also called lymphosarcoma, can develop in any lymph tissue anywhere on the body. Often the owner notices enlargement of one or many lymph nodes in the lower neck area.

Lymph gland cancers are devastating because they commonly spread throughout the body. Several breeds, including the Boxer, Basset Hound, Saint Bernard, and Scottish Terrier, have an increased risk for developing lymphomas. The lymphatic system also includes the blood cell-forming organs—bone marrow and spleen. Splenic hemangiosarcoma (cancer of the spleen) seems to affect middle aged to older German Shepherd Dogs most frequently. Affected dogs commonly are diagnosed on an emergency basis as their tumors rupture and cause pain, collapse, and severe bleeding, shock and eventually death if not treated. Unfortunately these tumors usually metastasize early and the expected lifespan after diagnosis is three to twelve months even with surgical treatment and chemotherapy.

Oral tumors account for about eight percent of all malignancies seen in the dog, and most growths in the middle-aged or older canine's mouth are malignant. Squamous cell carcinomas, melanomas and fibrosarcomas (cancers of connective tissue) affect the mouth, and all tend to spread throughout the body. Malignant melanomas tend to occur most frequently in dark-pigmented dogs. Scottish Terriers, black Labrador Retrievers, black Poodles and other dark dogs are most susceptible. Epulids are benign growths of the tissue surrounding the teeth which may need to be surgically removed for comfort. Watch for a mass on the gums, bleeding, mouth odor, or difficulty eating.

Bone cancer is another common canine cancer, rated by some in the top five. Osteosarcomas arising from the bone-forming cells are the most common type, and are almost always malignant. They have a high probability of spreading, often to the lungs. Typically they affect the long bones of the legs, or the skull, and are most common in large and giant breed dogs like St. Bernards, Great Danes and Newfoundlands; rarely does bone cancer occur in small dogs. The disease is excruciatingly painful. Affected dogs typically limp on the affected limb, which may have swelling.

Testicular cancer is considered relatively common in dogs; the testicle typically enlarges, or a mass grows on the scrotum. In cases where one or both testicles fail to descend from the abdomen into the scrotal sac (see CRYPTORCHID), there is a thirteen times greater incidence of tumors in the retained testicle. Fortunately, most testicular cancers tend not to spread, and neutering the dog usually cures the problem. Intact male dogs also tend to get perianal tumors—growths beneath the tail adjacent to the anus—that often are benign, but can be malignant.

The appearance of the tumor along with the dog's other symptoms (see chart) can point to cancer. Lumps that grow fast, change size or shape over weeks or months, ooze or break open, are firm and tightly fixed to body tissue, or are abnormally colored, are most likely to be malignant. However, only microscopic examination and identification of the tumor cells will render a definitive diagnosis. Your veterinarian may be able to collect a sample by inserting a needle directly into the tumor and withdrawing tumor cells into the syringe (see

CYTOLOGY). Other times, cancer cells may be identified in the circulating blood, or even in a urine specimen. However, often cancers require a biopsy (removal of a piece of tissue) for specialized laboratory analysis. A newer technique called lymphosyntigraphy injects radioactive tracers into the body. Cancer cells tend to absorb these compounds, which makes them easier to locate.

In 2010, a new blood test was unveiled for diagnosing cancer in dogs. BioCurex says the OncoPet RECAF test has detected 85 percent of a variety of cancers in dogs. The test detects whether RECAF, a universal marker for malignant cell growth in animals and people, is present in the blood. RECAF is related to rapid cell growth associated with cancer.

VETERINARY CANCER SOCIETY'S TOP 10 CANCER SIGNS

1. Abnormal swelling that persists or continues to grow
2. Sores that do not heal
3. Weight loss
4. Loss of appetite
5. Bleeding or discharge from any body opening
6. Offensive odor
7. Difficulty eating or swallowing
8. Hesitation to exercise or loss of stamina
9. Persistent lameness or stiffness
10. Difficulty in breathing, urinating, or defecating

Tests not only identifies the kind of cancer, but also evaluates its current state of progression. These two parameters define which treatment will be most effective (various cancers respond differently to available treatments), and help predict your dog's prognosis.

Prognosis depends on the type of the cancer, how advanced it is, and whether it has--or will--spread. It also depends on how healthy your dog is in other respects, because an elderly or ill dog may not handle the stress of cancer therapy as well as a robust dog. In the best circumstances when the cancer is detected early and treated aggressively, cures are possible.

Veterinary oncologists design treatments to remove, shrink, or stop the cancer growth, while also protecting the surrounding normal tissue. The same cancer treatments used in people are also used in dogs. These include one or a combination of surgery, radiation, and chemotherapy. Innovative therapies also may help, usually in combination with a conventional treatment.

Cure rates for malignant tumors in pets are 25 percent to 30 percent, which means cancer is more curable than commonly treated diseases like diabetes and heart failure. You don't have to "cure" in order to treat and improve and even extend quality of life.

The cancer treatment of choice in veterinary medicine is surgical removal of the tumor, and is particularly effective when the cancer is localized and has not spread. For instance, bone cancer is usually treated by amputation of the affected limb. Cost varies greatly depending on the cancer and the individual dog.

Unfortunately, surgical cure is rare because it's difficult to remove every cancerous cell. Leaving behind a single cell allows the cancer to recur and/or spread. In fact, the disturbance caused by surgery is sometimes thought to increase the chance that cancer cells will be disseminated; instead of conventional scalpels, lasers may be used to excise tumors to decrease this potential. Surgery alone may give your dog another six to twelve months. Other forms of treatment often follow surgery in an effort to rid the body of any malignant cells that may have been missed.

Some cancers that encroach upon vital organs, nerves or muscles can be difficult to surgically remove without damaging normal tissues. In those instances, radiation may be used.

Cancers of rapidly dividing cells (like bone marrow and the skin) are most sensitive to radiation therapy. Radiation works best on cancers confined to one area that are difficult to treat surgically, such as a skin cancer around the dog's eye. Radiation cures up to 80 percent of some kinds of cancers.

In order to irradiate only the target area, the dog must be anesthetized for each treatment. Anesthetic risk may be a concern when the dog is old or ill, as well as increasing the cost of an already expensive treatment.

Brachytherapy is one form of radiation treatment in which radioactive elements are actually planted into the tumor and left there for several days. However, it's not widely available. Conventional beam therapy is most commonly used, and consists of a beam of very intense X-ray being shot directly into the cancer to kill the cells.

Some of the newest linear accelerators (radiation machines) are designed to better target the tumor while sparing normal tissue. These technologies may incorporate CT scanners to help "see" the tumor in three dimensions and better plan the treatment. Washington State University has a linear accelerator that features a computerized 40-leaf collimeter that works like the iris on a camera to pinpoint the tumor with the X-ray beam. The head of the machine rotates around the pet's body and adjusts the dose of radiation as it moves.

Radiation therapy is most successful when used in combination with other treatments. Cancer cells aren't more sensitive than normal cells, and normal tissue can be damaged during treatment. The treatment regime varies, but often may be performed three times a week for a month.

DOG FACTS

Chemotherapy is the third cancer treatment commonly used with dogs, and is most useful in treating cancer that's spread throughout the body. A wide variety of cytotoxic (cell-poisoning) drugs are available and may be used singly or in combinations as pills or intravenous injections. The specific drug(s) used depend on the kind of cancer; many of the same human medications are effective against cancer in dogs. Often, initially intense therapy is followed by lower doses as treatment progresses.

The drugs are used to destroy as many cancer cells as possible, or at a minimum, to slow the growth rate of the tumor. But the drugs affect healthy tissue as well as cancerous growths, which is what causes unpleasant side effects in people. These symptoms vary depending on the drug and the dose; however, most dogs undergoing chemotherapy have few to no side effects compared to people. They may lose their appetite for a short time, or act lethargic during the most intense part of the treatment. But most dogs don't lose their hair, or suffer bouts of vomiting.

Toceranib phosphate (Palladia from Pfizer) has been shown to have effect against a number of canine tumors and is specifically approved for mast cell tumors. It works by killing tumor cells and by cutting off the blood supply to the tumor. An early study of Palladia showed 54 percent of dogs with a variety of tumors, including sarcoma, carcinoma, myeloma, melanoma, and MCTs, having some response to the drug. A subsequent study of Palladia showed a 59.5 percent biologic response in 145 dogs with inoperable mast cell tumors.

There is no such thing as a "standard" chemotherapy treatment. If the first drug you try doesn't work, it's not the end of the world.

Lymph gland cancers are considered one of the most rewarding canine cancers to treat using chemotherapy. Tumors shrink often within days of initial treatment, and up to 85 percent of treated dogs go into remission for nine to 18 months. A small percentage of these dogs are cured, or remain in remission for several years.

Because the drugs are prescribed according to the dog's body weight, cost of chemotherapy varies depending on the drug(s) and the individual dog. The cost for small animals tends to be relatively low, but can mount when your dog is quite heavy or is affected by other medical problems that increase the cost of treatment.

Chemotherapy is also a boon in treating bone cancer. Traditional treatment involves amputation, or sometimes replacement of the diseased bone with donor bone transplanted to "spare" the limb.

An experimental procedure called distraction osteogenesis induces the dog's body to grow a new bone. After the cancerous bone is removed, dogs wear an external brace with wires that go through the skin and bone, and out the other side. A small segment of normal bone is slowly moved each day by adjusting the frame. The owner turns a nut with a wrench three times a day, and that tricks the body into thinking it's trying to heal a fracture. Eventually the entire defect is replaced with the animal's own bone.

More experimental therapies are tested all the time. Immunotherapy employs special agents, including drugs, which help stimulate the body's immune system to prevent cancers from developing, or to help destroy existing tumor tissue. Gene therapy is the latest frontier in veterinary cancer treatments. For example, studies on genetically engineered tumor vaccines designed to target mouth cancers are being conducted.

In photodynamic therapy (PDT) sensitizing agents similar to chlorophyll, which the cancer absorbs, are injected into the dog's body. The cancer is then treated with laser light. The energy released within the sensitized cells kills the tumor but leaves normal tissue untouched. PDT is particularly useful against certain skin cancers, oral tumors and bladder tumors.

Heat therapy (hyperthermia) basically cooks the cancer to kill it, using sound waves that penetrate the body at specific depths and dimensions. Ongoing studies in hyperthermia cancer applications in animals continue at University of Illinois and North Carolina State University-Raleigh.

Cryosurgery uses selective freezing to damage and destroy cancerous tissue. A substance that produces intense cold—usually liquid nitrogen—is carefully applied directly to the tumor itself, leaving surrounding healthy tissue intact. Cryosurgery works best on localized tumors that don't invade too deeply into the body, such as oral tumors or perianal tumors.

Studies have shown that cancer causes changes in the body's metabolism of nutrition, and results in a syndrome known as cancer cachexia. This causes weight loss even when the pet eats enough food. Tumors thrive on glucose (blood sugar), but may have trouble using fat for energy. Therapeutic diets for dogs are now designed to "starve" the cancer while supporting dogs during treatments.

Your veterinarian may recommend PEMF therapy, which stimulate the electrical and chemical processes in the tissues to relieve inflammation and pain. Devices may be designed for whole body treatment or targeted areas of the body. Some of these devices have successfully completed efficacy studies and are FDA-approved. Therapeutic products may be available in mats, wraps or other devices from your veterinarian or over the counter (see PULSED ELECTROMAGNETIC FIELD).

Holistic veterinarians recommend a variety of therapies to help support pets with cancer, and these may be used alongside (not instead of) conventional treatments. Be sure to consult with your vet before adding a holistic treatment, though. An herb or vitamin may affect the impact of chemo, for example, so that less of a conventional drug is needed.

Extra antioxidant vitamins C and E have been shown to slow the growth and spread of some kinds of cancer. The mineral selenium also helps slow cancer growth, as do the omega-3 fatty acids in fish oil.

The herbs maitake and green tea help support the immune system, and have an antioxidant effect. Turmeric is thought to inhibit the growth of cancer cells. Noni juice, available in health food stores, is made from the morinda plant from the South Sea Islands. Noni juice can relieve pain often associated with cancer.

Medical marijuana (or cannabis) today is also available for pets, but must be formulated so that pets receive the medical benefits of the cannabis (hemp) plant while reducing potential toxic concentrations of the herb. Hemp can be used to reduce cancer associated signs. Ask your veterinarian if this supplement may benefit your pet.

With few exceptions, cancer cannot be prevented. You and your dog are best served by remaining vigilant to early warning signs, and seeking veterinary intervention as early as possible.

The maintenance of quality of life is the underlying goal of all cancer therapies, because a cure rarely is possible. Dogs also have no idea that they've been diagnosed with cancer, and are spared the fear and emotional distress people face. Dogs only know how they feel in this moment. Your veterinarian can help you recognize when a longer life isn't necessarily a better life. When the time comes, love will tell you the best decision to make for your dog (see EUTHANASIA).

CANINE CORONAVIRUS (CCV)

Canine coronavirus is a highly contagious gastrointestinal disease first identified in 1971 in a group of military dogs in Germany. The virus has since been found in Europe, North America and Australia, but likely occurs throughout the world.

The canine coronavirus is related to the feline forms that cause feline infectious peritonitis and feline enteric disease; however, CCV causes disease only in coyotes, foxes and dogs. All dogs are susceptible, but the signs are most severe in puppies, and may develop suddenly. Studies have shown that more than 25 percent of pet dogs have been exposed to CCV.

Dogs usually are infected through contact with sick dogs or their droppings. Once virus is swallowed, infection develops within one to three days. Many dogs will show no signs, while others become rapidly sick and die. Most cases are seen in kennel situations.

Early signs include loss of appetite (see ANOREXIA), sometimes fever, vomiting and depression. This is followed by loose to liquid diarrhea which may contain blood or mucus, and has a characteristic yellow-orange color and foul odor. Life-threatening dehydration can develop quickly.

CORONAVIRUS

SYMPTOMS: Loss of appetite; fever; vomiting; depression; liquid, yellow-orange diarrhea that may contain blood or mucus; dehydration
HOME CARE: Nursing care
VET CARE: Fluid therapy; antibiotics; medication to control vomiting and diarrhea
PREVENTION: Prevent contact with strange dogs; practice good sanitation by picking up yard; vaccination

CCV infects a specific part of the lining of the small intestine. The small intestine is lined with hill-shaped structures called villi that are covered with tiny hair-like projections (microvilli) which absorb nutrients. CCV infects the "hilltops" of the villi, compromising the body's ability to process food. However, the "valley" portion which contain microvilli-producing crypt cells can completely replace the tips about every three or four days. For that reason, the virus tends to produce only a mild to moderate, usually self-limiting disease; in most cases, dogs will recover within seven to ten days. However, some dogs may relapse three or four weeks following apparent recovery.

Diagnosis is made on the basis of symptoms, and sometimes identification of the coronavirus by electron microscope examination of a stool sample. There is no specific treatment for CCV, but supportive care helps speed recovery. It's mostly aimed at counteracting fluid loss, vomiting, and preventing secondary bacterial infection. Fluid therapy helps combat dehydration that often results from the vomiting and diarrhea, and antibiotics reduce the number of bacteria in the bowel so they do not infect the bloodstream through the compromised bowel lining. Medication is often prescribed to control the diarrhea and vomiting.

The disease by itself is rarely fatal; however, when the dog is already compromised by intestinal parasites or other illness, CCV can kill. In particular, dogs infected with canine parvovirus along with CCV can have up to a 90 percent mortality rate.

Prevention of the disease is best managed by avoiding contact with infected animals and their droppings. Sanitary procedures, such as picking up the yard and kennel area, help a great deal. Preventative vaccinations are available, and may be recommended for high-risk dogs such as those exposed through kenneling or dog shows.

CANINE DISTEMPER VIRUS (CDV)

Canine distemper, first recognized in Europe in the 18th century, is still considered the most important viral disease of dogs. CDV is similar to the human measles virus, and in dogs it is the most commonly known infectious disease of the nervous system. This highly contagious, often fatal virus is excreted in the saliva, respiratory secretions, urine and feces, and is transmitted through the air (sneezing and coughing) and by contaminated objects the same way a cold virus spreads in people. Contact with infected secretions spread the disease.

Rarely, unborn puppies are infected by their mother, which may result in stillbirths, abortions, fading puppy syndrome, and central nervous system signs in four- to six-week-old puppies.

CDV can infect and be carried by many species besides the dog, including the wolf, coyote, raccoon, ferret, mink, skunk, otter and weasel. These wild populations probably help maintain the infection, despite good preventative vaccination practiced by responsible pet dog owners. Unfortunately, even the highly effective commercial vaccines are not 100 percent effective, and even vaccinated dogs can become infected by and clinically ill from the disease.

Puppies are more susceptible than adult dogs, but during their lifetime, most dogs will be exposed to distemper. In particular, dogs that are kenneled or regularly boarded, and those that are routinely shown or hunted have a higher risk because of increased exposure to other dogs. Dogs obtained from the less-than-ideal conditions of some animal shelters or pet stores, particularly at nine to twelve weeks of age, are often affected. They may appear healthy but be incubating the disease when adopted (even if they've been vaccinated) then become sick once in their new home (see QUARANTINE).

DISTEMPER

SYMPTOMS: Loss of appetite; yellowish diarrhea; difficulty breathing; seizures; behavior changes; weakness; incoordination; thick discharge from the eyes and nose; sometimes thickened, cracked footpads
HOME CARE: Nursing care: VETERINARY CARE ESSENTIAL if the dog is to survive
VET CARE: Supportive care; fluid therapy; antibiotics; drugs to control vomiting and diarrhea; sometimes anticonvulsive medication to control seizures
PREVENTION: Vaccinate your dog as recommended by your veterinarian; prevent contact with other unvaccinated dogs

There are several strains of the virus, and some are more virulent than others. In general, about 85 percent of puppies exposed to the virus when they are less than a week old develop distemper within two to five weeks and die, while older puppies and adult dogs develop fatal disease only about 30 percent of the time. Older puppies and adult dogs have more mature immune protection, and so are better able to fight off the infection if they are exposed.

The virus attacks various body tissues, especially the epithelial cells that line the surfaces of the body like the skin, the conjunctiva of the eyes, the respiratory and urinary tracts, and the mucus membranes lining the gastrointestinal tract. It also infects lymph nodes, kidney, liver, spleen, and the brain and spinal cord. Whether or not the infected dog survives depends on the effectiveness of her individual immune system.

Within two days following infection, the virus spreads to the bronchial lymph nodes and tonsils, and then throughout the body's lymphatic system (bone marrow, spleen, and other lymph nodes). Within five days, virus infects and begins destroying the white blood cells, which results in leukopenia (low white blood cells), and a fever develops for a day or two.

By nine to fourteen days following infection, 75 percent of dogs that have competent immune systems will kill the virus and won't become sick. Dogs that aren't able to mount an early immune response develop sudden devastating signs of disease, including anorexia, yellowish diarrhea, trouble breathing, and central nervous system signs such as seizures, behavior changes, weakness and incoordination. A characteristic thick white to yellow discharge from the eyes and nose is often seen as well. This looks similar to signs of a cold, but dogs don't catch colds like humans do; this is a serious warning of illness.

Other symptoms vary, depending on what organs are affected by the virus. Infection of the respiratory system may prompt the dog to cough and develop pneumonia. Gastrointestinal infection can cause bloody or mucoid diarrhea. The eyes may ulcerate or even become blind, and the skin (particularly the footpads) may thicken, crack and bleed.

Dogs that survive infection during puppyhood may suffer enamel hypoplasia—poorly developed tooth enamel that's pitted and discolored—as adults. Even dogs that recover from infection may suffer permanent damage to the central nervous system that results in recurrent seizures or palsy for the rest of the dog's life.

Diagnosis of CDV is usually based on the signs of disease. Because of an impaired immune system, dogs suffering from distemper may also develop bacterial, fungal or parasitic infections that can make the dog even sicker and increase the risk of death. Without veterinary intervention, dogs experiencing severe symptoms usually die within three weeks.

There is no cure for distemper, only supportive treatment that addresses individual symptoms to make the dog more comfortable until—and if—her own body is able to overcome the infection. Hospitalization is usually necessary if the dog is to survive. Stricken dogs are treated with antibiotics to combat infections that often result from immunosuppression, along with fluid therapy and medications to control diarrhea and vomiting to counteract dehydration. Anticonvulsant medication may be necessary to control seizures. No one treatment is specific or always effective, and it may take ongoing therapy for up to six weeks to conquer the disease.

Dogs sick with CDV also shed the virus for up to 90 days and are sources of infection for other healthy dogs. Sick dogs must be quarantined away from healthy animals. The virus can live in a frozen state for many years, thaw out, and still infect your dog. However, virus is relatively unstable in hot or dry conditions, and can be killed by most disinfectants such as household bleach.

The decision to attempt to save the dog is based on her overall health, the seriousness of the disease, and potential for permanent health problems. Each dog responds differently to treatment. For some, symptoms get better, then worsen before recovery. Other dogs show no improvement despite aggressive treatment. Often, after consulting with their veterinarian, owners make the difficult decision to euthanize the sick dog.

Vaccinations work with the immune system to help protect the majority of dogs from contracting this disease. However, an unknown number of dogs do not develop an immune response (i.e., antibodies in the bloodstream) to vaccines, and these dogs may be susceptible to infection when exposed, even though they've received adequate vaccination. Stress and debilitation from other illness not only predispose dogs to contracting CDV, they also interfere with the effectiveness of vaccines. Occasionally, puppies that are born with a deficient immune system may actually become sick with CDV as a result of vaccination.

This is considered extremely rare, though, and the risk of disease from withholding vaccination is much greater.

The best way to protect your dogs from CDV infection is to vaccinate as recommended by your veterinarian, and prevent contact with other unvaccinated dogs.

CANINE HERPESVIRUS (CHV) Canine herpesvirus is one of a wide variety of herpesviruses affecting many species, and is the most common cause of fading puppy syndrome. A temperature of about 98 degrees is ideal for virus growth, which is why CHV attacks these youngsters rather than adult dogs whose body temperature normally ranges over 100 degrees. The virus can be found in the lower temperature areas of the genital and respiratory tracts of healthy adult dogs, where it remains dormant and doesn't cause deadly disease in the host, but may be shed intermittently.

The virus is transmitted through contact with infected oral, nasal, or vaginal secretions. Puppies may be infected during whelping—that is, as they pass through their mother's vaginal canal during birth. Carrier adult dogs, though not sick themselves, may spread infection to susceptible puppies. The virus can also spread to puppies by an owner who has handled an infected dog. Less commonly, puppies are infected by their mother before they're born.

At birth, puppies typically appear normal in every way, and nurse and even thrive. The virus attacks puppies five to 21 days after birth. CHV first infects the tonsils and nasal cavity, then is carried in the bloodstream to a variety of organs throughout the body. Within days of initial infection, many major organs including the kidneys, lungs, liver, gastrointestinal tract, lymph nodes, spleen and brain, are attacked by the virus. CHV kills the organs' cells and causes bleeding.

The first sign of disease is a sudden cessation of nursing. Then body temperature drops, tummies distend, and puppies lose coordination. They cry out during ongoing excruciating abdominal muscle spasms, and they excrete soft, odorless yellow-green feces. They may also have a nasal discharge or a rash on the tummy.

Late-stage disease results in central nervous system signs, such as blindness. Nothing is able to relieve their pain, and the puppies die within 24 hours. Those few babies that do survive the initial infection are likely to suffer permanent neurological and organ damage, are chronic carriers of the virus, and often succumb within six months.

Diagnosis of the disease is usually based on the signs. Mother dogs that lose a litter to CHV typically develop immunity to the virus, which they then pass on to subsequent litters that will not be affected. Unfortunately, there are no recommended preventative measures available, nor is there a recommended treatment for this devastating illness (see FADING PUPPY SYNDROME).

CANINE HERPESVIRUS

SYMPTOMS: Puppies stop nursing; swollen stomachs; loss of coordination; soft, odorless, yellow-green feces; nasal discharge or tummy rash; death within twenty-four to forty-eight hours
HOME CARE: None
VET CARE: Hyperimmune serum may reduce mortality
PREVENTION: Keep puppies warm and isolated from other adult dogs

CANINE INFLUENZA VIRUS (CIV) Canine influenza is a relatively new disease first recognized in racing greyhounds. In the spring of 2015, approximately 1000 dogs were affected by the Chicago-area outbreak of canine infectious respiratory disease (CIRD) caused by canine influenza virus.

As with human influenza, more than one virus may be implicated in the disease. ***Canine influenza (H3N8) virus*** is closely related to a common flu virus that has been found in horses for more than 40 years. It's thought that the virus mutated and became infectious to dogs, with the first reported outbreak on 2004. Today, H3N8 is considered a dog-specific canine flu.

The 2015 Chicago outbreak of dog flu was caused by a newer strain. This is the first appearance of ***Canine Influenza H3N2*** strain of the virus in North America; however, it was first detected in 2007 in dogs in South Korea.

CANINE INFLUENZA

SYMPTOMS: High fever; loss of appetite; nasal discharge; lethargy; wet cough; coughing up blood; red or runny eyes
HOME CARE: Nursing care
VET CARE: Cough suppressants; antibiotics; sometimes fluid therapy
PREVENTION: Avoid high risk areas; vaccinate your dog as recommended by your veterinarian

According to clinical studies by researchers at the University of Wisconsin, the CIV H3N2 may be shed for up to 24 days, which is far longer than what is seen with CIV H3N8. Experts estimate H3N2 produces ten times more virus than H3N8, which makes it far more contagious. As a result, the infection can spread quickly among social dogs in inner cities, doggie daycares, boarding facilities, dog parks, sporting and show events and any location where dogs co-mingle.

It's thought that this a "bird flu" adapted to affect dogs, and canine H3N2 virus has since been reported in China and Thailand where it reportedly can affect cats as well as dogs. However, studies indicate that neither virus transmits well to other companion animal species. Further, it is different from human seasonal H3N2 viruses. There have been no reports of dog-to-human transmission, and it is not considered contagious to people.

But dog flu is highly contagious between dogs. Nearly 100 percent of dogs exposed to the virus get it, since there is no natural immunity to this new disease, but not all dogs get sick. The virus is spread through direct contact with bodily fluids—sneezing, coughing, sniffing, and licking.

Stress caused by travel, confinement or interaction with strange dogs increases a dog's susceptibility. That means environments that promote canine congregation, such as boarding or dog parks, may be ground zero for spreading canine flu.

Both strains of dog flu cause high fever, loss of appetite, coughing, nasal discharge, and lethargy. Some dogs develop red or runny eyes, and in most cases, there's a history of contact with other sick or "carrier" dogs.

Dogs with mild symptoms may have a "wet" cough (resembling "kennel cough") with nasal discharge. In mild cases, these signs last ten to 30 days and usually go away on their own. Cough suppressants and/or antibiotics may be prescribed if a secondary bacterial infection exists. According to Cornell, some infected dogs won't show signs at all (some experts say probably 20 percent are asymptomatic)—however, they are still contagious and can spread the disease.

Symptoms may be more severe in cases caused by the H3N2 virus. Signs may be a high sudden fever (above 104 degrees Fahrenheit), followed by hemorrhagic pneumonia, coughing up blood and difficulty breathing. Illness can be complicated with bacterial pneumonia. Hospitalization with aggressive treatment with antibiotics, fluids are vital. Isolation to protect other dogs from contracting the disease is important.

Diagnosis is based on symptoms and a battery of tests that may include blood analysis, lung X-rays, and microscopic examination of samples from the lungs. There is a specific test available for the dog flu, but not the new variant. Cornell advises veterinarians that the Rt-PCR test may detect Influenza A H3N8, but the H3N2 may not be detected. However, an H3N2-specific serologic assay is under development and will be available soon.

Due to concerns over this emerging virus, the USDA issued a conditional product license to Merck Animal Health for a vaccine to protect against this newly identified strain. Canine Influenza Vaccine H3N2 became available to U.S. veterinarians November 23, 2015, and is recommended for healthy dogs six weeks old and older. Your veterinarian will advise you best whether the vaccination is a good idea for your dog.

CANINE PARVOVIRUS (CPV) Parvovirus, a highly contagious and often lethal virus was first identified in 1978, and is found throughout the world. It is believed that parvo arose as a mutation from wildlife or from the feline parvovirus (feline panleukopenia virus). Parvo also affects coyotes and some other wild canids.

Parvo affects dogs of any age but puppies are the most susceptible with up to a twenty percent mortality rate even in pups that receive treatment. Puppies stressed from fleas or ticks or from tail docking or ear cropping are at highest risk for severe disease. Rottweilers and Doberman Pinschers seem to be more severely affected by parvovirus than other breeds. The highest incidence of parvo occurs in kennels, pet stores, shelters, and poor-quality breeding facilities.

PARVOVIRUS

SYMPTOMS: Anorexia; bloody diarrhea; vomiting; fever; foaming at the mouth; convulsions; sudden death
HOME CARE: Nursing care; hospitalization usually required
VET CARE: Fluid therapy; antibiotics; medications to control vomiting and diarrhea; bland food
PREVENTION: Vaccinate your dog

The virus is shed in the droppings of infected dogs for about two weeks, and the disease is spread by direct contact with this infected material. Dogs are infected when they swallow the virus after licking contaminated material. Following exposure, symptoms occur in five to eleven days.

Symptoms include depression, fever of 104 to 106 degrees, refusal to eat or drink, and severe vomiting along with diarrhea. Vomiting is often the first sign, with diarrhea appearing within 24 to 48 hours. Vomit may be clear, yellow or blood-tinged; diarrhea is bloody, smells rotten, and may have mucus present. Because these signs are not restricted to parvo, diagnosis is only confirmed by finding the virus in the feces.

The acute form of the disease, however, may result in sudden severe stomach pain and depression, followed by shock and sudden death before any other symptom becomes apparent. A long illness is rare; dogs typically either recover quickly, or they die.

Parvovirus causes two forms of disease. Myocarditis affects the heart muscles in young puppies four to eight weeks old, and was more common when the disease first appeared. Affected puppies are infected before birth or shortly thereafter and typically stop nursing, gasp for breath and may cry in distress. Retching, convulsions and foaming at the nostrils or mouth may occur. Other times, the disease causes a sudden death syndrome that may occur within hours or a few days of onset. Those pups that survive initial infection may develop congestive heart failure and die weeks to months later. Today, this form is rare because puppies are usually protected by maternal antibodies.

The more common enteric form of parvo affects the intestines. The tonsils are infected first, and from there the virus travels to the lymphatic system which routes it to the bloodstream. Then virus travels throughout the body, ultimately infecting the crypt cells of the intestinal lining.

The small intestine is lined with hill-shaped villi containing tiny hair-like projections called microvilli. It's here the majority of digestive absorption takes place. Crypt cells down in the 'valleys' replace the microvilli every three to four days, and these new microvilli migrate toward the 'hilltops' of the villi. Parvovirus kills the crypt cells that make the nutrient-absorbing microvilli. It takes three to four days for crypt cells to heal, and begin to re-populate the villi. During that time, the puppy's body can’t process food and water.

Sick pups die from dehydration, electrolyte imbalance, shock, or secondary infections. Puppies often collapse and die in as little as twelve hours following the onset of symptoms. Immediate veterinary help is critical.

There is no cure or specific treatment for parvovirus, but early detection and treatment increase chance for survival. Therapy is centered upon good nursing and supportive care. Essentially, a sick dog must be kept alive long enough for his own immune system to suppress and clear the virus from his body. Dogs that survive for three to four days following the onset of vomiting and diarrhea generally recover rapidly, and will become immune to the enteric form of the disease.

An experimental treatment now in development by Avianix may hold hope for a successful treatment of the disease. Early tests of the new parvoONE antibody-based treatment, harvested from the yolks of goose eggs, showed a 90 percent cure rate, a potential breakthrough in animal care.

Food and water are usually withheld for two to four days to give the digestive system a chance to rest. Fluid therapy helps counter the devastating dehydration and returns electrolyte balance to normal. Antibiotics may be administered to fight secondary infection, along with medications to control vomiting and diarrhea. Once vomiting and diarrhea have subsided, water and a bland food like cottage cheese and rice or veterinary prescribed diet are offered in small amounts several times daily. The normal diet is then reintroduced gradually as the dog recovers over the next several days.

Strict isolation and quarantine helps control the spread of disease. Sick dogs should remain isolated for thirty days after recovery and be bathed thoroughly before brought into contact with other dogs.

Parvo can live in the environment for at least five months and sometimes for years. Direct dog-to-dog contact that spreads distemper isn't necessary to spread parvo. The virus can be picked up simply by walking through a yard contaminated with infected feces, or by contact with kennels or other objects that have been contaminated by an infected pet. You could carry the virus to your puppy on your shoes after you've walked through an infected area.

The virus is resistant to most common disinfectants and household detergents. But thorough cleaning with household bleach will kill the virus. A dilution of one part bleach to thirty parts water is recommended.

Protecting puppies with vaccination reduce the risk of your puppy catching the disease. Be sure your puppy stays away from exposure to other dogs until fully protected.

CANINE SCABIES

SYMPTOMS: Intense itching, skin inflammation; red papules; sores; crusting; hair loss; thickened, wrinkled skin
HOME CARE: Once diagnosed by vet, clip dog's fur; bathe with antiseborrheic shampoo
VET CARE: Same as home care; sometimes Ivermectin injections
PREVENTION: Prevent contact with strange dogs

CANINE SCABIES **SARCOPTIC MANGE**, also known as canine scabies, is caused by a circular short-legged microscopic mite that burrows in the skin. Canine scabies can affect any dog regardless of age, breed, or coat type. It's rare for only one dog in a multi-pet home to exhibit clinical signs. It is so contagious that if one is affected, all animals are infected.

The female mite burrows into the skin, forms a tunnel, and lays three to five eggs daily. Larvae emerge within another three to eight days, and after hatching, those that migrate across the surface of the skin often will die. But most larva stay in the tunnel or its extensions (called "molting pockets") where they develop into nymphs.

Some nymphs stay in the original tunnels and molting pockets, while others burrow and form new tunnels. A few wander on the skin surface, where the potential for transmission to yet another host becomes possible. The next molt produces adult male and female mites. The cycle from egg to adult takes 17 to 21 days. Adult females live about four to five weeks, while the males die shortly after mating.

The mite is usually transmitted by direct dog-to-dog contact. The mite lives out its entire life cycle on the dog, but mites can survive up to 48 hours off a host. This means your dog could pick up the mites simply by sleeping on a blanket used by an infested dog, or by sharing grooming tools like brushes.

It takes as little as a week for signs of disease to develop following exposure. The mite prefers sparsely-furred areas of the body, like the hock, elbow, area surrounding the eyes and muzzle, stomach, ear flap and root of the tail. The back is rarely involved.

Burrowing mites produce intense itching which prompts the infested dog to chew, scratch, and rub the affected areas. The scratch reflex in affected dogs can be easily stimulated; by merely manipulating the pinnae (ear flap) the dog will often kick a hind leg in reaction.

Excessive scratching results in skin inflammation, and red papules and sores and secondary infections often develop. Crusts form on the surface of affected skin, and as the disease intensifies, the skin thickens. Untreated dogs will have dry, deeply wrinkled and thick skin. Damaged skin causes loosened hair to fall out, and the sparseness of hair in turn provides the mite with an even better environment in which to proliferate.

Left untreated, the disease may continue for months to years. Victims with advanced mite infestation become irritable and are restless, and subsequently begin to lose weight. Diagnosis is based on signs of disease, and on finding the mite in microscopic examination of skin scrapings.

Scabies can be difficult to diagnose because the mites can be hard to find; only about 30 percent of canine scabies cases actually locate a mite in skin scrapings. For this reason, the condition may be confused with other skin conditions (see SEBORRHEA and flea allergy).

Treatment is often the best diagnosis. Dogs that respond favorably to therapy are deemed to have scabies. Treatment consists of clipping the fur, bathing with an anti-seborrheic shampoo, and treating with a miticide solution from your veterinarian.

Because the condition is so contagious, all dogs and cats in contact with the affected animal should be treated. Some dogs may be carriers of the mite, without ever showing clinical signs themselves. Several effective scabicides are available from your veterinarian. Multiple treatments over several weeks are generally needed for satisfactory results. Ivermectin, which is the active ingredient in some heartworm preventatives, is also effective against sarcoptic mange.

Secondary infections generally respond to the medicated shampoos and miticidal therapy, so antibiotics are not usually necessary. However, in severe cases of sarcoptic infection, use of concurrent therapy may be warranted. A high quality, well balanced food for affected dogs is important as well.

Canine scabies almost exclusively affects dogs, but can also cause skin disease in cats or in people. It most commonly affects owners who allow the pet to sleep in their bed or who hold him a great deal. In people, the mite causes itching and inflammation, and prolonged exposure may produce sores. However, the mite does not reproduce on people, and curing the pet typically also cures the owner within seven to 28 days following treatment of the affected dog.

Once cured, dogs are not immune to reinfection. Part of the treatment should include disinfection of the dog's bedding, grooming tools, collar, and carriers, to prevent reinfestation. Reduced exposure to other dogs, and vigorous treatment at the earliest warning will keep your dog free of this disease.

CARBON MONOXIDE POISONING

Carbon monoxide is an odorless, colorless, tasteless gas that is deadly to people and their pets. This natural by-product of fuel combustion is present in car exhaust and improperly vented gas furnaces or space heaters.

The gas causes the same problems in dogs as in people. However, carbon monoxide is lighter than air, so dogs that live at human knee level may not show symptoms as quickly as their owners. If you notice any change in your dog's behavior or your own symptoms that coincides with cold weather or the furnace coming on, consult your veterinarian and doctor.

Carbon monoxide passes into the lungs, and then binds with hemoglobin, the oxygen-transporting component of blood (see BLOOD). This effectively prevents the hemoglobin from utilizing or transporting oxygen to the body. The gas creates a kind of chemical suffocation.

The most common symptoms of human carbon monoxide poisoning are headache, confusion and disorientation, and flu-like sign with vomiting. Ultimately, the poison victim falls into a coma, and dies. We don't know if poisoned dogs suffer headaches, but they do act confused, lethargic, and drunk like human victims. A distinctive sign common to both people and pets are bright cherry-red gums in the mouth. When the victim is asleep during exposure to the poison, the dog—or the person—may never wake up.

The body can only get rid of the poison bound to the hemoglobin by breathing it out, or by replacing the poisoned hemoglobin with new. The liver and spleen replace hemoglobin about every ten to 15 days. When only a small amount of the blood is affected, the victim recovers without treatment as long as no more poison is inhaled.

But high levels of blood saturation will kill the person or pet unless emergency treatment is given. Twenty-five percent saturation level is considered dangerous for people. Usually, though, both people and pets should be treated when the carbon monoxide saturation level is ten percent or higher.

Administering high concentrations of oxygen is the treatment of choice, because it increases the amount of gas that is breathed out. Many hours of oxygen therapy may be required. In some cases, ventilation may be necessary. To protect yourself and your pets from carbon monoxide poisoning, have heating units inspected each fall before you start using them.

CARBON MONOXIDE POISONING

SYMPTOMS: Confusion; disorientation; difficulty walking; vomiting; lethargy; extreme sleepiness; cherry-red color to gums
FIRST AID: Provide fresh air. EMERGENCY! SEE VET IMMEDIATELY!
VET CARE: Oxygen therapy
PREVENTION: Safety check heating units before use

CARDIOPULMONARY RESUSCITATION (CPR)

CPR is the means of providing mechanical heart action and artificial respiration for dogs whose breathing and heartbeat have stopped. Heartbeat and respiration may stop due to poisoning, electric shock or injury like being hit by a car. CPR is a short-term method of keeping your pet alive, while stimulating her heart and breathing to resume working on their own.

Use CPR only when both the heart and breathing have stopped, and the dog is unconscious; you risk injury to the dog if CPR is administered when the heartbeat or respiration are normal. When the heart is beating, but the dog isn't breathing, refer to the section on artificial respiration.

Monitor the motion of the dog's chest to check for breathing. To find the heartbeat, place your flat palm on the dog's left side just above and behind the elbow of the front leg. If you still can't tell for sure, use the blink test. Tap her closed eyelid. Even unconscious dogs will blink unless the heart has stopped. If there's no movement, start CPR immediately.

CPR requires two people to apply artificial heart contractions and artificial breathing, one after the other, in an ongoing rhythm. A third person can drive you to the veterinary clinic while CPR is administered.

Experts agree that it is difficult and nearly impossible to restart a heartbeat without the specialized veterinary equipment. Although rare, an arrested heart may resume beating when stimulated by external compressions. The degree of heart compression depends on the size of the dog. About a fifty percent compression of the chest wall is required.

Dogs Under 20 Pounds: Perform the *cardiac pump technique* with compressions over the heart. That squeezes the motionless heart so that it pumps blood. Veterinarians recommend 100 to 120 compressions each minute, of 1/3rd to 1/2 of the chest width, according to the latest veterinary guidelines. It's also highly recommended to perform CPR in two-minute cycles, and switch who does the compression in each cycle so you don't wear yourself out.

Find the heart by flexing your dog's front left foreleg backwards. The center of the heart falls directly beneath where the point of the elbow crosses her chest.

Situate your dog on her right side on a flat, firm surface. Cup your hand over the heart, and squeeze firmly. Press in about ½ inch with your thumb on one side and fingers on the other.

For very small puppies that fit in the palm of your hand, perform compressions between your fingers. Cradle her in the palm of your hand, with your thumb over the heart and fingers on the other side, and squeeze rhythmically.

Dogs Over 20 Pounds: When a dog weighs more than 20 pounds, the space between the ribs and heart interfere with successful compressions. So instead, dogs this size best benefit from the *thoracic pump method*. When she's on her side, place your hands over the highest part of the chest and compress. That changes the chest cavity interior pressure which can move blood forward. Place one hand flat on her chest, and the other over top of the first hand, and press down 30 to 50 percent.

Barrel chested breeds like Bulldogs should be placed on their back before compressing the chest. Cross her paws over the breast, and kneel with her between your legs—tummy up. Hold her paws and perform compressions downward directly over the breastbone.

Acupuncture Resuscitation: When the pet's breathing and heart has stopped and resuscitation methods have failed, veterinarians suggest stimulating an acupuncture "alarm point." That prompts the body to release natural adrenaline (epinephrine), a drug commonly used in human and veterinary medicine in cardiac arrests to stimulate the heart and breathing.

The alarm point is in the center (midway point) of the slit found between your dog's nose and upper lip. Stick a needle, safety pin, paperclip, or even your clean fingernail into this point. Jab deeply to the bone, and repeatedly wiggle back and forth.

Don't be squeamish—this is your pet's life you hold in your hands! Continue administering the emergency acupuncture treatment for at least twenty minutes, until the pet revives or you reach the hospital.

Puppies and kittens dead at birth treated with this method have been revived more than an hour later, and survived to live long, healthy lives. A needle jab, with rescue breathing, can ensure your dog survives.

CARNIVORE A carnivore is an animal that eats other animals. The name comes from specialized molars, teeth in the side of the jaw that evolved with early meat eating mammals. These carnassial teeth offer a scissor-action that slices flesh and makes it easier to eat.

Although dogs prefer meat in their diets, they have evolved to be omnivores like people. This opportunistic ability, being able to survive on nearly anything at hand, means dogs are able to eat and thrive on both plant and animal source foods. When formulated correctly, dogs may do well on largely plant source based diets (see FOOD and NUTRITION).

CAR SICKNESS

CAR SICKNESS Young dogs often become sick to their stomachs during car rides. The motion of the car stimulates the area of the brain that stimulates vomiting. Stress and excitement also impact how well a dog tolerates car rides.

Young dogs may not have fully developed equilibrium and suffer from motion sickness as youngsters, but later outgrow the problem. Stress makes it more likely your dog will become sick, and when the dog remembers feeling bad and associates that with the car ride, this can become a vicious cycle.

Acclimate dogs slowly to car rides by making the experiences very short and pleasant. While he's still young, drive with him around the block, and end the ride with a special treat or favorite game so he associates the car with good things. If he shows signs of vomiting (salivation, excessive swallowing), stop the car and let him walk on leash for a moment or two to allow his stomach to settle.

CAR SICKNESS

SYMPTOMS: Agitation; whining; shivering; vomiting; excessive salivation or drooling
HOME CARE: Position dog/carrier so he has a view, or block his view with a towel
HOLISTIC HELP: Acupressure; homeopathy
VET CARE: Prescription sedative; Dramamine-type car-sickness medication
PREVENTION: Withhold food for six to eight hours prior to trip; acclimate dog to care in short trips; use favorite rewards to make experience more pleasant

Some dogs have less problems when allowed to watch the view, while others do better traveling blind; place a towel or blanket over the dog carrier or crate. Your veterinarian may prescribe a mild sedative to calm your pet's nerves, or a drug like Dramamine to soothe an upset tummy. A newer treatment, called Cerenia, is made specifically for carsick dogs.

Holistic veterinarians suggest using acupressure on the PC6 point to relieve nausea. This spot is located in the small depression on the underside of the front legs, just above the pad on the wrists. Press this point for one minute before you get into the car, and as often as needed during the trip, to help calm the tummy. A homeopathic remedy, Tabacum 30C also calms nausea. Put a couple of pellets on the cat's tongue two hours before traveling.

Ginger is another natural remedy that can relieve car sickness. The easiest way to give ginger is to sprinkle the contents of a capsule (available from health food stores) in a tablespoon of baby food, and give your dog about 20 minutes before the car ride. Dogs over 15 pounds can take 500 milligrams of ginger (smaller dogs half that amount). Some dog show professionals offer their dogs ginger snap cookies, which may also work, but do tend to stain white fur if the dog slobbers.

Dogs travel best on an empty stomach. Withhold food for at least six to eight hours prior to a long car ride, and give any veterinary-prescribed medication one hour before you leave. Never give your dog anything for car sickness without first consulting with your veterinarian. Most young dogs outgrow the problem.

CATARACT A cataract is the opacity of the lens inside the eye. The lens is located directly behind the pupil, and normally is transparent. Dogs suffer from cataracts more commonly than any other species. Cataracts can develop at any age, but most cases are found in dogs over five years of age.

Almost all dogs over the age of five years begin to have some degree of cloudiness to the lens of the eye, due to nuclear sclerosis, a normal part of aging. Dogs can see through this cloudiness without a problem. Cataracts, though, cause vision loss.

A cataract interferes with normal vision. It's often classified by age of onset—congenital, juvenile, or senile—along with the cause, and the degree of cloudiness. The opacity can vary from a little spot of white to a totally opaque structure that affects the entire lens. If the lens becomes completely masked, the result is blindness. Depending on the degree of opacity, you may notice cloudiness within the pupil space that looks like a white marble inside the eye.

Several things can result in lens changes. Trauma and/or resulting inflammation may cause a cataract, but usually to only one eye. Some puppies are born with the cataracts. Cataracts resulting from poor nutrition are possible, but rare because of modern advances in canine diets. And in some cases, the cataract is idiopathic, which means the cause cannot be identified.

Dogs most often suffer from senile, or "old age" cataracts; almost all dogs older than eight years suffer some degree of cloudiness to the lens of the eye. Cataracts in dogs also may result when the lens protein is injured by metabolic changes (see DIABETES MELLITUS).

But most canine cataracts are inherited, especially in certain breeds. Poodles, Cocker Spaniels, Boston Terriers, Wirehaired Fox Terriers, Siberian Huskies, Golden Retrievers, Old English Sheepdogs and Labrador Retrievers are reported to be affected most often.

A cataract may affect only a portion of the lens, and consequently some dogs show few signs at all. The cataract that covers the entire lens may still allow some vision. Treatment may not be necessary until a high degree of vision is lost and cataracts become problematic for the dog. Often, even blind dogs continue to do well in familiar surroundings by relying on their other acute senses. The underlying cause is treated when possible.

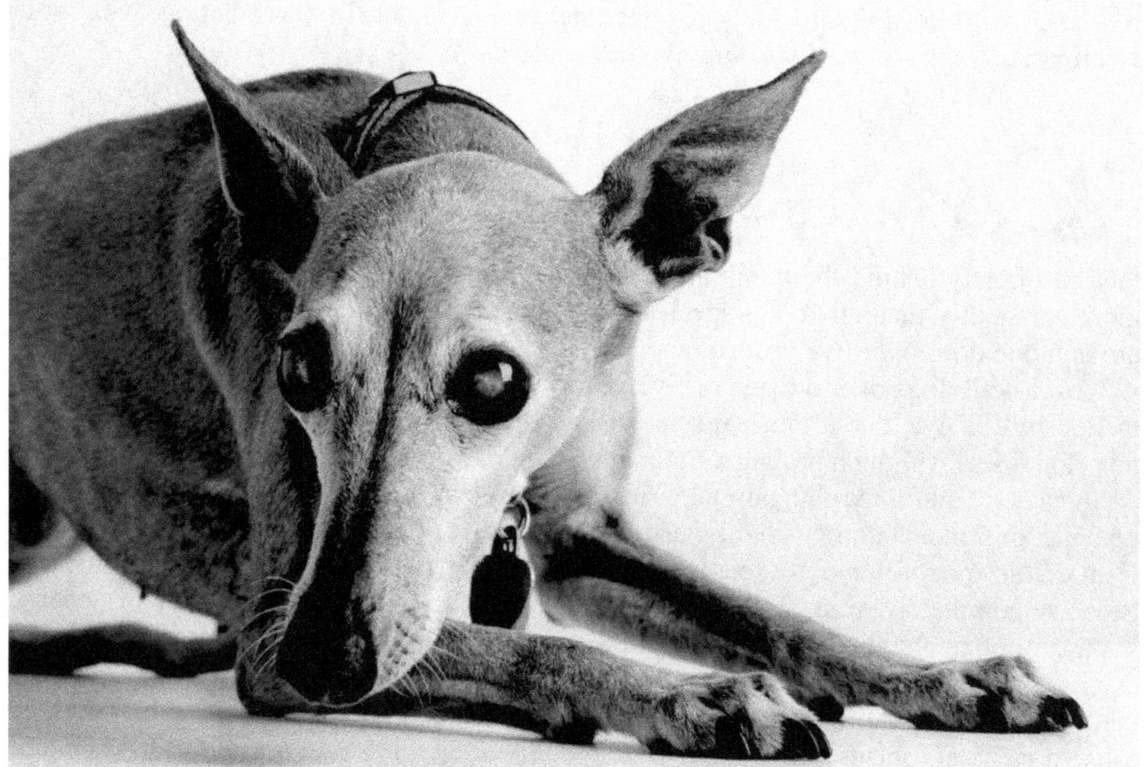

Puppies born with congenital cataracts can improve as they mature. The lens grows along with the dog, while the area of cloudiness on the lens remains the same size and, at maturity, is relatively small. By adulthood, many dogs born with cataracts are able to compensate and see "around" the cloudiness.

In dogs that have trouble navigating due to vision loss, sight can be restored to near normal by surgery. This procedure is not indicated when the cataract is caused by inflammation, however.

The same surgical techniques used on people for cataracts are applied to dogs. Most veterinary ophthalmologists in private practice or at a university can do the surgery. It is a long procedure done under general anesthetic that removes most but not all of the affected lens.

The lens itself is contained in a kind of capsule like an egg shell. Most commonly, surgery removes the front part of the shell and the contents inside, while leaving the back half of the capsule/shell intact. In some cases, the whole lens is removed and a new lens is transplanted to replace the damaged lens.

CATARACT

SYMPTOMS: Cloudiness to lens (inside) of eye; loss of sight; bumping into walls
HOME CARE: None
VET CARE: Address underlying cause; sometimes surgery
PREVENTION: None

A procedure called phacoemulsification produces high frequency sound waves—ultrasound—to break up the lens, which is then removed by suction, or aspiration. Dogs that have the surgery do quite well.

The healing phase is most critical the first couple of weeks after surgery. Dogs develop more eye inflammation after surgery than people do, and need eye drops to control that.

Dogs also react differently than people after the surgery. Their eyes will see right away, but how they're interpreting sight in their brain will be variable. Some dogs wake up from surgery and are immediately visual. Others may take several days or so before they're truly responding. This may be due in part to the effects of the anesthesia.

The surgery is quite expensive. If unable to afford the procedure, blind dogs still do well with accommodations to keep them safe and happy (see BLINDNESS).

Continue routine eye checks on dogs with cataracts, which can lead to other conditions such as inflammation of the eye (see UVEITIS) that can lead to glaucoma. The veterinarian can monitor the dog's eyes for uveitis, and if necessary, treat it using anti-inflammatory eye drops (see EYE and GLAUCOMA).

CESAREAN This procedure is a surgical delivery performed by the veterinarian when a natural birth is not possible. A difficult birth may occur even in the healthy bitch, and those in poor health often need assistance.

Sometimes, the bitch's uterus is too weak to propel puppies through the birth canal. In these instances, medications may be administered to stimulate uterine contraction.

A difficult birth also results when puppies are too large, which can occur in a single-pup litter. A single baby is common in miniature and small breeds like the Chihuahua, whose tiny frames also may impede normal delivery of a jumbo-size baby.

A small pelvis also can interfere with normal delivery. Trauma such as broken bones, nutritional deficiency, or heredity may result in a pelvic size and shape that makes natural birth difficult. In particular, brachycephalic (flat-faced) dog breeds like Boston Terriers, Bulldogs, and Pugs designed to have large heads with wide shoulders and narrow hips commonly suffer difficulty whelping naturally.

A cesarean is performed by the veterinarian, and the dog is under general anesthetic, with risk to the bitch usually nominal. Owners of breeds known to be prone to difficult births should consult with their veterinarian and plan for the possibility when the dog is bred. This reduces the risk of prolonged unproductive labor, dead puppies, uterine rupture or toxicity, which increase the risks for the bitch.

Within a few hours of the surgery, the mother is usually awake and able to nurse her puppies. She may or may not require a cesarean with future pregnancies, depending on the circumstances for the first (see REPRODUCTION).

CHASING ANIMALS/VEHICLES Dogs evolved as endurance specialists that use speed to run down prey. The urge to pursue moving objects is hardwired into the canine brain, and is a natural hunting behavior that is demonstrated whenever your dog chases a ball, Frisbee or squirrel. However, chasing inappropriate objects like bicycles or cars, or animals like the neighbor's cat or livestock, can become a problem that may have unfortunate or even deadly consequences.

All dogs enjoy the chase, but particular breeds developed for specific kinds of work are typically more obsessive than others. For instance, sighthounds like Greyhounds and Whippets, and most terriers are attracted to pursuing and even attacking small animals, and can pose a danger to cats, smaller dogs, or farm animals like chickens or rabbits. Shepherd breeds are more likely to chase larger livestock, as well as cars, bicycles, and jogging people in a misguided effort to herd them.

The owner of a dog that chases inappropriately is liable should property be damaged or a person injured. The chasing dog is also at risk from being injured or killed by the vehicle, or by the other animal or person defending themselves. In some areas, property owners are within their rights to shoot dogs that harass livestock.

To teach what not to chase, your dog must first be trained to leash walk nicely and to understand basic commands. Then expose your dog to staged situations that prompt chasing behavior, such as livestock or cars.

Place your dog on a long six-foot leash (as a safety precaution, should he bolt), and give him the sit/stay command. Next, have a friend slowly ride the bicycle, drive the car or jog by the dog, while you continue to enforce your dog's sit/stay position.

Distract your dog with a food or toy reward, praising him for not chasing. As soon as he begins to agitate about running after, make an about-face and walk the other direction while praising and offering treats. You want the dog to associate the car/bike/jogger presence with his favorite reward as he WALKS AWAY from the enticement.

Gradually increase the speed of the vehicle, and continue to intermittently reward your dog for sitting still as it approaches, and then turning away to get treats once it's near. Drill with these set ups over and over until he looks at YOU after he sees the car/bike/jogger rather than wanting to approach and chase.

Mail deliveries are notorious for enticing dogs to want to chase. Enlist the aid of your mail carrier, by providing a favorite treat or toy and having the mail delivery person toss this to the dog. That way the dog associates the delivery with good stuff. Otherwise, when the delivery person walks away the dog is rewarded for barking and chasing—which he thinks drove the "scary" person away.

It's impossible to totally eliminate chasing behavior, but it can be redirected. Prevent inappropriate chasing habits from the beginning; remember, what's cute in a ten-pound puppy is dangerous in a 50-plus pound adult.

Reduce opportunities for mistakes by enforcing boundaries. A fenced yard or leash confinement when off your property, teaches him the rules and prevents him from chasing your neighbor's livestock. Offer safe outlets to satisfy this normal urge. Interactive games such as fetch not only satisfy your pet, but provide a bonding experience for the two of you.

Relieving your dog's boredom can help avoid chase behaviors that arise from frustration and loneliness. There are also organized dog sports such as herding trials for shepherd breeds, lure-coursing for sighthound breeds, and go-to-ground for terriers that reward these innate behaviors in controlled settings (see HUNTING and TRIALS).

CHERRY EYE This condition occurs when the pinkish-red tear gland at the inner corner of the eye protrudes, or prolapses. The smooth mass of this third eyelid swells to the size of a small cherry. There may be a purulent discharge if infection is present.

It is most commonly associated with a congenital weakness in the anchoring tissue of the gland in the dog's eye. The cause of the prolapse could be due to scrolled or everted cartilage in the third eyelid, abnormal cells in the third eye, or a prolapse of fat in the dog's eye. It's not known if this is inherited, but it does appear to be more common in younger animals and certain breeds.

Cherry eye can occur in one or both eyes of any breed dog. However, it is most common in Beagles, Bloodhounds, Boston Terriers, Boxers, Bulldogs, Cocker Spaniels, Lhasa Apsos, Mastiffs and Chinese Shar-Peis. Prolonged exposure of the gland can cause irritation to the eye. Sometimes, anti-inflammatory topical medications may resolve the problem. More commonly, surgery is necessary to correct the condition.

CHERRY EYE

SYMPTOMS: Red, swollen tissue at inside corner of the dog's eye, sometimes with a discharge
HOME CARE: None
VET CARE: Anti-inflammatory ointments; more often, surgery
PREVENTION: None

CHEWING Just like human babies, puppies put things in their mouths as a way to explore their world. Particularly when teething, young dogs chew objects to relieve the discomfort. But unlike people, dogs don't outgrow the habit of mouthing and gnawing.

Your dog doesn't have hands, and instead uses her mouth. Canines are mouth-oriented creatures with an incredible ability to control the intensity of their bite. Modern pet dogs use their powerful teeth and jaws to pick up and carry things, to eat, for defense, and for recreational chewing. Gnawing objects simply feels good to dogs.

This oral fixation tends to get dogs into trouble, however, because they aren't always particular about the objects they target. Canine chewing not only can damage your property, but can injure the dog when teeth are broken or an object is swallowed (see SWALLOWED OBJECTS and PERIODONTAL DISEASE).

Items that carry their beloved owner's scent—like leather shoes—are often targeted, but nothing is sacred. Dogs who are bored and have nothing else to do tend to be problem chewers.

Chewing is normal, natural behavior for dogs and cannot—should not—be eliminated. It is up to owners to provide their pets with appropriate and safe chewing outlets to satisfy these doggy cravings.

Avoid offering objects that may confuse your dog. If she's not to chew your new shoes, don't offer the old ones; dogs may not be able to tell the difference. The key to solving problems is to reduce your dog's opportunities to make mistakes. Don't leave tempting items scattered about the house, and confine your dog to a "safe" zone when you aren't there to supervise her activity. When you catch her chewing a forbidden object, tell her "no" and take it away (or remove her from the table leg), and provide her with a legal alternative. A product like Bitter Apple applied to dangerous objects like electrical cords will help train your dog to leave forbidden items alone (see ELECTRICAL SHOCK).

NEVER OFFER YOUR DOG COOKED BONES. Cooked bones can splinter under the dog's assault. Swallowed fragments potentially can cause lethal internal trauma by puncturing or blocking the gastrointestinal tract.

A number of commercial chew objects are available, including sterilized raw bones and a variety of flavored rawhide toys. Rawhide is fine in moderation, but large dogs tend not only to chew, but to eat the things. In excess, rawhide can interfere with sound nutrition when your dog eats these treats instead of her food. They can also cause blockage if large enough pieces are swallowed (see CONSTIPATION). Commercial hard rubber chew objects are available in sizes and even chicken and liver flavors to suit nearly every dog.

CHEYLETIELLOSIS Also called walking dandruff or cheyletiella dermatitis, this condition in dogs is caused by a mite called *Cheyletiella yasguri*. The mite lives on the surface of the dog's skin and causes a contagious disorder that tends to be limited to scaling and crusting of the skin.

Typically, the dog's fur looks filled with dandruff. The skin may be itchy or not, and occasionally the lymph nodes swell. Some dogs may harbor the mite without showing any signs, yet spread the parasite. Any dog is susceptible, but the bug most commonly affects puppies and young dogs. It is contagious to other pets and to people.

This mite is quite large, and an infection looks like white specks on the dog's skin or fur. It can be seen with (sometimes without) the aid of a magnifying glass. The entire life cycle—egg, larva, nymph, adult—is completed on the host. However, adult female mites can survive for an extended period off the host, increasing the risk of contagion to other victims.

Diagnosis is based on the signs and by finding the mite during microscopic examination of skin debris. Cheyletiella mites are easily killed with flea treatments as recommended by your veterinarian. In fact, the condition is rarely a problem in areas where routine flea prevention is practice. Treatment should be applied to other pets (including cats) that are in contact with a diagnosed animal, and environmental treatment is also recommended.

WALKING DANDRUFF

SYMPTOMS: Scaly, crusty skin; dandrufflike flakes in fur; itchy skin; swollen lymph nodes
HOME CARE: Flea treatment
VET CARE: Same as home care
PREVENTION: Routine flea prevention

CHIROPRACTIC Chiropractic care is a holistic manipulative therapy that carefully flexes the affected joints to return them to proper alignment. Treatment plans are customized to the individual pet. Advocates say that appropriate adjustments can affect your pet's emotions, as well as how the organs work, due to the viscera-somatic, or "organ-to-muscle" reflex.

Manipulative therapies also include physical therapy and massage. While massage focuses on the tissues surrounding the bones, chiropractic care and physical therapy focus on the proper functioning of the joints and related muscles, including the spine.

Science and holistic methods work hand-in-paw with these hands-on modalities both in people and in pets. Veterinary chiropractors often require X-rays before attempting any adjustments. While a human chiropractor can't prescribe drugs unless also an M.D., a chiropractor with a veterinary degree can incorporate medications to help.

It may take only one "adjustment" or instead require several. The longer the problem has existed, the more treatments will be necessary, and chiropractic manipulations (especially of the spine) require a trained veterinary chiropractor because it can be very easy to injure your pet unless you know what you're doing.

Physical therapy techniques, though, can often be performed by you at home to help loosen up your pet's stiff legs, shoulders and necks. This increases joint mobility, and also stimulates production of synovial fluid, a substance manufactured by the body that nourishes and lubricates the joints to keep them healthy.

Be careful not to over-extend a muscle or joint, though, and pay attention to the dog if he tells you to stop. Flinching or crying out during physical therapy means it's painful and you should stop and have a vet check out the pet for any problems.

A chiropractic technique called motion palpation can be safely done at home. Motion palpation helps flex and extend the joints of the back. It can have an additive effect, so that even tiny amounts done daily help pets feel better over the long term. It's particularly helpful for creaky older pets, but athletic animals will enjoy and benefit from this gentle treatment that keeps them flexible and may help prevent injury.

Ask your dog to stand or lie down in a comfy position. Feel for the individual vertebrae, the bumpy bones in the back. Pay particular attention to the dents or "valleys" between each bone.

Start at the neck, right where his skull meets the spine. Position your thumb and index finger on each side of the first dent between the first vertebrae and his skull.

Press down very gently with your fingers, and release. Then move to the next dip, and repeat the quick gentle pressure—each press shouldn't take more than one second, so you can count, "One-one-thousand" and then move on. Continue to move downward from his furry head toward his wagging tail, pressing each "valley" in turn and then releasing.

CHOCOLATE TOXICITY

Many dogs have a sweet tooth and relish the taste of chocolate, but the candy is toxic to both dogs and cats. Dogs are poisoned most often probably due to their less-than-discriminatory eating tendencies, and the incidence increases around the holidays when owners have more candy available.

Chocolate is made from the roasted seeds of cocoa plants, and contains a substance called theobromine along with small amounts of caffeine; both are toxic to pets. Milk chocolate found in candy bars contains about 42 milligrams of theobromine per ounce. Typically, a toxic dose of milk chocolate is five ounces per pound of body weight, so while a bite of chocolate generally isn't a concern, a 10-pound dog may get very sick from eating as little as eight ounces of milk chocolate.

Unsweetened baking chocolate is much more dangerous because it contains nearly ten times as much theobromine as milk chocolate, about 450 milligrams of theobromine per ounce. Baking chocolate is used to make brownies, chocolate cake, and other deserts. A lethal dose of theobromine is .67 to 1.3 ounce of baking chocolate per 2.2 pounds of dog. That means your ten pound dog can become sick simply by licking off the chocolate frosting on a large cake.

CHOCOLATE TOXICITY

SYMPTOMS: Drooling; vomiting and/or diarrhea; excessive urination and thirst; hyperactivity; irregular heartbeat; muscle tremors; seizures; coma; sudden death
FIRST AID: EMERGENCY! SEE VET IMMEDIATELY! If ingested in last two hours, induce vomiting
VET CARE: Induce vomiting; give activated charcoal; flush stomach; supportive care, like fluid therapy and sedatives
PREVENTION: Keep chocolate out of dog's reach

Signs of chocolate poisoning are often delayed for up to eight hours following ingestion, with death occurring 12 to 24 hours post-poisoning. Some dogs show few signs, then suddenly die of heart failure. If you suspect your dog has eaten chocolate, don't wait for symptoms; get help immediately!

The theobromine and caffeine are stimulants that affect the dog's nervous system, causing hyperactive behavior along with other signs. Dogs may pass large amounts of urine due to the diuretic effect of the drug which also relaxes bladder control. Dogs often drool, act thirsty, and may suffer vomiting and/or have bouts of diarrhea. The drug may either increase the dog's heart rate or cause irregular heartbeat. The signs of poisoning may eventually include muscle spasms or tremors, seizures, coma, and ultimately death.

There is no antidote for chocolate poisoning. Affected dogs are offered supportive treatment to prevent further absorption of the poison and hasten elimination, along with symptomatic treatment.

When your dog has eaten chocolate, it's generally recommended that the owner make the dog throw up as soon as possible. Chocolate isn't absorbed very quickly, so emetics may be helpful for six to eight hours after ingestion.

Refer to the section on ADMINISTERING MEDICATION. An effective emetic is one tablespoon of a 3 percent solution of household hydrogen peroxide for every ten pounds of pet. Repeat the dose in ten minutes if the first dose doesn't do the trick. Whether successful in inducing vomiting or not, bring your dog to the veterinary hospital so further help can be offered.

Activated charcoal may be administered to help prevent additional absorption of the theobromine into the dog's system. Signs of shock are addressed with fluid therapy, and seizures, heart irregularities, vomiting and diarrhea are each specifically treated with appropriate medications. The treatment is often prolonged, because the half-life of theobromine—the time it takes the body to eliminate it—is 72 hours in dogs.

The best way to deal with chocolate toxicity is to prevent the problem from ever happening. If your dog has a sweet tooth, keep chocolate out of reach (see POISON).

COCCIDIOSIS

SYMPTOMS: Mild diarrhea with mucus and blood; loss of appetite; weight loss; dehydration
HOME CARE: None
VET CARE: Sulfa-type drugs; fluid therapy; blood transfusion
PREVENTION: Prompt cleaning of feces from yard; disinfect runs and kennels; prevent dogs from eating wild animals; preventative prescription medication may help

COCCIDIOSIS Coccidiosis is an intestinal disease caused by coccidia, a common protozoal parasite that affects both domestic and wild animals. There are 22 species of coccidia with four species of *Cystoisospora* being most common in dogs.

Coccidiosis is relatively common in dogs, with the parasite thought to be present in 3 to 38 percent of dogs. The parasite colonizes the lining of the intestine, and adult dogs often have coccidia in their system without getting sick. Puppies less than a month old are affected most often with intestinal disease.

Dogs are infected by swallowing the immature parasite. Five to seven days later, the eggs, called oocysts, develop in the dog's intestine and are passed in the stool. These microscopic oocysts require several days in the soil to become infective. Dogs contract coccidia by swallowing this infective stage either from licking themselves or contaminated objects, or by eating raw meat or other infected animals.

Puppies stressed by other illness, an unsanitary environment, and/or the crowded conditions of pet stores and shelters, are at highest risk for coccidiosis. The earliest sign typically is a mild diarrhea which becomes more severe until it contains mucus and sometimes blood. Anorexia, weight loss, and dehydration follow. This acute phase lasts up to ten days, and severely affected puppies may die. Diagnosis is made by finding oocysts during a microscopic examination of a stool sample.

Puppies are usually treated with a sulfa-type drug for five days to two to three weeks to eliminate the parasite. Sulfadimethoxine is the only drug that is currently approved to treat enteritis resulting from coccidiosis, but many other drugs and drug combinations have been used with differing success. Ponazuril, one of the newer drugs, appears to be promising.

Resolution of the symptoms is slow once signs develop, and it may require a week of therapy before improvement is seen. Severe cases may demand hospitalization to counter dehydration with fluid therapy. Sanitation is the single most important prevention of coccidiosis, particularly in kennels or other environments where large numbers of dogs are housed.

Environmental control is important. Remove feces promptly from the yard or kennel to prevent infection or reinfection. Coccidia are resistant to common disinfectants, but a strong ammonium hydroxide solution or heat treatment using boiling water, steam or a flame gun (on cement or gravel runs) is effective. Disinfect runs, cages and food bowls every day to destroy infective organisms.

COGNITIVE DYSFUNCTION All dogs tend to suffer some memory loss as they age. A percentage of old dogs develop more severe symptoms, technically called canine cognitive dysfunction, which could be compared to human senility. The older the dog is the more likely he is to show impairment in this area.

Studies show that 30 percent of dogs aged 11 to 12 had one or more symptom, and 68 percent of the 15 to 16 year old dogs had one or more symptom—35 percent of this group had two or more symptoms. Castrated male dogs were significantly more likely to have problems with disorientation than spayed females, but there were no differences between the sexes in other categories.

Dogs are one of the few species that develop a beta amyloid pathology in the brain. Beta amyloid is a starch-like protein that becomes waxy once deposited in the brain tissues. Beta amyloid has been associated with Alzheimer's disease in people. The deposition of beta amyloid material is somewhat different in than in the humans. In the dogs it's very diffuse and doesn't consolidate into distinct plaques as it does in humans.

Alzheimer's patients develop huge ventricles—spaces inside the brain that contain fluid, due to cell death. Basically, the brain shrinks and these ventricles become bigger. The same thing happens in affected dogs.

Getting lost in the house or yard, going to the wrong door, forgetting how to signal to go outdoors for urination or defecation—these and other signs correlate with some of the age-related degenerative changes in the dog's brain that are involved with memory and learning.

It's important to diagnose cognitive dysfunction correctly. Behavior changes in the aging dog often have other causes. For example, a break in housetraining might be due to kidney disease or diabetes, while disorientation and personality changes could be caused by a brain tumor or neurological disruptions from liver disease.

When the symptoms are caused by cognitive disorder, owners typically put their elderly dogs to sleep. Surveys of veterinarians indicate that in the United States, up to 500,000 dogs with cognitive disorder are put to sleep each year. However, there is now medical help that can reverse the condition in a percentage of affected dogs, and preserve the bond between the owners and their pets, at least for a short time.

COGNITIVE DYSFUNCTION

SYMPTOMS: Disorientation: wanders aimlessly; acts lost and confused; may not recognize family members or other familiar people or places; gets "stuck" in corners or lost in the house
Interaction changes: no longer greets family members; dislikes or avoids petting; not as interested in getting attention, interaction changes with other pets
Sleep changes: is awake and active at night; sleep cycles are disrupted or reversed
Housetraining is forgotten
Anxiety or compulsive behaviors; tremors; howling; repetitive pacing; licking the floor or other objects; circling; tail
HOME CARE: None
HOLISTIC HELP: Nutraceuticals
VET CARE: Sometimes drug therapy
PREVENTION: Keep dogs active and their minds engaged

The human medicine selegiline hydrochloride (Anipryl) has been FDA-approved to treat canine cognitive disorder. Anipryl may work to prevent ongoing damage to the brain. It acts on one of the neurotransmitters in the brain responsible for nerve-to-nerve communication. The drug slows the natural destruction of the chemical compound dopamine in the brain. The medicine works very well in about 1/3rd of cases, nominally well in another 1/3rd and not at all in the final percentage of dogs. Anipryl also is a temporary fix, and doesn't stop the progression, but only reverses signs for a year or two. Dogs will need to be on the drug for about four weeks before any results can be expected.

A natural component of some foods, called phospholipids, can help reverse signs of cognitive disorders by helping brain cells send and receive nerve impulses more effectively. Choline and phosphatidylcholine, two common message-sending compounds, are found in a dietary supplement called Cholodin, which is a less expensive alternative to Anipryl. The products are available through veterinarians, and come in a pill form or powder to be mixed into the food.

Some specialized therapeutic diets are now available that also help temporarily reverse brain aging changes. Diets containing alternative energy sources such as fatty acids from medium-chain triglycerides (MCTs) may prove beneficial in offsetting cognitive decline.

Medical marijuana (or cannabis) today is also available for pets, but must be formulated so that pets receive the medical benefits of the cannabis (hemp) plant while reducing potential toxic concentrations of the herb. Hemp can be used to aid in decreasing the severity of dementia. Ask your veterinarian if this supplement may benefit your pet.

As with humans, it's important to keep dogs active and mentally engaged. That can help slow or even prevent some of the "brain rust" that slows down cognitive abilities. Teach tricks and obedience drills, and offer interactive puzzle toys. That exercises not only his body, but his mind, and preserves the bond of love you've developed together.

COLITIS

Colitis is an inflammation of the lining of the large bowel or colon, which is at the end of the gastrointestinal tract. Colitis accounts for about half of diarrhea problems in dogs (see DIARRHEA).

The colon acts as a dehydration organ, pulling water from the solid waste that's passed. Inflammation inhibits water removal and interferes with organ contraction and movement of the fecal material.

Signs of colitis include urgent straining and painful defecation. Affected dogs commonly produce very frequent (several in an hour) liquid stools that have a great deal of mucus and bright red blood.

Colitis may be caused by a variety of conditions, including intestinal parasites (see WHIPWORMS, HOOKWORMS and GIARDIA). When the causative parasites are eliminated through proper treatment, the colitis usually goes away. Rarely, the inflammation is due to a food allergy, and avoiding the food ingredient will relieve the situation (see ALLERGY).

Sometimes, a specific cause for the colitis can't be determined. Cases of idiopathic colitis may benefit from high-fiber low-fat diets fed in small frequent meals (three to six times a day). The diet content and feeding schedule may slow the transit time of the material in the dog's colon, allowing the organ to better function. Your veterinarian may also prescribe oral medications (see INFLAMMATORY BOWEL DISEASE).

COLITIS

SYMPTOMS: Straining to defecate; frequent liquid stools containing mucus and bright red blood
HOME CARE: None
VET CARE: Address the specific cause; oral medications and high-fiber diets
PREVENTION: Prevent intestinal parasites; avoid abrupt diet changes

COLLAPSED TRACHEA This syndrome occurs when the normally rigid structure of the trachea—the breathing tube leading down the throat to the lungs—weakens. The trachea is then easily collapsed from such things as the dog tugging against his collar, or heavy panting during exercise. The cause of tracheal collapse is unknown, but it is most common in toy and miniature breeds like terriers and Poodles, and frequently in obese dogs. Although the syndrome can occur alone, dogs can also have concurrent respiratory or heart disease.

Signs are a chronic honking cough along with difficulty inhaling or exhaling. In mild cases, the dog may show signs only during heavy exercise or excitement. In more extreme cases, dogs at rest or only mildly excited suffer coughing fits that end with gagging, retching or even vomiting; occasionally, the dog passes out.

Tracheal collapse is suspected whenever an otherwise healthy small breed dog suffers a chronic cough. Diagnosis is confirmed by X-rays or endoscopic examination (see ENDOSCOPE).

Dogs suffering from this syndrome often can lead relatively normal lives. Most mild cases can be controlled by restricting the dog's activity, reducing opportunities for excitement and stress, and treating the dog with cough suppressants. When the dog is obese, weight reduction is important (see OBESITY). Attaching leashes to front-attach harnesses rather than collars is recommended.

When other medical conditions are present, they must be treated as well. Antibiotics and bronchodilator drugs may be helpful. Severe cases that threaten the dog's life may be helped surgically by removing and replacing the portion of trachea that is affected, or implanting a prosthesis to hold the airway open.

COLLAPSED TRACHEA

SYMPTOMS: Honking cough; difficulty inhaling or exhaling; exercise intolerance; coughing fits with gagging, retching, or vomiting
HOME CARE: Restrict dog's activity; avoid stress; use vet-prescribed cough suppressants
VET CARE: Antibiotics; bronchodilator drugs; sometimes sugary
PREVENTION: Keep dog trim; prevent excess stress and activity; do not let dog overheat

COLLIE EYE ANOMALY (CEA) This is an inherited condition of Collies and Shetland Sheepdogs, and is an interruption in the development of the eye which impairs vision.

Also referred to as collie eye defect, this is an inherited congenital condition affecting 70 to 90 percent of smooth and rough Collies in the United States and Great Britain. The condition also affects 2 to 3 percent of Border Collies, and it's seen in Australian Shepherds, Shetland Sheepdogs, and other herding dogs.

Lesions form on the retina at the back of the eye, and on the optic disk which is the contact point at the back of the eye for the optic nerve leading to the brain. In some cases, the retina is detached. Puppies are born with CEA in both eyes, and the condition is static and does not worsen over time.

The degree of vision impairment varies from dog to dog. Mild cases can result in "blind spots" that don't bother the dog and may be hard for your veterinarian to detect. CEA characterized by retinal detachment will ultimately result in complete blindness.

The condition is caused by a defect in chromosome 37, and only happens in dogs that have one or both parents that carry this genetic mutation. The parents may not be affected and so may not have been diagnosed. Other genes may also be involved.

Genetic analysis can determine if your dog has this defect even before symptoms are seen. Signs of progression may include eyeballs looking smaller than normal, or sunken in their sockets, or a cloudy appearance to the cornea. Prompt diagnosis and treatment helps manage the disease and may delay or prevent signs.

There is no treatment for CEA. Reputable breeders are working with researchers to discover how the problem is inherited. It is hoped that eventually the incidence can be reduced or even eliminated from these breeds (see BLINDNESS and EYES).

COMMUNICATION Communication is a process by which information is transmitted from one individual to another using a system of common signals. Understanding each other becomes particularly important when individuals must frequently interact (see SOCIAL STRUCTURE).

Canine communication is a complex system of sign language, vocalization, and even scent cues (see MARKING) that serve to reinforce the dog's social position within the group. Dogs are quite flexible regarding members of their group, particularly when the dog has been properly socialized (see PUPPY). In other words, your dog considers you—and other people and pets in the household—to be a part of his family group, and acts accordingly.

If your relationship is to reach its full potential, it is important that you, and not your dog, be in charge. For this to happen, you must understand each other's language.

Human hearing and scenting limitations make it impossible to understand subtle signals of canine language. But an attentive owner can learn to interpret the more obvious canine signals, and pave the way for smoother interspecies communication. Many dogs meet us halfway by learning a large human vocabulary, particularly when words are used with consistency (see TRAINING).

Dogs are more highly attuned to body language, however, and this silent communication is given greater weight. Your dog's dedicated observation can make him appear psychic—he always hides when a bath is imminent—when in fact he's simply reacting to non-verbal cues you may be unaware you're broadcasting. That's why when you smile during a verbal reprimand, your dog reads amusement rather than reproach, and acts accordingly.

Each type of communication has advantages and disadvantages. Sound carries over long distances, but a bark may alert adversaries as well as family members. A body posture can be held nearly forever, while a growl can only be sustained one breath at a time. And scent signals can be left behind for others to read the way people leave voice mail.

Dogs use combinations of each technique to communicate meaning. Very basically, canine communication is used to decrease the distance between individuals with signals that solicit attention, or to increase distance between individuals with warning signals. Most often, vocalizations punctuate what the body movements are saying in the same way people use inflection to impart emotion and meaning. And because dogs realize people rely on verbal communication, our dogs have become much more vocal than their ancestors.

For instance, barking is rare in wolves, but is the most common vocal signal in dogs. It's used during play, defense, and as a greeting, and is considered a sign of dominance but not necessarily of aggression. Barking is a canine fire alarm, a call to action that alerts the family group to the unusual. This may be anything from the arrival of friend or foe, to an unexpected sound like thunder, or the strange sight of you wearing a hat. Some dogs bark to relieve boredom, particularly when left alone for hours at a time. Dogs also bark together as a joyful expression of happiness; that's why yelling at a dog to stop barking rarely works. He thinks you're joining in a communal bark-fest, and barks even louder.

Canine body positions

Dogs use howls to express emotion, and to announce their location to missing family members. Usually, a howl is a dog's cry of loneliness that implores others to come join him; dogs left home alone, or sequestered by themselves in a room may howl. Howls seem to be contagious, with a single lone call often answered by any other dog within hearing. Dogs may interpret a siren or even human singing as an invitation to sing along.

Whining, whimpering and yelping are used to communicate submission, pain or fear. They may also be used as solicitations to a dominant individual (usually the owner) for attention, food, or to go in or out.

A dog laugh sounds similar to a human saying, "Ha-ha-ha-ha!" but without sounding the "a" vowel and is simply a breathy exhalation. There's also research that points to a dog sneeze in certain circumstances to being similar to a "canine giggle" of delight. Recordings of the panting-laugh sound played at shelters has helped calm dogs' stress. Sneezing can prompt a reciprocal sneeze in your dog, too—because after all, laughter is catching and good medicine.

Growls and snarls are distance-increasing signals that are warnings to stay away. Snarls display the teeth and aren't always accompanied by sound; they signify slight fear. Growls indicate deeper concern, and can be made with the mouth open or closed. A dog's growl is used in defense, and as a threat. Dogs that aren't sure how they feel may bark, snarl and growl all at the same time, which usually means they're more scared than aggressive.

Silent canine communication makes use of the dog's body from nose to tail. The position and movement of his tail, his facial expression, even his posture is telling. Eyes communicate volumes. Droopy eyelids indicate pleasure, and your dog may squint and moan with delight when his ears are rubbed. Alert dogs keep their eyes open wide. An unblinking stare is a challenge and shows dominance, while averting the eyes shows canine submission. The pupils of a dog's eyes indicate aggression and imminent attack when they suddenly dilate wide. Avoid locking eyes with a strange dog, for such a challenge may incite him to attack.

The dog's mouth is also quite expressive. In general, when the lips lift vertically to show the long dagger-shaped canines, the dog is showing aggression or fear. Lips pull back horizontally to show more teeth in a canine grin of submission, which is often used as an appeasement gesture toward a dominant individual. A flicking tongue signals intent to lick, which when aimed at the face or hands is also an appeasement gesture. The relaxed, happy dog may sit with his mouth half-open and tongue lolling out as he pants.

The ears are barometers of mood. The shape of the dog's ears, whether prick or drop, also influence how easy ear language is to understand. For the sake of this discussion, the ear conformation of the German Shepherd Dog will be used. When erect and facing forward, the dog is interested and possibly aggressive. The ears flatten against the head by degrees depending on how fearful or submissive the dog feels.

Tail talk is perhaps the dog's most obvious signal to people. Again, the conformation of the dog's tail, from long to docked, corkscrew or curled, will determine the extent of your dog's tail semaphore.

In most cases, a wagging tail is a distance-reducing signal that declares the dog to be friendly. However, what the tail says depends to a great degree on what the rest of the body is doing.

A relaxed pet's tail curves down and back up in a gentle U. As interest grows, the higher the tail will be held. Dominant and confident dogs hold their tails high, and wag rapidly in tight sharp arcs. Aggressive dogs also hold their tails high, often tightly arched over their back with just the end jerking very quickly back and forth. This indicates imminent attack, and usually includes relevant vocalizations and facial expressions.

Holding the tail in a low position indicates submission. A dog shows his deference by wagging in loose, wide low arcs that often include hip wags as well. Tucking the tail between the legs signals submission and fear. A tucked tail is the canine equivalent of hiding the face. Tucking the tail between the legs covers the genitals, and interferes with the sniffing behavior that identifies him to other dogs.

Your dog's carriage and even his fur position show how he feels. Dogs bump, push or lean against people or other animals as a sign of dominance. Erect posture is a sign of confidence typical of dominant dogs, who seem to nearly stand on tiptoe when in the presence of another dog they want to impress. The aggressive dog leans forward toward whoever they want to cow, while the fearful dog leans backward. Piloerection—fluffing the fur along the ridge of his back (the hackles)—makes the dog look bigger and more impressive, and may be used to bluff. Both fearful and aggressive dogs raise their hackles.

The opposite is true when a dog shows submission. He tries to look smaller than he is. Dogs cry uncle by flattening their ears, tucking their tail, crouching as low as possible and perhaps offering a paw in a placating gesture in prelude to rolling over. Exposing the tummy, perhaps even urinating in this position or when crouched before the aggressor, is the dog's ultimate sign of deference.

All these signals must be read together to place your dog's meaning in proper context. Often, mixed signals may be sent, with the snarling front half of the dog indicating aggression while the back half wags submissively. Dogs may "pretend" to be aggressive to invite play, and indicate it's a game by using exaggerated signals (see PLAY).

Canine language serves to smooth relationships, offering a way for dogs to get along with each other and the people who make up their families. Communicating deference to a dominant individual reinforces each's position within the family group. For the most part, place is determined simply by posturing alone, and fights are rarely necessary. Dominant dogs practice chivalry, and let lower-ranking dogs off the hook when they cry uncle.

CONSTIPATION

Constipation refers to the difficult, less frequent than normal passage of dry, hard feces. If defecation is delayed and feces remain in the colon for two or three days, too much moisture is removed by the organ, which makes elimination painful. A constipated dog may squat and strain unproductively for long periods of time. Ongoing constipation may result in a loss of appetite, and the dog losing weight. When the condition becomes chronic, the bowel lining may become inflamed which stimulates a release of dark fluid that accompanies the hard, dry fecal matter.

Dogs may become constipated for a variety of reasons (see SWALLOWED OBJECTS. Beside the danger of puncture, swallowed bone fragments turn feces into cement-like masses that block the colon. Dogs are notorious for chewing and swallowing non-digestible objects like paper, sticks, grass, and cloth, which turn into wads that cause impaction. Rawhide chews, if eaten in excess, promote constipation.

CONSTIPATION

SYMPTOMS: Straining without passing stool; hard, dry stools accompanied by dark brown liquid
HOME CARE: Offer milk; nonflavored Metamucil; bran cereal; canned pumpkin, or squash; offer fresh celery; increase exercise
HOLISTIC HELP: Homeopathy; aromatherapy
VET CARE: Suppositories; enemas; laxatives; sometimes mechanical removal of blockage; fluid therapy if dehydrated
PREVENTION: High-fiber diets; groom to remove mats; keep dog from ingesting nonfood items; limit rawhide-type treats; avoid bones

High meat diets with little fiber produce stools that are smaller and sticky, and difficult to pass. Stress influences the condition; dogs boarded or in strange surroundings may voluntarily delay defecation and become constipated. Elderly dogs commonly suffer bouts of constipation, which may be due a combination of weak abdominal muscles, reduced exercise, or improper diet (see GERIATRIC DOG). Poor grooming, especially of longhaired dogs may also promote constipation when fur beneath the tail mats with feces and causes anal inflammation that results in painful defecation; mats may even cause external blockage that interferes with normal defecation. Keep the anal region of longhaired dogs clipped to prevent mats from developing (see GROOMING).

Another common cause of constipation is prostatitis. In unneutered male dogs, the prostate swells and blocks the colon in the pelvic region. Rectal exams should be part of the annual exam for intact males over five years of age. Tumors of the prostate, rectum or perianal region can cause constipation.

Constipation can also be a sign of kidney disease or diabetes; with either condition, there is excessive urine production which prompts the colon to conserve water—and that causes a dry stool that can lead to constipation (see KIDNEY DISEASE and DIABETEST MELLITUS).

Laxatives may be helpful, but human medications can be dangerous and should only be given with veterinary approval. Your veterinarian may prescribe enemas or suppositories;

ask for a demonstration before attempting to administer these treatments yourself or you risk injuring the dog. Many times, evacuating the colon requires a veterinarian's help, and often the dog must be sedated.

Treating constipation must address the specific cause to be effective, but in general, treatment for canine constipation is the same as people. Feeding a diet containing 7 to 13 percent fiber (look on the label), drinking lots of water, and a regular exercise regimen (a daily 20 minute walk) are beneficial, as is increasing the dog's exercise. Old dogs may benefit from a higher water content diet. Feed canned food, or soak the kibble with equal parts water for twenty minutes before feeding.

The homeopathic remedy Nux vomica 6C liquid may help. Holistic veterinarians recommend diluting 20 drops of the remedy in an ounce of spring water, and giving your pet half a dropperful three times a day to relieve the constipation. Aromatherapy using lavender may also help. Place a drop or two of the essential oil on a bandana for the dog to wear. The oil works for up to six hours so you'll need to repeat the treatment a few times a day until the constipation resolves.

Veterinary approved stimulant laxatives are available, but shouldn't be overused or they may interfere with normal colon function. Mild cases of constipation may benefit from temporarily adding milk to the diet, which has a laxative effect in some dogs. Give your small dog 1/8 cup twice a day, and a large dog 1/2 cup twice a day until they're regular again.

A better choice is laxatives like Metamucil that contain cellulose ingredients which attract water and add bulk to the stool. Mix non-flavored Metamucil with your dog's food. One teaspoon twice a day for small dogs, and two to three teaspoons twice a day for large dogs is helpful. Bran cereals, and canned pumpkin or squash are natural sources of fiber that also work well, and dogs seem to like the flavor. To promote regularity, add ½ teaspoon to your small dog's food, or about two tablespoons to the big dog's diet.

For dogs that relish vegetable snacks, offer a stick or two of carrot or celery; the fiber and liquid help reduce constipation, and also gives your dog an outlet for chewing urges. Only give your dog rawhide or sterilized bones and supervise his chewing so he doesn't swallow them.

COPPER POISONING

Copper naturally occurs in certain foods, such as organ meats like liver and kidneys. Copper is an essential nutrient affecting the formation of bone, and is normally metabolized in and the excess removed by the liver.

However, some dogs, particularly Bedlington Terriers and West Highland White Terriers, have an inherited tendency to an increased sensitivity and aren't able to get rid of excess copper. Doberman Pinchers are also prone to copper toxicity secondary to liver disease (see LIVER DISEASE). The inherited tendency is similar to Wilson's Disease in people in which copper cannot be metabolized, but collects in various organs and causes damage.

In dogs, the copper typically accumulates in and damages the liver. Although excess copper can be demonstrated in the liver by six months of age, signs of disease usually aren't evident for several years. Symptoms are the same as for liver disease and damage to the organ is irreversible once signs develop. Without treatment, the dog will die.

Up to 50 percent of Bedlington Terriers develop the disease, and West Highland White Terriers are also at high risk. It is recommended that dogs of these breeds be fed a low-copper diet from puppyhood on as a preventative measure. Such a diet is indicated in any dog diagnosed with the condition. Ask your veterinarian for a recommendation.

In addition, zinc supplements may prove beneficial as a preventative and treatment in such dogs, since it inhibits copper absorption and may even help eliminate copper stored in the liver. Some drugs also increase the excretion of copper in the urine, and may be helpful for dogs with this condition.

COPPER POISONING

SYMPTOMS: Loss of appetite; vomiting; diarrhea; weight loss; lethargy; jaundice; swollen abdomen; bloody urine and/or feces
HOME CARE: None
VET CARE: Drugs that help the body excrete copper in the urine; zinc supplements
PREVENTION: High-risk breeds should be fed low-copper diet and be given zinc supplements

COPROPHAGIA This is a fancy term for the disgusting practice of a dog eating feces, his own or another animal's. In fact, this is a common behavior of dogs. Mother dogs ingest their puppies' stool as a means of keeping the nest clean. Outside of this context, though, the behavior becomes objectionable to most owners.

Usually the behavior is first noticed in puppies aged four to nine months old, with the frequency increasing after one year of age. Some dogs outgrow the nasty habit, but it can persist throughout the dog's life. In some dogs, the behavior may indicate a nutritional or gastrointestinal disorder in which food isn't being completely digested. Pancreatitis, parasites, or starvation may prompt the dog to eat his own waste in an effort to utilize the nutrients that it contains.

But in most instances, nutritional deficiency has nothing to do with the behavior. Dogs are historically scavengers, and this is a scavenger behavior that causes some dogs to relish cow piles or to eat from the cat's litter box.

The behavior can be an attention-seeking behavior, or a bad habit prompted by anxiety or boredom. Increase playtime with your dog. Most need about 45 minutes of aerobic exercise each day to stay healthy. And increase the number of toys in the house to keep him busy when you're away.

Retraining is also key, and preventing the dog access to feces is the obvious answer. Walk the dog on a leash, and pick up droppings promptly. A muzzle may be beneficial to prevent the dog from eating anything when he can't be supervised. Put a cover on the cat's litter box, and/or use a baby gate to limit the dog's access to the cat's toilet area.

The behavior resolves in some dogs fed a high-protein low carbohydrate ration twice a day. Adding a tablespoon of vegetable oil to the food every day seems to help in some cases.

When all else fails, a commercial product called ForBid can be added to your dog's diet. When eaten with his food, the powder makes the dog's feces taste bad. Feeding the dog MSG, garlic, or pumpkin is also thought to give feces a bad taste and make it less attractive to the dog. ForBid and other commercial products are available at many veterinary offices or pet supply stores.

CROPPING Otoplasty refers to the practice of surgically altering the shape of the dog's external ear. The procedure may be done to correct congenital defects or damage from injury or disease.

Historically, ears were cropped on protection and "varmint" dogs to prevent ears from being mauled during fights with prey or each other. Also, erect "prick" ears are said to be healthier because they allow air flow that's blocked in hanging or "drop" ear conformation of dogs like Beagles.

Truthfully, the procedure rarely is required for the dog's health. Usually it's done purely for cosmetic reasons to change a folded or hanging ear conformation to an erect look favored by dog show fanciers.

In the United States, ear cropping is historically performed on more than fifty breeds. These include Boston Terriers, Boxers, Doberman Pinschers, Great Danes, and Schnauzers to conform to the specific look of each breed standard.

The surgery is performed on eight to ten week old puppies (Bostons more typically at four to six months of age). These early age surgeries create stress that can predispose at risk puppies to health problems (see DISTEMPER and PARVOVIRUS). Ear cropping requires general anesthesia and the expertise of a veterinary surgeon familiar with individual breed standards.

Various breeds' standards dictate the preferred shape of the ear. A "show trim" often looks longer and more extreme on a Great Dane destined for the show ring than for a pet. And breeds like the Bull Terrier or American Pit Bull Terrier calls for shorter ear cropping.

Splinting and other specialized ear-bandaging techniques help form the puppy's ears for a week or more following the surgery, and will need to be monitored and changed as the ears heal. Discomfort from the bandaging and wound can make healing a challenge since pups paw at bandages and shake heads to relieve the discomfort. Pain medicine is recommended.

In recent years, the ethics of cosmetic ear cropping has been called into question both in the United States and abroad. The American Kennel Club breed club standards for these breeds generally include descriptions of both the ideal cropped, as well as a natural ear conformation. Some dog show fanciers believe cropped dogs do more favorably in competition and continue to crop in order to succeed in the show ring. Show dogs in some other countries may be disqualified if the ears are cropped.

The practice of surgically altering the conformation of a dog's ears is expensive, painful, requires tedious owner follow up, and is not always successful. Changing the way ears look may also interfere with the dog's body language. If conformation dog shows are not in your plans, there's no reason to put your puppy through ear cropping. Please consult with your veterinarian and consider your own motives before putting your puppy through this elective procedure (see DOCKING).

NOTE: The American Veterinary Medical Association passed the following policy, mirroring that of the American Animal Hospital Association and the Canadian VMA: **The AVMA opposes ear cropping and tail docking of dogs when done solely for cosmetic purposes. The AVMA encourages the elimination of ear cropping and tail docking from breed standards.**

CRYPTORCHID The testicles of puppies are generally descended into the scrotal sack by ten days after birth. Male puppies that fail to have their testicles descend into the scrotal sack by eight weeks of age are said to be cryptorchid; occasionally, the organs will descend by six months of age. When they don't, the testicles are retained within the abdomen. When only one is retained, it's called monorchid.

Cryptorchid dogs are sterile, but monorchid dogs may be able to father puppies. This isn't considered a good idea, though, because the tendency to retain a testicle is thought to be inherited; it is more common in purebred dogs. Dogs with a retained testicle cannot be shown in conformation, and surgically moving the organ into the scrotum is considered unethical.

The testicles generate male hormones even when they are retained in the abdomen, which means cryptorchid dogs exhibit the same behavior as any intact male (see REPRODUCTION). These dogs are also at higher risk for testicular cancer. For all these reasons, cryptorchid dogs should be neutered. The veterinarian must surgically go into the abdomen to find and remove the organs.

CUSHING'S DISEASE More correctly referred to as hyperadrenocorticism, Cushing's Disease was named for the doctor who first described this syndrome in people. It is a common metabolic disorder of dogs in which the adrenal gland produces too much steroid hormones, especially cortisol. It usually occurs around eight to ten years of age.

CUSHING'S DISEASE

SYMPTOMS: Increased appetite and thirst; excessive urination; lethargy; sometimes pacing, circling, drunken behavior, or seizures; symmetrical hair loss on the body; potbellied appearance; thin, wasted legs; skin disease
HOME CARE: None
VET CARE: Surgery to remove tumor when possible; drug therapy to control symptoms; sometimes radiation therapy
PREVENTION: Avoid the overuse of steroid drugs

Cortisol affects the metabolism of carbohydrates, proteins and fats. It also suppresses the body's inflammatory and immune responses. Too much secreted into the system reduces the body's resistance to bacteria and viruses. Beagles, Boston Terriers, Boxers, Dachshunds, and Toy and Miniature Poodles appear to have an increased risk for the condition. The disease is a progressive one that is slow and insidious.

There are different forms of the disease. In the pituitary form of Cushing's Disease, a tiny and otherwise benign tumor causes the pituitary to over-stimulate the adrenal gland. Smaller breed dogs tend to get tumors of the pituitary gland.

About 20 percent of Cushing's disease is the adrenal form, in which cortisol-secreting tumors develop on the adrenal glands themselves. Larger breed dogs are more likely to develop tumors of the adrenal gland. Yet another form of the disease can be induced by the overuse of cortisone-type medications, which are often used to control itchy skin conditions (see ALLERGY).

Signs of Cushing's disease are increased appetite and thirst, excessive urination, and lethargy. When caused by a tumor in the brain, neurologic signs may include pacing, circling, a drunken walk, head pressing, or seizures. Dogs also typically suffer a symmetrical hair loss on their body, and often develop a progressive pot-bellied appearance, with wasting and weakening of the leg muscles. Color changes in the fur and/or the skin are typical, along with skin disease that includes thinning and loss of elasticity, flaky scales, bumpy irregularities, black head pimples particularly surrounding the nipples and genitals, and bleeding. Complications of Cushing's disease include increased risk of infection, high blood pressure, congestive heart failure, pancreatitis, diabetes, and blood clotting abnormalities.

Only a veterinarian can diagnose Cushing's Disease using a battery of laboratory tests. Blood tests evaluate the adrenal gland function by measuring the amounts of circulating hormones when the dog is at rest, and in response to adrenal gland stimulating and suppressing drugs.

But about 40 percent of dogs with Cushing's have an abnormal test result. The dog's history and physical examination are most important. The urine cortisol-creatinine ratio is quite sensitive but not specific. The low-dose dexamethasone suppression (LDDS) test is sensitive and relatively specific if the test is performed on dogs with appropriate history and physical examination results. Treatment depends on where the tumor is located.

The pituitary form of the disease is treated with oral medication that controls cortisol secretion from the adrenals. Lysodren (Mitotane), also known as o,p'-DDD, is most often prescribed and it works in almost all cases. It is structurally related to the insecticide DDT, and is cytotoxic, that is, it destroys the adrenal gland cells. Typically, Mitotane is given for the rest of the dog's life, and quickly reverses many of the symptoms within days to weeks.

Ketoconazole (Nizoral) is an alternative drug treatment for dogs that do not respond well to Mitotane. It inhibits adrenal hormone production and is considered less toxic than Mitotane. It is not FDA approved but off-label use in dogs is common and is considered accepted practice.

When the dog has an adrenal tumor, some experts recommend treating with the drug trilostane for several weeks prior to surgery. Surgical removal of the affected gland is the treatment of choice for the adrenal form of Cushing's. When the tumor is on only one gland, removing that gland cures the disease. In dogs that do not respond well to any medication, both glands may be removed, followed by oral medication to replace the missing hormones.

S-Adenosylmethionine (SAMe) is a nutraceutical antioxidant that may be helpful in Cushing's patients with liver complications. A commercial S-Adenosylmethionine supplement (Denosyl SD4) has been demonstrated to improve liver function in these pets.

Treatment for Cushing's disease reverses the symptoms and improves the dog's quality of life. It helps the dog live an average of 18 months longer. Dogs diagnosed at an earlier age and successfully treated often live for another five to ten years.

CUTEREBRA This is the larval stage of the bot fly, a parasite that afflicts rabbits and mice, and can infect pets that hunt these creatures. Cats are at highest risk, but dogs are not immune. Cuterebra infection is seen most often during the summer months.

Bot flies lay up to 2000 eggs in their lifetime, infecting the soil or vegetation surrounding mouse and rabbit runs. Eggs are triggered to hatch when sensors pick up the body heat of a nearby host. The larvae enter the body through the nose or mouth when the dog sniffs or lick-explores an infected environment. Once inside, the parasite migrates and forms a cyst beneath the dog's skin usually in the chest or neck region. This area swells as the parasite matures.

Initially the swelling is firm, then softens as it fills with fluid, which escapes from a central vent-hole through which the parasite breathes. The larva continues to grow and molt, and the spine-covered brownish cuterebra may reach over an inch in length and a half inch in diameter. After about a month spent in the host, the parasite exits the skin and drops to the ground, where it spends the winter in a pupal stage. Pupae hatch into adult bot flies in the spring.

CUTEREBRA

SYMPTOMS: Soft swelling beneath skin of usually the neck or chest
HOME CARE: None
VET CARE: Surgical removal
PREVENTION: Prevent dogs from hunting and roaming

Dogs aren't generally bothered by cuterebra infection, but the cysts may become infected. In very rare instances, the cuterebra may migrate into the nostrils, spinal column or scrotum, or even into the brain, which can have life-threatening consequences.

Do not attempt to remove the parasite yourself, and never squeeze the swelling to express the cuterebra from the skin. Crushing the parasite may cause a life-threatening anaphylactic reaction in your dog. Cuterebra parasites are carefully removed through the vent hole by surgically enlarging the opening. The empty cyst is cleaned and treated to prevent infection.

Prevent your dog from unsupervised roaming and hunting to reduce cuterebra exposure and risk of infection.

CYST A cyst is a sack-like cavity filled with foreign matter that is contained by a thickened capsule of tissue. Cutaneous cysts (those found in the skin) are quite common in dogs, and can appear anywhere on the body. Some breeds, including Kerry Blue Terriers, Schnauzers and spaniels, tend to be affected most often.

Cutaneous cysts are usually filled with fluid or a semisolid cheese-like substance. They are firm to soft, well defined round areas that move freely beneath the skin. The most common type in dogs are follicular (epidermoid) cysts that arise from the hair follicles; they are commonly—and erroneously—referred to as "sebaceous cysts."

Cysts often grow to an inch or more in diameter, and may rupture and drain from a central opening. Manual expression of a cyst can cause severe inflammation, and is discouraged. Surgical removal is the recommended therapy.

Fluid-filled ovarian cysts may develop in intact female dogs and can grow quite large, producing hormones that interfere with the dog's fertility. Surgical removal of the cysts may correct the problem and allow conception to occur. Spaying removes the reproductive organs, including the affected ovaries. Spaying your dog before her first heat cycle prevents the problem from ever occurring (see SPAYING).

CYSTITIS Cystitis is an inflammation of the membrane lining the urinary bladder, and is usually caused by bacterial, viral, or fungal infection. Bacterial urinary tract infections are common in dogs, estimated to affect more than 10 percent of all dogs. Cystitis typically affects females more often than males. The condition can occur at any age, and may be present prior to or in conjunction with the development of bladder stones.

People suffering from this condition may feel the need to urinate more frequently, and suffer pain during urination. Such signs in dogs, though, may not be noticed unless a housebroken dog has an accident in the house. Occasionally, the dog's urine contains blood.

Left untreated, the infection and inflammation can ascend into the kidneys, and cause scarring or even kidney failure. The condition may lead to prostate infection, or invade the testicles of male dogs; in both male and female dogs, untreated urinary tract infections may cause` infertility.

Diagnosis is made by examination of the dog's urine. Both a urinalysis and a urine culture may be performed to identify the cause of the infection, so that an appropriate medication can be prescribed.

Holistic veterinarians may recommend using an herbal tincture called Goldenrod Horsetail Compound to reduce the bladder's irritation. You can also look for a combination of goldenrod, horsetail, parsley, marshmallow root and elderberry, sometimes called Urinary Tea Blend. Dogs weighing under 15 pounds can have half a dropperful of the tincture twice a day until they feel better. Larger dogs can take between one and two droppersfull a day. The easiest way to give this is mixing it into the dog's food.

The homeopathic remedy Cantharsis 30C helps to reduce the pain of urination, particularly when there is blood in the urine. Cranberry, often recommended for the same condition in people, also works well, but most pets hate the taste. You can use the supplement called CranActin from health food stores. As your vet for the proper dose.

Cystitis is typically treated with an antibiotic for two to three weeks. To help prevent future bouts, provide your dog with access to plenty of clean fresh water, offer ample opportunities for appropriate elimination, and encourage your dog to exercise regularly.

CYSTITIS

SYMPTOMS: Dribbling urine; urinating in unusual locations; frequent voiding of small amounts of urine; sometimes bloody urine
HOME CARE: None
HOLISTIC HELP: Herbal treatment; homeopathy
VET CARE: Antibiotics; sometimes therapeutic diets
PREVENTION: Offer lots of fresh water; provide plentiful bathroom breaks; encourage exercise

156 DOG FACTS

CYTOLOGY When owners discover a lump or bump on their dog, they don't want to wait for answers about how serious the problem might be. While pricy diagnostic tools like MRI or CT-scans provide detailed information, one of the simplest tests offers quick, inexpensive answers.

Cytology is a noninvasive, pain-free way to look at cells under a microscope. Cytology can detect many health problems, including inflammation, infection, fungi, parasites, bacteria, and cancer. Cytology often can determine within minutes if the dog's lump or bump is cause for concern.

A trained pathologist can look at cells and tell what kind of cells they are. Once cells are identified, the veterinarian can plan the most appropriate treatment.

Diagnosing a lump or bump is one of the most common times cytology is used. Cells are collected by using a fine needle aspirate. The veterinarian uses a syringe similar to those used to give vaccinations. The needle is passed into the mass and the plunger of the syringe drawn back to collect material from the mass into the needle. A fine needle aspirate can be used to collect cells from masses on the skin surface or from deeper in the tissue. For masses inside the chest or abdomen, a longer needle would be required, as well as sedation and an ultrasound probe to guide the needle to the right place.

The cells are put onto a microscope slide, treated with a series of stains to make them more visible, and then examined under the microscope.

Pathologists often can distinguish benign from malignant processes by how the cells look, and sometimes even identify the type of cancer. Some tumors are more easily diagnosed with cytology than others. That depends on how readily the tumor exfoliates—sheds cells.

Round cell tumors such as mast cell tumors and lymphomas exfoliate best and are very easy to diagnose with cytology. Carcinomas that arise from epithelial tissue such as the lining of the mouth or intestinal tract also can be diagnosed with cytology.

Benign fatty tumors (lipomas) occur under the skin and are very common in dogs and typically aren't a serious problem. They are very easy to diagnose by an aspirate, although not many cells are collected that way. The sample is clear fatty-looking greasy material when it's a lipoma, and those don't even need to be stained to diagnose them.

Tumors that don't exfoliate well or are difficult to sample with a needle may not be candidates for cytology. For instance, sarcomas—tumors of connective tissue such as muscle, ligament and tendon—are often the most difficult to diagnose cytologically. A biopsy may be needed in conjunction with a fine needle aspirate to get a definitive diagnosis.

Biopsy is the gold standard for making a diagnosis because it preserves the tissue architecture. Instead of a few individual cells, biopsy obtains a piece of tissue either with larger bore needle, or an incision that removes a piece of tissue with a blade. The sample is preserved in formalin, embedded in paraffin wax, stained, and then fine slices are made. "The cells look the same under the microscope as with cytology, but biopsy preserves the relationship of cells to each other.

That's important because biopsy samples allow the pathologist to "grade" the seriousness of a cancer—an assessment of how malignant and bad it's likely to behave. Grading can be done with biopsy but not with an aspirate.

A biopsy typically costs two or three times more than cytology because it requires general anesthesia, a pathologist's report, and hospital stay. It also takes two or three days to get the results. But it offers a more complete and accurate diagnosis.

Veterinarians almost always perform cytology as the first step in diagnosis, though, because the procedure can be done in the exam room with no sedation. The cost might run $25-50 to collect the sample, and another $100-150 if sent out for the pathologist report. Cytology is a fast, economical way for your veterinarian to determine next steps for your dog's diagnosis and treatment—and in happy cases, quickly gives owners the good news that the lump is nothing to worry about.

DAM The term "dam" is used by canine professionals in reference to a dog's mother.

DEAFNESS Hearing loss is being recognized more and more in many purebred dogs. There are several causes. Conductive hearing loss occurs when there's a problem with sound waves traveling through the inner ear.

Pets can be born with conductive hearing loss or can acquire it later in life. Puppies can be born deaf when there are problems with the auditory nerve that transmits sound from the inner ear to the brain. Called sensorineural hearing loss, the condition may be inherited and is more likely in breeds such as Dalmatians and Jack Russell Terriers.

The most common cause is chronic ear inflammation and infection of the external or middle ear. Parasites, inhalant and food allergic dermatitis, and the yeast *Mallasezia canis* are the most common causes of ear inflammation and infection (see EAR MITES, HEMATOMA and OTITIS). Temporary hearing loss may occur with the rupture of the eardrum but should return as the membrane heals.

A sensory disorder is caused by nerve problems in the inner ear. Sensorineural hearing loss, usually congenital and possibly inherited, is present from birth. The pet can have partial or complete hearing loss.

Dog breeds predisposed to congenital deafness include Dalmatians, English setters, bull terriers and Jack Russell terriers. Chemical or noise-induced damage can also cause irreversible or progressive hearing loss. Nearly 200 drugs and chemicals can prove toxic to hearing. The most common include certain antibiotics, diuretics, the anticancer drug cisplatin and some antiseptic preparations.

Age-related hearing loss (presbycusis) is not associated with a specific cause, but is a gradual degeneration of one or more areas of the ear. It is believed to be the most common form of hearing loss in dogs.

There is a reflex that contracts the two tiniest muscles in the body inside the middle ear. This self-protective reflex acts like a biological muffler. By contracting those muscles, the sound that reaches the inner ear is reduced. Before a dog barks, that muscle contracts so the dog's own vocalization doesn't damage his hearing, but a percussive sound such as gunfire happens too fast. That can cause a cumulative hearing loss and the ear does not recover from that.

Holistic veterinarians don't know why it sometimes works, but some hearing problems can be improved with acupressure. There are two points near the base of the ear that you can stimulate. TH17 is located just below the ear, and SI19 and GB2 are both located just in front of the ear. Press each point with your finger once a day for 30 seconds to a minute, then release.

Dogs often overcome deficits in one of their senses by compensating with another. That's why it's hard to detect hearing loss in pets, even if present from birth. Dogs normally have a range of hearing of sound frequency that's close to three times that of humans, so pets can often suffer from congenital or acquired hearing loss and the owner never notices.

Dogs can't tell us they don't hear something, so diagnosis can be tricky. Behavioral audiometry, a hearing test, presents sounds to the patient, and then the resulting behavior indicates if the animal detects the sound. Both conscious and reflexive responses can be monitored, but it's still tough to interpret. For instance, did the pet actually "hear" the sound or "feel" the vibration through the floor?

Impedance audiometry measures changes in the eardrum mobility as pressure in the external ear changes. In a healthy ear, the air pressure in the external ear canal will be the same as the air pressure in the middle ear. By comparing the two, a hearing impairment can be diagnosed.

Acoustic reflex, another test using impedance audiometry, is the involuntary action of the middle ear in response to a sound. When a loud noise is heard, the muscles of the middle ear in normal pets contract to decrease the movement of the eardrum, protecting the inner ear from damage. The reaction can be measured, and an acoustic reflex less than normal indicates inflammation of the middle ear, or disease of the cochlear nerve, which transmits the sound impulses to the brain.

Most owners realize there's a problem during training when voice commands are ignored or other noise fails to draw the dog's attention. Deaf dogs may bark less than other dogs, and the voice may sound odd. They frequently develop behavior problems because of their inability to understand human communication, and because they may be easily startled or frightened by the unexpected.

Deaf dogs are often taught to respond to the porch light flashing on and off, rather than being called to come in. They can be "clicker trained" using a flashlight beam, rather than a sound cue. Although they can't hear, deaf dogs can still feel vibration, so a slammed door or stomped foot or vibrating collar may work as a signal. It's particularly important to give the deaf dog some sort of warning of your presence to avoid a startle/bite reflex. Some deaf dogs may be able to hear the frequencies of special whistles, and may compensate enough for day-to-day living.

Dogs with a gradual hearing loss tend to do well as long as they remain in familiar, safe surroundings. Routine ear cleaning is important to stay ahead of possible health problems (see GROOMING). Dogs with hearing loss are a challenge for many owners, but can be trained with patience to understand hand signals rather than voice commands.

DEHYDRATION Dehydration is a water deficit of the body. Dogs lose water every day during elimination, the exhalation of each breath, and through the evaporation of saliva during panting. About 75 percent of water loss is due to urination, and another 20 percent occurs through the respiratory tract, mouth and skin. These fluids are replaced when the dog eats and drinks. Anything that increases the fluid loss, or interferes with the body's recouping moisture, may result in dehydration.

Dehydration can occur as a result of any illness that causes diarrhea or vomiting, or an excessive fever (see HYPERTHERMIA and TEMPERATURE). Excessive urination that occurs in diabetes mellitus and kidney disease, bleeding, or any condition that causes a reluctance to eat or drink can result in dehydration. A normal adult dog's total body water is approximately 60 percent of his body weight. Signs of dehydration become apparent with losses of as little as 5 percent of normal body water. A 12 to 15 percent loss of total body water results in shock, and imminent death.

DEHYDRATION

SYMPTOMS: Loss of skin elasticity; dry mouth; stringy saliva; delayed capillary refill time; sunken eyeballs; muscle twitches; cold paw pads
HOME CARE: Give lots of water and/or solutions like Pedialyte as directed by the veterinarian
VET CARE: Fluid therapy; supportive care; sometimes blood transfusion
PREVENTION: Provide lots of fresh water at all times: offer shelter from the heat

The earliest noticeable sign of dehydration is dry mucus membranes in which the dog's gums and tongue are sticky instead of wet. The saliva may become sticky or even stringy.

A more obvious sign is loss of skin elasticity. A dog's skin normally fits like a comfortable coat, with some room to move particularly in the shoulders. Grasp the skin over your dog's neck and shoulders, and gently lift; when normally hydrated, the skin quickly springs back into place upon release. The skin retracts slowly when the dog is 7 to 8 percent dehydrated; a dehydration of ten percent or more is serious, and the skin will remain in a ridge when retracted, and not spring back into place.

Capillary refill time is an accurate measure of hydration. This is the time it takes for blood to return to tissue after pressure is applied, and can be demonstrated by gently pressing a finger against your dog's gums. This briefly blocks blood flow so the tissue turns white when the pressure is quickly released. When your dog's hydration is normal, it takes less than two seconds for the white to return to normal pigment. A dehydration of 7 to 8 percent dehydration will delay capillary refill time for two to three seconds. Longer than four or five seconds indicates severe dehydration, an extremely dangerous situation. These dogs also exhibit sunken eyeballs, involuntary muscle twitches, and cold extremities. Dogs suffering

from moderate to severe dehydration require immediate veterinary attention if they are to survive. Intravenous fluid therapy will be required to rehydrate the dog and return his electrolyte (mineral) balance to normal.

In mild cases in which vomiting is not a problem, simply getting the dog to drink water will be helpful (see ADMINISTER MEDICATION). Under normal circumstances, a thirsty dog willing to drink is able to recoup a six percent water deficit in about an hour. Your veterinarian may prescribe products like children's Pedialyte, which also provides lost minerals.

The underlying cause of the dehydration will also need to be treated. Specific medication may be required to prevent further fluid loss (see DIARRHEA and VOMITING).

DEMODECOSIS

SYMPTOMS: Hair loss on face or forelegs with or without itching; patchy hair loss on body; red, crusty skin; swollen paws; "mousy" body odor
HOME CARE: Once diagnosed, Goodwinol Ointment on localized lesions; benzoyl peroxide shampoos and/or dips as prescribed by vet for generalized disease
VET CARE: Medicated dips; sometimes antibiotics
PREVENTION: None

DEMODICOSIS Demodicosis, caused by the demodectic mange mite is not contagious. Puppies are infected the first two or three days after birth through close contact with an infected mother. In normal dogs, a few of these mites may be found in the hair follicles of the face. A normal immune system keeps the mite population in check, so that no disease results and the puppy's hair coat remains normal.

The life cycle of the mite is spent entirely on the host animal, and takes about 20 to 35 days to complete. Spindle-shaped eggs hatch into small, six-legged larvae, which molt into eight-legged nymphs, and then into eight-legged adults.

Demodicosis typically affects puppies three to 12 months old. Usually it is the immune-compromised individual unable to stop mite proliferation that develops disease. Two forms of demodectic mange occur: Localized and Generalized.

The condition always begins as the localized form, which is limited to a spot or two on the face and legs. **Localized demodicosis** is quite common in puppies, and is a mild disease that goes away by itself. It consists of one to five small, circular, red and scaly areas of hair loss around the eyes and lips, or on the forelegs. The lesions may or may not be itchy. In most cases, the localized form resolves as the dog's immune system matures and gets the bugs under control. It rarely recurs.

When the localized form spreads, involving large areas of the body with severe disease, it is termed **generalized demodicosis** and is considered uncommon. Again, it is youngsters that are most commonly affected with generalized demodicosis, usually prior to the age 18 months. Such dogs may have a genetic defect in their immune system.

Any pup may develop the disease, but an inherited predisposition appears to increase the incidence of the disease in the Afghan Hound, American Staffordshire Terrier, Boston Terrier, Boxer, Chihuahua, Chinese Shar-pei, Collie, Dalmatian, Doberman Pinscher, English Bulldog, German Shepherd Dog, Great Dane, Old English Sheepdog, American Pit Bull Terrier and Pug.

Generalized demodicosis is a severe disease characterized by massive patchy or generalized hair loss and skin inflammation, often complicated by bacterial infection that may cause the feet to swell. Mites (all stages) may also be found in lymph nodes, the intestinal wall, blood, spleen, liver, kidney, bladder, lung, urine, and feces. The skin turns red, crusty and warm, and has many pustules. It bleeds easily, becomes very tender, and has a strong "mousy" odor due to bacterial infection on the skin. The condition can ultimately kill the puppy.

Diagnosis is based on signs of the disease, and finding the parasite in skin scrapings or biopsies. Treatment is not always necessary for localized demodicosis, which often resolves by itself. Generalized demodicosis requires aggressive therapy, however. Typically, the pup is shaved to offer better access to the skin, and is given weekly or every-other-week whole-body dips with a miticidal preparation prescribed by the veterinarian. Some puppies and breeds are sensitive to these preparations, though, and may suffer side effects such as drowsiness, vomiting, lethargy, and drunken behavior. Use such products only with veterinary supervision.

Antibiotic therapy is required to fight secondary infections. Repeated baths with exfoliating shampoos such as those containing benzoyl peroxide are helpful. Unfortunately, dogs suffering from generalized demodicosis have a guarded prognosis and may never achieve a cure. Euthanasia is sometimes the kindest choice. Because of the potential heritable components involved in this disease, dogs that have suffered generalized demodicosis should not be bred.

DERMATITIS

DERMATITIS Dermatitis refers to skin disease, and is an inflammation that can involve the entire body, or be isolated to specific areas. Canine dermatitis is most often associated with allergy or skin parasites that cause mange. It can also result from metabolic disorders like Cushing's disease, or from sunburn, and very rarely is a psychological disorder related to stress. Signs and treatment vary depending on the cause (see ALLERGY and PARASITES).

DIABETES MELLITUS

DIABETES MELLITUS Diabetes is a general term that refers to several disorders that share similar symptoms but have different causes. Diabetes insipidus typically affects puppies or young adult dogs, and results from a lack of the hormone vasopressin (ADH) that controls water resorption in the kidneys. Diabetes mellitus is much more common, and most dogs are middle-aged or older when they develop symptoms.

Diabetes mellitus is a metabolic disorder in which insulin is not produced by the pancreas in sufficient quantities (Type I, insulin dependent), or the body is unable to use the insulin that's present (Type II, non-insulin dependent). Insulin is a hormone that makes possible the movement of glucose (sugar) from the blood into the cells of the body where it is used for energy. Although the dog's body may be able to process food into glucose, the diabetic animal is unable to use this energy and slowly starves.

The pancreas, a gland located near the stomach and liver, produces the hormone insulin. Insulin resistance is often seen in dogs suffering from hyperadrenocorticism (see CUSHING'S DISEASE), and can result from overuse of glucocorticoid (steroid) drugs. A large percentage of body fat also tends to suppress insulin function, which means obesity doubles, triples or quadruples risk for diabetes. Damage to the pancreas also can cause the disease (see PANCREATITIS).

DIABETES

SYMPTOMS: Increased appetite; weight loss; increased thirst; increased urination; breaks in house-training
HOME CARE: Insulin injections as instructed by veterinarian
VET CARE: Stabilize dog with fluids and other medications: regulate diet and monitor urine and blood; determine proper insulin dosage
PREVENTION: Prevent obesity; trim down pudgy pooches

About one in 200 pet dogs are estimated to develop the condition. Females are affected twice as often as males. Although any dog can develop disease, there appears to be an increased incidence in Beagles, Cairn Terriers, Dachshunds, Miniature Poodles, Miniature Schnauzers, Keeshonden, Golden Retrievers, Labrador Retrievers, and Doberman Pinschers.

The onset of diabetes is insidious, and is often undiagnosed until relatively advanced. Signs are increased consumption of water and food, increased urination, and weight loss. Diabetic dogs also can suffer sudden blindness (see CATARACTS).

The food eaten by a diabetic dog is turned into glucose by digestion, but without insulin, it cannot be further used. Glucose levels in the blood continue to rise as the dog eats more and more to satisfy her hunger. Eventually, the glucose in the blood is excreted in ever-increasing volumes in the urine, and the sugar in the urine causes an osmotic diuresis that pulls even more liquid out of the dog's body. The resulting increase of urination makes the dog thirsty, so she drinks more water, which increases urine volume, and so on. The increased need to urinate may cause a break in housetraining, which may be one of the earliest signs an owner may notice. Left untreated, the diabetic dog will eventually begin to rapidly lose weight.

Diagnosis is based on the signs of disease, along with evaluation of the blood and urine. Sugar and sometimes acetone in the urine along with a high blood sugar indicate diabetes mellitus. Pet owners may notice the dog has sticky urine.

Left untreated, dogs develop a life-threatening ketoacidosis. When the body is unable to metabolize glucose for energy, it instead switches to catabolism, a destructive process in which fat and muscle tissue are broken down for energy. Ketone bodies are a normal byproduct of fat metabolism, but an excess of ketone bodies in the blood and urine results in a diabetic coma and death. A characteristic sign is a sweet-smelling breath similar to the odor of nail polish. Treatment for ketoacidosis should include fluid and electrolyte replacement, insulin therapy, and bicarbonate may be needed to correct acid-base balance.

Diabetes mellitus cannot be cured, but in most dogs it can be controlled. Treatment addresses any complications of the disease, and replaces the insulin the dog's body cannot provide. Management is accomplished more easily in some patients than in others, however.

Dogs suffering from Type II (non-insulin dependent) diabetes mellitus improve when fed high fiber diets. These diets appear to reduce insulin requirements and also help overweight dogs lose weight. High fiber diets help relieve the surge of glucose that increases insulin requirements shortly after eating certain foods, and are helpful in any dog that suffers from diabetes mellitus. Most dogs with the condition, though, also require insulin injections.

The trick is to find the right type and amounts of insulin, balanced with proper diet and exercise. Commercial insulin is derived from a variety of sources, most notably beef, pork, and synthetic human insulin, or combinations thereof; all are effective in dogs. These products are categorized by promptness, duration, and intensity of action. The mixture most appropriate for your dog's condition must be determined by your veterinarian. Typically, the dog's blood and urine glucose levels are monitored for several days, and hospitalization is often required to obtain these baseline readings. Even then, adjustments to the dose may be necessary, and the dog should be reevaluated by your veterinarian two or three times a year.

Dog owners usually become quite adept at giving their dogs insulin injections once the dosage has been determined by a veterinarian. Most dogs require twice daily beneath-the-skin (subcutaneous) injections. In addition to insulin, how often and how much the dog is fed and exercised influence treatment success. Too much or not enough of either may cause problems. Therefore, the diabetic dog's diet and exercise must remain constant, with regularly scheduled feedings, and no unauthorized snacks or romps.

Diabetic coma may result if not enough or too much insulin is given, if the dog doesn't eat on schedule or exercises too much, or if the insulin has expired and isn't effective. The dog loses consciousness, and can't be roused. This is an emergency that your veterinarian must address.

Too much insulin can cause insulin reaction, referred to as hypoglycemia. Symptoms include disorientation, salivation, weakness and hunger, lethargy, shaking, or head tilt. Without treatment, the dog will suffer convulsions, coma, and then death. Giving the dog a glucose source, such as Karo syrup or honey, should reverse signs within five to fifteen minutes. Then get your dog to the veterinarian immediately.

DIARRHEA

The frequent passage of soft or fluid stools is referred to as diarrhea. Diarrhea is not a disease, it is a sign of illness and is typical of a variety of health conditions. Any change of bowel habits that continues for more than 24 hours should be addressed by the veterinarian.

Dogs frequently suffer gastrointestinal upsets, and diarrhea is the most common sign. The condition may be of acute (sudden) onset, or chronic, which is an ongoing condition.

Food normally spends about eight hours in the dog's small intestine, where most of the bulk and nearly 80 percent of the moisture is absorbed. As the remainder moves through the colon, the waste is concentrated as much of the remaining water is removed. Diarrhea results when food passes too quickly through the intestine, and is incompletely digested. Rather than solid, well-formed feces, the waste is soft or liquid.

Diarrhea results from an irritation of the bowel lining that causes the rapid transit of food. Common causes include intestinal parasites like hookworms or viruses like canine distemper and canine parvovirus. Dogs are notorious gorgers, and overeating or an abrupt change in diet may bring on diarrhea. Unhealthy table scraps can cause upset digestion. Milk causes problems for many dogs because they may lack the dietary enzyme that allows them

to digest it properly. Indiscriminate eating habits, such as snacking from the garbage, eating varmints, or ingesting toxic substances (see POISON) also may result in diarrhea. Some dogs develop allergies to their food. And swallowing foreign material may also result in diarrhea (see SWALLOWED OBJECTS).

Treatment must address the underlying cause whenever possible. If the problem is due to parasites, deworming medicine is given. Diarrhea resulting from viral diseases may require treatment to counteract such consequences as dehydration. Only in the mildest cases would an antidiarrheal medication be the sole treatment, because if the underlying cause isn't removed, the condition will return.

DIARRHEA

SYMPTOMS: More frequent than normal bowel movements; soft or fluid feces
HOME CARE: Withhold food for 24 hours; offer ice cubes to lick; offer bland first meal in several small servings; gradually introduce regular diet over several days; offer natural wheat bran or Metamucil to food
VET CARE: Specific medications for parasites; antidiarrheal medication; fluid therapy; specific medications depending on diagnosis
PREVENTION: Vaccinate dogs against viral illnesses; pick up yard to reduce parasite risk; keep outside dogs confined to yard to prohibit them from eating vermin; avoid sudden diet changes, table scraps, garbage and milk treats

Acute diarrhea is treated by withholding food for at least 24 hours to rest the gastrointestinal tract. As long as there is no vomiting along with the diarrhea, offer small amounts of water or ice cubes during this time.

The first meal should be bland and offered in four to six servings throughout the day rather than one big meal. A therapeutic diet prescribed by your vet may be helpful, or you can feed a mixture of one part broiled lean hamburger and two parts cooked rice, or one part cottage cheese or boiled egg mixed with two parts rice or cooked macaroni. Feed this diet for three days, even if the dog's diarrhea has stopped. On the fourth day, mix this special diet half and half with your dog's regular diet. Reduce the mixture until by the end of the week, your dog is again eating only his normal ration. Sometimes mixing in a tablespoon of a fiber supplement helps firm the stool; try natural wheat bran or unflavored Metamucil.

You also can use Kaopectate at a dosage of ½ to 1 teaspoon per five pounds of pet, up to a maximum of 2 tablespoons every eight hours. Pepto-Bismol also may be used temporarily at a dose of 1 teaspoon per 5 pounds or a maximum of 2 tablespoons up to three times a day (or one tablet per 15 pounds up to three times a day). Your veterinarian may prescribe a specific dosage of other antidiarrheal medication for your dog.

When diarrhea becomes a chronic problem, symptomatic treatment usually doesn't work. Whenever you suspect your dog has swallowed something dangerous, or if the stool contains blood, see a veterinarian immediately. A black, tarry stool indicates upper digestive tract bleeding, while bright red blood or clots arise from the colon.

If diarrhea doesn't resolve with the above steps, is accompanied by other signs like refusal to eat or vomiting, or if it persists for more than 24 hours, see your veterinarian. A further diagnosis is necessary to understand what's causing the problem before it can be appropriately treated (see COLITIS, ENTERITIS, INFLAMMATORY BOWEL DISEASE and MALABSORPTION SYNDROME).

DIGGING Dogs excavate for a variety of reasons. Digging is a natural canine behavior that evolved as a means of survival. The dog's footpads are very thick and callused, and are the toughest area of her body. Dogs use their claws and paws to shovel dirt when pursuing burrowing varmints, to bury food or toys for safe-keeping, and to create nests in the snow or dirt that protect them from the cold of winter, or the heat of the summer. Dogs also dig to escape, by tunneling beneath fences meant to confine them from harm.

All dogs dig, but terrier breeds live for the joy of kicking up dirt. The word "terrier" means "of the earth;" terriers were developed specifically to dig in pursuit of below-ground prey.

Digging becomes a problem when your dog is given no opportunity to indulge the urge; left to her own devices, she'll often choose an inappropriate outlet. Dogs dig holes in the yard, un-plant your flowerbed or potted plants, empty the cat's litter box, or even attempt to tunnel through carpeting, upholstery, and hardwood floors. When confined, dogs often scratch at doors or the floor in an effort to get out.

Digging becomes particularly problematic in dogs that are bored, and conversely, digging enthusiasm can be dampened by giving the dog something better to do. First, be sure you provide your dog with at least 20 minutes (40 is better!) of aerobic exercise every day. Burn off her energy by playing games of fetch or taking her on a brisk walk. If you have a terrier and space allows, provide her with a "legal" area like a sandbox in the yard where she can dig to her heart's content.

If your dog is caching toys or food, then only allow her to have these items for fifteen or twenty minutes at a time. Take them away when she begins to lose interest, and offer them again at a later time. Some dogs bury objects to prevent another dog from stealing them. Give your dog privacy away from the competition if this is the case.

Digging holes to stay cool can be cured by providing your dog with a shaded area out of the sun, such as access to the covered porch or patio. A dog run with a concrete floor and shaded roof will provide a secure, comfortable outdoor area for the dog that can't be pockmarked by digging.

For hard-case diggers, build a sand box for his legal excavation. A shaded area about three feet wide, six feet long and two feet deep will satisfy most dogs. Let him see you bury one or two of his toys (very shallowly) and then encourage him to dig them up. Get down on your hands and knees and show him by pawing the sand with your hand.

Dogs that dig to escape confinement may be discouraged when their holes are filled with bricks—eventually the dog should become convinced he'll run into bricks wherever he digs. Dogs also dislike digging up feces, so you may discourage a hard-case digger by "planting" his own feces in the holes, and covering them up as a sort of booby-trap.

Indoor digging may require more specialized corrections. Provide some distraction, like legal chews or a favorite toy, to give the bored dog something better to do. Put a cover on the cat's litter box, or move it out of reach. Cover the surface of large potted plants with gravel or larger rocks to make the contents unattractive to canine diggers.

Obedience training is the single most important step dog owners can take to prevent and correct problem behaviors like inappropriate digging (see TRAINING).

DISC DISEASE Just like their owners, dogs may suffer debilitating spinal injury and back problems. Disc disease is most common in small breeds, and particularly in those with long backs and short legs like Dachshunds and Basset Hounds.

The spine is a chain of bones held together by ligaments, with intervertebral discs in between each vertebra that act as cushions. These discs provide the spine's flexibility. The spinal cord is strung through a bony canal inside each vertebra, and is the neurological highway that speeds nerve impulses from the brain throughout the body.

DISC DISEASE

SYMPTOMS: Weak, wobbly gait in rear legs; hunched, painful posture; refusal to move; paralysis
HOME CARE: Confinement; restrict activity, especially running or jumping; physical therapy; pain medication only if prescribed by vet
HOLISTIC HELP: Chiropractic; acupuncture; massage
VET CARE: Same as home care; sometimes pain medication; commonly anti-inflammatory drugs; occasionally, back surgery
PREVENTION: Prevent obesity; restrict jumping; remain vigilant for problems; enforce rest when necessary

The discs act as shock absorbers for the back and are filled with fluid, collagen and other substances. Disc disease typically begins as early as seven months of age, when the disc suffers a loss of this fluid and begins to calcify and loses its resiliency. Eventually, the degenerated disc may rupture, which compresses the spinal cord. That causes the dog severe pain in the neck or back, and may compromise function and feeling in the legs (see PAIN).

Signs depend on the site of the damage. Ruptured discs located in the lower back cause a weak, wobbly gait in the rear legs. Ruptured discs located in the neck cause the dog to tilt his head down in a hunched, painful posture, and refuse to move, and may cause front leg weakness. The most severe signs are complete paralysis due to compression and/or damage to the spinal cord.

Diagnosis is based on signs, and sometimes X-rays confirm the condition and pinpoint the location of the problem. Treatment depends on the severity of the signs, and prompt veterinary help improves your dog's chance for a complete recovery. Initially, confinement and enforced rest for four to six weeks may return the dog to mobility.

The discomfort helps restrict the dog's activities; otherwise, the dog may move too much and cause further damage. For that reason, pain medication and anti-inflammatory drugs like steroids are prescribed carefully. Most dogs improve from mild symptoms after three or four days of crate rest.

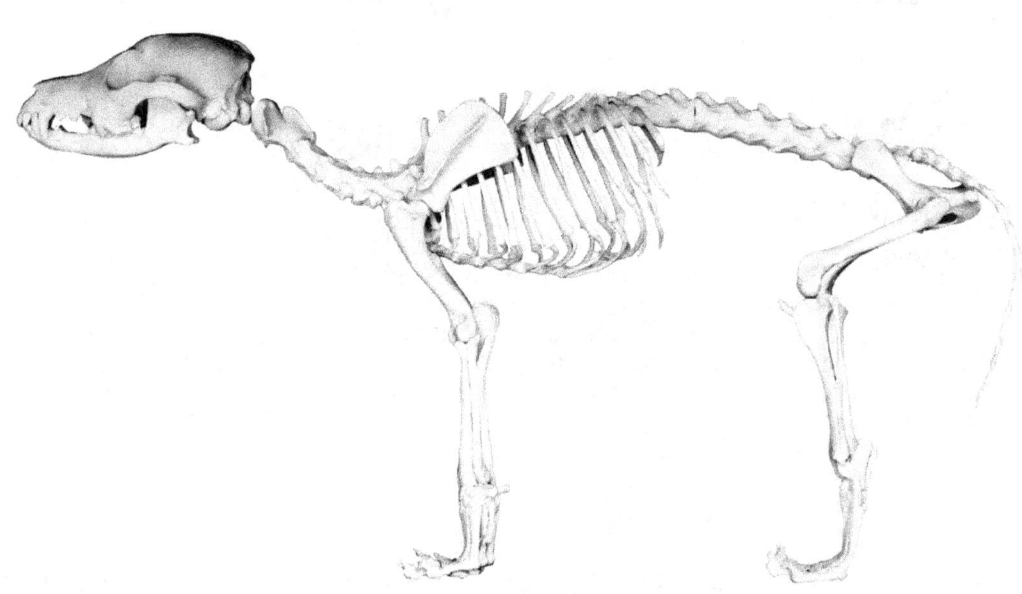

Today, many veterinarians include physical therapy such as swimming or underwater treadmill to exercise and strengthen the dog both before, during and after other modalities. Acupuncture may help with pain, and chiropractic adjustment helps a percentage of dogs. Supplements like Cosequin (a glucosamine and chondroitin combination) may help relieve or slow further injury to the disks.

With more severe symptoms or those that don't improve with rest, more aggressive therapy such as surgery may help. Surgical decompression of the spinal cord creates a "window" in the vertebrae to remove the encroaching disk material from the spinal canal. Prognosis can vary depending on the severity of the signs, and how long the dog has suffered the problem. Some veterinary researchers report significant improvement in some dogs suffering disk disease by combining conventional therapies with veterinary acupuncture treatments. Complete recovery may take as long as six months and typically requires physical therapy.

However, dogs may suffer permanent nerve damage so that full recovery isn't possible. A veterinarian can best evaluate each individual situation (see WOBBLER'S SYNDROME).

DOCKING

Docking refers to the amputation of all or a portion of the puppy's tail. Tails can be docked for medical reasons, such as damage from frostbite or fracture if the pup's tail gets shut in the door. Some dogs like Labradors retrievers are "tail beaters" in a constant state of bloody injury from flailing their tails against objects. Other times, a puppy is born with a "crook" in the tail that may catch on objects and cause injury, and so this is removed for safety reasons.

But most puppy tail docking happens for cosmetic reasons, so that the dog will look a certain way. Hunting dogs and terrier breeds most typically have docked tails. Historically, tails were docked (or "curtailed") to prevent injury to them during work. Centuries ago when only nobility were allowed to own certain kinds of dogs, a commoner's "cur" dog had his tail docked to easily tell him apart from purebred dogs owned by the aristocracy. Today the American Kennel Club member dog breed clubs includes docked tails in more than forty breed standards.

The length of the docked tail varies depending on the specific breed. Some are docked quite short and close to the body. The Pembroke Welsh Corgi standard calls for tails to be "docked as short as possible without being indented." Other breeds are kept rather long—the Wire Fox Terrier standard calls for a three-quarter dock. If a puppy of a normally "tailless" breed is born with a tail this may be corrected with docking. Typically, the surgery is performed on three to five day old puppies often without anesthesia. Yes, puppies feel pain and cry when the procedure is done.

The puppy tail is measured, and the amputation made between the appropriate vertebrae. Absorbable stitches or tissue glue ensure a more cosmetic healed tail with skin closed over the stump of the bone, rather than just lopping off a portion of the tail. It should be done under sterile conditions by a veterinarian familiar with breed standards.

As with ear cropping, today, the practice is more a tradition than a health consideration. In fact, dog registries in Europe forbid tail docking as inhumane. The practice is controversial, even in the United States.

When you adopt at a conventional age of eight to 12 weeks, your puppy likely already had his tail docked. While the majority of puppies may never suffer known physical problems, some veterinarians believe docking may predispose dogs to urinary incontinence later in life. Docking a dog's tail also cuts off tail talk to a great extent, which potentially could cause communication problems between dogs. Purebred and mixed breed puppies with natural tails and ears are no less loveable, trainable, or beautiful (see CROPPING, and COMMUNICATION).

DOMINANCE

DOMINANCE Dominance is behavior used to achieve command over another individual. Most dogs are happy to simply belong to a family, and know their ranking within that social group. However, some dogs that have forceful personalities aren't satisfied unless they are in charge.

The canine social system defines how your dog behaves (see SOCIAL STRUCTURE). It is based on a hierarchy of dominant and submissive individuals. Submissive dogs defer to those in power, be that another dog or pet, or the owner. A dominant dog wants to call the shots, and may challenge an owner's authority. However, dominance is not necessarily expressed as aggression; even the tiniest and seemingly compliant pet may assert his dominance, and wrap the unsuspecting owner around his furry paw.

Dominant behavior may be expressed in a variety of ways. Dogs that beg constantly for food, attention, to go inside or out are asserting their dominance. Such dogs may growl or snap at another pet or the owner when displeased or challenged, demand the choicest resting areas like the sofa or your bed, hog all the toys, and eat from other pet's bowls. A dominant dog isn't necessarily large, either; tiny dogs like a Chihuahua or Toy Poodle often buffalo their owners into pampering them.

It is vital that you, as the owner, be the leader in your dog's social group. Dogs communicate dominance with attitudes expressed through posture, vocalization and body position (see COMMUNICATION). Use your dog's language to establish yourself as leader; speak with a commanding voice, stand tall, and make eye contact, and enforce your authority with appropriate training.

Don't allow yourself to be trained by the dog. If he whines and pushes against you for attention, then only pet him when he's quiet and ignore him when he's noisy. If he begs to be fed, feed him before he turns up the noise, and don't give in to pleas at any other time. Consistency is key; owners reinforces the dog's identity as king by giving in just one time. Dogs know that if it worked once, it will likely work in the future. Have the dog earn your attention. The person in the family group that controls access to food, toys and attention is the leader. Rule judiciously and with benevolence.

Dogs are particularly sensitive to territorial issues. Dogs consider their house, the yard and their owner to be owned by them, and defend this "property" against threat. Dominance becomes most problematic in multi-pet households where property must be shared. If your dog feels his territory is threatened—the mailman or a strange animal crosses the yard, a new baby is taking your time, the cat sits on his favorite chair—the dominant dog may react with pushy behavior or some other action to reestablish his position.

It is very important in multi-pet homes that owners do not interfere with or try to influence a dog's social status among his furry peers. Dangerous aggression cannot be permitted, but in all else, allow the pets to work out their own ranking. There is often posturing and skirmishes before one is established as Top Dog, and your interference prolongs this sorting out process and can make life miserable for the lower-ranking pet. Treating a low-ranking animal the same as his superior puts the dominant dog's nose out of joint, and he feels compelled to reinforce his position by harassing his subordinate. The best way to handle the situation is to support the dominant pet; dog society is not democratic, and you must recognize this.

Remember that most dogs don't care if they're the leader; they are perfectly happy as long as they know their place within the family group. You can help them by reinforcing their social standing.

Feed the dominant dog first. If he routinely steals from the other pets, feed them in separate rooms. And when the dominant dog chases your other pet off the sofa, don't try to correct the situation; simply allow the lower-ranking dog quality time with you when the dominant dog is otherwise engaged.

Most dogs sort out their own social order with few squabbles. The dominant dog typically is a confident, secure individual that has nothing to prove—after all, the other pets know he's King, and reinforce his status by displaying submissive behaviors, so King Dog can afford to be tolerant (see COMMUNICATION, INTRODUCTIONS, SUBMISSION, and TRAINING).

DREAMING

Animals with highly developed brains dream, and it's no surprise that dogs indulge in these canine fantasies. At birth, the area of the puppy brain that keeps her awake and alert is poorly developed; consequently, puppies spend the first two weeks of their life sleeping 70 percent of the time (the remainder is spent eating). This early sleep is characteristic of the dream state in older animals and people, and is punctuated with muscle twitches and vocalizations. As the puppy's brain matures, another type of non-dreaming quiet sleep develops; however, like people, dogs continue to dream throughout their lives.

Why people and animals dream isn't known, but like their owners, dogs appear to relive the activities of everyday life in their dreams. The dog's muscles relax, and her eyes move rapidly beneath her eyelids (REM, or rapid eye movement phase) during dream sleep, and she is difficult to wake up. A trusted owner whose scent and touch are familiar may even be able to move the dog without awakening her. A dreaming dog's paws, legs or tail may move, and she may whine, whimper or growl as she fetches a dream ball.

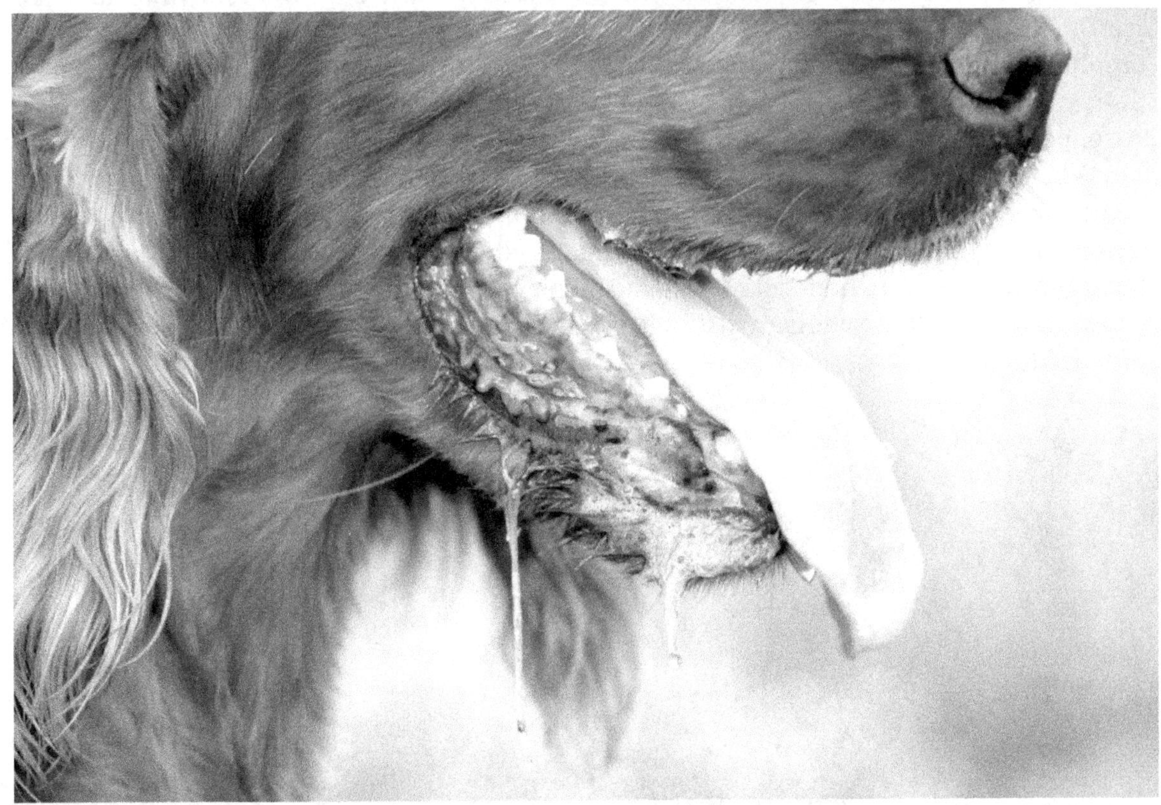

DROOLING Saliva that escapes from the mouth is referred to as drooling.

Saliva is the alkaline fluid produced by four pairs of salivary glands which help lubricate the mouth, food, and aid in digestion. The evaporation of moisture from the mouth and tongue helps control the dog's body temperature (see PANTING). An excess production of saliva results in drooling.

Dog breeds that have loose, pendulous lips and jowls tend to drool more than others. In particular, Bloodhounds, Great Pyrenees, Newfoundlands and Saint Bernards produce an excess of thick, mucoid saliva that tends to hang from the corners of their mouths.

The secretion of saliva may be stimulated by a variety of things. A dog's mouths may water in the presence of enticing food. Conversely, dogs drool when they feel sick (see

VOMITING). Illnesses as innocuous as car sickness, to deadly ones like rabies and canine distemper may be associated with drooling. Stress may cause dogs to drool when they are fearful or nervous. Injury or foreign objects in the mouth, throat or esophagus often cause drooling (see FOREIGN BODY, STOMATITIS and PERIODONTAL DISEASE); a sore throat may prompt a reluctance to swallow, resulting in drooling (see KENNEL COUGH). Also, poison like arsenic also causes excessive drooling.

When drooling is a problem, treatment depends on discovering the underlying cause and addressing it. Owners of dog breeds that have a tendency to drool may benefit from frequently wiping the dog's face, and shielding furniture and carpets with towels. Sedatives, tranquilizers or anti-motion-sickness medications are available that may help relieve stress-caused drooling. Your veterinarian may prescribe a drug to help reduce the amount of saliva produced.

DROWNING Drowning is suffocation resulting from inhaling water. Water in the lungs impairs or even stops normal respiration, and may also stop the heart.

Dogs are natural swimmers, and certain breeds (especially retrievers) are drawn to water. Other dogs may prefer dry land, particularly if a heavy coat tends to become waterlogged and uncomfortable. Puppies and small dogs are at highest risk for drowning, because their inexperience, curiosity, and fearlessness may prompt them to explore, yet be unable to climb out when they fall into even small bodies of water. However, all dogs are at risk for drowning. Hazards like ponds, rivers and streams are often involved, and are especially dangerous during winter months when dogs venture out on thin ice and break through. Swimming pools and hot tubs are a year-round risk.

DROWNING

SYMPTOMS: Loss of consciousness; no breathing apparent; dog found in or near water
FIRST AID: Swing dog downward to express water; begin resuscitation; once dog is breathing, keep warm and get to a vet.
VET CARE: Oxygen therapy; possible rewarming therapy; precautions against pneumonia
PREVENTION: Bar the dog from exploring dangerous waterways; supervise young puppies and dogs around toilet bowls, whirlpools, bathtubs, swimming pools, or other bodies of water

Treatment requires removing water from the lungs, and getting the dog to resume breathing. For a large dog, one person should grasp him about the abdomen just in front of his hind legs, and turn him upside down with his head pointing to the ground, while the second person thumps both sides of the dog's chest with the flat of each palm so water runs out of his throat and windpipe. With small to medium size dogs, one person can grasp the dog with both hands about the lower abdomen, and swing the dog's head down for 20 to 30 seconds. This should remove most of the water, and in some cases, the dog will begin breathing again.

If he's still not breathing, begin artificial respiration to get air into the dog. If the water was cold, the dog's body will need to be warmed as quickly as possible. Seek veterinary attention immediately. Such pets are frequently at risk for pneumonia. (See ARTIFICIAL RESUSCITATION and HYPOTHERMIA).

DRY EYE (KERATOCONJUNCTIVITIS SICCA)

This condition is exactly what it sounds like, an insufficient lubrication of the eye. Normally, tears are secreted by specialized glands that keep the eye wet. Dry eye results from a malfunction of these glands resulting in inadequate tear production.

Injury or disease can damage the nerves of the tear glands or the tear glands themselves, so that tear production is reduced or stopped. Normal age changes in the elderly pet may result in problems, or chronic eye infections may block the tear ducts. The syndrome can also occur as a result of corrective surgery which may remove one of the tear glands (see CHERRY EYE). In most cases, the condition affects older dogs.

Signs are dullness to the surface of the eye, along with a thick, stringy discharge that's difficult to clean away. Without enough lubrication, blinking begins to cause pain and the eye will become infected and inflamed, and develop ulcers. Dogs suffering from dry eye typically squint the affected eye and are reluctant to blink. In some cases, the nostril on the same side is also affected, and the dog will repeatedly lick his nose to keep it moist.

When the cause is reversible, most cases recover within 60 days with appropriate treatment. Treatment consists of reestablishing the flow of tears, controlling infection with antibiotics, and reducing inflammation in the eyes with appropriate medications. Your veterinarian may prescribe drugs that stimulate the production of tears.

Holistic veterinarians may recommend the herb eyebright, since it’s an antioxidant and anti-inflammatory that nourishes and soothes eye irritation. It can be given as eye drops, or as a compress. You can also get eye drops that combine eyebright and goldenseal from your health food store. Always consult with your veterinarian before putting anything in your dog’s eyes.

When dry eye is the result of nerve damage or age changes, the condition may be permanent. Artificial tears provide some relief for the dog, but usually must be administered throughout the day at two to four hour intervals to be effective. Some ointment-based medications are available (see ADMINISTER MEDICATION).

A drug called cyclosporine (Optimmune) can increase the animal's own natural tear production. One of the salivary glands can be transplanted to the eye to provide moisture from saliva.

Early diagnosis and treatment is essential for best recovery results, and to preserve vision in your pet's eyes.

DRY EYE

SYMPTOMS: Dull-looking eye; thick, stringy discharge; redness or ulcer; squinting; sometimes excessive licking of nose
HOME CARE: Artificial tears administered at two-hour intervals; meds as prescribed by vet
HOLISTIC HELP: Herbal therapy
VET CARE: Prescription drugs (ointments or drops) to stimulate tear flow; sometimes surgery
PREVENTION: None

EAR The dog's ears are sensory organs of hearing, and also provide a sense of equilibrium, or balance. Canine hearing is remarkably acute; it's used in hunting, protection, and play, and is an important tool that keeps dogs in touch with their world.

The structure and function are categorized as the external, middle, and inner ear. The visible portion, called the pinna, is a triangular cartilage flap covered on both sides by skin and fur. The size and shape varies among breeds. Some are erect (prick ears) like the German Shepherd Dog, folded to some degree (drop ear) as in the Collie, or pendulous as in Cocker Spaniels. The pinna of some dogs is surgically altered to conform to a breed standard (see CROPPING).

The pinna is extremely mobile, with more than twenty separate muscles that provide 180 degrees of movement. This mobility helps collect, capture and direct sound further into the organ. It also aids in canine communication by offering a host of expressive ear positions.

The pinna funnels sound down the L-shaped auditory canal. This configuration, a vertical passageway ending in a right-angle turn inward (the foot of the L), helps protect interior structures. However, it also makes dogs prone to ear infections when debris collects in the foot of the L. Hair that grows in the ears of a number of dog breeds may compound the problem (see OTITIS).

Sound waves pass through the auditory canal, and strike the tympanic membrane, or eardrum. The resulting vibration is passed to a chain of three tiny ossicles (bones called the hammer, anvil and stirrup) of the middle ear. The eustachian tube which helps equalize pressure within the ear is also located in the middle ear, and connects this area to the back of the throat.

Vibrations are transmitted by ossicles to the inner ear, a bony chamber containing four fluid-filled organs responsible for hearing and balance. Chalk-like particles float in the fluid inside the semicircular canals, utricle and saccule, and as the dog moves his head they brush against tiny hairs that line these organs. That signals directional information to the brain, and gives the dog his sense of equilibrium.

Sound vibration is read by the fluid-filled cochlea, a snail shell-like coil of tubing lined with a membrane called the cochlear duct that spirals its length. The "organ of Corti," a specialized area of this lining, is where hearing actually takes place. Vibration-sensitive hairs that cover the organ of Corti pass information through the auditory nerve to the brain, where the vibration is interpreted as sound.

These intricate organs enable your dog to hear sounds you cannot detect, particularly at high frequencies and at soft volumes. People are able to hear low-pitch tones about as well as dogs, but while we typically hear sound waves up to 20,000 cycles per second, dogs may hear frequencies as high as 100,000 cycles per second. The size of the dog doesn't matter, with Chihuahuas able to hear just as well as Great Danes. However, age tends to temper the dog's hearing, and young dogs hear better than old dogs.

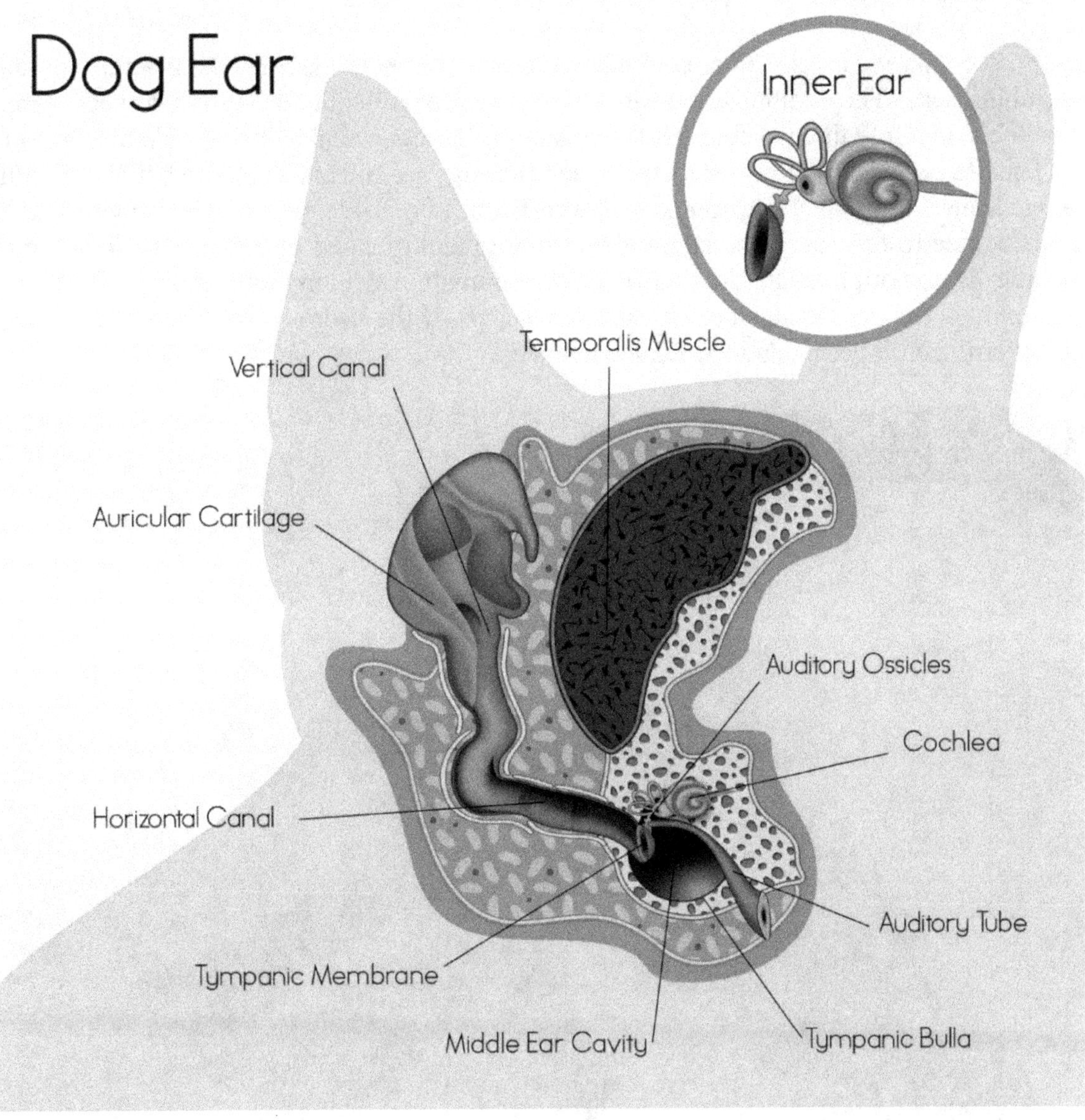

EAR MITES These aggravating parasites commonly afflict dogs, and often lead to secondary ear problems. Ear mites (*Otodectes cynotis*) are a type of arthropod that resembles ticks. They colonize the ear where they feed on cellular debris and suck lymph from the skin. Only three or four adult mites in the ear can wreak considerable discomfort.

The life cycle takes three weeks from the time eggs are laid and cemented in place within the ear canal. Eggs incubate four days, then hatch into six-legged larvae which feed for another three to ten days. The larvae develop into eight-legged protonymphs, which molt into the deutonymph stage. At this point, the immature deutonymph attaches itself to a mature male ear mite using suckers on the rear legs. If the deutonymph becomes a female adult, fertilization occurs and the female bears eggs.

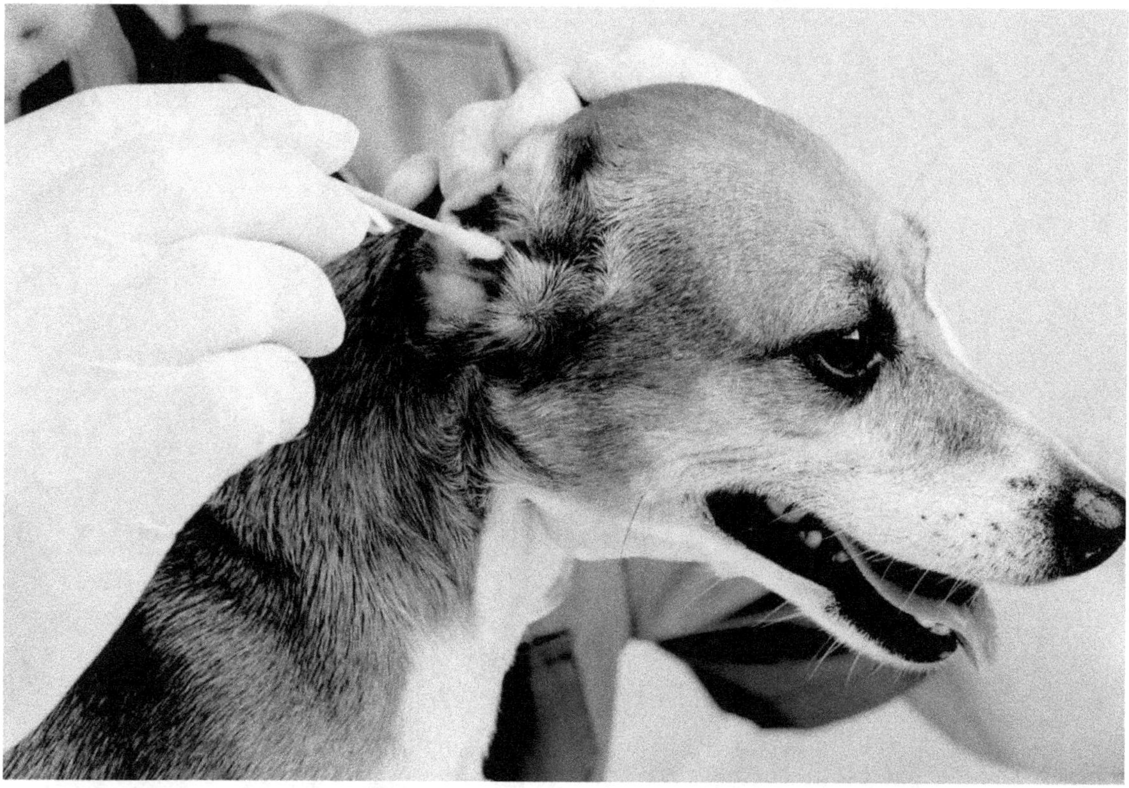

Ear mites are the most common cause of otitis, and signs of infestation include a brown crumbly debris in the ear canal, and/or crust formation. Mites crawling about inside the ear cause intense itching, and dogs typically shake their heads, dig at their ears, or rub their heads against the floor or furniture.

Trauma to the ear often results when the dog's efforts to relieve the itch bruises the pinna, the external ear flap. Scratching and head shaking, especially in pendulous-eared dogs like Beagles, often results in a kind of blood blister (see HEMATOMA).

Ear mites are extremely contagious, and also affect cats, rabbits, ferrets and other pets. Puppies often acquire ear mites from their mother. If one pet has ear mites, all animals in contact with that pet must be treated to prevent re-infestation. When left untreated, ear mites can lead to infections of the middle and inner ear which can damage hearing or affect balance (see OTITIS).

Characteristic dark ear debris and behavior signs generally point to ear mites. The veterinarian confirms the diagnosis by finding the mite in a sample of ear debris that's examined under the microscope. The parasite is tiny, white, and nearly impossible to see with the naked eye. Never treat your dog for ear mites until the diagnosis has been confirmed, or you risk masking other ear problems, or complicating their proper diagnosis and treatment.

The ears are treated by flushing away the debris and mites using an insecticide such as a carbaryl or pyrethrin that kills the bug (see GROOMING, EARS). The medication is often suspended in a bland medium, like mineral oil, which when squirted into the ear helps float debris out of the ear canal as the ear base is gently massaged.

Holistic veterinarians may recommend using a green tea rinse, since it's a natural antiseptic and can gently remove the ear debris caused by the mites. Steep a tablespoon of green tea leaves in a cup of hot water for three or four minutes, strain it, and allow to cool to room temperature. Flush your pet's ear canal with the tea, using a small dropper.

A natural traditional way to treat ear mites is to suffocate the bugs with oil. Place two or three drops of vegetable oil in the pet's ears, and massage. The oil also soothes the itch, but you'll need to treat the ears daily for at least a month to catch all the maturing bugs, and your dog's oily head may not be to his (or your) liking.

A number of commercial products are available for treating ear mites; ask your veterinarian for a recommendation. Treating the ears twice a week for at least three weeks is necessary to get rid of the problem, because eggs will continue to hatch for at least that time, and can quickly re-infest the ears. Steroid medications may be necessary to soothe inflammation, or antibiotic ointment to treat bacterial infections.

Ear mites sometimes travel outside of the ear to other parts of the dog's body. Resulting sores may resemble an allergy to fleas; the condition is called otodectic mange. When your dog is diagnosed with ear mites, don't neglect the rest of his body. Flea products also kill ear mites, so choose an appropriate product and do whole-body treatments along with ear treatments.

Ear mites may infest the environment for several months, and premise control is helpful particularly in homes with many pets. Follow the same procedures and use the same products

for premise control of fleas to get rid of ear mites in the environment. Treat your house and yard for at least four weeks; experts suggest treating the environment two weeks beyond the pet's apparent cure.

Often, the dog's ears are so sore that sedation is necessary for the initial ear treatment. Some dogs are too difficult for owners to continue treating at home, and in certain instances, an oral or injectable medication may be recommended. Ivermectin is an effective treatment for ear mites, but can be toxic in some dog breeds. Dog breeds susceptible to Ivermectin toxicity include Collies, Shetland Sheepdogs, Australian Shepherds, English Shepherds, Longhaired Whippets, McNabs, Silken Windhounds, and Old English Sheepdogs. Your veterinarian can run a genetic test for the mutation of the ABCB1 gene (available at the University of Washington) to see if your dog may be at risk.

EAR MITES

SYMPTOMS: Black to brown tarry or crumbly debris in ears; itchy ears; scratching or rubbing of ears; shaking head; holding ear toward ground
HOME CARE: After diagnosis by vet, clean ears with prescribed medication
HOLISTIC HELP: Herbal treatment; oil the ears
VET CARE: Sometimes sedation to flush ears; medication to reduce inflammation or itching; mite-killing medication
PREVENTION: Monitor ears; prevent contact with other possibly infected animals

EATING Dogs are passionate about food. In fact, many dogs will eat anything that doesn't move faster than they do, and it's up to owners to ensure the canine diet is appropriate.

The canine style of eating is rooted in evolution. Dog ancestors hunted in packs and required large animal prey to sustain the group. The mouse or rabbit an individual might catch was eaten outright, but larger animals posed a problem. What wasn't eaten immediately drew scavengers ready and willing to steal leftovers out of canine mouths.

That's why most modern dogs are gorgers. Like their ancestors, dogs can eat huge quantities of food at one time. Such a meal would last wild canines several days, which meant they didn't need to hunt or eat as often. Modern hunting breeds—Labrador Retrievers and Beagles are notorious—tend to be gorgers that gulp mouthfuls of food without chewing until they reach the bottom of the bowl.

Dog ancestors also developed the ability to benefit from vegetables, which is why modern canines share the human enthusiasm for sweet foods. Sweetness is the signal that a plant has reached ultimate ripeness and highest nutrient value. This diet flexibility gave dogs an edge in survival by allowing them to eat whatever was at hand.

A dog's teeth are designed for an omnivorous diet, that is, one composed of both animals and vegetables. Dagger-shaped canine teeth are designed to hold and slash prey, while the small incisors across the front of the jaw gnaw flesh from bone. Molars are used to crush bone, shear meat, and grind vegetable matter.

Dogs are happy to eat anytime—or all the time—but it's healthier and easier for you to manage feeding on a routine basis. Feed your dog in the same place and at the same time every day. Most dogs consider eating a social event, and enjoy company while dining. However, if you have more than one pet, competition may be a problem. Dogs tend to eat more when another pet is present because of their gorger mentality; if I don't eat it, he will. Make sure each pet has his own bowl, and feed them at separate ends of the kitchen, or even in separate rooms, if necessary.

Drinking is accomplished by curling the tongue into a backward spoon to scoop liquid. In this way your dog throws water up into his mouth, and swallows every two to three laps. Plenty of clean water should be available at all times. Dogs otherwise seek out less than stellar water sources, like the toilet, which has a constant supply of cool, aromatic, and oxygenated tasty water. You can provide the same allure in a more hygienic fashion with a dog water fountain.

A number of bowl designs are available, from trendy fashion statements personalized with your dog's name, to disposable paper trays. The best are utilitarian, easy to clean dishes that stay in place.

Lightweight plastic bowls are difficult to keep clean, and may skid about the room when under canine assault. Ceramic dishes are a better choice because of their solid weight and ease in cleaning. Buy American, though, as the glazes of some products manufactured in foreign countries may contain lead. Heavy glass bowls are also good choices, but be careful of using breakable dishes. Stainless steel bowls are the veterinarian's choice because they are easily sterilized and won't break. But empty pans may turn into dog toys or chew-objects.

Specialty bowls come in designs to keep long ears from falling into food, or with platforms so that tall or arthritic dogs won't have to bend to eat. There are also bowls that keep water from freezing in winter, or keep food and water cool in warm weather. A variety of automatic bin feeders and waterers are also available.

Puppies should be weaned by the age of six to seven weeks, and eating an appropriate commercial puppy ration. Puppy tummies are too small for them to eat adequate amounts at one feeding, so offer puppy food three to four times a day. Stick to the same schedule every day, which will also aid in potty issues (see HOUSE TRAINING). Moisten dry foods to make the kibble easier to eat by mixing three parts dry food to one part water (not milk) to soften the food. Offer each meal for about twenty minutes at time, and allow the puppy to eat his fill. Always throw out the uneaten portion, because wet food spoils if left out too long.

Soft diets may be fed for your dog's lifetime, but can be quite expensive for large dogs, and also tend to contribute to dental plaque or tartar. Puppies are able to eat plain dry food with appropriately-sized kibble by about three months of age. Gradually decrease the amount of water over a week's time until the food is completely dry. Feed your puppy a commercial puppy ration as long as he is growing, at least for a year; some breeds continue to grow beyond this point, so asked a knowledgeable breeder or your veterinarian for a recommendation. You can reduce the feeding schedule to twice a day once your puppy is four or five months old, and to once a day when he reaches eight to nine months old. However, some dogs continue to do better on twice-daily feedings throughout their life.

When he's stopped growing, most pet dogs thrive on a commercial adult maintenance ration. If you choose to home-prepare food for your dogs be sure to consult with your veterinarian for appropriate formulations. Change to a new diet gradually to avoid causing upset stomachs that can result in diarrhea. Introduce new food over a week's period by mixing it with the familiar food. Gradually increase the proportion of new food while reducing the amount of old ration until the dog is eating only the new diet.

The quantity of food required depends on the dog and the individual food. Big dogs need more than small dogs, working dogs like hunters or herders require more than couch-potato lap pets. Dogs need to eat less of nutrient dense super premium foods than other category diets. But dogs that weigh less than 20 pounds need about 30 percent more calories per pound of body weight than dogs weighing 20 to 75 pounds. And dogs weighing over 75 pounds require about 15 percent fewer calories, pound for pound, than dogs in the 20 to 75 pound group. Commercial dog foods publish feeding guidelines on their packages, and your veterinarian can offer recommendations. However, the best indication is your dog. If he begins to gain weight, reduce the amount he is fed; conversely, if he is losing weight, increase the amount or choose a more nutrient-dense product.

Your dog's appetite may vary some from day to day; sometimes, he may not feel like eating, then the next day act perfectly fine. A loss of appetite for several days may indicate illness, so see a veterinarian.

Most dogs do best being meal fed, that is, having food offered only once or twice a day for a limited period of time. This also helps alert owners when he may be feeling ill, aids in scheduling bathroom breaks, and limits the amount of food a gorger otherwise would eat. Canned rations must be meal fed, as they will spoil if left out all day.

Some dogs, particularly small dogs and miniature breeds, do well on free feeding of a dry food. The kibble can be left in the bowl all day without spoiling, so the dog can nibble at his leisure. This is convenient for both the dog and the owner (see FOOD and NUTRITION).

ECLAMPSIA Eclampsia is a condition caused by a low calcium level in the blood. Also called milk fever, eclampsia is associated with a large litter of puppies that deplete the bitch's calcium stores. Most commonly, the condition arises in the first weeks following the birth during the heaviest nursing, but may also develop prior to whelping or (more rarely) into the sixth or seventh week of nursing. Eclampsia usually affects Toy breeds and small dogs that have large litters.

ECLAMPSIA

SYMPTOMS: Restlessness; pacing; ignoring puppies; stiff-legged gait; drunkenness; rapid breathing; high fever; grimacing expression; pale lips and gums; drooling; collapse with muscle spasms
HOME CARE: EMERGENCY! SEE VET IMMEDIATELY!
VET CARE: Intravenous calcium treatment; therapy to counter high fever
PREVENTION: None; avoid over-supplementing with oral calcium

The mother dog initially acts restless and anxious. She leaves her babies and paces, breathes rapidly, and sometimes exhibits a stiff-legged uncoordinated gait. Her temperature may sore as high as 106 degrees. The condition causes tetany, a constriction of the muscles, and the affected dog's face may tighten to expose her teeth in a strange grin. Her gums and lips will appear pale. Finally she collapses, suffers muscle spasms with all four legs kicking wildly, and drools. Left untreated, eclampsia results in respiratory failure, brain damage, and hyperthermia; the combination can be fatal within a few hours. This is an emergency that must be immediately addressed by a veterinarian.

Diagnosis is based on characteristic signs in a nursing bitch. Immediate administration of an intravenous organic calcium solution, such as calcium gluconate, is the treatment of choice. Given in time, treatment results in a rapid, dramatic improvement within 15 minutes of administration. When the dog's temperature exceeds 104 degrees, treat her for heatstroke as well (see HYPERTHERMIA).

Puppies should be remove from nursing, and bottle-fed with an appropriate milk replacer (see MILK, AS FOOD) for at least 24 hours. Depending on the mother's condition and the age of her puppies, you may need to take over feeding for Mom permanently, or perhaps wean the puppies. Puppies may be weaned at three weeks in these instances.

Be aware that a bitch that has previously suffered an episode of eclampsia is at higher risk for a recurrence during subsequent pregnancies. However, adding calcium to the bitch's diet prior to whelping will not prevent eclampsia and in fact may promote the condition. Feed only a complete and balanced ration that contains the recommended calcium-to-phosphorus ratio.

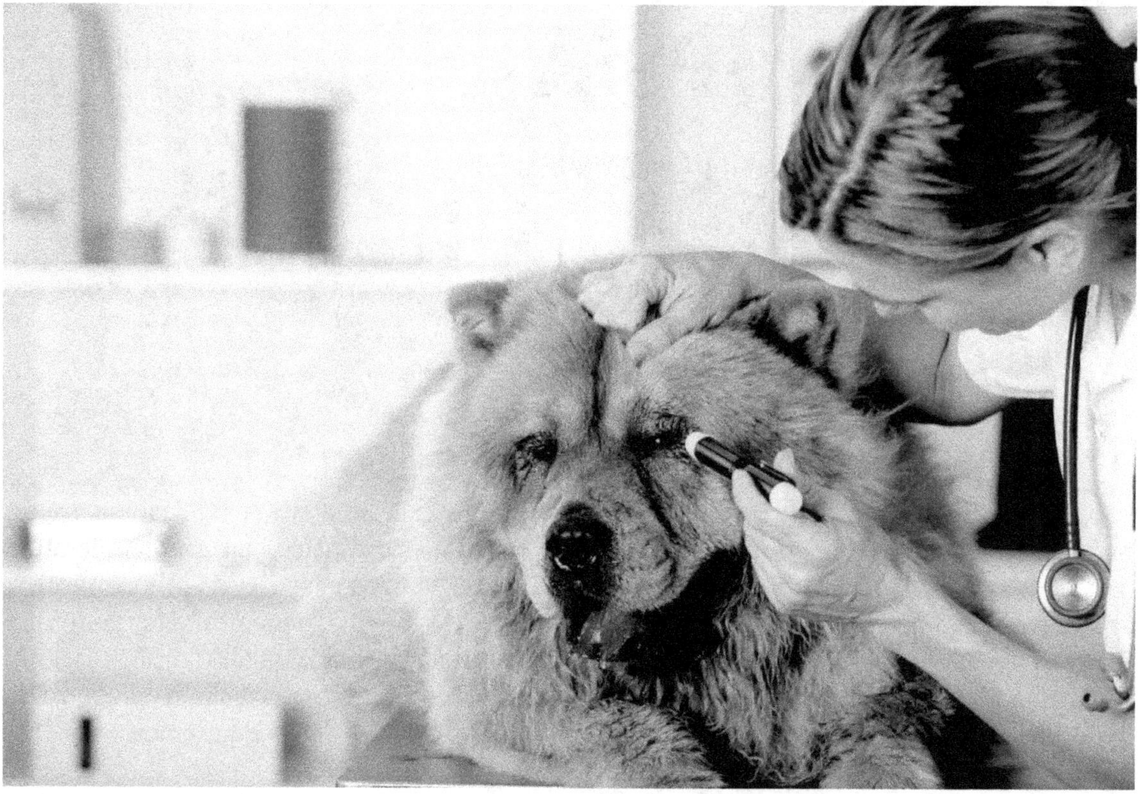

ECTROPION/ENTROPION These terms refer to the abnormal conformation of a dog's eyelids. Entropion is the rolling inward of the lid, while ectropion is the reverse in which the lower eyelid turns outward.

In either instance, the eye may become damaged. Inward-turning lids place eyelid hairs and lashes against the sensitive cornea, and interferes with the tear coating that keeps it healthy. An eversion of the eyelid increases the chance of irritation or injury by exposing the eye, and is mostly seen in dogs with loose facial skin like hounds and spaniels.

Ectropion and entropion eyelids are usually congenital, and often inherited. The highest incidence of entropion occurs in Basset Hounds, Bernese Mountain Dogs, Bloodhounds, Bulldogs, Chesapeake Bay Retrievers, Chinese Shar-Peis and Chow Chows. Ethical breeders are aware of the inheritance factors predisposing certain dogs to such conditions, and are seeking to reduce the incidence of these problems. Surgery is often required to correct the defect.

ECTROPION/ENTROPION

SYMPTOMS: Rolling of the eyelid margins; red, watery eyes; reluctance to blink; mattery discharge
HOME CARE: Keep eyes clean by wiping away discharge; vet care required
VET CARE: Surgical correction
PREVENTION: None

EHRLICHIOSIS This disease goes by many names, including tropical canine pancytopenia, canine typhus, canine hemorrhagic fever, Nairobi bleeding disease, and tracker dog disease. Canine ehrlichiosis is caused by one or several species of Ehrlichia bacteria, most commonly *Ehrlichia canis* (*E. canis*) or *Ehrlichia lewinii* (*E. lewinii*). This specialized bacteria requires an intermediate host, or vector, to infect its victim. The brown dog tick and the Lone Star tick are the primary vectors.

The disease has been reported worldwide wherever these ticks are found. Most cases in the United States occur in dogs living in the Texas Gulf coast regions and other southern states. All dogs are susceptible, but those with greater exposure to ticks—outdoor dogs, working dogs and hunting dogs—are at highest risk. Doberman Pinschers and German Shepherds seem to be more severely affected. Ehrlichiosis is diagnosed most often during the warm months of tick season.

Dogs suspected to have ehrlichiosis may instead be infected with anaplasmosis, or have a concurrent infection with both. Deer ticks, western black-legged ticks, and the brown dog tick carry this bacteria. Anaplasmosis produces similar signs of disease (painful joints, fever, vomiting, diarrhea), and is diagnosed and treated similarly to ehrlichiosis.

The tick becomes infected when it bites an exposed dog and ingests infected blood. The tick may transmit the disease for up to five months after engorgement with infected blood. Once infected, transmission of the disease to dogs can occur in any stage (by larva, nymph, or adult tick). It is even possible for ticks to survive winter months and infect susceptible dogs in the spring.

The organism is passed to dogs in the tick saliva when the infected parasite takes a blood meal. Blood transfusion from an infected donor dog also has the potential to transmit the disease. *E. canis* initially invades and damages the white blood cells of the host dog. From there, the rickettsiae spread via the blood to lymphatic tissue including the liver, lymph nodes and spleen.

Signs of the disease can vary greatly from case to case, making canine ehrlichiosis an extremely frustrating disease to diagnose. Dogs suffering stress are also more susceptible.

There are both acute and chronic stages of the disease. Dogs suffering from the acute phase exhibit sudden severe symptoms, or show few or no signs at all. Signs include a week-long fever, eye and nasal discharge, loss of appetite, depression, swollen legs, stiffness and reluctance to walk, and weight loss, and some dogs show neurologic symptoms such as muscle twitches. X-rays may reveal signs of pneumonia. The acute stage lasts two to four weeks; dogs either recover, or proceed to the chronic phase of disease.

The chronic stage of the disease can last for several months, and appears to affect dogs with suppressed immune systems. The bone marrow is compromised, resulting in a reduction in the production of blood cells. Often, the dog will develop kidney disease. Low platelet counts may cause bleeding tendencies, and long nosed breeds like shepherds may suffer nose bleeds. Fatigue, bloody urine, discoloration and bruising of the skin occur in all breeds.

Diagnosis is based on signs of disease along with history of tick exposure. Polymerase chain reaction (PCR) testing, which isolates the DNA of the causative agent, is now commonly employed for confirmation. The PCR test, in combination with a test for antibodies to the *Ehrlichia* infection, is typically the best way to make a concrete diagnosis.

The antibiotic doxycycline is effective against *E. canis* when administered early in the course of the disease. Dogs may require six weeks or more of treatment before being cured, and some may benefit from fluid therapy or blood transfusions. Infection does not impart immunity and dogs can be reinfected. Dogs with chronic disease in which bone marrow is irreparably damaged may require months of therapy before any improvement is apparent, but prognosis is not good and often the dog dies despite treatment.

There is no vaccination available to prevent canine ehrlichiosis. The best way to protect your dog is to reduce or prevent his exposure to ticks. In high-risk environments (i.e., kennel situations where the disease has been diagnosed), a daily low-dose of antibiotic may be used as a preventative.

EHRLICHIOSIS

SYMPTOMS: Presence of ticks; fever; eye and nasal discharge; anorexia; depression; swollen legs; lameness; muscle twitches; weight loss; nosebleeds; bloody urine; bruising

HOME CARE: Remove ticks; vet care required

VET CARE: Remove ticks; antibiotic therapy

PREVENTION: Use appropriate insecticides to keep ticks off your dog; promptly remove ticks that do attach to the dog

ELECTRICAL SHOCK Dogs are often injured or killed from encounters with electricity. Lightening, fallen electrical cables, or faulty circuits offer opportunities for disaster, but most accidents result from the puppy or dog chewing through an electric cord. Electrical current may cause muscle contractions that make your dog bite down even harder, and prevent her from releasing the cord.

If you find your dog in such a situation, shut off the current and disconnect the plug before attempting to touch her or you risk being shocked, too. If the dog has stopped breathing, begin resuscitation (see ARTIFICAL RESPIRATION).

ELECTRICAL SHOCK

SYMPTOMS: Mouth burns; difficulty breathing; convulsions; loss of consciousness; shock
FIRST AID: Shut off current first then administer resuscitation if dog isn't breathing. EMERGENCY! SEE VET IMMEDIATELY! Nutritionals support during convalescence
VET CARE: Oxygen therapy; drugs to rid fluid from lungs; surgical removal of burned tissue; antibiotics; possible placement of feeding tube and prescription nutrition
PREVENTION: Supervise dogs and puppies around electrical cords

Injury varies depending on the degree of the voltage and the pathway taken through the body by the current. Usually, electrocution causes burns at the point of contact, usually the mouth area in dogs. The lungs often fill with water within twelve hours after the incident, due to electricity rupturing tiny capillaries in the lungs. The fluid which leaks into the lungs makes it difficult to breathe.

Current passing through the heart may prompt an irregular beat and circulatory collapse, while a central nervous system injury affects breathing and other bodily functions. Unless treated promptly, the dog may fall into a coma, suffer convulsions, and die. Pets who survive can suffer permanent nerve damage. The trauma causes shock, and should be treated accordingly (see SHOCK).

Burns from electrical shock may need surgery to remove the damaged tissue. Antibiotics fight possible infections, and when mouth burns are severe, a feeding tube may need to be passed through the nose to bypass the damaged oral cavity. Drugs are often used to stabilize an irregular heartbeat, and fluid therapy combats circulation problems and shock. Diuretic drugs help eliminate water in the lungs, and bronchodilating drugs and oxygen therapy help the dog breathe. Some dogs may need mechanical help breathing until their lungs can compensate. Electrical shock victims must be seen by a veterinarian as soon as possible.

It's easier to prevent electrical shock than deal with the consequences. Puppies that are teething are at particularly high risk, but all dogs investigate their world with their mouths. Unplug appliance that aren't in use, and tape down cords to make them less tempting. Use a dog repellent like Bitter Apple on dangerous items to keep them out of your dog's mouth. WATCH your dog to prevent her from dangerous contact with electrical cords.

ELIZABETHAN COLLAR

An Elizabethan collar is a cone of stiff material placed about the dog's neck to prevent him from bothering, licking or biting at healing wounds. The contraption is named after the elaborate ruffled stiff collars of the Elizabethan period. In veterinary medicine, it's typically made of plastic or cardboard and extends outward in a cone to just beyond the end of the dog's nose. Pet supply stores and veterinarians offer the collars in various sizes.

You can make a serviceable Elizabethan collar by cutting the bottom from a plastic pail or waste basket, or using stiff cardboard. Size depends on the dog's dimensions. Cut out a twelve to eighteen-inch circle and at the center cut a neck-sized opening (plus an inch or so). Measure the dog's collar for the right size; the depth should reach from point of neck-contact to the tip of the dog's nose.

Remove a pie-shaped wedge from the circle (about one-fourth of the diameter) and tape the edges to form the cone. Buffer the inside opening with tape to cushion the dog's neck, and punch three to six holes to accept string to bind the contraption to the dog's collar. Some dogs aren't able to eat or drink while wearing the collar, so remove it for dining. The collar impairs peripheral vision, and dogs shouldn't be allowed outdoors unattended while wearing the collar.

Ask your veterinarian about alternatives to the stiff collar. Soft cervical type collars may be as effective and less stressful for your recovering dog.

ENDOSCOPE The term endoscopy means "looking within," and the technique is another noninvasive way to examine the internal structures of a pet's body. The respiratory, digestive, and urinary tracts, as well as some areas of the abdomen or chest, can be viewed with an endoscope. Before the method became available, the stomach and intestines were most commonly examined by having the pet swallow a contrast medium, like barium, and then taking pictures with X-rays. Exploratory surgery was often the only way to gain a true diagnosis.

Endoscopy is the unsung workhorse of veterinary medicine. It goes beyond retrieving all the odd and dangerous things your dog inadvertently swallows. Endoscopy offers a minimally invasive alternative to surgical procedures and can provide great results often with less pain and quicker recovery than surgery. That's especially important for critically ill patients.

Endoscopes are used to collect biopsies of the intestines, stomach, colon, nasal cavity, liver, bladder, and urethra. Foreign matter in the esophagus, stomach, or trachea can also be removed. Endoscopes also magnify the view, which means an even closer look than might be possible to "eyeball" during surgery.

The term endoscopy means "looking within." Endoscopy is performed with either rigid or flexible scopes. Flexible scopes work best to examine the stomach and intestines while rigid scopes more typically evaluate the nasal passages and female urinary and reproductive tracts. Rigid scopes also are more useful for abdominal evaluation and biopsy of organs such as the liver.

The endoscope tube can be inserted into any opening—mouth, nose, rectum or surgical incision. The fiberoptic endoscope includes a light source and can also transmit therapeutic laser impulses through optical fibers to treat a lesion, for example. More recently, endoscopes employ video chip cameras which make them more versatile and less fragile.

The image captured on the inside of the dog's body is transmitted to a screen for the veterinarian to view. That allows the doctor to guide the instrument from the outside of the body to get an up close look at what might be wrong, collect samples, or treat problems.

Endoscopes also have at least one channel through which tiny tools can be passed. For example, the tools may be used to collect tissue samples for cancer biopsies, or retrieve inhaled seeds or ingested bones that have lodged in the dog's respiratory or digestive tract. Endoscopy also may be used to control bleeding, stretch narrowed passageways or insert therapeutic devices.

Anesthesia is almost always required. It's rare to have complications but anesthetic risks are possible in some dogs. There's also a small risk of perforation especially in dogs with severe intestinal disease being scoped for biopsy of the stomach or small intestine. Dogs with foreign material stuck in the esophagus for more than 24 hours are at increased risk of perforation.

In pets, the respiratory, digestive, and urinary tracts, as well as some areas of the abdomen or chest are most often viewed with an endoscope. Here are the most common reasons that endoscopy is performed.

Endoscopy is the term used for gastrointestinal causes. Endoscopy is used for investigating the reasons behind vomiting, diarrhea, weight loss, loss of appetite, abdominal pain, evidence of an abnormal mass on ultrasound or radiographs, foreign body removal, or esophageal disorder. The endoscope can view the esophagus, stomach, upper duodenum, colon and the ileocecocolic junction.

Cystoscopy refers to endoscopy for the urogenital system. This is used for conditions such as straining to urinate, blood in the urine, painful urinations, abnormal discharges, and suspicion of a mass. It is performed to obtain biopsies, remove stones, and to look for evidence of kidney hemorrhage. It also is used to identify and correct ectopic ureters—a birth defect resulting in urinary incontinence in young dogs—and the laser ablation of ectopic ureters. Endoscopy can assist in the placement of stents in the ureter and urethra, and is useful in canine reproduction procedures to examine the vulva and vagina and to assist in artificial insemination.

Cystoscopy also can be used to perform Laser-Induced Shock Wave Lithotripsy. The scope is passed through the dog's urethra into the bladder so the surgeon can actually "see" the stone. Then a laser light beam transmitted through fibers in the endoscope shatter the stone into smaller and smaller pieces so the powdered stone can pass painlessly out of the body when the dog urinates.

Bronchoscopy is the use of endoscopy for the respiratory tract. A dog that suffers chronic or acute coughing episodes may be evaluated with bronchoscopy and have both the upper and lower airway tract evaluated. Bronchoscopy is used for suspected pneumonia, for difficulty breathing, and to assess for tracheal collapse. Bronchoalveolar lavage—rinsing out the airways—can be performed to obtain a sample for cytology and culture, to obtain biopsies for the airways, and to remove tracheal foreign bodies.

Rhinoscopy refers to endoscopy of the nose and sinus. This is used to evaluate conditions of nasal discharge and nasal bleeding. Rhinoscopy can look for nasal foreign bodies, diagnosis fungal or bacterial infections in the nose and sinuses, and treat for those infections. Rhinoscopy also can biopsy masses located in the nasal and nasopharyngeal areas as well as place nasopharyngeal stents to treat areas of stenosis—narrowed areas of the nose and sinuses.

Laparoscopy views the inside of the abdomen. A spay or neutering of a cryptorchid dog can now be done using a tiny incision and laparoscopy, rather than an invasive incision that takes longer for the dog to recover from. The procedure also might be used to place a stent in a blocked bile duct, take biopsies of tumors or remove them. And laparoscopic-assisted gastropexy surgery may be performed for preventative treatment of gastric dilation and volvulus syndrome (see BLOAT).

Thoracoscopy is using an endoscope to view the chest cavity. It might be used for the removal of the pericardium (the sac around the heart) to stop bleeding into the pericardial sac, for example. Thoracoscopy also is used to biopsy the lung, remove a lung lobe, or for cancerous or inflammatory lung conditions.

Arthroscopy is used to look at the joints. The veterinarian can view the joint and decide if there are lesions, foreign bodies, loose fragments of cartilage or bone to remove or infection and treat accordingly. Arthroscopy also is used in tendon transplants performed at some specialty practices (see KNEE INJURY). Another innovative procedure used in people and as yet only rarely in dogs is Electrothermal Assisted Capsulorphy (ETAC). The new therapy uses radio frequency energy to shrink connective tissues to tighten the laxity of joints, which may be therapeutic for dogs with intact but unstable cruciate ligaments in the knee, hip dysplasia, and shoulder problems.

ENTERITIS

SYMPTOMS: Loss of appetite; vomiting; watery diarrhea
HOME CARE: Withhold food For 12 to 24 hours; offer ice to lick; if symptoms persist, see a veterinarian
VET CARE: Fluid therapy; diagnostic tests; treatment specific to cause
PREVENTION: Feed smaller portions; cut out table scraps; when diet change is necessary, do so gradually

ENTERITIS An inflammation of the small intestines and/or stomach is called enteritis, and can result from several diseases. Dogs suffering enteritis may lose their appetite, and commonly exhibit watery diarrhea along with periodic vomiting (see DIARRHEA and VOMITING).

Most cases of enteritis in dogs arise from their less-than-discriminatory eating habits. Raiding the garbage, eating table scraps, food allergy, swallowed objects, or simple gluttony often result in gastrointestinal upset. Any sudden change in diet, even from one commercial food to another, potentially may cause enteritis.

When acute signs are due to dietary indiscretion, vomiting and diarrhea usually resolve simply by resting the gastrointestinal tract and treating the symptoms. Withholding food for twelve to 24 hours is often all that's required, but in some instances, your veterinarian will prescribe medication to control the diarrhea.

When signs don't respond to symptomatic therapy, a diagnosis of the underlying problem is necessary if the condition is to be reversed. A number of viral diseases cause similar signs and can be life-threatening, and intestinal parasites are also a common cause. In some instances, fluid therapy may be required to counteract dehydration resulting from diarrhea and vomiting (see ALLERGIES, COCCIDIOSIS, CORONAVIRUS, GIARDIA,

HOOKWORMS, LEPTOSPIROSIS, PARVOVIRUS, ROUNDWORMS, SWALLOWED OBJECTS, and WHIPWORMS).

EPILEPSY

EPILEPSY This generic term describes a brain disorder characterized by seizures, also called convulsions or "fits." a seizure is a loss of motor and/or emotional control which results from abnormal nerve impulses in the brain.

The brain employs neurons as messengers, which function by sending tiny electrical charges through the nervous system. The nervous system is structured like a web of highways, a neural network that provides pathways to every area of the body so that instructions from the brain can be delivered to prompt body functions.

Epilepsy happens when neurons misfire. A kind of biological power-surge blows out the breakers of the brain, and temporarily shuts down normal function. The result is a seizure.

Seizures can be acquired, and develop as a result of head trauma, poison, or metabolic disease. Toxicities resulting from antifreeze or inappropriate use of flea preparations often result in seizures. A blow to the head from being hit by a car can injure the brain and seizures may not begin until several days or even weeks following the accident. Severe kidney or liver disease, tumors, or organic or infectious disease like canine distemper or diabetes mellitus may cause seizures. Eclampsia, heat stroke, intestinal parasites, and tick-borne diseases may induce seizures.

When the cause is identified and successfully treated, seizures may be eliminated. Seizures may occur only once in the dog's life, or continually recur. Seizure disorders in dogs may also be inherited. Beagles, Belgian Turvurens, German Shepherd Dogs, Golden Retrievers, Irish Setters, Keeshonds, Labrador Retrievers, Poodles and St. Bernards are predisposed to inherited epilepsy.

When the first seizure occurs in a dog older than six, it's usually due to a tumor (see CANCER). Acquired disease may appear at any age, but usually occurs for the first time in older dogs. The majority of epileptic dogs are between one and five years of age, and act normally between episodes; this form is typically termed idiopathic epilepsy, which means the cause cannot be determined. Seizures in dogs less than a year of age are likely caused by inherited problems, infections or toxins. Idiopathic and inherited epilepsies may appear in the first year, but more commonly are noticed during the dog's second year.

Dogs usually suffer major motor seizures, also called the grand mal or tonic/clonic episodes, which affect the entire body. Partial motor seizures strikes only specific groups of muscles; for instance, an ear may flick or the dog's lip may spasm.

Psychomotor seizures affect behavior; the dog suddenly hallucinates, becomes aggressive or fearful, or exhibits compulsive/obsessive behavior. During an episode, the dog may chase his tail, a ball or stick. Some dogs inexplicably attack objects, owners, invisible items without warning, or may even maim themselves. English Springer Spaniels, Cocker Spaniels and Bull Terriers appear to be prone to obsessive/compulsive disorders and rage syndrome which some experts believe may be caused by psychomotor seizures. King Charles Spaniels may exhibit "fly-catching" behavior, snapping at the air when nothing is there.

EPILEPSY

SYMPTOMS: Seizures; falling down; jerky or paddling motions of legs; grinding of teeth; loss of bladder and bowel control
FIRST AID: Keep cool; avoid noise; shut off lights; do not touch; seizures lasting longer than five minutes are a MEDICAL EMERGENCY! SEE VET IMMEDIATELY!
HOLISTIC HELP: Acupuncture
VET CARE: Diagnostic tests; medications to control seizure episodes
PREVENTION: Once diagnosed, medication may reduce the frequency; there is no prevention

Seizures rarely last longer than a few minutes, and are characterized by three phases. The first is an altered period of behavior immediately prior to the seizure, called the aura. Dogs stare, seem "out of it" or act disoriented, apprehensive or restless. They may sniff the air or snap as though seeing or smelling a hallucination. Your dog may seek you out during this period, and whine.

In the next stage the convulsion begins. The dog loses consciousness and falls over with legs rigid and outstretched, and breathing stops. This rigid phase lasts ten to thirty seconds. It's followed by the agitated phase in which dogs paddle or jerk their legs, chew and grind their teeth, blink their eyes, drool and foam at the mouth. They often urinate or defecate, eyes dilate, and the fur stands on end. The first two phases typically last one to three minutes.

During the post-seizure phase, the convulsion stops but the dog acts exhausted or confused. Complete recovery varies between individuals; some are back to normal within minutes, while others act disturbed for hours. The dog may immediately suffer another seizure, particularly if stimulated by loud noises, bright lights, or excitement.

Leave your dog alone during a seizure. He isn't aware of his actions, and the involuntary muscle contractions may result in you being severely bitten. DON'T TRY TO PUT ANYTHING IN YOUR DOG'S MOUTH. Move a seizuring dog only if he might fall and further injure himself. Turn on the air conditioner or a fan to help keep the area cool. A seizure burns so many calories, it can overheat your dog. Outside noises or sights can prolong the seizure or prompt a new one, so avoid talking or touching your dog. Turn off the lights and any music, and cover with a sheet to help shut out external stimulations. Very young puppies may suffer seizures as a result of low blood sugar (see HYPOGLYCEMIA) if they don't eat enough, so giving your puppy a dribble of honey or Karo syrup may be helpful, after the seizure ends. When the convulsion stops, take him to the vet.

Most convulsions in dogs are more frightening than dangerous. However, seizures that continue for longer than five minutes are an emergency, and need immediate veterinary attention. Rapidly recurring seizures without recovery between, or ongoing prolonged convulsions are referred to as status epilepticus. Uncontrolled seizures can cause permanent brain injury, severe metabolic problems, and death. The seizure itself burns so many calories that body temperature rises and blood sugar levels drop; both conditions stimulate seizures to continue. Intravenous administration of valium is the treatment of choice to stop status epilepticus.

Seizures are usually controlled with oral anticonvulsant medication the owner gives the dog at home. Maintenance therapy is only warranted when dogs suffer recurrent seizures that interfere with a quality life. One seizure rarely prompts medication, and dogs who suffer only occasional episodes may not require medication at all.

The condition is not curable; in certain instances where metabolic disease damage can be reversed, epilepsy may be transient. Treatment for ongoing epilepsy, however, attempts to reduce the frequency, shorten the duration, and/or reduce the severity of seizures, with a minimum of side effects. Limiting recurrence to one or two seizures per month is considered a success.

Some of the same human medications for controlling seizures are also used in veterinary medicine. Phenobarbital and primidone are most often used in dogs; Dilantin, which works well in people, is metabolized too rapidly in dogs to be particularly helpful to them. An experimental drug that is effective in some dogs is potassium bromide, and is available at some veterinary schools. Some dogs suffering from psychomotor seizures have been helped with medications that control obsessive/compulsive disorders, such as Prozac and similar drugs. Ask your veterinarian for the best program for your dog.

Dosage varies from dog to dog, and it's important to work closely with your veterinarian to find the ideal maintenance dose. Side effects such as sedation, increased thirst, appetite, or urine output are seen in some patients. Once anticonvulsant therapy has begun, missing a dose can actually cause a seizure, so owner attention and compliance is important if the dog is to do well.

Acupuncture treatment for seizures has been used for centuries and documented as early as 770 B.C. by a group of Chinese physicians. Until recently, acupuncture was used in Western medicine only as a last resort in seizures that could not be managed by conventional means. No one knows for certain how acupuncture works, but a major advantage is the lack of side effects like depression or drowsiness often common with drugs. Acupuncture appears to increase the level of inhibitory discharges in the cortex of the brain, which suppresses seizures. Research has documented acupuncture increased levels of endorphins, natural painkillers produced in the brain that are known to have anticonvulsive effects (see ACUPUNCTURE).

Gold beads are often implanted at acupuncture points to cause long-term stimulation of these sites. In one study of 40 dogs with epilepsy, 50 percent were able to be taken off all anticonvulsant medication after receiving gold bead implants, another 25 percent were able to reduce their medication and 25 percent had no response to the therapy.

Medical marijuana (or cannabis) today is also available for pets, but must be formulated so that pets receive the medical benefits of the cannabis (hemp) plant while reducing potential toxic concentrations of the herb. Hemp can act as a neuroprotective agent reducing seizure frequency and intensity. Ask your veterinarian if this supplement may benefit your pet.

Most dogs are helped by therapy, but about 20 to 30 percent require intensive medical attention. Most dogs with idiopathic epilepsy can, with treatment, enjoy a quality life.

EUTHANASIA

Euthanasia is the act of causing merciful death. When your dog suffers an injury or illness with no reasonable hope of recovery, euthanasia may be the kindest choice. Deciding to put your dog "to sleep" isn't easy, and should be made with the understanding and guidance of a compassionate veterinarian.

All of us who love and care for dogs understand that we will outlive our pet, and ultimately have to say goodbye. But knowing that doesn't make the reality any easier. Quality care can prolong the lives of our pets only for so long.

It is incumbent upon caring owners to make the wisest, most compassionate—and certainly, the most difficult—decisions for our dogs. The time will come when a longer life isn't necessarily a better life. When the joy of living is gone, when pain replaces pleasure, and when your dog is ready to leap forward into the next adventure beyond your side, you can grant her the greatest gift of all—a merciful death.

Often, you will somehow "know" when the time is right. But many dog lovers may have trouble recognizing what's best, particularly when we want so very much not to lose our beloved dog. Either situation is normal. Ask your veterinarian to help you make this decision.

Today, many clinics provide a separate room that allows you to have private time alone with your dog before, during, and after the euthanasia. The first step typically involves placing a catheter in the vein, to make it easier to administer the euthanasia solution when the time comes. Chronically ill dogs may already have an IV catheter in place.

Occasionally, the dog will be sedated first, which makes her very sleepy. You may prefer to forgo the sedation, so that she remains alert up to the end, and you are better able to interact with the dog you know and love during your goodbyes.

Once you have had time to visit, the veterinarian will return and ask if you're ready. The procedure should be explained to you in advance, so you know what to expect. As the drug relaxes the dog, sometimes she will involuntarily urinate, so if you want to hold your dog you may want to cuddle her in a towel. If the dog has not been sedated before, she may receive that injection now so she's relaxed and has a smoother transition. Then a slow IV injection of the euthanasia solution, a barbiturate anesthetic-type drug, is administered. It can be very quick acting; usually within a minute or two the dog will be gone. The veterinarian will listen for a heartbeat to confirm that the dog is dead.

After the pet is gone and the heartbeat stops, sometimes the dog will twitch or have last minute breaths, but it's just an automatic response by the body. At this point, most people wish to spend some time alone with their dog. Don't hesitate to ask for this consideration if it's not offered.

A beloved pet's final moments are often difficult for your veterinarian and staff, too. Many practitioners offer counseling and emotional support.

EYES

The dog's eyes are sensory organs that translate images carried by light into meaning. Besides providing vision, dog eyes are also important in canine communication.

Structurally, the canine eye is similar to our own. It is designed to function well in both high and low light situations. Eyes situated toward the front of the face provide binocular vision and an acute depth perception important for a successful predator. But eye placement—and so, visual acuity and field of vision—varies from breed to breed, with flat-faced dogs like the Pug more forward-facing, and narrow-headed breeds like the Collie placed further toward the sides.

Each eyeball is cradled in fat and positioned inside a bony socket in the dog's skull. Eyelids support the front of the eye, and glide across the eyeball on a coating of tears. Dogs have a third eyelid that begins at the inside corner of the eye. Called the nictitating membrane or haw, this membrane lubricates and protects the eye. It is more prominent in some breeds than others, but is usually not particularly noticeable when the other eyelids are open. It functions by sliding across and wiping the surface clean.

A thin layer of clear cells, called the cornea, cover the front surface of the dog's eyeball. The "white" of the eye, or sclera, isn't nearly as obvious in dog eyes as in our own. The conjunctiva is a thin, protective layer of tissue that covers the inside of the eyelids, sides of the nictitating membrane and sclera. Tear glands located in the eyelids produce lubricants that also contain bacteria-fighting substances which help protect the eyes from infection.

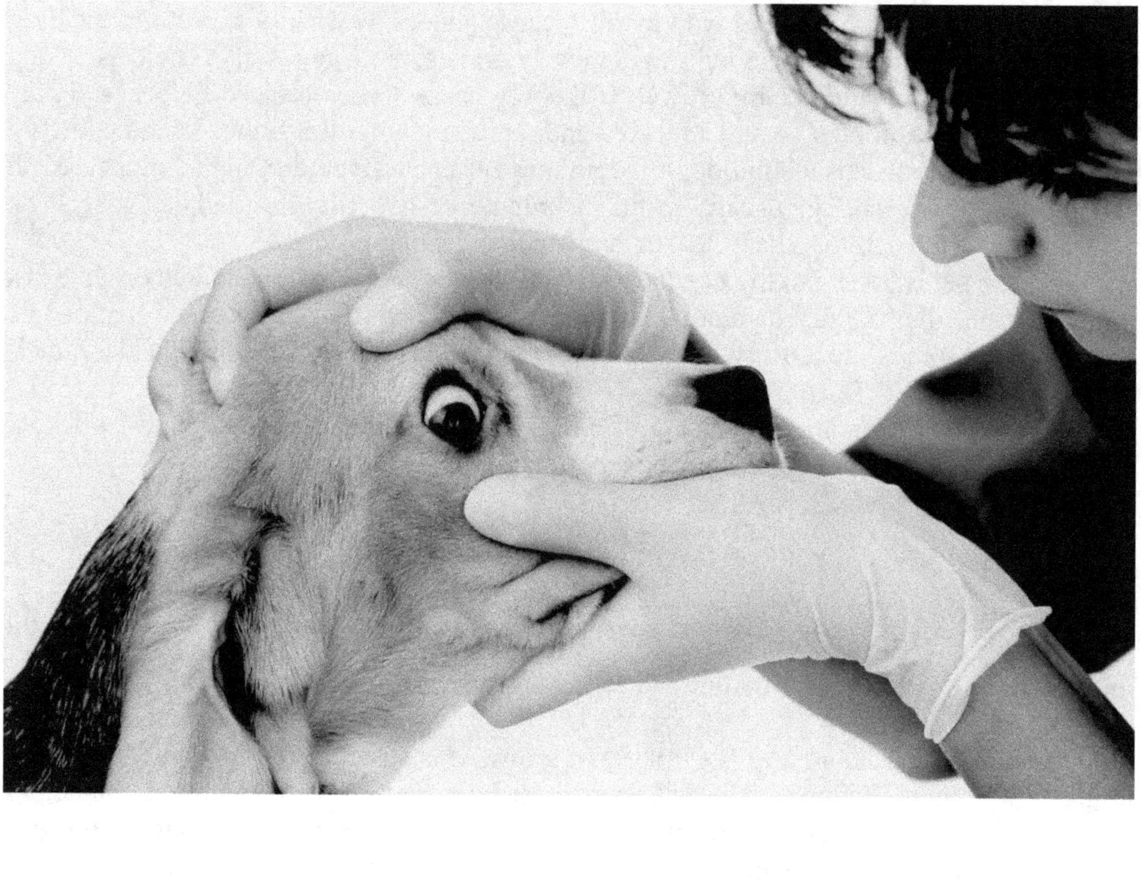

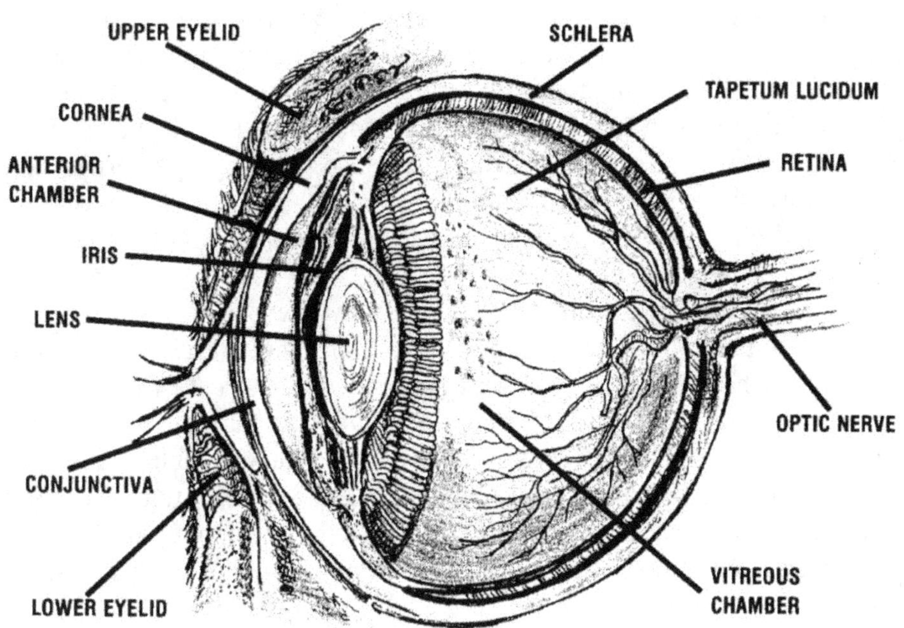

Behind the cornea, the front portion of the eye is filled with watery fluid that holds the structures of this anterior chamber in place. The center black area is the pupil, an opening directly behind the cornea through which light passes into the eye. Surrounding the pupil is the colored portion of the eye, called the iris. It is actually a special muscle that controls the opening and closing of the pupil to regulate the amount of light allowed into the eye. In very bright light, the iris closes the pupil to a pinpoint, while in low light, it is dilated in a wide circle to capture as much light as possible.

The posterior chamber of the eye is situated behind the pupil and iris, and contains a gel-like material that helps give the eye its shape. Called vitreous, this substance keeps the inner structures like the lens in place. The lens focuses light that enters through the pupil onto the retina at the back of the eye.

The retina is covered with highly specialized light-receptor cells, called rods and cones that react to the light in various ways. Cones provide color sense, while rods allow the dog to see shades of white, black and gray. The optic nerve is connected to the retina, and carries these signals to the brain's visual center, where the impulses are translated into meaningful images.

The dog's cones allow him to see a dichromatic, or two-color system (blue and green, and their combinations) rather than the three (red/yellow/blue and combinations) which people see. Dogs can be readily trained to distinguish between certain colors, but probably don't see them the same way that we do. Under normal light, dogs likely see blue and green as much brighter than red, because they have few to none red-sensitive cones.

This lack of color perception is balanced by dogs having many more rods than people do. The retinal illumination of the dog is about three times more efficient than ours, which means dogs see much better in low-light conditions than people. A layer of reflective cells behind the retina, called the tapetum lucidum, enhances the light-gathering efficiency of canine eyes by nearly 40 percent by reflecting any light that enters the eye. This gives the dog's eyes a second chance to use existing light, and also accounts for the eerie glow of canine eyes at night as light escapes.

Eyes that face forward allow the dog's field of vision to overlap, providing three-dimensional or binocular sight. The degree of binocular vision varies from breed to breed, with flat-faced dogs having more, and narrow-headed dogs less. Cocker Spaniels and Greyhounds have about 80 degrees of binocular vision, compared to our own 120.

Dogs tend to see better at middle to far distances, and have trouble focusing on objects closer than about ten inches. Rather than focus, dogs tend to rely more on motion. That's why dogs may be unable to see the last piece of food in the bowl, but will respond to strong hand signals at a distance of up to a mile away. And they may not recognize an owner who wears a hat until scent or sound of voice offers further identification.

Many of the short-nosed dogs like Pugs have high density vision cells arranged in a single spot on the retina, called the area centralis. The area centralis has three times the density of nerve endings as the visual streak found in long-nose breed dogs. Some researchers report this may be why short-nose dogs seem to react to the TV screen, or perhaps appear more sensitive to human facial expressions.

This may be why smaller breeds become so cherished. Dogs able to see well in near-vision (lap-to-face) distances have the physical ability to be more responsive to our moods and emotions.

Eyes are prone to conditions which can be extremely painful to the dog and require immediate veterinary attention. Signs of a painful eyes include squinting, tearing, avoiding light, and tenderness to touch. A visible nictitating membrane is often a sign of pain. Flat faced breeds that have more prominent eyes like the Pekingese may require routine cleaning of their eyes (see GROOMING) and be more prone to eyeballs popping out of the socket (see PROPTOSIS OF EYEBALL). Signs of injury and/or disease may include any kind of eye discharge, redness, crusting, cloudiness to the eye, or a hard or soft eye (see CATARACT, CHERRY EYE, DRY EYE, ECTROPION/ENTROPION, GLAUCOMA, and UVEITIS)

FADING PUPPY SYNDROME This term refers to puppies which appear healthy at birth, then inexplicably "fade away" and die. Such puppies fail to gain weight, stop eating, and become weak. It is likely that a variety of conditions result in the syndrome, either singly or in combination. Factors such as the immune competence of the dam, environmental stress, congenital defects, viruses or even inherited blood defects such as neonatal isoerythrolysis (see BLOOD) may contribute. If the cause is treatable and can be identified in time, the condition may be reversible (see BRUCELLOSIS and CANINE HERPESVIRUS)

FADING PUPPY

SYMPTOMS: Puppies failure to thrive; refusal to eat; weak; crying; sudden death
HOME CARE: Nursing care; supplemental feeding; keep warm
VET CARE: Supportive care; treatment depending on cause
PREVENTION: Ensure the mother dog is healthy and has been wormed and vaccinated prior to pregnancy

FALSE PREGNANCY Also called pseudo pregnancy, this condition is exactly what it sounds like; the dog exhibits physical and behavioral signs of pregnancy following estrus when in fact no puppies have been conceived. The condition may occur whether the dog has been mated or not, and is an exaggeration of a clinically normal condition.

False pregnancy is a relatively common occurrence in intact female dogs. Behaviorists believe the condition in wolf ancestors served a survival function. Female wolves that did not become pregnant were nevertheless biologically prepared to nurse and mother the offspring of other pack members.

False pregnancy results when ovulation occurs but fertilization does not take place. It is not caused by an excess of progesterone, though. The level of this hormone, which prepares the dog's body for pregnancy, remains normal, but the body is somehow fooled into behaving as though it has become pregnant.

Signs develop about six to ten weeks following estrus, and vary from dog to dog. Some exhibit only subtle changes in appetite with perhaps a slight swelling of the abdomen. Other dogs "adopt" and mother inanimate objects like a stuffed animal or a shoe, or other puppy substitutes. Dogs suffering a false pregnancy often produce milk, and may even go through labor.

Treatment is rarely necessary for this condition, which will resolve by itself within one to three weeks following the onset of signs. However, producing milk without nursing puppies to relieve the pressure can prove uncomfortable for the dog, and is a potential cause of infection (see MASTITIS). Dogs suffering from false pregnancy actually stimulate the ongoing production of milk by mothering objects or licking their own breasts; even the presence of another dog's puppies may prompt milk production. An owner's efforts to relieve the dog's distress can make the condition worse; cold or warm packs applied to the swollen mammary glands also stimulates milk production.

If the condition doesn't resolve within three weeks, try removing the "adopted" objects and apply an Elizabethan collar to prevent the dog's continued self-stimulation. In some instances, more aggressive intervention by a veterinarian may be required.

Dogs that suffer from false pregnancy once will likely do so again. When puppies are not desired, sterilization prevents future occurrences (see REPRODUCTION and SPAYING).

FEAR Fear is a strong emotional response to a perceived threat. Dogs typically exhibit fear when confronted with unfamiliar people, animals, or situations. This normal emotion is a protective mechanism that prompts the dog to either fight or flee the danger.

Fear is a strong emotional response associated with the close proximity of another object, individual or social situation that threatens the animal. This common emotion becomes abnormal or inappropriate only within certain contexts.

Anxiety is the fearful anticipation of a future event, and this tends to be an ongoing but less severe response that can turn into full-blown fear. Phobias result, on the other hand, in an immediate, extreme and severely abnormal response, like a panic attack or catatonia. Some experts believe that one phobic experience "primes" the individual to fear future events. Just the memory of the first event is enough to trigger subsequent attacks.

Properly socialized dogs tend to be more confident when faced with new experiences, and they are less likely to suffer abnormal anxiety or fearful behavior later in life. Pets frightened by something during this impressionable period, though, may forever after react with anxiety when faced with a similar situation. For instance, a pup abused by a male caretaker is likely to be fearful as adult pets when exposed to any other male.

Pets either try to escape the scary situation and run away, or when that's not possible, they may become aggressive to drive off the perceived threat. Some dogs try to defuse the threat with submissive behaviors, such as urinating to "cry uncle." Punishing pets for fearful behavior doesn't help. More likely, punishment makes the behavior worse or turns the fear into aggression toward the owner.

Researchers have determined that a functioning amygdala is required to learn fear, and a functioning forebrain is required to unlearn fear. The amygdala is a tiny portion of the brain considered the "primitive brain." It deals with emotions and the fight-or-flight response. The forebrain is the seat of personality, and it also deals with logic. Many human fear disorders seem to result from the inability to inhibit a fear response. It's theorized that fear arises in part from the overreaction of the amygdala, or the failure of the amygdala to switch off once the threat is gone.

PET (positive emission tomography) scans have been used to study regional brain flow as it corresponds to emotion. Some dogs respond more quickly or with more intensity to various stimuli than other dogs. This "hyper-reactivity" is probably truly pathological—that is, caused by a physical or chemical abnormality. Once they've gone beyond this threshold, it can be nearly impossible to interrupt the fear cycle.

There are limitless circumstances that may prompt fearful or anxious behavior in the dog. Anything outside the dog's experience is typically perceived as a potential threat, particularly by submissive dogs. Strange noises, being left alone, or a stranger's approach are common triggers of fear. Dogs may react fearfully to unfamiliar animals, children or babies; people in uniforms or wearing hats are common fear inducers.

The dog's response to fear depends on the circumstances and how dominant or submissive the dog may be. When the opportunity is available, dogs may run away or try to hide from the threat. Dogs fearful of being left alone (see SEPARATION ANXIETY) may try to escape by clawing windows or doors, and crying or howling for company, or even chewing or eliminating inappropriately. When escape isn't possible, when the dog feels cornered, or is defending his property (the yard, an owner), the result may be a fear-induced aggression (see AGGRESSION).

Your dog communicates his fear and tries to drive the threat away using growls and snarls, barks, raised hackles and/or flattened ears (see COMMUNICATION). If these distance-producing signals don't work, the dog may attack. A submissive dog crouches in a low position, rolls on his back, and urinates submissively (see SUBMISSION and SUBMISSIVE URINATION) in an attempt to appease the perceived threat.

Many young dogs tend toward shyness during adolescence, at about four to five months of age. However, most of these fear-related behaviors fade as the dog matures, gains confidence, and becomes used to the triggering situation. Exceptions can develop into problem behaviors, though. In particular, some of the northern breeds like Siberian Huskies, as well as larger breed dogs like German Shepherd Dogs and Labrador Retrievers tend to be more likely to develop phobias about loud noises like thunderstorms or fireworks (see NOISE PHOBIAS). And a dog that is frightened by something specific during the socialization period (see PUPPY) may thereafter react in a fearful manner.

Dogs that are particularly submissive may benefit from obedience training and interactive play sessions. Nothing builds canine confidence like being praised for doing something well. Tug-of-war with a towel is a great confidence boost for dogs; let him win.

Punishing the dog for fearful behavior does not work, and in some instances will escalate the behavior. The best way to prevent fear in dogs is to build confidence at an early age by exposing them to a variety of positive new experiences.

When the dog is older, a program of desensitization is required. In effect, the dog is trained to recognize a benefit to conquering his fearful behavior. He is exposed to the fear-inducing situation time after time—a man in a hat, tape-recorded thunder, the departure of a loved one—initially for extremely short periods followed by progressively longer sessions. He is rewarded (praised, given a treat, etc.) only when he behaves appropriately. Eventually it is hoped that the dog will learn to relate the formerly fearful encounter with good things for himself.

The pheromone produced by mom-dogs as they nurse signals the babies to 'have no fear' and these no-fear pheromones work on adult dogs, too. Several products are now available, including "Good Behavior Calming Collars" and "D.A.P." (dog-appeasing pheromone) products. Pheromone products are particularly helpful to soothe noise-phobic dogs, puppies going to new homes, or any fear-related situation. They are available as a spray, a plug-in product, and an impregnated collar the dog wears. These products also can help with your dog's separation anxiety issues.

FENCE A good dog fence makes good neighbors and safe pets. You may think you're indulging your new puppy by allowing her to roam. But not only can roaming pets turn into pests or worse (coyote bait comes to mind), they can become lost, contract disease or spread illness to other beloved pets.

You wouldn't let your four-year-old human toddler roam outside unsupervised, and let him "learn the hard way" if something goes wrong. The cost of safe fencing is offset by saved emergency room bills and lost sleep.

Dog containment takes some thought, and depends on your individual pet. Just because your dog follows the rules doesn't mean other dogs will. Avoid tethering or chaining your dog. Some localities have laws against this, unless it's for very short periods of time while under your supervision. Physical barriers are the safest and most reliable options.

You'll need to figure out if your dog is a jumper or a digger before investing and planning the fencing. What contains a Border Collie puppy may not do the job once he's an adult. The paws of digging terriers probably won't manage tunneling until he reaches adult size, but plan now for excavations.

Privacy fences made of wood may work for the vaulting maniacs, as they won't be as easy to climb out.

They'll need to be six to nine feet high to stop the leaps. Chain link fencing works well for most dogs. Some athletic dogs also can climb out, in which case a top may be needed.

For the diggers, the fence should either be sunk into the ground—frankly, that doesn't work so well—or install a "lip" of fencing flat against the ground all around the perimeter. It can be installed at the bottoms of privacy or other barrier fences, too, to keep the dog from digging out.

Landscape (vine roses, for example) help camouflage any unsightly fences. The thorns also help persuade dogs from either side of the fence to keep their distance. Grass grows up through the lip of fencing and can be mowed with ease.

Sometimes housing developments won't allow physical fences. "Electronic fences" may be popular but I cannot recommend them. According to experts including the American Veterinary Society of Animal Behavior, punishment training including use of shock training devices can cause " . . . potential adverse effects which include but are not limited to: inhibition of learning, increased fear-related and aggressive behaviors, and injury to animals and people interacting with animals."

Electronic fences are only as good as the training, and they are not magical or foolproof. Invisible Fence, for example, insists on slow, careful training of the pet with the help of professionals. But there are other "do it yourself" products and unless you have good training skills, your puppy could be hurt by the training—or training failure when he escapes the fence despite the shock. Besides, there are more humane and equally effective alternatives to electronic containment.

A similar underground "invisible barrier" technology uses a warning beep sound first and then a burst of citronella spray should the dog breach the barrier. Cornell University studies showed that citronella (an aversive scent) collars were much more effective than electric shock collars to train. They're also more humane.

A major downside to non-physical fences is they won't prevent other animals or people from coming into the pet's yard. A goofy puppy intent on the exciting chase could follow a squirrel and cross the boundary—and then the collar's shock or scent prevents him from coming home. People may not recognize your dog is "confined" and this could invite strangers to pet the dog or even steal him.

Fences do more than keep pets safely inside. They keep temptations and dangers out, and reduce our liability as pet owners. When you have a clueless dog that attracts trouble like a magnet, it's even more important to supervise, even when you have a fence. And that's peace of mind for us, and our beloved animal friends.

FERAL

As it applies to our pets, feral refers to a domesticated dog that has reverted to the wild state. Feral dogs are usually lost or abandoned dogs forced to live on their own (see STRAY). Some may crave human attention, but most learn to fear people and avoid close contact.

Feral dogs are found in both cities and farm settings. They typically survive as scavengers, eating from dumpsters or overturning garbage cans, or from the handouts of sympathetic humans, and sometimes by stealing cat or dog food left out for other pets. They are rarely effective hunters, but may catch the occasional rabbit, or feed on dead livestock or road kill. Occasionally, a dog or group of feral dogs learn to kill young calves or sheep, pet cats or small dogs.

Groups of feral dogs rarely are larger than three individuals, with these small groups sometimes interacting loosely with other small packs. Larger groups may hang out together for only short periods of time. Although the group may collectively help guard puppies that are born, and protect territory from trespass, the interactive group-rearing that is typical of wolves has not been observed in feral dogs. In fact, because of high levels of disease, poor nutrition, and the threat of injury from automobiles or other predators, puppies born to feral dogs rarely survive to adulthood.

Well-meaning individuals who feed these dogs without addressing other issues may perpetuate the problem. Feral dogs are a nuisance, and pose a health risk to pets and people. Particularly in the southwestern United States, populations of feral dogs provide a reservoir for the spread of rabies. Local health departments may resort to trap-and-kill programs to control the problem.

Some feral dogs can become pets again, or at least learn to tolerate human contact. However, this often requires great patience and dedication on the prospective caretaker's part, and should not be undertaken lightly. Animal welfare organizations and concerned citizens groups may be able to offer educational support for people who are interested in helping feral dogs in their area.

FLATULENCE

Also referred to as passing gas, this condition is both offensive and embarrassing to a dog owner. Gas is produced naturally in the intestines during digestion, and some dogs produce more than others. Usually, the obnoxious condition isn't dangerous, but flatulence can be the sign of a health problem.

FLATULANCE

SYMPTOMS: Passing gas; offensive odor
HOME CARE: Offer a more digestible diet; cut out table scraps; feed activated charcoal; add yogurt to the diet
HOLISTIC HELP: Flower essences; digestive enzymes
VET CARE: Prescription for gas control; sometimes antibiotics for bacterial overgrowth
PREVENTION: Slow gulping of food; feed free choice; offer multiple but smaller meals; feed away from other pet competition; limit rawhide treats

What and how the dog eats influences how much gas will be produced, and ultimately passed. Inappropriate food supplements, snacking from the garbage, or any sudden change in diet can make the problem worse. Diets that include highly fermentable substances, large quantities of milk, or simply gulping air when eating or drinking are common causes.

Gorging allows food to stay in the stomach for extended periods, and tends to make dogs more prone to gas. Feed your dogs separately to cut down on competition. Slow the gulper by placing a large non-swallowable ball in the bowl so she must eat around it. Invest in a foraging feeder, bowls designed to make dogs work to reach the food.

Try offering the dog a more digestible diet. Check the ingredient list on the package (see READING FOOD LABELS) and ask your veterinarian to recommend an appropriate choice. Change diets gradually over a week's period, by initially mixing two-thirds of the old diet with one-third new. Progress to half and half, then one-third to two-thirds, and finally the new diet entirely.

The flower essence crab apple can help bring the body back into balance. Add two or three drops onto your pet's tongue or in his drinking water each day. Adding digestive enzymes to your dog's food may also help. As your holistic veterinarian for a recommendation.

Another helpful option is garnishing the dog's regular diet with a tablespoonful of plain yogurt, which contains beneficial bacteria that helps digestion and reduces flatulence. Many dogs love the flavor. As a last resort, your veterinarian may prescribe a human medication that contains simethicone and activated charcoal to control the gas. There is also an anti-gas veterinary product called CurTail that contains an enzyme that aids food digestion and reduces flatulence.

FLEAS

FLEAS A flea is an external blood-sucking parasite, and is the most common complaint of dog lovers. There are more than 250 kinds of fleas in the United States, but the cat flea *Ctenocephalides felis* afflicts pets most often. With the exception of pets living in mountainous regions exceeding elevations of 5000 feet, or dry areas like deserts that are inhospitable to fleas, every dog is at risk for flea infestation. Fleas thrive in warm summer weather, but because most dogs spend time both outside and indoors, fleas carried into homes often set up housekeeping, and afflict dogs all year long.

Fleabites can cause a variety of problems, and while some dogs don't seem bothered at all, others suffer skin irritation, itchiness, or even severe allergic reaction (see ALLERGY). Blood loss from fleas can cause anemia or even death, especially in very young or ill dogs (see ANEMIA). Fleas should never be taken lightly, because they are also potential carriers of other diseases and parasites (see PLAGUE and TAPEWORMS).

Fleas belong to a group of insects designated Siphonaptera, meaning "wingless siphon," which refers to piercing-sucking mouthparts. The flea cuts into the dog's skin and inserts a suction tube to feed upon blood. They are also equipped with a specialized protein, called resilin, which functions like elastic to propel the flea great distances. The resilin is compressed by leg and thorax muscles, then quickly released, and the recoil action flings the flea as much as eight inches vertically and sixteen inches horizontally. Six hooked legs are used to cling to any host within reach.

The flea's flat body is armored with cuticle plates that make it nearly crush-proof, and the narrow profile promotes easy movement through fur. An adult flea can live from a few weeks to more than a year, but more typically lives about thirty days. Fleas set up permanent housekeeping on the pet, and stay there unless involuntarily evicted.

However, adults represent only about 5 percent of the total flea population. The remaining 95 percent of the bug count is composed of immature life stages: eggs, larvae and cocoons.

After mating, female fleas store sperm to use as needed; a blood meal stimulates her to lay eggs. She can produce over 2000 eggs in thirty days, and up to 50 each day. Eggs typically fall from the host, and may remain dormant in the environment (the carpet or yard) for as long as six months. But normally, eggs hatch into tiny, maggot-like larvae within one to two weeks. They are virtually invisible to the naked eye, and subsist on the waste passed by adult fleas (sometimes referred to as "flea dirt), and other organic material.

Larvae spin cocoons in about three weeks, where they mature into adults. From inside the cocoon, the flea's antennae and bristles are able to detect body heat and odor, changes in light, touch and moisture, and even traces of carbon dioxide exhalation of a nearby host. This prompts the flea to emerge from the cocoon, and immediately snag a canine victim. The cycle from egg to adult takes about 30 days.

FLEAS

SYMPTOMS: Presence of fleas; black pepperlike residue on skin; itchiness, particularly of the back above the tail; tapeworm segments; lethargy; pale lips and gums
HOME CARE: Treat dog and environment with appropriate insecticides
VET CARE: Fluid therapy; blood transfusions; flea treatment; sometimes steroid therapy
PREVENTION: Routine flea control; confine dog to finite outdoor areas

Flea infestation is diagnosed by actually seeing the bugs on the dog, but fleas move so quickly they may be hard to find. Other incriminating evidence, like dark brown specks of digested blood excreted by the flea, also diagnoses the condition. The parasite tends to like the dog's flanks and lower back above the tail. Flea dirt can be found on the skin in these areas by parting the fur. Try standing your dog on a light-colored towel or sheet, and comb his rear quarters, and the evidence will pepper the fabric below. When the specks are placed on a damp cloth, they dissolve and turn red. Evidence of tapeworms also points to flea infestation. Look for dried rice-like grains in the dog's bedding, or in the fur below the dog's tail.

A range of products is available for addressing the problem, but flea control is complicated by both flea biology and pet sensitivity. Simply put, there is no quick fix.

Because the lion's share of the flea population isn't even on the dog, it's crucial to treat the environment as well as your pet. Treating only your dog may kill the adult fleas, but leaves the remaining life stages to mature and begin the cycle all over again. Dogs that come indoors for even brief periods will seed flea eggs in your house which, given time to mature, quickly turn your house into a flea hotel. And if your dog spends any amount of time outdoors, he is exposed to fleas and is potentially re-infested. The weapons you choose to battle fleas depends on your particular circumstances.

Historically, flea control relied on various classes of chemical insecticides applied to the dog or environment as sprays, bug "bombs," powders, shampoos and dips. Inappropriate or careless application of chemical insecticides are potentially toxic to the pet. Always read, understand, and follow product directions for use.

The effects of a class of chemicals called cholinesterase inhibitors can be cumulative. What may be safe when used by itself can become toxic or even deadly when combined with another product. For instance, dipping your dog with one product, then spraying the house with another can result in toxic levels that poison the dog. This group of chemicals includes organophosphates such as chlorpyrifos (Dursban), Malathion, diazinon, cythioate and fenthion, and carbamates like carbaryl and propoxur. Products containing chlorinated hydrocarbons (DDT, lindane, methoxychlor) are highly toxic, and must be used with extreme caution.

Botanicals are chemical compounds derived from plant sources, and typically are less dangerous to the dog. Pyrethrins, made from a relative of the chrysanthemum flower, are one of the safest insecticides for pets available. They kill fleas quickly on initial contact, but have little residual effect; because they degrade when exposed to ultraviolet light, pyrethrin-based products aren't particularly effective for environmental protection. Synthetic pyrethrins called pyrethroids include permethrin and provide a broader and longer flea-killing action than natural pyrethrins.

Some products are combined with synergists, compounds like piperonyl butoxide (PBO) that increase the effectiveness of insecticides and allow lower, safer concentrations of the chemical to be used. Microencapsulation is a technique used to reduce toxicity to the pet while enhancing the product's long-term effect; the chemical is encased in permeable microcapsules that release small amounts of insecticide over a longer period of time.

Insect Growth Regulators (IGRs) are a relatively new class of flea control which are extremely safe for pets because they affect insects, not mammals. Methoprene and phenoxycarb are two of these hormone-like compounds. IGRs work by changing the insect's metabolic process to prevent maturation of the flea, or reproduction. In either case, the life cycle is broken. Some IGR products are used in the environment, while others address the dog. The IGR lufenuron (Program) is given to the dog as a once monthly pill; fleas that bite a dog treated with lufenuron won't produce eggs able to hatch. However, fleas that bite still cause itchy skin, so this isn't the best choice for flea-allergic dogs.

New chemical products are also available for flea control that are safer for the dog and the environment, while providing better and longer-lasting flea control. Imadacloprid (Advantage) kills adult fleas, and fipronil (Frontline Top Spot) kills both adult fleas and ticks by affecting the insects' nervous system, not the dog's. Both products are applied once a month as drops to the skin of the dog's shoulder blades. Imadacloprid spreads through the skin, while Fipronil spreads to the hair follicles, where it coats each hair as it grows. These products kill fleas before they bite, which prevents the allergic reactions sensitive dogs suffer.

How the product is applied influences ease of use and effectiveness. Flea collars, shampoos, dips, powders and sprays are traditional delivery systems. The "one-time application" of flea collars appeal to dog owners for their easy use, but historically haven't been particularly effective; after all, the collar is on the dog's neck, while fleas are on his rump. Newer collar products which spread the flea-treatment over the entire pet are more effective.

Shampoo products kill fleas only while on the dog; rinsing off the suds eliminates the action (see GROOMING/BATHING). Powders and dust last longer, but are messy and can dry the skin. Sprays for small dogs may be a good choice, because they offer a good initial flea kill, and some repel fleas or offer residual protection; they can be costly for big dogs, though. Dips are applied wet and allowed to dry, and offer good residual protection because they penetrate the hair—but typically must be applied three times a month for complete protection. Again, these can be messy to apply, particularly if your big dog objects to bathing. Some dogs are sensitive to these strong dips.

"Natural" products are touted as an alternative to chemical flea control; however, please be aware that some of these work better than others, and the claim "natural" does not necessarily mean it is safe for your dog. Rotenone and d-limonene are effective when used properly, and are considered botanicals, which are made from roots and citrus fruit extracts. Desiccants are drying agents that cause fleas to dehydrate and die; derivatives of borax used by some commercial pest control companies on carpet do kill flea larvae which helps break the life cycle. Desiccant diatomaceous earth (DE or Diatom Dust) also has a drying effect against a certain percentage of fleas and larvae, but is messy to apply. Certain kinds of nematodes (worms) that eat immature fleas are sold in pet stores and garden shops in powder form, to be mixed with water and sprayed in the yard. And herbal preparations in the environment like peppermint shoo away fleas because of the strong odor, but don't kill fleas—and the smell may be as offensive to your pet as well as the flea, and can sometimes be toxic to pets.

Compounds claiming to have activity against parasites are required to pass EPA guidelines for safety and effectiveness claims, and will have an EPA registration number on the label. Some products avoid these expensive tests by calling themselves "natural." A product without the EPA registration may work and be safe, or it may be dangerous, and ineffective. There's no way to predict.

For the most effective and safest flea treatment protocols for your individual needs, consult with your veterinarian. In many cases, (such as flea-allergic dogs) the best options are to use an IGR-containing product that breaks the flea life cycle, along with an appropriate adulticide product to kill adult fleas on the dog. Today, parasite preventive products designed to protect against heartworms often also protect against fleas (see HEARTWORMS).

Outside treatments are effective only if your dog is confined in a limited area; it's impossible to treat the whole of the great outdoors. The ideal flea habitat is moist and cool; fleas tend to avoid the hot, drying sun, so focus treatment in shaded areas of the yard. Trim grass short, and pick up the brush to let the sun chase the bugs away. Check with your local County Extension Agent to learn what environmental insecticides are approved for use in your area. Some products containing IGRs can control fleas for up to twelve months, but be aware that some IGRs may also affect beneficial insects, like bees or butterflies, so choose your weapons wisely.

Vacuum carpets several times to lift the flea eggs and larvae to the surface so flea products can reach them. Change the vacuum bag frequently to keep surviving bugs from re-infecting the house. Follow product directions to treat the house and yard, and don't allow pets or people access until these areas are completely dry.

FLOWER ESSENCES Flower essences are a type of "vibrational therapy" made from the essential oils of wild plants, trees, and bushes said to offer benefits to the emotional state of pets. Several brands are available. One of the best known, Bach Flower Remedies, consists of 38 individual essences made by infusing spring water with wild flowers either by steeping in the sun or by boiling.

Bach Flower Remedies were created by British physician Dr. Edward Bach in the early 1900s. He believed disease to be a physical sign and end product of unhappiness, fear and worry, and identified twelve "pathological emotional states" in people that the essences are designed to treat:

Fear, Terror, Mental torture or worry, Indecision, Indifference or boredom, Doubt or discouragement, Over-concern, Weakness, Self-distrust, Impatience, Overenthusiasm, Pride or aloofness

We can't know with certainty that pets feel the same emotions as people do, but holistic veterinarians have used the remedies with success, by attempting to identify the pet's emotional state.

The great thing about Bach Flowers is they can be used safely by anyone. Even if you use the wrong remedy, although it may not help it won't cause problems. The essences are easy to use. They don't work in all cases, but when they do, they tend to work very quickly. You can combine them, but will get the best results by limiting to no more than three at a time.

Each individual flower essence treats a specific type of anxiety. The essence Mimulus, for example, is good for soothing fears while Rock Rose deals with terror. Vervain calms nervous energy and Vine helps stop aggression. Holistic veterinarians also attribute some physical healing properties to various flower remedies. They won't cure behavior or health problems by themselves, but can help when used alongside other techniques.

Occasionally more than one flower essences is combined into one remedy. The premixed Rescue Remedy, for example, contains the essences of Impatiens, Star of Bethlehem, Cherry Plum, Rock Rose, and Clematis. Rescue Remedy is considered an “emergency remedy” good for any kind of sudden stress or shock.

You can find Bach Flower Remedies at most human health food stores. A number of veterinarians and pet product stores also carry them, and they’re available over the Internet. They come in individual glass bottles, and need to remain in glass and be kept away from direct sun, microwaves or heat.

While you can take the remedies undiluted, it’s best to prepare a treatment bottle from the full-strength “stock bottle” you purchase.

Obtain a glass 30 ml (1 oz.) dropper bottle and fill with spring water (not tap water).

Add two drops of your chosen Remedy to the new bottle of spring water. It’s best to limit this to three Remedies in the same bottle. Shake well, at least ten times (practitioners call this “succussing”).

(Optional) Add one teaspoon of EITHER brandy, apple cider vinegar or vegetable glycerin to the treatment bottle as a preservative. Be aware that this changes the flavor so choose wisely based on how you plan to administer the remedy to your pet. I suspect that most pets do best with no preservative or the vegetable glycerin.

Store the stock bottle and treatment bottle in a dark, cool place. The stock bottle should last for a very long time in this way.

To treat your dog, use the treatment bottle and shake it each time before putting three drops in the water bowl for the dog to sip all day. It won’t hurt if the other pets also drink. Alternatively, you can mix the drops into a teaspoonful of plain yogurt for the dog to take as a treat.

Since it’s a vibrational energy medicine, practitioners say that simply dripping the two drops on the pet’s forehead or a paw also works. But when giving the drops directly don’t let the dropper touch the skin, fur or mouth or you’ll contaminate the bottle.

Holistic veterinarians usually advise giving three drops, one to four times a day as needed, until your pet acts like she feels better. More is NOT better—Bach Flower Remedies work best over a longer period of time.

FLUKES

SYMPTOMS: Coughing; diarrhea
HOME CARE: None
VET CARE: Medication to kill the parasite
PREVENTION: Keep dog from eating varmints

FLUKES This is a kind of trematode, a flatworm parasite that varies from a few millimeters to two inches in length. There are many kinds of flatworms, but they are uncommon parasites of dogs. When they do infest dogs, they are found in the intestines or lungs.

Typically, the fluke is covered with hard cuticle scales or spines, and has a pair of suckers on its underside. Most flukes have both male and female reproductive organs, and are capable of independent reproduction. There are five life-stages from egg to adult, and each stage may depend on a specific host for development. Dogs contract the parasite when they eat one of these host animals.

Lung flukes cause a chronic cough as a result of cysts that form in the dog's lungs. Dogs may contract lung flukes by eating infected crayfish or snails, or the frogs, birds, snakes or rodents that eat these snails or crayfish. The highest incidence occurs in dogs that live near the Great Lakes, and in the Midwest and southern states.

Intestinal flukes are most common in dogs of the Pacific Northwest, and are contracted by eating raw fish. Most commonly, they cause an enteritis with diarrhea. However, this parasite is particularly dangerous because it carries a rickettsial disease that can be deadly (see SALMON POISONING).

Diagnosis is based on signs of disease, and on finding the eggs during fecal examination. Occasionally, lung cysts will be seen on an X-ray. A medication like praziquantel effectively kills the parasite.

Prevent your dogs from contracting flukes by keeping them from hunting along waterways where infective snails, crayfish or frogs are found. Do not allow your dog to scavenge dead fish.

FOOD

FOOD Food is organic material consumed by an organism to nourish and sustain life. Food promotes body growth, repairs tissue, maintains vital bodily processes, and provides the energy necessary for work and play. Like their hunter/scavenger ancestors, our dogs enjoy chasing the occasional bunny or raiding the garbage. But left to his own devices, your dog's gustatory adventures can get him into all kinds of nutritional trouble. It's up to responsible owners to provide balanced and complete foods for their dogs.

An appropriate diet must consider the individual dog. The right recipe for your dog is influenced by his age, lifestyle and activity level, health status, and sometimes breed. Growing puppies need more calories than adults, and dogs with special health conditions as well as geriatric dogs often require specific diets. Formulating dog foods is extremely difficult, even for professional canine nutritionists. Homemade diets can be appropriate for your dog when designed by a veterinary nutritionist.

You will find a wide array of commercial food choices for your dog, which are designed to provide appropriate nutrition for every dog and condition imaginable. Reputable pet food companies invest years in ongoing research to ensure the diets they produce fulfill the various needs of pet dogs.

Commercial dog food companies design their products to please owners, as well as the pet. Dog food must be attractive to human consumers because unless you buy the product, your dog will never eat it. Certain elements, like the color of the food, are designed to prompt owners to open their wallets. Dogs don't care what food looks like. Just think of some of the things your dog puts in his mouth. Try not to be swayed by packaging; choose a food that best addresses your dog's nutritional requirements.

Commercial pet food products typically fall into one of three broad categories: super premium products, premium products, and low-cost products. The category that is best depends on the age, the body condition, and activity level of the individual pet.

Super premium foods tend to be highest in nutrient density and digestibility, and use high dollar quality ingredients; consequently, this category is the most expensive. Higher fat content makes the foods very tasty so dogs tend to eagerly accept these diets. Nutrient density means the dog doesn't need to eat as much volume as in other categories, while high digestibility allows his body to use a high percentage of nutrients; the end result is less waste, and a smaller volume of stool to clean up from the yard. Super premium foods are marketed primarily through specialty pet product stores or veterinary clinics.

Grocery stores typically stock premium name brand products, which may also be found at large pet stores and some department stores. These diets are more economical than super premium dog foods, and the average dog will thrive on the nationally distributed brands. However, because premium name brand products aren't as nutrient dense as super premium diets, dogs must eat more to obtain equivalent calories. Select products made by reputable manufacturers that have been tested through feeding trials to ensure the diet is of a consistent quality and provides complete and balanced nutrition.

Low-cost products are known for being the least expensive pet foods, and typically are sold in the grocery store or discount chain stores sometimes as the "store brand." These foods often are not as readily accepted by the dog because they may not be particularly tasty, a result of using the least expensive ingredients to keep cost down. This also results in lower digestibility, which means a great deal of the diet isn't useable and instead ends up out on the lawn. House-brand products claim nutritional value equal to national name brand products, but at a lower cost. Some dogs may do fine on these foods; however, dogs may have trouble eating enough of these diets to obtain adequate nutrition. It's very difficult to predict the quality of these low cost products, which can vary from batch to batch. If a product costs less per pound of food, but your dog must eat more volume to meet his needs, the food is no longer "cheap." Avoid generic dog foods. Choose quality over cost to ensure your dog receives the best possible nutrition. Ask your veterinarian whether a super-premium, premium, or other product is most appropriate for your dog's circumstances.

Before making your final choice, also consider the form of the food. Dog foods come in three basic forms; soft-moist, canned, and dry. These vary in the moisture content, cost, palatability, convenience to the owner, and the amount of nutrition delivered per pound of food.

Soft-moist foods appeal to consumers primarily for their convenience; they can be stored without refrigeration, and typically come in single-serving packages which are particularly helpful when traveling with the dog. Ingredients like corn syrup that keep the food moist and prevent it from drying out tend to make the dog thirsty. High quality soft-moist foods are more palatable than dry (but less than canned forms); these foods tend to be more expensive than dry foods. Semi-moist foods contain about 16 to 25 percent protein, 5 to 10 percent fat, 25 to 35 percent carbohydrate and 30 to 50 percent water.

Canned dog food and human canned food products are processed in the same way. Once nutritionists design the formulation (recipe), the ingredients are ground together and placed in cans at high-speed filling lines run by computers. The food mixture in the cans is cooked and sterilized in giant pressure cookers, sealed, then labeled and shipped. This process preserves food without adding chemicals. Until it's opened, a canned product stays fresh nearly indefinitely. Canned dog foods contain about 8 to 15 percent protein, between 2 and 15 percent fat, and 72 to 78 percent water.

Dry food ingredients are mixed into a dough or batter, cooked under extreme pressure for a short time, then pushed through a die plate to give the food its characteristic shape. Called extrusion, this process dries the kibble and gelatinizes the starches in the grain ingredients to make them more digestible. Dry dog foods generally contain 18 to 27 percent protein, 7 to 15 percent fat, less than 12 percent water, and about 35 to 50 percent carbohydrate.

The quality of the diet—whether name-brand, premium or super premium—depends more on the ingredients, formulation and processing rather than form of the food. Complete and balanced nutrition may be obtained from any of the forms, but some food types may have certain advantages or disadvantages for an individual dog.

Canned diets tend to have a higher protein and fat content and lower carbohydrate content than dry foods. Carbohydrates don't can well, so only small amounts are used in canned foods. There is a perception that canned dog foods contain primarily meat and fat, and in fact some do and only add necessary vitamins and minerals to balance the diet. Meat meal is more typically used in dry foods, while canned products often contain fresh meats cited on the label as beef, chicken, and meat byproducts. However, some canned products contain an extruded soy product that is less expensive but looks like meat. The label identifies such ingredients as textured vegetable protein, soy protein, or soy protein isolate. As long as it's formulated correctly, soy ingredient diets are fine for the dog.

The lower carbohydrate and fiber content of canned diets may result in the dog producing softer stools since fiber helps form feces. Carbohydrates are useful in formulating low-calorie rations, and again, canned "lite" diets are difficult to produce. And because carbohydrates help food retain its form, canned foods must instead rely on gum Arabic, xanthan gums and vegetable gums as viscosity enhancers to help the food set up. These ingredients create the "gravy" that owners (not necessarily dogs!) are so fond of in canned products. Color enhancers like iron oxide and caramel may be added to make the food look more like something the owner would want to eat. Some products are designed to look like human beef stew, complete with veggies.

Canned foods are extremely palatable because water releases odor and flavor, both appealing to canine taste buds. The canning process requires liquid (raw meat is approximately 83 percent water) which is why canned foods are high in moisture. Some foods add palatability enhancers like garlic powder, caramel, and onion powder.

Canned foods are also easier to chew. Small dogs with very small mouths, or older dogs with no teeth prefer to eat them. However, canned and soft-moist foods tend to stick to teeth and may impact the dog's dental status (see PERIODONTAL DISEASE).

Canned foods also appeal to dog owners who fear their dog will become bored with one food. Dry products are available in larger quantities, while canned foods are packaged in single servings. This makes offering the dog a buffet of choices easier for the owner.

A drawback of canned diets is they spoil quickly once opened, cannot be fed free choice, and leftovers must be refrigerated. Canned dog foods compared to dry forms cost much more, because dogs may need to eat three times as much canned food as dry to compensate for the bulk added by water. This may make feeding canned diets cost prohibitive for certain breeds; it takes many cans to satisfy the appetite of a 120-pound dog.

Dry dog foods offer two advantages to the owner; cost and convenience. Dry diets can be purchased in large quantities, the bags are easily stored, and do not require refrigeration after being opened. Owners can feed dry diets free choice, filling the dog's bowl with food and allowing him to eat at his convenience. Most experts believe feeding two to three small measured meals is healthier for the dog, particularly for very large and deep-chested breeds (see BLOAT). Dry diets tend to be more energy dense than canned or soft-moist forms, which means your dog can eat less volume of the food, while getting the same amount of energy.

Palatability of a given food is influenced by "mouth feel" as well as flavor and smell. Some dogs prefer crunchy food which offers the dog an opportunity to indulge his love of chewing.

While the food form does influence dental disease, feeding a dry diet will not prevent tooth problems. Kibble won't stick to teeth the way canned foods do, and eating dry foods may slow down the development of tartar or even help reduce dental plaque. But veterinary dentists estimate the detergent action of eating a dry diet, at best, helps by about ten percent. Only proper veterinary dental care, including regularly brushing your dog's teeth, will control tartar.

Fat makes foods taste good so the dog will eat them. However, if fat isn't protected with preservatives, it deteriorates (oxidizes) within hours of a dry food's manufacture. To slow down this process and prevent fats from turning rancid, preservatives keep dry food fresh for up to a year after manufacture so that optimum nutrition is delivered when the food is eaten. Antioxidants like BHA, BHT, ethoxyquin, vitamin E and vitamin C are often used to help maintain freshness (see FOOD ADDITIVES, NUTRITION and READING FOOD LABELS).

FOOD ADDITIVES These are ingredients included in diet formulations that enhance the food in some way. Food additives may be nutritional, or non-nutritional.

Nutritional additives are the vitamins, minerals, and fats which are incorporated to make the diet nutritionally complete and balanced. Flavorings, texture enhancers, colors and preservatives are non-nutritional additives added to enhance the taste or appearance of the food. Laws that regulate pet food require that any additive in pet foods be proven harmless to pets. Many currently used in dog foods are also approved for use in people foods.

Organic food dyes such as caramel or carotene, and artificial colorings like iron oxide provide a consistent appearance, or distinguish between various particles in multi-particle foods. Sugar-type additives like guar gum, gum Arabic, xanthin gum, carrageenan and cellulose flour are used to give foods a characteristic texture. These ingredients create the aspic or jelly-like consistency of certain canned foods, as well as the gravy-like sauces. They prompt owners to buy these foods by making dog food look more like something people would want to eat themselves. Texturizers also are designed to make food "feel good" in the dog's mouth.

Some pet foods add flavor enhancers to increase palatability. Palatability is incredibly important, because a food has no benefit unless the dog accepts and eats it. Dogs love the flavor of animal digest, which is enzymatically degraded (pre-digested) meat or animal organs; animal digest is often sprayed on dry foods to make them taste good to the dog. Canned foods typically are already highly palatable, but some add flavorings like garlic powder, caramel, or onion powder.

Food additives also include preservatives, which are designed to guard the nutritional quality of foods by slowing or preventing food from degrading (spoiling). Canned diets rarely contain preservatives, because the canning process itself offers the necessary protection. However, dry and semi-moist forms of food require preservatives to prevent the break down (oxidation) of the nutrients. Oxidation is the reaction of oxygen with other compounds, especially fats, and has been described as a kind of biological rust. Preservatives, also called antioxidants, help food taste fresh, protect fat from becoming rancid, and keep essential fatty acids and fat soluble vitamins at optimal nutrient value.

A variety of natural and synthetic antioxidants are used in commercial pet foods. Chemical preservatives such as sorbic acid or potassium sorbate are humectants that hold water and help keep soft-moist products moist, and also protect these foods from mold and bacterial growth. The synthetic antioxidants most commonly used in dry pet foods include ethoxyquin, BHT (Butylated Hydroxytoluene) and BHA (Butylated Hydroxyamisole).

Ethoxyquin has been used in pet foods since the mid-1950s when five year efficacy and safety studies were done. Ethoxyquin is considered by many pet food nutritionists to be the most effective preservative on the market, with BHA and BHT rating fairly close behind.

Ongoing questions regarding the safety of ethoxyquin have been raised, and many pet food companies forego their use.

Natural antioxidants are preservatives found in nature, and include ascorbic acid (vitamin C), and tocopherals. Tocopherals are chemical compounds collectively referred to as vitamin E. Natural antioxidants are typically used in combinations, and potentially provide good preservation but don't tend to last as long as synthetic forms. Foods preserved with mixed tocopherals should usually be used within three to six months of manufacture, or by the product's expiration date.

FOOD SUPPLEMENTS

A food supplement is anything fed to the dog above and beyond an otherwise complete and balanced diet. Dogs who eat homemade diets, and dogs suffering from certain medical conditions may benefit from dietary supplementation. Food supplements may be necessary to stimulate a dog's food intake, particularly hard-working dogs or bitches nursing a litter which require higher levels of energy. Always consult a veterinarian before supplementing your dog's diet.

Food supplements range from nutritional components like vitamins and mineral tablets, to table scraps and commercial treats. When a dog is already eating a complete and balanced diet, food supplements potentially can throw the nutrition out of balance. Choose a complete and balanced diet for your dog (see READING FOOD LABELS).

Nutrients work together, and are needed in the right combinations and amounts; too much can sometimes be as bad as too little. High quality commercial dog foods formulate products with a safety margin for all the essential nutrients, to compensate for any normal loss through processing or storage, and for variations in the needs of individual dogs. Further, offering your dog vitamins or other treats beyond what's required can potentially cause nutritional imbalances, and can be dangerous.

For instance, too much dietary calcium can cause bone and cartilage deformities, and interferes with absorption of phosphorus, iron, zinc and copper, which may cause deficiencies of these minerals. Such deficiencies can result in skin disease, reproductive problems, nervous system dysfunction, and impaired immunity.

Feeding excessive amounts of raw liver can cause a calcium deficiency and possibly vitamin A toxicity, resulting in crippling bone disease, weight loss, anorexia, even death. And a deficiency of vitamin D (which is involved in the absorption of calcium) may result in rickets. Vitamins D and E are found in wheat germ, liver and fish oils, and dogs may relish these treats. Too much can cause toxicities that can result in skeletal deformity, reproductive problems, and even calcification of soft tissues. Eating onions or garlic in excess (equal to or greater than 0.5 percent of the dog's body weight) can cause hemolytic anemia that can kill the dog (see ANEMIA).

Adding raw egg white to the diet can cause a vitamin deficiency. A protein called avidin is found in raw egg whites; avidin destroys biotin, one of the B vitamins, and can result in poor growth and hair loss in the biotin-deficient dog. Raw foods must be carefully prepared to avoid parasites and bacteria (see SALMONELLA).

Because dogs are omnivores willing to eat anything, they often beg for and relish scraps from the table. Such treats increase your dog's risk for obesity, gastrointestinal problems that result in upset tummies with signs like vomiting or diarrhea, or even metabolic problems (see PANCREATITIS). Table scraps should make up no more than 5 to 10 percent of the total amount of food your dog eats and even then should be healthy scraps—that is, vegetables, grains and fruits along with the occasional meat tidbit—never exclusively fat trimmings. But many veterinarians recommend no table scraps at all.

Cooked bones are never a good choice, as they tend to splinter and can lodge in the dog's mouth or intestinal tract and cause life-threatening blockage (see SWALLOWED OBJECTS). Raw bones splinter less often, but are unsanitary and may break the dog's teeth. And although your dog may relish sweet treats as much as you do, candy of any kind is a no-no, and can drastically increase dental problems or even be deadly (see CHOCOLATE TOXICITY and PERIODONTAL DISEASE).

Beware of diet supplements marketed as "natural;" there are few regulations that apply to such products, so approach them with caution. In fact, manufacturers can avoid certain expensive efficacy and safety tests by saying their product is natural. Many times this term is used as a marketing buzzword, because "natural" is often equated with "healthier." Unfortunately, natural is not necessarily healthy, or even safe; some of the most dangerous poisons are natural. Ask questions of the manufacturer, and if you don't like the answers, or can't get any answers, avoid the product to protect your dog. Rely on the reputation of well-known pet food companies that have been around for a while, and have the nutritional research to back up their claims. And always ask your veterinarian's advice, as some "natural" products may have health benefits for your dog when used under an expert's supervision.

Treating your dog with an occasional healthy snack probably won't cause any problems. Dogs and owners seem to benefit most from the bonding experience of doing something "special" for the dog. A wide variety of commercial dog treats are available, and some are formulated to be complete and balanced so they don't cause nutritional difficulties (other than added calories).

If your dog isn't eating enough, a veterinary exam can rule out possible health problems. Adding one teaspoon of vegetable oil for every eight ounce cup of dry food may tempt his appetite, and also help improve his coat condition. A strong-smelling or flavored top dressing like warm chicken broth often prompts dogs to eat up to ten percent more of the food. However, a better choice for dogs with small appetites and big energy needs is a more energy-dense ration, like a complete and balanced super-premium food. Such diets provide more calories even if the dog eats less volume.

A good way to treat the dog without unbalancing his diet is to reserve a portion of his regular ration. Offer this reserve as special tidbit feedings throughout the day (see NUTRITION and FOOD).

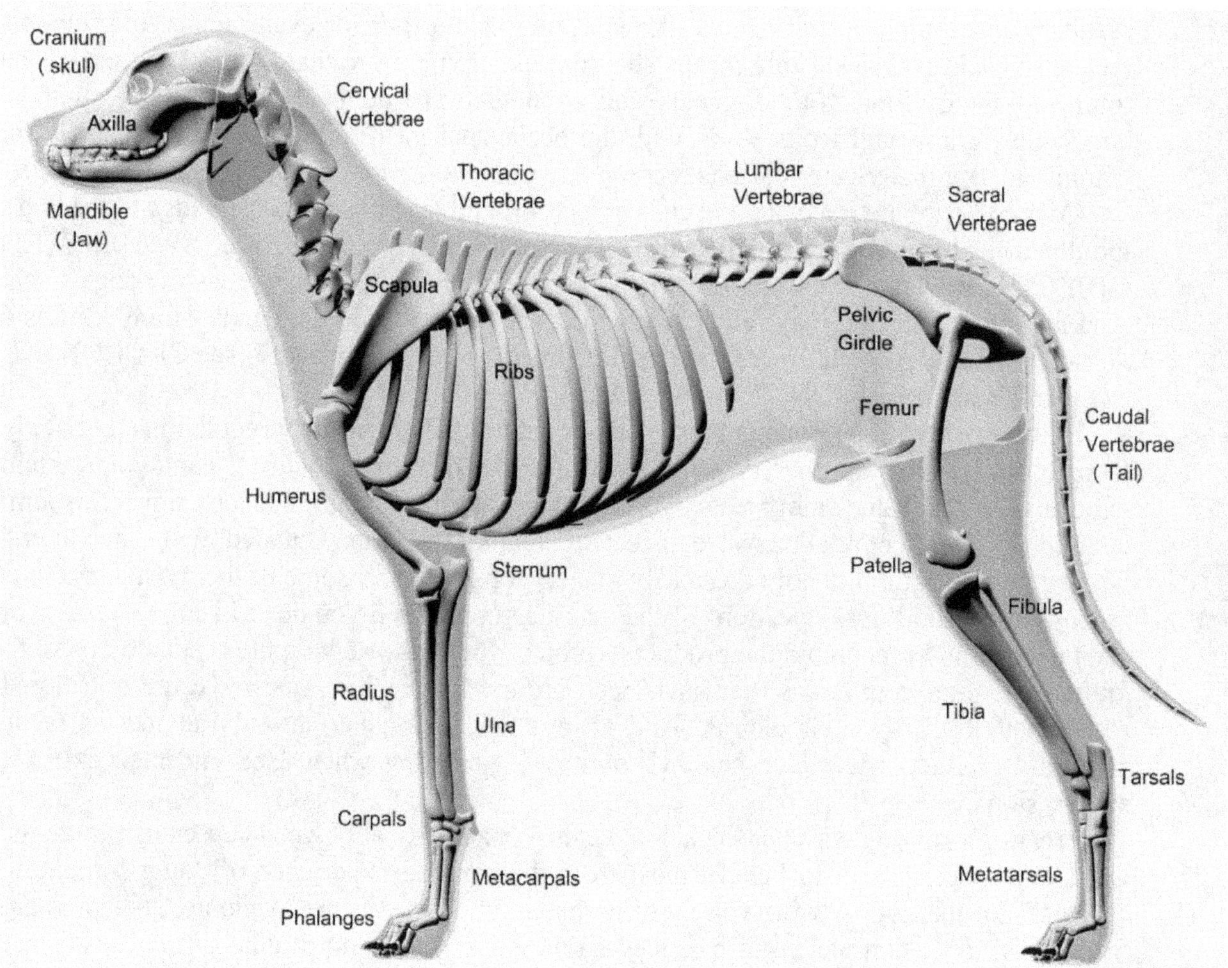

FRACTURE A fracture is an injury that results in partial or complete breakage of bone. The skeleton is a collection of bones that form the scaffold-like structure that gives each dog her shape. Selective breeding has varied the size and shape of the canine skeleton, making the tiny dome-headed Chihuahua distinctive from the giant narrow-headed Wolfhound. Despite these differences, all dogs—no matter the breed—remain surprisingly similar beneath the fur, with about 319 separate bones making up the average canine skeleton.

Fractures most typically result from trauma. Bones can withstand only small amounts of stress without fracturing. Other times, disease weakens the bone until only minor stress results in damage.

Fractures are categorized as fatigue fractures, pathologic fractures, or traumatic fractures. Fatigue fractures result from ongoing stress to a bone; they are not common in dogs, but may occur in dogs that do repetitive strenuous work. Illnesses like cancer or hyperparathyroidism may weaken individual bones or the entire skeleton and result in pathologic fractures. The disease as well as the fracture must be treated in these instances. The growing bones of puppies tend to crack or split rather than break; these fractures are called greenstick fractures. Elderly dogs may develop brittle bones that break more easily than healthy adult dogs.

Dogs most commonly suffer traumatic fractures, which usually result from being hit by cars. A broken bone is often only one part of a litany of other injuries. A fracture is painful, but conditions like bleeding and shock may be life-threatening and must take precedence before anything else. Your dog should see a veterinarian as soon as possible.

A complete break in the bone is classified by whether or not the skin is breached. It's called a closed fracture when the skin is not broken; when bone protrudes from the skin, it's termed a compound, or open fracture. Such injuries increase the risk for tissue or bone infections, which are painful and can result in limb loss or even death.

Although any bone may be broken, some are more susceptible to fracture than others. The dog's pelvis is broken the most often. The femur (thigh bone) is the next most common fracture site. The lower bones of the hind legs (tibia/fibula), and the forelegs (radius/ulna/humerus) also commonly suffer fractures, especially when dogs jump from high surfaces.

Dogs can also suffer fractures of the skull which could cause brain injury or concussion. A broken palate (roof of the mouth) or jaw (mandible) are common injuries. Severe damage including paralysis may result from spinal fractures, and broken ribs may puncture internal organs and threaten the dog's life. Crushing injuries may occur when a tail is caught beneath a chair, or shut in a door.

There may be blood present with compound fractures, which also have the bone exposed. Closed fractures may be more difficult to detect. Dogs suffering from a fracture often hold the affected limb off the ground at an odd angle, or may limp. The leg or tail may move or hang disjointedly. The injured area may be swollen. Dogs with pelvic fractures often trouble standing or supporting their weight, and may walk with a wobbly gait in their hind limbs. Some dogs will simply refuse to move.

If you suspect your dog has suffered a broken bone, limit his movement as much as possible. Avoid touching or manipulating the affected area. Broken bone is sharp, and fooling with the injury may punch bone through skin, or damage veins, arteries, internal tissues, organs or nerves. Handle your dog carefully to prevent further injuries to him, or to yourself (see RESTRAINT).

If you are more than thirty minutes away from the vet, fractures of the leg below the elbow or knee are best immobilized using a temporary splint. The splint must extend both above and below the injury to be effective. Cover open wounds with sterile gauze or a clean cloth before splinting to help prevent infection. If the fracture is above the elbow, wrap a towel about the dog to hold the limb snug against the body.

Nearly any long, stiff material will work as a temporary splint. A rolled newspaper, or a cylinder of cardboard from the core of a roll of paper towels may work. Split cardboard tubes up the center so that the injured limb can be laid inside without any attempt to straighten or reposition the fracture. A simple hand towel or bubble wrap about the limb may be sufficient, just enough to stabilize the injury. Place the stricken dog on a towel in a box or carrier, and get your pet veterinary attention as soon as possible.

For pelvic injuries, and especially suspected back fractures, limit the dog's movement as much as possible. Ideally, the dog should be placed on a rigid surface for transport to the veterinarian. For small dogs, a cookie sheet, T.V. tray, even the flat blade of a snow shovel may work. A large board or something like an ironing board may be better for a larger dog. If rigid material of an appropriate size isn't available, use a sheet or blanket. Place the conveyance on the ground next to the dog, and carefully slide (don't lift) her onto it. For large dogs, you'll need a person at the head-end and one at the tail-end (and possibly a person in the middle) to move the dog all in one motion. With fabric carriers, try to keep the blanket taut and as level as possible during transport. Once the dog is in the car, get her to the emergency room as soon as possible, and let your veterinarian get the dog out of your car. He'll have the appropriate dog-size stretcher.

Fractures may be obvious, but more often require specific diagnostic procedures to determine the best procedure for repair. Veterinarians palpate (feel) the injury and use X-rays. Sedation or anesthesia may be required to take the X-rays and treat your dog. Treatment consists of setting the fracture (called reduction). A range of procedures are available to position bone appropriately so that healing will take place. The type of fixation depends on the kind of fracture, its location, the individual dog and owner compliance.

Greenstick fractures and breaks in the mid-portion of the legs may be sufficiently treated with a simple splint or cast. This method has the greatest success when bone fragments fit back together easily. However, fractures near to a joint, or bones with multiple fractures are more difficult to fix.

FRACTURE

SYMPTOMS: Floppy, "unhinged" legs or tail; limping; swelling; exposed bones; reluctance or inability to move
FIRST AID: Immobilize with temporary splint
VET CARE: X-ray; application of cast, surgical plating, wire, or pinning; sometimes antibiotic therapy; occasionally amputation
PREVENTION: Prevent car accidents; confine dogs to yard or leash; remain vigilant slamming doors, falls, or dog jumping from your arms or furniture

Complicated fractures may require intramedullary pinning, which is the insertion of a stainless-steel rod that strings the pieces back together like threading a needle. Small external metal pins may be inserted through the skin and muscle and into the bone, with the visible portions outside fixed to a single connecting bar that holds everything in place. Metal plates and wire may be required to surgically fix bone fragments back into place, so that healing can begin. The hardware may become a permanent part of the dog, or may be removed after the fracture heals.

Canine bones heal relatively quickly and easily, especially those of growing puppies. Pelvic fractures may heal by themselves even when multiple fractures are present, although sometimes surgery must repair the damage when the pelvis is too unstable. In either case, the dog's mobility must be restricted, so that new bone called callus forms across the fracture site and helps stabilize it. Hard bone formation follows shortly, with an eventual return to normal function.

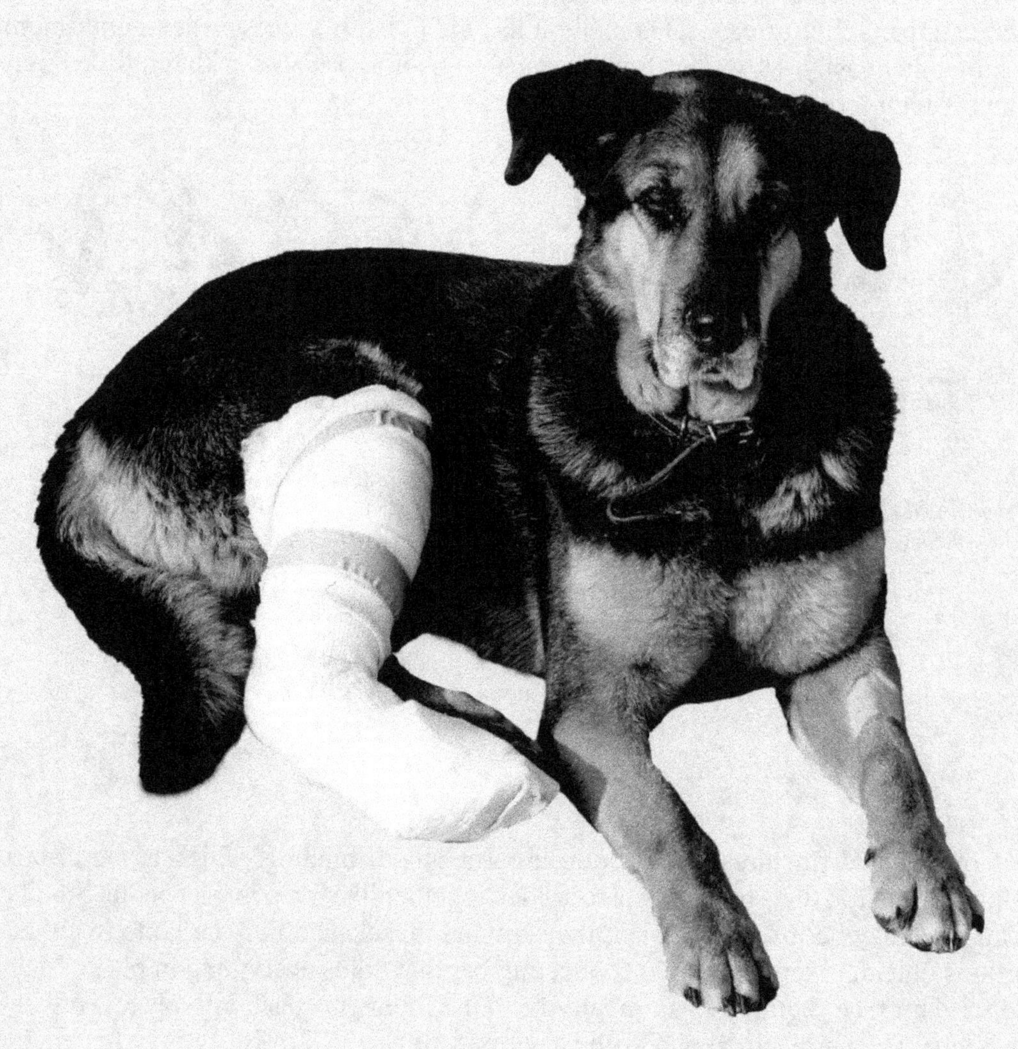

Dogs that fracture the ball and socket formation of the hip may regain partial to full limb function within three to five weeks simply by resting the affected leg. In some instances, the damaged femoral head and/or neck are surgically removed, and the body creates a new false joint out of tissue that functions like the original.

Sometimes a fracture refuses to heal; this often occurs with broken tails or toes, and amputation may be necessary. Dogs rarely seem to miss toes or tails, and many do quite well when they have lost a leg.

Unsupervised outdoor dogs are at highest risk for fractures from car accidents. But indoor injuries can also result in fractures when the dog or puppy falls from an owner's arms, or lands wrong after jumping on or off furniture. Most tail and paw injuries can be prevented by remaining aware of rocking chairs and slamming doors that can crush legs or tails.

FROSTBITE

SYMPTOMS: Pale to white flesh on ear tips, nose, testicles, tail, and toes; swollen, red, or blistered tissue; blackened peeling tissue
FIRST AID: Soak in 104-degree water until tissue is flushed; apply antiseptic ointment; veterinarian must evaluate damage
VET CARE: Antibiotics; pain medication; possible amputation of affected tissue
PREVENTION: Confine dogs in doors during cold weather; provide outdoor shelter

FROSTBITE Frostbite refers to partial or complete freezing of the extremities of the body. Dogs most typically suffer frostbite on their ears, toes, scrotum and tail.

Like our own, a dog's body is composed of more than 90 percent water. Freezing causes great damage because water expands when frozen, rupturing the integrity of the living cells

and destroying tissue. Frostbite causes severe tissue damage, infection, and even loss of body parts.

Cases of frostbite are categorized from mild to severe. Mild frostbite turns the affected area white and pale. As the area re-warms and blood circulation returns, the injury reddens and may swell. Severe frostbite looks similar to burns. The affected area first blisters, then peels, and dead skin eventually sloughs off.

Treatment consists of rewarming the frozen area. First aid at home is extremely important to minimize damage. Do not massage or rub the area, and don't apply snow or ice; that will further damage the tissues, and make recovery more difficult. To thaw frozen tissue safely, soak in warm 104 to 108 degree water for 15 to 20 minutes until the skin becomes pink. The area will begin to weep serum, and as feeling returns, the dog will feel pain. Apply a triple antibiotic ointment like Neosporin to the affected area. Restrain the dog from licking or biting the area (see ELIZABETHAN COLLAR).

It may be difficult to evaluate the extent of the injury until a few days have passed. Often, an area that appears only mildly affected on initial examination later exhibits severe damage. Frostbite should always be evaluated and monitored by a veterinarian. Prescription antibiotics and pain medication may be necessary, and severe cases may require surgery to remove damaged or dead tissue. Healing may take several weeks. Dogs that have suffered frostbite in the past are prone to recurrence.

Prevent frostbite by confining your dog indoors during cold weather. Outdoor dogs require protection from the weather; a warm, dry shelter away from the wind is best (see HYPOTHERMIA and OUTDOOR SHELTER).

FUNGUS

FUNGUS A fungus is a kind of primitive plant that lacks energy-producing chlorophyll, and instead subsists as a parasite. The term "fungus" refers to molds, mushrooms, and yeast; they function to promote decay and decomposition of organic matter.

A variety of fungi are able to produce mild to serious disease in dogs. The most common types affect the skin or mucus membranes, and tend to be self-limiting problems that are relatively easy to treat (see RINGWORM).

Candidiasis is a relatively uncommon yeast infection of the mucus membranes in the mouth, genitals and respiratory tract. Signs of localized infection are ulcers, moist dermatitis, or a purulent white discharge from the genital tract. Candidiasis is diagnosed by culturing the organism or by finding the organism during microscopic examination of a skin scraping or tissue sample. Localized infections are typically treated with topical antifungal medications. Occasionally, the infection spreads throughout the body, resulting in a variety of signs from fever and generalized pain, to abscesses and lymph node enlargement. Whole-body or systemic disease caused by fungus is quite rare in dogs, and most commonly affect dogs with immune system defects. These organisms may be resistant to treatment, and can be life-threatening to the host. Prognosis for this form of fungal infection isn't good.

Blastomycosis, coccidioidomycosis, cryptococcosis and histoplasmosis are four other kinds of systemic fungal diseases that can affect dogs. Each are found in specific geographic regions. In each, the organism is inhaled by the dog, and in most cases, this prompts a strong immune response that keeps the dog healthy and protected from infection. In rare instances the dog succumbs to infection, and the organism spreads from the lungs throughout the body infecting the organs and tissues. Diagnosis is made by microscopic examination of affected tissues that identifies the organism.

Systemic illness can be difficult to treat and isn't always successful, and dogs diagnosed with systemic fungal disease may ultimately be euthanized. When treated, prolonged systemic antifungal therapy is required, which also can cause side effects in the dog. The medication can have adverse effects on the kidneys and liver, with side effects that include diarrhea, vomiting, kidney failure and anemia.

Blastomyces dermatitidis causes **blastomycosis,** and is found in moist, shaded soil rich in rotting organic matter like bird droppings. The organism is most prevalent along the Ohio/Mississippi river valley, north-central states, and mid-Atlantic seaboard. Young male dogs, especially hunting breeds, are most often affected. Infection causes skin, eye (see UVEITIS), and respiratory disease, and may result in neurological signs. The most common signs are coughing, labored breathing, pneumonia, weight loss and anorexia. Prognosis is guarded, and treatment takes weeks to months of aggressive therapy.

Coccidioides immitis is the organism that causes **coccidioidomycosis,** also called "valley fever." It is found in the same regions where the creosote bush thrives, in the dry soil of the southwest, from California to Texas. Most cases cause only mild flu-like signs; but other times, infection spreads beyond the lungs into the bones and joints, eyes, kidneys, liver, and even the spinal cord and brain. Signs include chronic harsh cough and fever, anorexia, lethargy, weight loss, lameness, joint enlargement, draining tracts over infected bones, and neurological signs. Treatment takes six to twelve months, and can be successful but lifetime therapy may be required.

Cryptococcus neoformans causes **cryptococcosis,** a yeast-like fungus that prefers tissues of the central nervous system. It is most commonly found in pigeon droppings. Cryptococcosis is uncommon in dogs, but when it occurs, lower respiratory signs are most common. Other signs may include neurologic involvement such as head tilt, rapid eye movement, circling, varying degrees of paralysis, disorientation, incoordination and seizures. Dogs may exhibit dilated pupils and blindness. Diagnosis can be made from examination of nasal discharge, skin scrapings, or biopsy. Treatment is difficult but can be effective.

The soil fungus *Histoplasma capsulatum* causes **histoplasmosis,** and is found most commonly in the Ohio, Mississippi and Missouri River valleys. The organism likes to grow in bird, chicken and bat droppings. Signs of infection are usually mild coughing, lethargy and fever, with watery to bloody diarrhea, and mucus in the stool; more severe disease may include anemia, chronic cough, and coughing up of blood. A minimum of four to six months of systemic antifungal therapy is required.

Keeping a dog in optimum health is the best prevention. Additionally, prevent dogs from access to bird droppings.

GERIATRIC DOG Geriatric refers to the condition of aging, which is a gradual decline in the effective functioning of the body. Dogs age at different rates, and this is dependent to a large degree upon an individual animal's genetics. Big dogs tend to age more quickly than small dogs. Breeds like Great Danes are elderly at age seven, German Shepherd Dogs are considered old when they reach nine to ten years of age, medium-sized dogs are aged at ten to 12 years, while smaller breeds like Toy Poodles and Yorkshire Terriers are considered geriatric at 14 to 16 years old. But just like their owners, signs of aging are extremely variable. The better care a dog receives throughout his life, the longer he can be expected to live.

Stray and feral dogs that don't have these benefits rarely live to experience geriatrics. They die early and young, usually from a combination of disease, malnutrition and trauma. But pet dogs are living longer, healthier lives than ever before, due in great part to advances in canine nutrition and medicine.

Canine longevity means owners are faced with more geriatric issues than ever before. Many parallel the health issues that people can expect as they age. Elderly dogs are less active, sleep more, and may become forgetful. They aren't able to withstand extremes of temperature (heat or cold) as well as youthful dogs. They lose muscle, and may become unsteady on their feet or unable to sustain the activities of their youth. Typically, the thighs and forelimbs become thinner while the neck and body thicken, and abdomen sags; exertion may result in tremors of fatigue. Joint pain from arthritis is a common complaint, and often slows the dog down or results in a short temper. Like a set-in-his-ways human, the oldster canine gets cranky and less tolerant of changes in routine.

The dog's senses tend to dull with age, which can be upsetting to your pet when he can't see, smell or hear the way he used to. Most old dogs suffer some degree of dental problems, which can be painful (see PERIODONTAL DISEASE). Senior dogs tend to eat less and may lose weight due to pain when eating or due to other problems; this is a sign something is wrong, and should be checked by the veterinarian. More often, geriatric dogs suffer from eating more than they need and exercising less (see OBESITY). In fact, being fat shortens lifespan, while lean dogs live up to two years longer.

Old dogs may have problems with irregularity (see CONSTIPATION), may suffer from senility, and often their house training becomes less reliable. The skin loses elasticity, and tends toward dryness when oil-producing glands slow down. When activity declines, so does the normal wear of toenails, which may seem to grow faster. Special attention to your aging dog's grooming helps him look and feel healthier.

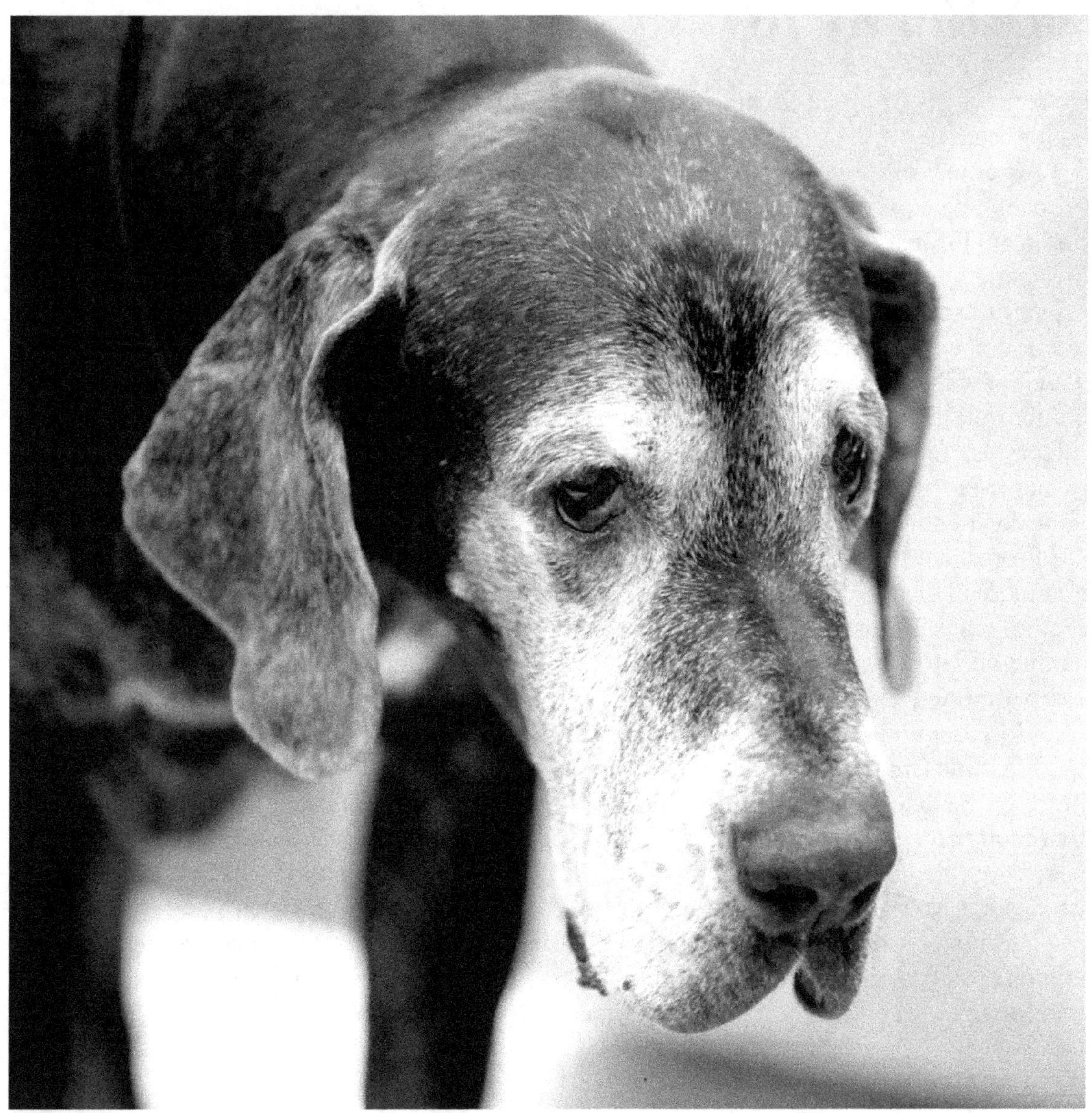

The geriatric dog's health becomes more fragile because the immune system's competence also fades with age. Old dogs get sicker quicker, and recover more slowly than healthy young dogs. It is vital to provide prompt veterinary attention to keep old dogs healthy.

Recognize that dogs age more rapidly than humans; after age three, each canine year is roughly equivalent to four human years. More frequent veterinary evaluations are therefore particularly important for the aging dog; twice a year after age eight is a good goal. Canine geriatric medicine attempts to reduce physical discomfort and emotional stress, as well as slow the signs of aging as much as possible. Often, special nutritional concerns must be addressed.

A number of diseases and conditions typically affect geriatric canines. Renal failure is probably the most common cause of death in aged dogs (see KIDNEY DISEASE). Kidneys just seem to wear out more quickly than other organs. Heart disease is another consequence of canine aging, because the muscle tends to weaken after a lifetime of use. Cystitis and urinary tract infections also occur frequently in aging dogs. The risk of cancer increases as the dog ages. Cataracts are very common in old dogs, and glaucoma or dry eye may also develop with age. Intact male dogs may develop prostate infection. And because of a compromised immune system, geriatric dogs may suffer a wide range of opportunistic infections. Elderly dogs may not tolerate hospitalization that separates them from their owners very well, though, and in these cases your veterinarian may show you how to treat your dog at home.

Proper nutrition is vital to the old dog's health. "Mature" or "senior" formulations of commercial diets are available for the special needs of older dogs. In most animals, energy requirements decrease with age, and since this is thought to be true in dogs, most commercial canine geriatric rations are reduced in calories. Often, elderly dogs do best on food that's easily digested and/or chewed.

Most dogs can live comfortably and happily into old age, but some environmental modifications may help. If stair steps are a problem, provide a ramp to make familiar haunts more accessible. Move sleeping quarters to a warm, cozy spot. Keep your dog warm when he accompanies you on outings by perhaps providing him with a sweater. Daily grooming keeps your dog looking and feeling good, and also provides an opportunity to find problems early. Give your old dog lots of attention and understanding; he's given you the best times of your life, now be his comfort and friend during these golden years. Encouraging moderate exercise will keep him fit and limber longer, and make the last years of his life more comfortable and enjoyable for you both (see COGNITIVE DYSFUNCTION).

GIARDIA

SYMPTOMS: Soft stools; poor hair coat; swollen abdomen; trouble gaining or maintaining weight
HOME CARE: None
VET CARE: Drug to kill parasite
PREVENTION: Keep yard clean; restrict access to mud puddles or other unsanitary water sources; vaccinate as recommended

GIARDIASIS This is an illness caused by a protozoan of the Giardia species, a single cell organism that parasitizes the small intestine. Canine infection is becoming more common, and typically affects pups.

The organism compromises the dog's ability to properly process food. Signs of infection are diarrhea sometimes mixed with mucus and blood. Other times the stool may simply be soft and light colored, or even normal-appearing, but the dog develops a poor hair coat and the tummy swells from gas. Infected dogs may have trouble gaining or maintaining weight.

The infective cyst stage of the organism lives in the environment, most usually in standing water. Dogs tend to contract the parasite by drinking from mud puddles or other contaminated water sources. The disease is also spread through contact with infected feces.

Diagnosis is made by finding the protozoan during microscopic examination of stool samples. However, infected dogs pass the organism only intermittently, and a fresh stool sample may be negative even when giardia are present. Repeated tests are often necessary before the tiny parasite is detected. Some dogs may not show signs of illness themselves, yet are infected and spread the parasite.

Giardia can be treated with a prescription drug called Flagyl (metronidazole) to kill the parasite. This drug can injure unborn puppies, however, so medication such as albendazole may be safer option for treating pregnant bitches. Keeping the yard picked up and restricting your dog's access to unsanitary water helps prevent the chance of infection.

Water-borne diarrheal disease in humans is also commonly caused by giardia (see ZOONOSIS); however, it's not known if the same kind of organism affecting dogs causes the disease in people. Reasonable hygiene practices (washing hands after cleaning up after puppies) prevents the possibility of contracting the infection from a pet. Researchers at the University of Calgary (Alberta, Canada) are in the process of developing and testing a new protective vaccination against Giardia infection in puppies.

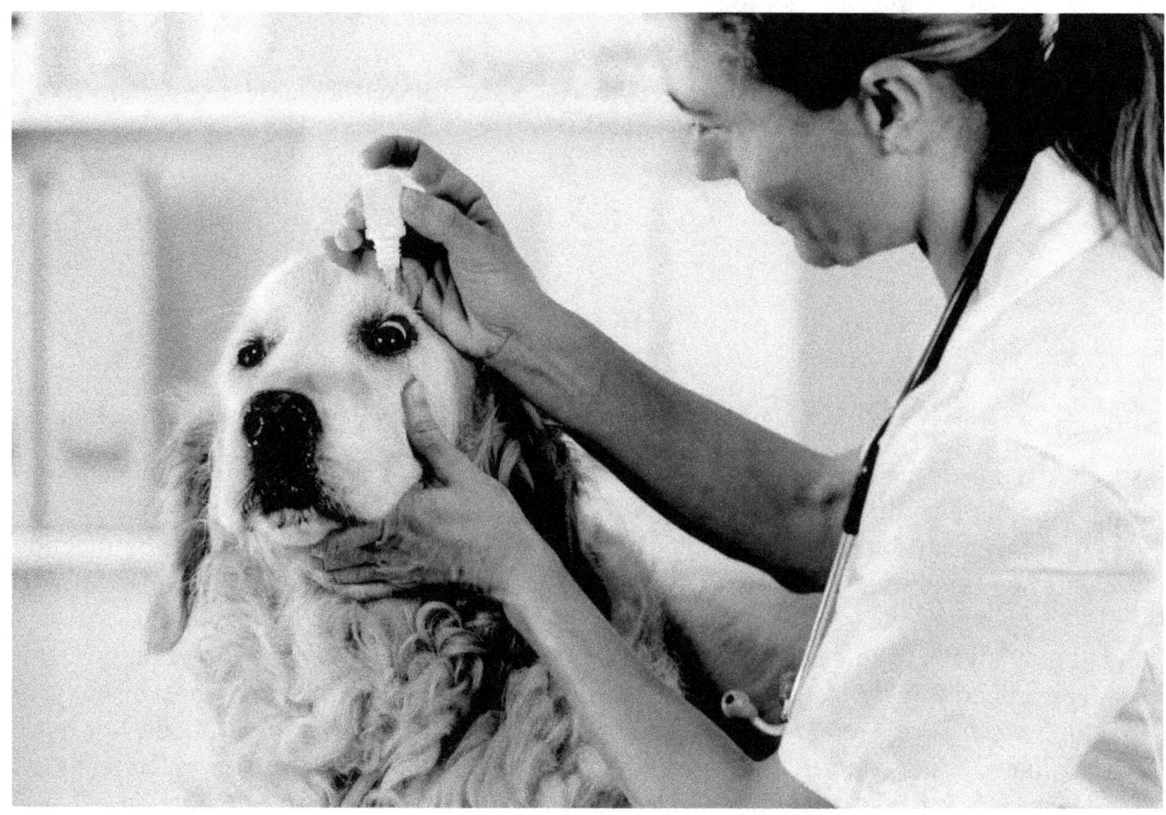

GLAUCOMA

Increased pressure inside the eyeball is referred to as glaucoma. It causes damage to the retina and optic nerve, which results in blindness if not treated in time. While glaucoma is a gradual disease in man, it's very aggressive in dog (see

EYES). It can cause sudden blindness in as little as 24 hours, or can develop over weeks to months.

Any dog may be stricken with glaucoma, but it's more common in some dogs than others. Glaucoma is categorized as either primary or secondary. Primary glaucoma arises spontaneously due to congenital or inherited conditions. It's an inherited defect in Beagles, and also commonly affects Cocker Spaniels and Basset Hounds.

Secondary glaucoma results from an injury or disease. Most often, the condition develops due to trauma that causes bleeding inside the eye or that displaces the lens. Conditions like uveitis, untreated cataracts or tumors that cause intraocular inflammation also may result in glaucoma.

Directly behind the cornea, the front portion of the eye is filled with aqueous humor which is manufactured by a membrane called the ciliary epithelium. This specialized liquid holds the internal structures in place, and the fluid level is constant, but not static. It drains out, but at the same time is replaced with fresh by the membrane. The excess fluid drains through the iridocorneal angle where the cornea and iris meet. Anything that interferes with the drainage can result in glaucoma when pressure rises from the increased liquid inside the eyeball.

It's similar to over-filling a balloon, which expands when there is no outlet for the pressure. In glaucoma, the sphere of the eye keeps filling and swells when the drain is plugged and the fluid can't escape.

The condition is excruciating for the dog. Increasing pressure destroys vision by pushing the internal structures out of position.

Signs of glaucoma may occur suddenly, or appear gradually and be quite subtle. Often, signs aren't noticed until they become severe, at which time it may be too late to save the dog's vision. High intraocular pressure can permanently damage the eye within only a few days, and suspected glaucoma should be considered an emergency with veterinary evaluation sought immediately. The painful eye produces excess tears, is cloudy or bloodshot, and the dog squints or paws at the eyeball that eventually swells. Finally, the dilated pupil no longer responds to light.

An instrument such as a Schiotz tonometer or Tono-Pen measures the pressure inside the eyeball to diagnose the condition. The tonometer is gently balanced on the dog's cornea (after drops numb the area), and a scale on the instrument indicates the pressure. The Tono-Pen is much smaller and contains a computer microchip that registers a reading when it's merely tapped on the surface of the eye.

Gonioscopy uses a special lens to examine the drainage (iridocorneal) angle. Most dogs with primary glaucoma have goniodysgenesis, so this evaluation can help determine the proper treatment. Gonioscopy is generally only performed by veterinary ophthalmologists. High resolution ultrasonography (HRUS) also can help determine the type of glaucoma, prognosis, and response to treatment.

The condition is treated very aggressively. Administration of a single drop of topical prostaglandin (PG) derivatives may dramatically lower the pressure within thirty minutes to two hours, and the treatment usually is repeated if the pressure is not reduced in one hour. If the pressure is still not decreased another hour later, traditional glaucoma therapy should be pursued.

Eye drops such as Xalatan and latanoprost are particularly helpful for dogs. The drops help to relieve the pain, contract the pupil and reduce the inflammation. Unfortunately, such treatment rarely prevents progressive visual loss in the long term. If medication fails to control the condition, surgery may be necessary.

GLAUCOMA

SYMPTOMS: Painful eye; squinting; pawing at the eye; tearing; bloodshot or cloudy-looking eye; swelling of the eyeball; dilated nonresponsive pupil
HOME CARE: None
VET CARE: Medications to control pressure: pain medications; possibly surgery; sometimes removal of affected eye
PREVENTION: None

When glaucoma affects one eye as a primary cause—not from an injury—it often eventually develops in the other eye as well. Veterinary ophthalmologists offer a couple of different surgical options. Tiny shunts may be implanted to help control the pressure by draining away excess fluid. Cryosurgery to freeze the fluid-producing cells in the ciliary epithelium also is an option. One of the most recent and successful innovations uses an ophthalmic-size laser to perform a procedure called laser ciliary body ablation. The laser selectively destroys fluid-producing tissues in the eye, and so reduces fluid production.

When the disease has progressed to where the pupil no longer responds to light, the dog has lost vision in that eye. If medication can't control the pain, then several surgical options are available. The most common procedure involves a schleral prosthesis—a silicon ball—that's placed inside the damaged eyeball after the painful internal structures have been removed. This is also a good cosmetic procedure, in which the dog keeps his eye, and the eyeball will still move, but he'll have no vision.

Another possibility is to remove the eyeball altogether, in a procedure called enucleation. If enucleation is performed, a prosthetic implant may be placed, or sometimes the socket is left empty, and the eyelid is sewn shut.

Dogs that have lost the vision in one or both eyes tend to do extremely well and adjust quickly. Removing the pain often returns the dog to a higher activity level because she feels so much better. Because dogs tend to rely more on hearing and scent for orientation, blind dogs do very well in familiar surroundings (see BLINDNESS).

GRAPE/RAISIN TOXICITY

SYMPTOMS: Vomiting; diarrhea; loss of appetite; lethargy; weakness; abdominal pain; dehydration; passing no urine, or very small quantities of urine; death
FIRST AID: Induce vomiting; offer activated charcoal; EMERGENCY! SEE THEVET ASAP
HOME CARE: None.
VET CARE: Gastric lavage; fluid therapy; dialysis
PREVENTION: Prevent dogs eating grapes or raisins

GRAPE/RAISIN TOXICITY Both fresh and dried grapes (raisins) are quite toxic in dogs. The exact poisonous substance that causes reaction isn't known, and sensitivity varies from dog to dog. No dog should eat any amount of this fruit because even a small dose can be fatally toxic for your dog.

The most dramatic and serious problem caused by grape/raisin toxicity is sudden kidney failure with lack of urine production. For unknown reasons, kidney failure is not seen in all dogs after ingestion of grapes or raisins. Researchers continue to investigate why some dogs die and others are not affected by the poison.

The first signs of distress often include vomiting and/or diarrhea with only a few hours of ingestion. After about 24 hours, you may see grapes or raisin pieces in the feces or vomitus. Affected dogs lose their appetite, become lethargic and unusually quiet. They may suffer abdominal pain, and "hunch" their back from the discomfort. Dehydration develops from the diarrhea and vomiting, but they only pass small amounts of urine. Eventually they stop urinating at all when the kidneys ultimately shut down. Prognosis is guarded, even when treated, and most dogs die once the kidneys stop producing urine.

Grape/raisin toxicity is an emergency that needs prompt veterinary intervention. If you see or suspect your dog has eaten grapes or raisins, induce vomiting immediately (but only if the dog remains conscious).

You can give your dog 3 percent household hydrogen peroxide, one tablespoon for each ten pounds he weighs. If vomiting doesn't happen within ten minutes, repeat the dose, but then get your dog to the emergency room. Take a sample of the vomitus or feces if available to help the doctor be sure of the diagnosis.

Diagnostic tests include blood count, biochemistry profile and a urinalysis to measure the functioning status of the dog's kidneys. An ultrasound may also be helpful to evaluate the kidneys. Unless actual evidence of grapes/raisins present, the veterinarian often must base a presumptive diagnosis on symptoms alone.

Treatment includes washing out the stomach, along with fluid therapy to combat dehydration and shock. IV fluids may be required for 48 hours or longer, along with medication designed to increase urination. Where available, the dog may also receive support by dialysis. Sadly, most dogs do not recover from grape/raisin toxicity, even when timely treatment is given. Early treatment improves the chance for survival. Keeping raisins and grapes out of your dog's reach is the ideal prevention.

GRASS, EATING

Dogs are omnivores, which means they can eat nearly anything, including vegetables or fruits. Wild canids like coyotes typically eat vegetable matter found in the stomach and intestines of prey animals, but may also eat roots, grasses and even fruit. Our dogs often beg for and enjoy snacks of raw vegetables like lettuce, green beans and carrots.

Most pet dogs occasionally eat grass, which may be used as a natural emetic to stimulate vomiting when the dog feels unwell. However, grass eating does not always result in vomiting; some dogs may simply relish the flavor or texture. Some speculation exists that grass grazing may provide trace elements of vitamins.

Indoor dogs may indulge their urge to graze by nibbling houseplants which, depending on the plant, may be dangerous (see POISON). Occasional grass eating isn't a cause for concern. However, if grazing becomes a habit, and especially if grass eating prompts vomiting more than two days in a row, your dog should be examined by a veterinarian to rule out a health problem.

GRIEF

SYMPTOMS: Change in behavior; acting withdrawn or depressed; hiding; searching for missing pet friend; crying; refusing to eat
HOME CARE: Emotional support; spend time and talk with pet
HOLISTIC HELP: Flower essences; herbal therapy; music therapy; TTouch
VET CARE: Possibly medications
PREVENTION: None

GRIEF Grief over pet loss can be difficult and heartbreaking for people, but it can be an even greater challenge to help the surviving pets deal with pet loss. Dogs do, indeed, grieve.

They cannot tell us how they feel. And the owners in the family may overlook behavior changes while dealing with their own sense of loss. Not every pet will react at all, while a percentage seems to suffer greatly. When pets grieve, they usually show their sense of loss with behavior changes. In fact, separation anxiety is one form of grief; your dog only understands someone she loves is gone.

The surviving pets often begin to act differently when the cat or dog first becomes sick or starts to decline. For people, this can be a time of preparation, and some of our grieving may be done well in advance of the pet's actual death. Grief counseling often is part of what caring veterinarians naturally do.

We can't know if surviving pets realize their companion animal friends will soon die, but they certainly do act as though aware a change has (or will) occur. In fact, many sensitive dogs and cats react to their owners' emotional upset and grieve in response to our own changes of behavior over the heartache.

The surviving pet may seem withdrawn and depressed. Often the personality changes and a shy dog becomes more demanding of attention, while a demanding dog instead hides. One of the most heartbreaking situations occurs when the surviving pet cries and searches for the missing loved one for days or even weeks.

Although it sounds macabre, sometimes it can be helpful to allow the surviving pet to say "goodbye" to the body after a furry friend has died. They may sniff and examine the body, cry or ignore it all together, and any reaction should be considered normal.

That's the only way we can explain to them what has happened to their friend, and why a beloved cat- or dog-friend has disappeared from their life. Viewing the friend's body allows them to understand he's not coming back. They still grieve, but aren't driven to look for their missing buddy.

People go through several stages of grief—denial, anger, bargaining, depression, acceptance—but not necessarily in this order. While anthropomorphic to think pets might "bargain" *(I'll let you have my toy if only you come back!)* it's certainly within the realm of possibility that they might feel anger or depression over the loss. Pets do in fact seem to finally work through the situation to acceptance. It takes some pets much longer than others just as people get over a loss in different time frames.

Many of the same things we do for each other can help our pets. Allow the grieving and even validate it with each other by simply offering compassion and support. Help your pets manage grief with these simple tips.

Talk to them. Try to be positive around your grieving pets. They may not understand the words but will pick up on your emotions. Simply say, *I'm sad, and I feel awful, but it's not your fault, and I know you feel awful, too.* You'll want to avoid babying, though, because that can reward the pet for acting depressed.

Music, particularly uplifting, faster tempos to lift depression. Harp music can have a soothing effect. But any music that your pet associates with positive times could be helpful (see MUSIC THERAPY).

Flower essences also helps a percentage of pets. The Bach Flower remedy called Star of Bethlehem is said to be particularly helpful for relieving sorrow and grief. You can find

Bach flower remedies or other brands at many health food stores, holistic veterinary clinics or online.

Also, the herb St. John's Wort acts as a natural antidepressant but must be dosed according to a veterinarian's advice. If the depression doesn't lift and lasts too long, your veterinarian may be able to prescribe an antidepressant drug.

Give your dog the gift of time to grieve. It hurts terribly, for you as well as your surviving pet. Still, the capacity to grieve honors the memory of the departed, and is a measure of the depth of our love. And that truly is a legacy to celebrate.

GROOMING

Grooming refers to the proper cleaning and conditioning of the body. Grooming keeps your dog looking and feeling good, and requires attention to the hair coat, ears, eyes, toe nails, anal glands and teeth. Grooming not only addresses the dog's physical needs, but promotes bonding between the owner and pet because the contact and attention simply feels good (see TOUCH).

Grooming promotes healthy skin. The sebaceous glands at the base of each hair root secrete an oily substance, called sebum, which is spread over the fur during grooming. Sebum helps waterproof the fur, and gives the hair coat its healthy sheen. Grooming also removes loose hair that can tangle the fur and produce painful mats.

A healthy coat is not only attractive, it's the dog's first line of defense against injury. Fur lies in loose protective layers that shields skin from damage, and provides insulation from temperature extremes. A properly groomed coat is weather-resistant and sheds rain, and keeps the dog warm in the winter and cool in the summer. A dog's sweat glands are not particularly effective for cooling (dogs pant to cool off) and the coat must remain free of mats to allow air to pass between the hairs when it's hot. Healthy fur traps warm air next to the skin when it's cold.

Dogs attend to some grooming themselves. They scratch with rear toenails, use their teeth to nibble burrs, dirt or parasites from their fur (see FLEAS, TICKS, and LICE), and clean their genitals by licking. Some breeds are more fastidious than others. For instance, the Basenji licks himself all over like a cat to keep clean. Dogs may also become overly enthusiastic in licking or nibbling, and develop hot spots, lick granulomas or hair loss. For the most part, dogs must rely on the owner for proper grooming care.

GROOMING YOUR DOG: The length and type of coat varies from breed to breed. Dogs with smooth short hair require less coat care than longer-furred breeds, but every dog benefits from regular grooming attention. Besides making your dog look and feel good, grooming provides an excellent opportunity to examine your dog for health problems.

Begin grooming your dog during puppyhood, so he'll learn to anticipate and enjoy the attention. Even reluctant dogs accept grooming when the sessions are kept brief. There's no rule says you must groom the whole dog at one time so break off the session if it becomes a struggle, and finish later. Make grooming as enjoyable for you both as possible by being prepared. Have all your supplies and equipment close at hand, stop before your dog becomes antsy, and then reward his patience with a treat or game.

Big dogs can be groomed on the ground as you kneel beside them; medium to small dogs should be placed on a table at waist level, which helps confined their movements. Your dog may accept grooming better if lightly restrained by a second pair of hands while you handle the comb and/or brush. Many dogs, though, love the sensation of being brushed, and will beg you to go on and on.

A wide variety of tools are available, especially for show-grooming. A professional groomer or breed expert can best guide you regarding the extravagant show trims of curly or woolly-coated dog breeds like Poodles. But even if your dog isn't a show contestant, you should learn how to keep the fur clean, and prevent painful mats.

Teflon-coated combs are best, because they don't break or pull the fur and reduce static electricity shocks that turn many dogs off to grooming. Combs are designed with fine, medium and coarse teeth, which is the amount of space between the tines. The widest-toothed comb is best for long, thick fur, while fine-toothed combs work well on dogs with short fur.

Brushes also come in many styles. Dogs with short fur can get by with a rubber curry brush to smooth the coat and pull off dead hair. A slicker brush has bent wire bristles set close together in a rubber pad, and is designed to remove mats and shed fur; they come in small, medium and large for different size dogs. The pin brush, with long rounded stainless steel or chrome-plated pins, works well on long thick coats. A pin palm brush has round-tipped pins set in an oval rubber pad, and is designed for brushing the face and leg fringes of terriers. The bristle brush has natural and/or nylon bristles for smoothing the coat of short, medium or long coats. There are also electric clippers, stripping knives and other specialized grooming equipment for specific coat situations.

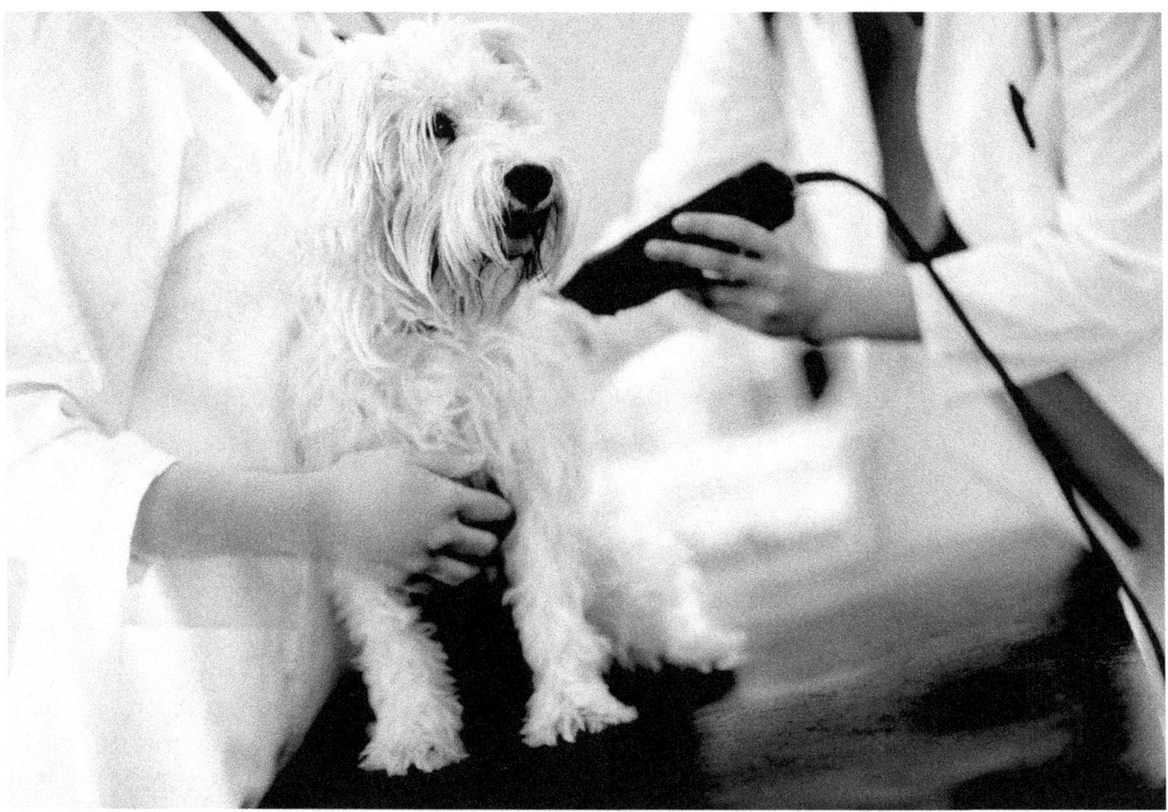

There are five basic coat types, and care is slightly different with each. Long fur with undercoat includes breeds like Collies and German Shepherd Dogs, and requires two or three times weekly combing followed by brushing. Non-shedding curly coats includes the Poodles and Bedlington Terriers; their fur grows continuously, and must be trimmed with electric clippers about every two months, and combed weekly in between. Silky coat breeds include the Afghan Hound, Lhasa Apso, Maltese, Pekingese, setters and spaniels. They may require daily combing and brushing to prevent matting. Smooth coat dogs include the Boxer, Rottweiler, and Greyhound, which are maintained with a comb and/or bristle brush; very short coats may only need a curry brush or chamois cloth. Slip an old pair of pantyhose over your hand, and stroke the dog with that, which works as well as expensive grooming equipment to polish the fur. Wiry coat dog breeds include most terriers and the Schnauzer. These breeds need weekly combing. They may also require plucking about four times a year, which removes the dead hairs from tight wiry coats; a professional groomer can show you how.

For routine care, always begin by allowing your dog to sniff and investigate the grooming tools, especially if the experience is new to him. Start with petting, or finger-combing, your dog, to familiarize yourself with the contours of his body and discover any problem areas like mats ahead of time. Initially comb or brush with short, light strokes in the direction the fur grows. Thick, long fur needs to be combed before brushing; comb through the surface first, and work your way deeper until you're combing clear to the skin. Always be careful not to press too hard, though, or you risk hurting tender skin.

Create a grooming ritual that's always the same, so your dog knows what to expect. Groom him in the same time and place, and always finish with something pleasant like a game or treat, so he'll equate the experience as positive.

Begin by grooming each side of his face, progress to his throat and neck, then move to the sides of his body. The backbone and nipples are tender areas, so use a light stroke in these areas. Don't forget the tail, especially the underside. Dogs generally let you know what they like by moaning with enjoyment; they particularly like having their chest and tummy brushed. Pay attention to the flanks inside and out.

When old, dead fur falls out and is caught in long outer hairs, painful knots develop. These mats often form during spring and fall shedding, but can be a problem year round in silky-coated dogs. Problem areas are the "armpit" regions of all four legs, behind the ears, and beneath the tail. Regular grooming can prevent mats from developing. Minor mats may be teased out with a coarse toothed comb, starting at the very tips and slowly working deeper. Don't use scissors; inevitably, you'll also cut the skin. A badly matted coat may require electric clippers, and is best addressed by a professional.

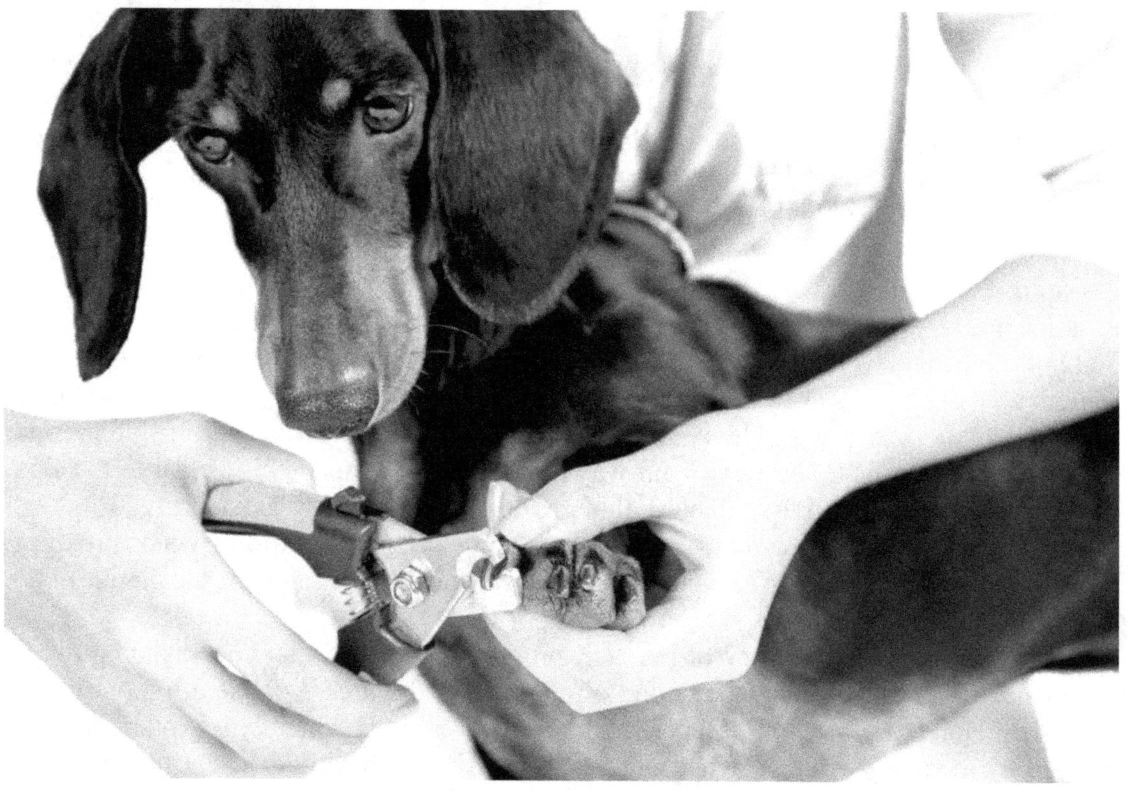

CLIPPING YOUR DOG'S NAILS: Most active dogs allowed to run outside naturally wear the nails to a manageable length, and may not need frequent trimming. However, dogs that spend most of their time inside often require monthly nail attention. The toenails of some dog breeds like the Chihuahua seem to grow quickly and may need more frequent trims.

Over-grown nails tend to curl, can become caught in bedding and carpets, and may split or tear. Keeping the toenails trimmed is healthier for the pet, and helps reduce inappropriate digging some dogs are prone to indulge. Dewclaws on the inside of the lower leg need particular attention since they never contact the ground.

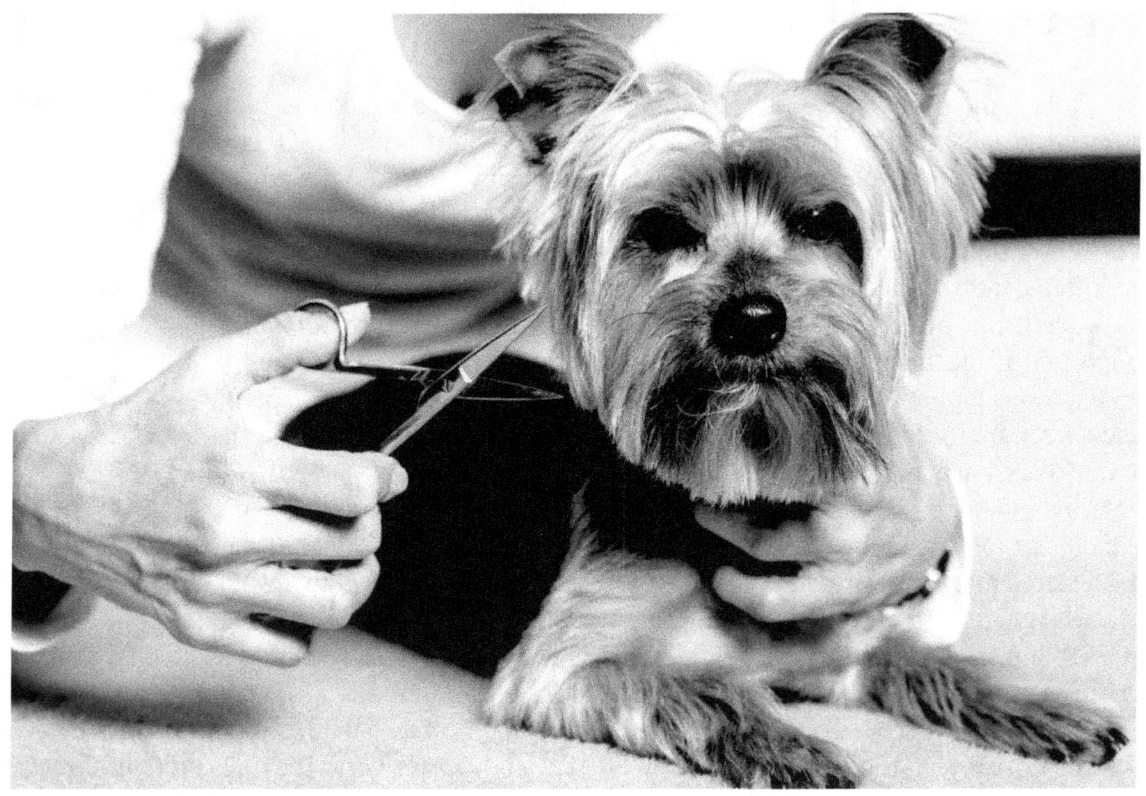

A variety of commercial nail trimmers are available from your veterinarian, pet-supply store or online source. They are typically either scissor-action or guillotine type clippers designed to cut the dog's toenails at the proper angle without splitting or crushing the nail. The clippers you choose must be sharp, and you must be comfortable using them. Dog nails may also need to be filed after trimming. Use an emery board, or a nail file available from a pet supply store to smooth the edges, and keep them from getting caught in the carpet.

It's helpful to regularly handle your puppy's paws and trim just the tip of his nails, even if they don't need it. This gets him used to the idea. What he learns to accept as a puppy is more easily endured as an adult. This is particularly helpful with large-breed dogs that can be handled more easily while puppy-size.

All four feet don't have to be done in the same session. If you're having difficulty getting the job done, finish the other toes later. It's helpful to have two pairs of hands during nail trimming; ask someone else restrain and steady the dog while you wield the clippers (see RESTRAINT). A wiggling dog makes it more likely you'll "quick" the nails, cut into the living vessels that feed the nail bed, and cause them to bleed. Also take care not to catch the fur in the clippers. This is uncomfortable for your dog, distressing for you, and will make you both reluctant to try again in the future.

DOG FACTS

Nails at their longest should just clear the ground when the dog is standing. If you hear him "clicking" over the linoleum like a tap-dancer, he needs a trim. Overgrown nails cause the foot to spread or splay, and can even curl and grow back into the dog's flesh.

When the nails are white or clear, the pink quick is visible and makes it easy to avoid the danger zone. Clip just outside the pink line showing in white nails. However, dog toenails are often dark or opaque, and the quick can't be seen. Rather than trimming blind and taking too much, clip off only the tips, the hook-like portion that turns down. This is especially important if the nail has been allowed to overgrow, because the quick will grow further down, too. Tipping the nails will prompt the quick to draw back up, so you can trim a little each week until reaching the proper length. Don't forget the dewclaws, the extra "toe" that some dogs have high on the inside of their legs. Dewclaws are often removed by the veterinarian soon after a puppy is born (except in the Briard and Great Pyrenees breeds, which call for this in the standard). If you do happen to quick a nail, use a styptic pencil or corn starch and direct pressure to stop the bleeding, or rake the claw through a bar of soap.

Always reward your dog for enduring a nail trim. Tell him what a good dog he is, and engage him in a game to show how pleased you are. Dogs like to please us, and consistent positive reinforcement helps make future sessions less traumatic.

BATHING YOUR DOG: Dogs tend to be bathed oftener than is necessary. Excessive baths can strip natural oils from the coat and dry the skin. Unless they get quite grubby or are show animals, most dogs that are regularly groomed shouldn't need a bath more than one to four times a year, depending on coat type.

Puppies shouldn't be bathed until they are at least four weeks old. Old or sick dogs can be stressed by bathing. Puppies and geriatric dogs have trouble regulating body temperature, and can become chilled and easily develop pneumonia. If your dog is in one of these categories, consult with your veterinarian before taking the plunge.

Poodle-type coats require the most bath time, and should be washed with each trim about every two months. Silky and wiry coats do well with four baths a year. German Shepherd Dogs and similarly coated dogs need a bath a couple of times a year; spring and fall is good, following their normal shed. Smooth coated pets like Rottweilers may need a bath only once a year, and then only if they get smelly or dingy-looking.

Assemble all the supplies you need beforehand. Be sure there are no mats by thoroughly combing and brushing your dog; water turns mats into solid masses impossible to remove without electric clippers. Bathe large to medium dogs in the bathtub, or if the day is warm, the garden hose in the back yard or patio may be appropriate. A waist-high sink works well for small dogs, and is easier on your knees.

Use only shampoos approved for pets. People products, even human baby shampoo, are so harsh and will dry the dog's skin and possibly cause allergic reactions. Do not use dishwashing soap, laundry detergent, turpentine, gasoline, kerosene or other household cleaners or chemicals; they can be toxic to your dog. Should your dog get paint, tar or tree sap in the coat, it's best trimmed out with electric clippers. Try soaking the area in vegetable or mineral oil for 24 hours, then wash out with dog shampoo. Some sticky substances like chewing gum may be removed by rubbing peanut butter into the mass, and then washing it

out. Strong odors or toxins may need specific attention (see POISONS and SKUNK ENCOUNTERS).

Dogs object to baths when they're frightened, so prepare ahead of time out of his sight. You'll need dog shampoo, mineral oil, cotton balls, a washcloth, and towels. The bigger the dog, the more towels you'll need. Place everything near your sink, tub, or patio within easy reach. When bathing indoors, the area should be warm and draft-free. Be sure to push shower curtains and any breakables out of the way that could spook your dog. If you're container-bathing, fill the tub or sink with dog-temperature water (about 102 degrees) before you bring in the victim—er your pet. Making him watch isn't nice.

It's easier to bathe your dog when two hands are free. Bath tethers are available that have a suction cup that secures one end to the tub or sink while the other clips to the dog's collar. When bathing outdoors, tether the dog with a short lead to a fixed object.

Before beginning, place cotton in the pet's ears to keep out the water. A drop of mineral oil or artificial tears in each eye helps protect them from errant suds. Place the dog in the standing water. It doesn't need to cover him; level with his knees is fine, and lets him feel he can stand above it without risk of drowning.

Use a plastic cup or ladle to dip water over the pet, or use a hand-held sprayer. Many dogs are frightened by sprayed water, so use only a low force and keep it against the coat to soak the fur. Don't spray or dunk the dog's face; that is very scary and upsetting to the dog. Instead, use a washcloth to clean and rinse the face. Once the fur is wet, apply a thin stream of pet shampoo along the back—or lather the shampoo in your own hands and then apply—and suds your dog thoroughly, then rinse. If you're using a flea product, suds the dog's neck first to create a flea barrier the bugs won't cross. Most shampoos, especially flea products, work best if left on the dog for ten to fifteen minutes.

The most critical part of bathing your dog is the rinse cycle. Leaving soap in the coat can cause an allergic reaction, can attract dirt, and makes the fur look dull and dingy. After you've thoroughly rinsed the dog, do it once more before calling it quits. Then allow your dog to do what he's been yearning for the whole time--a good shake. If his shaking doesn't fling out the cotton, then you remove it from his ears. Leaving the cotton in can cause ear infection. Always dry your dog's ears after bathing with a commercial drying solution and/or a cotton ball and cotton swabs to prevent ear infections.

Smooth coated dogs air dry very quickly. Dogs with more fur require lots of towels. As much as dogs may dislike the bath, they often relish the toweling-off afterwards. Some dogs will tolerate a blow-dryer on a low setting, which will help fluff up the fur. Be sure the dog is dry to the skin before allowing him outside if it's a cold day.

CARING FOR YOUR DOG'S EYES: Just like people, dogs may develop "sleepy-crust" in the corners of their eyes when tears spill out and dry. Some dog breeds like Poodles and Maltese have large prominent eyes that tend to water.

Others that have many nasal folds, like the Pekingese, Pug, and Bulldog, may have hairs that grow too near the eye and cause irritation. Tears can stain the fur, particularly in white or light-colored pets, and can crust the fur, irritate the skin, and lead to infection. A groomer can show you how to use electric clippers to keep these areas trimmed, and prevent eye irritation. Wipe out the skin folds regularly with a warm wet cloth to help prevent skin irritation or infection.

Clean the dog's eyes each day to prevent problems from developing. A cotton ball or soft cloth moistened with warm water or contact lens saline solution works well to soften the secretion, and wipe it away. Stained fur is usually at the inside corners and below the dog's eyes; commercial products available from pet stores can help remove the stain from fur.

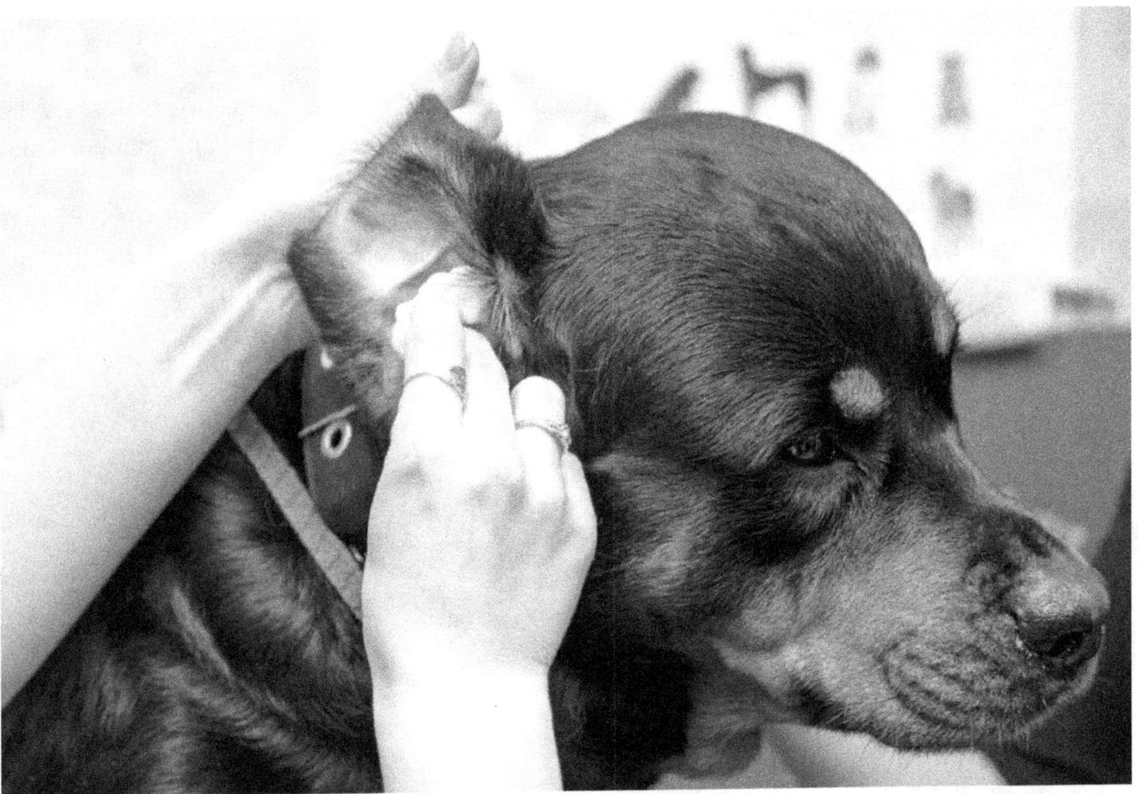

CARING FOR YOUR DOG'S EARS: Different dogs require various amounts of ear care. Healthy ears are pink, and a small amount of amber wax is normal and helps protect the ear canal. A discharge, bad smell, and/or dark or crumbly material may indicate an infection or ear mites. Check your dog's ears at least once a week, and clean at least monthly unless oftener is recommended by your veterinarian.

Commercial ear cleaning solutions are available from veterinarians and pet stores, but a 50/50 vinegar and water solution is fine for general cleaning. Place a small amount of solution on a cotton ball, soft cloth or cotton swab, and gently wipe out only the visible portions of the ear. Never drip cleaner or put any instrument down into the ear canal unless instructed to do so by your veterinarian. You may inadvertently damage your dog's ear.

The pendulous ears of breeds like Cocker Spaniels can trap moisture, and the poor air circulation provides a perfect environment for ear infections. If your dog has this type of ears, he'll benefit from a weekly cleaning with a drying agent (epiotic solution) or "airing out." Draw the ears up over his head or behind his neck, and tape them in place for a few hours. It looks funny, but can prevent ear problems down the road.

In Poodles, Cocker Spaniels, Schnauzers, Lhasa Apsos, Bouvier de Flanders, Old English Sheepdogs and some other breeds, hair actually grows inside the ear canal. This blocks air circulation, holds moisture, and makes these dogs prone to ear infections. Every one to three months, use electric clippers to trim the hair around the ears, and pluck out the fur growing inside the ear.

Serum that oozes from the hair pores after plucking is an ideal medium for bacterial growth. Follow ear plucking with an antibiotic ointment as recommended by your veterinarian to prevent infection (see OTITIS). You may be able to perform plucking service for your dog once a veterinarian or professional groomer shows you how.

DOG FACTS

HAIR Hair is the colored thread-like structure made of keratin that grows outward from the skin. Individual hairs combine to make up your dog's distinctive coat.

Fur is a protective barrier shielding the dog's skin from the elements, and regulating body temperature. Hair also acts like a "wick" which routes scent-producing chemicals related to identification and sexual status from the skin into the air.

All healthy dogs have fur, but the amount and type of hair coat varies in individuals and from breed to breed. Even the hairless breeds have hair on the face, feet and tail.

Hairs are composed of the hair shaft, which is the visible portion of the hair, and a root that's generated by a hair follicle within the skin. Dogs have compound follicles, which means multiple hairs are produce (as many as 20) from a single pore; people have simple follicles, which produce only one hair for each pore (see SKIN).

In general, dogs have three kinds of hairs, which are characterized by length and diameter. Guard or primary hairs are the longest, coarsest hairs of the outer coat. Secondary hairs of various lengths make up the undercoat. Medium length awn hairs make up the intermediate coat, and undercoat is soft, short cotton-like fur that's curly or crimped. All three types may sprout from a single compound follicle. Sinus hairs, also called whiskers or vibrissae, are found on the face and offer specialized sensory input.

The length of the hair shaft, and the ratio of guard to undercoat hairs varies from breed to breed. When the hair follicle that produces the hair is slightly twisted, the hair that grows is curly. These differences, as well as a variety of colors and patterns, produce each dog's distinctive coat.

Hair grows from the root outward in a cycle of rapid growth called anagen, shrinkage (called catagen) in which the root detaches from the follicle, and a resting period, termed telogen. Old loose hairs in the telogen phase are pushed out by new hairs as the anagen cycle begins (see SHEDDING). Shed fur is composed of telogen hairs.

A single human hair may grow for up to six years before being shed and replaced by a new one. The growing cycle of canine hair is much shorter and more synchronized, which accounts for the massive shed. It varies from breed to breed, but the growth cycle averages about 130 days. The exception is the so-called "non-shedding" breeds like the Poodle and some terriers, whose coats actually grow for several years before being replaced.

A healthy coat is possible only with proper nutrition, because hair is 95 percent protein. Your dog's coat retains its healthy glow from the proper balance of fats and other nutrients. Poor nutrition is first reflected in the skin and hair coat by dry, lifeless fur or abnormal hair loss. Grooming is beneficial for all dogs, and particularly important for dogs with thick long coats (see GROOMING).

HAIR LOSS Also referred to as alopecia, hair loss is normal for dogs as new growth replaces old dead fur (see SHEDDING). Dogs with long, thick coats like the Chow Chow typically lose heavy undercoats in clumps, which may give them a shocking moth-eaten appearance. But normally, every time a hair is lost, it is replaced like clockwork.

Isolated areas of hair loss not due to normal shedding can arise from parasite infestation or skin disease (see ALLERGIES, FLEAS, DEMODECOSIS and CANINE SCABIES). A veterinary diagnosis is necessary before the proper treatment can begin.

Also known as canine pinnal alopecia and acquired pattern alopecia, pattern baldness is a common syndrome found in Boston Terriers, Dachshunds, Manchester Terriers, Miniature Pinschers, Whippets, Italian Greyhounds and Chihuahuas. Typically, dogs show a slow, progressive thinning of the coat, particularly of the ears, but also of the neck, chest, thighs, abdomen, and around the anus. There is no associated itchiness or inflammation. For Dachshunds with hair loss on the outer ear flaps, complete hair loss typically results by age eight or nine, and the exposed skin becomes dark. In some cases, partial regrowth of fur is attained with oral treatment of melatonin supplements.

Hair loss may occur when the normal hair growth cycle gets out of synch, and the telogen phase is prolonged (see HAIR). In almost all instances, this is due to an underlying metabolic disease (see CUSHING'S DISEASE). Hair loss may also occur secondary to the dog pulling or plucking out his own hair, but this is more common in cats than in dogs. Stress from metabolic insult, a high fever, or serious illness may also cause a sudden loss of coat, which usually re-grows two to three months later.

Destruction of the hair follicles from bacterial or fungal infection (see RINGWORM) may also cause permanent hair loss. It may also develop from constant traction placed on the hair from rubber bands or barrettes used to decorate toy breeds like Poodles, Yorkshire Terriers or Maltese.

Occasionally, dogs suffering psychological stress lose hair by obsessively licking, biting and pulling at their fur. This can become a habit if the stressful conditions are not addressed. Sometimes, these dogs may be helped with antianxiety drugs.

HEART DISEASE

SYMPTOMS: Tires easily; weakness; blue tinge to skin; swollen abdomen or legs; coughing, especially at night; labored breathing; sitting with "elbows" out
HOME CARE: Nutritional support; prescribed medications
HOLISTIC HELP: Nutraceuticals; herbal treatments; homeopathy; flower essence
VET CARE: Diuretic drugs; medication to support/regulate heart function
PREVENTION: Heartworm preventative; routine dental care; prevent obesity; encourage moderate exercise

HEART DISEASE A number of conditions can adversely affect the function of the heart. Heart failure results when the damaged muscle is no longer able to move blood throughout the body properly. Without treatment, the dog will die.

Signs of heart disease vary from type to type, but many times the affected dog suffers exercise intolerance (becomes exhausted quickly), may act weak, or have a bluish tinge to the skin from lack of oxygen. In most cases of chronic (long-standing) heart failure, the dog's body retains fluid (edema). This is due to the body trying to compensate for reduced heart efficiency; the result is a retention of sodium and fluid, increased blood volume and constriction of the blood vessels, and increased blood pressure. Heart disease has a cascading effect on the whole body, and can lead to damage of other organs like the kidneys, liver and lungs.

When the left side of the heart fails, fluid collects in the lungs (pulmonary edema) and results in a cough, labored breathing, and panting. Obesity complicates heart disease and makes it more difficult to treat, but some dogs suffer weight loss and seem to waste away. Dogs sit with elbows spread and neck extended while straining to breathe, and may even try to sleep in this position to ease respiration.

When the right side of the heart fails, fluid collects and swells the abdomen (ascites), accumulates beneath the skin (edema--the legs may swell), and/or fills the chest cavity (pleural effusion). This fluid accumulation results in congestive heart failure. Often, dogs suffering from heart failure will have a heart murmur (see ARRHYTHMIA). Many times, right heart failure develops as a result of the strain from existing left heart failure.

Patent Ductus Arteriosus The most common congenital heart disease, patent ductus arteriosus (PDA) affects Miniature Poodles and German Shepherd Dogs most often, but any dog may have the problem. It may or may not be inherited. Normally, the ductus arteriosus, a short blood vessel, allows blood to bypass the lungs of an unborn puppy. If the duct fails to close after the puppy's birth, blood leaks back into the heart through the opening and leads to left heart failure. Surgery can cure the problem when performed early, and in the past this has been the treatment of choice.

A thoracotomy opens up the entire chest wall to offer access to the heart, and then the hole is repaired. A new method, interventional catheterization, uses a catheter (flexible tube) to reach and close the hole. Pets recover more quickly with this procedure than thoracotomy, and other more invasive surgeries. Catheters may also be used to lodge little stainless steel fiber-embedded coils into the "holes," to stimulate clotting that induces the body to patch itself.

Pulmonic Stenosis is another heart problem, which means a narrowing of the connection between the right ventricle, or lower heart chamber, and the pulmonary artery that leads to the lungs. Affecting small breed dogs most often, this congenital defect makes the heart work harder to push blood through the narrow opening. Heart muscles sometimes compensate by growing stronger, but many times the heart defect becomes life-threatening.

New catheter techniques can also treat pulmonic stenosis. Performed under anesthesia, the procedure requires a small incision into a blood vessel, and a fairly large catheter with a balloon on the end is passed through the vessel to reach the heart. Once it reaches the narrowing, the balloon is inflated with saline, and enlarges the opening to normal size. The procedure is identical to that performed on children with pulmonic stenosis. Heart catheterizations are specialized procedures, and only a few centers across the country do them.

Aortic Stenosis affects large breed dogs like Golden Retrievers. This is a narrowing of the connection between the left ventricle and the aorta. Again, the heart tends to compensate for this condition by enlarging so blood can be pumped with more force. Although many dogs show no signs of problems, a few may collapse after exercise, or die suddenly without warning. Surgery is the treatment of choice, but is risky, expensive, and only available at veterinary schools or specialists that have access to cardiopulmonary bypass machines.

Acquired valvular heart disease is the leading cause of heart disease in dogs. Valvular heart disease affects about 1/3 of all dogs over the age of 12, and about 75 percent of dogs with heart disease have chronic valvular heart disease (CVHD). The heart valves simply begin to wear out, and leak blood backwards instead of pumping it all forward. This puts extra strain on the heart muscle.

Unlike congenital forms, acquired heart diseases develop over time, and commonly are due to other conditions like cancer, parasites (see HEARTWORM DISEASE), or infectious diseases (see PERIODONTAL DISEASE). Bacterial endocarditis also causes the dog to develop a fever, and may prompt the formation of blood clots that can cause lameness when they block blood flow to a leg. Along with therapies aimed at relieving the heart failure, bacterial endocarditis is also treated with antibiotics.

Dilated cardiomyopathy may also cause heart valve problems. Cardiomyopathy is a disease of the heart muscle rather than the valves, and the dilated form results in systolic dysfunction—the heart muscle loses the ability to adequately contract and pump blood out of the heart. The heart itself enlarges, but becomes flaccid and the muscle walls become thin. It is not a disease of old age, but typically develops between the ages of two to five years old, although signs may not become apparent right away. The disease is thought to have a genetic factor, because more than 90 percent of canine cases occur in Boxers, Cocker Spaniels, Doberman Pinschers, German Shepherd Dogs and Golden Retrievers. Most times the cause remains unknown, but Boxers, Dobermans, Saint Bernards, and Cocker Spaniels that develop the condition may respond to nutritional supplementation with the amino acids taurine and/or carnitine (see NUTRITION). Most dogs with dilated cardiomyopathy die within six months to two years of diagnosis. Treatment is designed to prolong life and make them more comfortable during this period.

Simply listening with a stethoscope may detect a murmur or excessive fluid in the lungs. X-rays of the thorax will typically show an enlarged heart, and you might see changes in the lungs consistent with fluid.

An echocardiogram, or ultrasound of the heart, is the ideal way to diagnose heart disease. That requires specialized equipment that general practice veterinarians usually don't have. Typically dogs will be referred to a veterinary cardiologist or internist. The echocardiogram tells the veterinarian how strongly the heart is able to contract, and if there are any leaky valves, an idea of the heart chamber size, and the thickness or thinness of the walls. Thorough testing helps determine which medications will work best for the dog.

Dogs with acquired valvular heart disease can often be helped with drugs that improve the heart's performance and reduce fluid accumulation. Digitalis or related medicines such as Cardoxin or Lanoxin help improve heart muscle performance. Calcium channel blockers such as diltiazem, or beta blockers such as propranolol may help.

A diuretic drug such as Lasix (furosemide) forces the kidneys to eliminate excess salt and water. However, high doses of diuretics can contribute to kidney problems, and cause the dog to drink more water and urinate more frequently, so extra bathroom stops will be necessary until the body adjusts to the medicine. ACE inhibitors, such as Enalapril

(Enacard), benazepril (Fortekor), and Lisinopril, are vasodilator drugs that ease the workload on the heart by opening up the arteries. Newer treatments target the neurohormonal abnormalities that accompany heart failure.

Holistic veterinarians may recommend giving hawthorn berries, said to make the heart muscle stronger. The homeopathic remedy Apis is a mild diuretic that can help get rid of excess fluids of plural effusion. Pets with heart problems also may benefit from supplements with coenzyme Q10.

Specially designed therapeutic diets that are low in sodium help the dog compensate for the potassium, chloride and magnesium lost due to increased fluid excretion, and help them avoid fluid retention. A variety of brands are available, and it's important to choose one that will both be good for the dog, and that he'll readily eat. It may be helpful to feed several small meals to help stimulate the appetite and reduce gastrointestinal upset.

Treatment for congestive heart failure does not correct the problem, it only seeks to alleviate the worst symptoms. Most, though not all, patients who experience congestive heart failure survive as long as they receive treatment promptly, but the long-term outcome for patients is guarded. The goal is to keep the dog comfortable, and maintain a good quality of life despite heart problems.

HEARTWORM DISEASE

SYMPTOMS: Difficulty breathing; shortness of breath; reluctance to exercise; weight loss; sudden collapse; coughing, sometimes of blood; swollen abdomen or legs

HOME CARE: Supportive care; reduce stress; limit activity; requires vet treatment

VET CARE: Medication to kill both adult and immature heartworms

PREVENTION: Routine heartworm blood testing; heartworm preventative medication

282 DOG FACTS

HEARTWORM DISEASE Heartworm disease was first described in 1922, and is caused by a type of roundworm called *Dirofilaria immitis* that belongs to a group of parasites termed filarids. Adult worms live in the pulmonary arteries and right heart chambers, and can damage the heart muscle and interfere with its function. An intermediate host, the mosquito, is necessary to transmit the disease to dogs. The life cycle takes about six to seven months.

All dogs can get the disease, but those exposed more often to mosquitoes—outdoor dogs living in close proximity to mosquito breeding grounds like swamps or standing water—are at highest risk.

An infected dog's blood contains circulating microfilariae, the immature stage of the heartworm. Mosquitoes become infected by ingesting baby heartworms when taking a blood meal from an already infected dog. The immature parasite spends about three weeks developing inside the mosquito, then the larvae migrate to the mouthparts of the insect. When the mosquito again takes a blood meal, larvae are deposited upon the skin and gain entrance to the new host's body through the bite wound left by the mosquito.

The heartworm undergoes many more molts and development stages during the next several months, during which time it migrates inside the animal's body, ultimately arriving at the heart and pulmonary arteries where it matures. Adult worms can reach four to 12 inches in length. Adults mate and females shed as many as 5000 microfilariae each day into the dog's bloodstream. These microfilariae must be ingested by a mosquito to continue their development, but can remain alive and infective in the dog's bloodstream for up to three years.

It's not uncommon for infected dogs to carry dozens of worms; more than 250 have been found in a single dog. Heartworm disease is a chronic condition in which worms live in the dog for up to five years. Initially, the dog may not show any ill effects, but symptoms develop and grow worse over time. Common signs are coughing, shortness of breath, and reluctance to exercise. Dogs may faint after exertion. Eventually the dog becomes weak, listless, loses weight, and may cough up blood. Severe signs of late-stage disease are congestive heart failure, including labored breathing and edema. The condition may result in sudden collapse and death.

Heartworm disease is diagnosed based on signs of disease and blood screening techniques. Traditional tests look for microfilariae in the blood. However, a dog can be infected without microfilariae being present. This may result from single-sex infections–worms present in the heart are the same sex—in which reproduction can't happen. Other times, the dog's immune system clears away the microfilaria, but leaves the adults in the heart. Newer, more accurate tests detect antigen that worms release into the bloodstream, or screen for antibodies made by the dog's immune system in defense against the worms. Tests may be used in combination, or occasionally, X-rays or echocardiograms may help diagnose the disease.

Once diagnosed, dogs are evaluated for liver and kidney competency--and treated for problems, if necessary--before being treated. Very rarely are the worms removed surgically. Sometimes they are treated with injections of a drug called thiacetarsamide (Caparsalate), which is a derivative of arsenic. It's administered intravenously in two doses each day for two days, and hospitalization is required to monitor the dog for any adverse reactions to the drug. The medication is also toxic to the liver, and may cause loss of appetite, vomiting, or jaundice (yellow-tinge to skin) from liver involvement. Treatment is stopped if the dog suffers these side effects; when begun again a month later, side effects rarely recur. The medication kills about 70 percent of the worms. Some dogs require a repeated treatment to address the remaining worms.

The newest and safest treatment is with a drug called Immidicide. One injection is given in the muscle daily for two days. This drug eliminates virtually all side effects and is much more effective in producing a complete cure.

The treated dog can go home, but must undergo an enforced rest for several weeks until the dead worms are absorbed by the body. This prevents the sudden movement of dead worm debris that might result from sudden exertion, and could cause a life-threatening blockage, or embolism, when the parts of the worm lodge in an artery in the lungs. Embolism can cause lung damage and/or heart failure. In severe cases, treating the dog with buffered aspirin before and after treatment appears to reduce this risk by helping make the blood less "sticky."

In three to six weeks following adult worm treatment, the dog is treated with an oral medicine like Levamisole, Interceptor or Ivermectin to kill the microfilariae that still circulate in the bloodstream. Any one of these drugs may cause side effects, such as vomiting and listlessness or diarrhea. Ivermectin, however, can cause life-threatening reactions in Collies, Collie-crosses and Australian Shepherds, and should not be used in these dogs.

It is much easier and less expensive to prevent heartworm disease than to diagnose, treat and cure it once infection is present. Preventing mosquito bites will eliminate the risk of disease; however, this is nearly impossible. Keeping dogs indoors during mosquito feeding times, like late afternoons and evenings, will help. Preventative medications are a more effective option, and are quite safe.

Several preventatives have been available for dogs for many years, and are generally given as daily or monthly pills. Some also prevent certain intestinal parasites. Always have your dog tested to ensure she is not already infected with heartworms before giving her a preventative medication; some medications can cause dangerous reactions if given when microfilariae are present in the dog's body.

HEMATOMA This term refers to a blood-blister, a swelling beneath the skin that contains blood. Hematomas typically result from a bruise or blow and usually resolve by themselves. Surgical drainage may be required when the hematoma is large.

Dogs most commonly suffer aural hematomas in the skin of the ear flap (pinna). This results from scratching or rubbing the ear, due to parasites or ear infection. The ear cartilage is separated from the skin when the area between suddenly swells with blood and fluid. The soft swelling is usually on the inside but can be on the outside surface of the pinna. Aural hematomas most commonly affect dogs with floppy pendulous ears that easily bruise when the head is shaken to relieve itchy ears. The underlying cause must be treated as well as the hematoma (see OTITIS and EAR MITES).

HEMATOMA

SYMPTOMS: Soft swelling of (usually) the inside or sometimes the outside of the ear flap
HOME CARE: None
VET CARE: Surgical drainage and repair; medication to treat underlying cause
PREVENTION: Routine ear cleaning to prevent self-trauma from scratching

The trapped blood must be drained to prevent the ear cartilage from scarring. When the hematoma is small, removing the fluid with a syringe, followed by firm bandaging for seven to ten days, may be sufficient. More commonly, the hematoma recurs in a day or two as new blood and serum fills the cavity.

Surgery offers the best results. The dog is anesthetized, and a small incision opens the inside surface of the pinna. The opening is drained and cleaned, and the separated flaps of cartilage and skin stitched back together. A narrow opening is left at the incision line so that fluid will drain as the incision heals rather than re-inflating the wound. Often, a soft padded bandage is used to help the ear retain normal shape as it heals, and may anchor the ear against the head or collar to prevent a recurrence of ear-flapping injury. Dogs that undergo this surgery are fitted with an Elizabethan collar to prevent them scratching at the wound.

HEMOPHILIA

HEMOPHILIA Hemophilia is an inherited bleeding disorder, and has been found in nearly all of the popular dog breeds. Affected dogs lack an essential clotting component of blood. The body is unable to stop bleeding from even minor injuries.

Signs of the condition include recurrent bruising or blood pockets beneath the skin (see HEMATOMA), bleeding into the joints and resultant lameness, and internal hemorrhage that often results in severe anemia and death. Dogs diagnosed with hemophilia should not be bred, as the condition can be passed on to offspring (see VON WILLEBRAND'S DISEASE).

A team of scientists led by David Wilcox at the Medical College of Wisconsin in Milwaukee reported in November 2013 that they had successfully fix a flawed gene in dogs suffering from hemophilia. Ask your veterinarian about gene therapy for your dog.

HEMOPHILIA

SYMPTOMS: Recurrent bruising; blood pockets beneath skin; lameness; failure of bleeding injuries to scab or clot; anemia
HOME CARE: None
VET CARE: Blood transfusions; supportive care
PREVENTION: None; once diagnosed, avoid trauma and elective surgeries and remain vigilant for signs; seek prompt treatment should bleeding occur

HERBS Herbs may be considered old fashioned in today's cutting-edge world of medicine, but holistic veterinarians continue to use herbs. Many of these plants are the foundation of modern drugs and medications, but don't cause the same side effects as the modern drugs. That's because the chemicals derived from herbs have been isolated to a single ingredient that works quickly but can sometimes be too harsh.

The original plant, though, has other components that buffer these effects. For instance, willow bark contains a chemical that works similarly to aspirin. But while aspirin can predispose to gastric ulcers, willow bark protects against them.

Most herbs contain active ingredients within their bark, seeds, roots, and leaves so a single plant could be effective in multiple conditions. For example, slippery elm not only can ease diarrhea, it also will soothe a sore throat. Because they have many active ingredients, but are relatively safe, herbs may be effective even when the veterinarian hasn't been able to pinpoint what's causing the problems.

Herbs are rarely used by themselves. They work well alongside conventional treatments. Care must be taken, though, because the chemical components of the herb may interact with the medications your dog already takes. It's always best to check with your veterinarian about any herbal products before giving them to your pets.

One reason is that herbs are not as regulated as drugs. The strength of a given herb may vary and be much weaker—or even triple the strength—of the exact same herb from another company.

Here's another dangerous scenario. A common drug given for heart problems is digitalis. The herbal remedy for heart problems is hawthorn (*Crataegus laevigata*). If the two are given together they can amplify the effects of both the drug and the herb and create an overdose that could potentially kill your pet.

The U.S. Department of Agriculture has cataloged more than 80,000 herbs and choosing them can be confusing. Think of herbs as medicines, and the best person to prescribe medicines is your veterinarian after diagnosing a health concern.

Herbs also come in many forms—fresh, dried, concentrated, or packed into capsules—and the form may be chosen based on the best way to administer to your pet. Even when the active ingredients are the same, herbs have different effects depending on how they're prepared and packaged.

Apothecaries sell bulk herbs as fresh green plants, as dried or as powdered. Bulk herbs are usually prepared by steeping them in boiling water to make teas and tonics quickly absorbed by the body. This can be pretty easy to administer as liquids.

Fresh and dried herbs don't last forever. Look for expiration or harvest dates on the label and give them the sniff test. If they smell dry or musty, they've probably given up their essential oils and won't be as effective. Store herbs in a cool dark place or they lose strength when they're exposed to light and heat. Some herbs will react with chemicals in plastic containers, so it's better to store them in glass, instead.

Extracts and tinctures are concentrated liquid forms of herbs and work very quickly. They can be mixed in a glass of water and poured on your pet's food or administered directly into the dog's mouth. Some tinctures are made by soaking herbs in alcohol making them taste bad and some can be potentially dangerous because of the alcohol so only a vet should prescribe these.

Herbal capsules and tablets are just as effective as fresh herbs but are absorbed less quickly by the body. When speedy action isn't an issue they may be recommended for convenience of administration when it's easier to simply pill your pet.

The strength of herbs varies from batch to batch due to differences in climate, soil conditions, and which fertilizers were used. The only way to be sure you're getting the best quality every time is to rely on a reputable supplier. Ask your vet for a recommendation or purchase directly from the veterinarian.

HERNIA

SYMPTOMS: Soft, compressible, but painless swelling; hard and painful swelling adjacent to the navel or genitals; labored breathing following trauma, such as being hit by car
HOME CARE: None; hard, painful swelling that can't be moved; respiratory distress following trauma are EMERGENCIES! SEE VET IMMEDIATLEY!
VET CARE: Surgery
PREVENTION: None; remain vigilant for signs; seek prompt treatment

HERNIA A hernia is the abnormal protrusion of abdominal contents through a natural or unnatural opening in the body wall. Hernias are characterized as either reducible or non-reducible (incarcerated). The reducible type is characterized by a soft, painless, and compressible swelling that's easily manipulated back into place, and may vary in size from time to time. A non-reducible hernia is hard and painful, and cannot be moved. A non-reducible hernia should be treated as an emergency, because the protruding tissues may die as a result of strangulation if blood supply is pinched off.

There is no way to prevent congenital hernias. When a dog is born with a hernia, inguinal (groin) or umbilical (naval) hernias are the most common. Typically, congenital hernias are corrected during spay or neuter surgery.

Occasionally, adult dogs suffer from perineal herniation, which is the protrusion of the rectum through the pelvic muscles. Affected dogs are typically six to eight-year-old unneutered animals, and incidence seems highest in Boston Terriers, Boxers, Collies, Corgies and Pekingese. You'll see a bulge alongside the anus that may grow larger as the dog strains. The feces caught in this area can become impacted, and block normal defecation. Surgery corrects the defect.

Herniation can also be the result of trauma. The severe blow a dog suffers when hit by a car often causes a diaphragmatic hernia. The diaphragm is the muscle and tissue structure that divides the abdominal cavity from the chest. The tear allows abdominal organs to intrude into the thorax, which interferes with the dog's ability to expand his lungs. Affected dogs typically exhibit labored breathing while sitting with the neck extended or head hanging in an effort to ease respiration. Diagnosis is based on signs, a history of trauma, and X-rays. Surgical correction is the only treatment.

Sometimes a dog suffers an abdominal or thoracic hernia during an attack by a larger dog. The sharp canine teeth can penetrate the muscles of the abdomen or thorax and tear the body wall sometimes without even causing a noticeable skin injury. These hernias also require surgical repair and the entire contents of the abdomen or thorax should be evaluated since trauma can also occur to structures like the intestines, kidney, spleen, bladder or lungs. Supervising your dog's outdoor adventures, confining him to the yard, and keeping him safe from cars can reduce the risk of traumatic herniation. Prognosis is guarded when repairing a traumatic diaphragmatic hernia.

HIP DYSPLASIA Hip dysplasia is a progressive degenerative disease that causes joint instability due to an abnormality of the hips and/or head of the femur (thigh bone). It is the most common cause of rear-end lameness in dogs, and is most often seen in large breeds like German Shepherd Dogs, St. Bernards, and Swiss Mountain Dogs. However, any size dog may be affected. Male and female dogs are affected with equal frequency.

The cause of canine hip dysplasia isn't known. Dogs suffering from hip dysplasia should not be bred; their puppies will be two times more likely to develop the disease as puppies born to parents with normal hips. Genetics accounts for about 25 percent of a dog's chance for developing hip dysplasia, and even dogs with normal parents can develop the condition.

Hip dysplasia is considered "polygenetic" by veterinarians, which means the genetic component of HD can be influenced by lifestyle, nutrition, weight and activity level. Severe disease may be seen as early as four months of age, but usually develops in nine to 12-month-old pets. They tend to have trouble getting up, difficulty jumping, limp after exercise, or display a classic wavery or bunny-hop gait.

Dogs typically are born normal, but as the puppy matures, the hip joint alignment becomes progressively worse. Normally, the pelvis has a kind of a cup or socket (acetabulum) into which the rounded head of the femur fits. This ball and socket arrangement forms the joint, and muscles and tendons hold the joint together and allow the leg movement. Dogs suffering from dysplasia typically have a very shallow socket and/or loose muscles and tendons. This allows the joint to work loose, which places abnormal stress and wear on the bones when they rub together, and causes further joint degeneration. Bones respond to stress by growing thicker, which makes the fit even worse.

However, hip dysplasia is not a finite condition; there are degrees of severity, and some dogs may show minimal to no signs at all. Mild cases may go undiagnosed until the dog reaches middle age or older. How quickly or to what extent degeneration occurs is in part determined by the dog's activity level. While healthy, normal hips probably won't be adversely affected by hard work, the dog with mild to moderate hip dysplasia develops more severe signs more quickly when excessive stress is placed on these joints.

As the hip joint becomes damaged, inflammation of surrounding tissues weakens the joint further. The ligaments become swollen and stretched, and ultimately rupture. The cartilage that covers and cushions the bones is worn down. Thigh muscles and muscles of the hip joint atrophy. Dogs with hip dysplasia often develop joint pain (see ARTHRITIS).

Outward signs may point to a problem, but for a conclusive diagnosis, X-rays are performed while the pet is under anesthesia. The dog is placed on his back and the veterinarian looks for the typical arthritic changes and subluxation (laxness) of the bone fit. Some changes may not be evident until the dog reaches two years old.

HIP DYSPLASIA

SYMPTOMS: Lameness; limping; favoring of rear legs; difficulty rising, running, or jumping; wavery gait; bunny hop when running
HOME CARE: Encourage moderate exercise; provide good nutrition; offer pain relievers as recommended by vet
HOLISTIC HELP: Supplements; heat treatment; herbal treatment; massage
VET CARE: Pain medications; sometimes surgery
PREVENTION: None; provide good nutrition and keep dogs lean to delay progression of disease

HD is a developmental problem and changes dynamically as the dog grows. There can be tremendous changes from six to nine months to a year. That's why OFA certification cannot be done prior to age two in dogs. The Orthopedic Foundation for Animals (OFA) provides a consulting service for purebred dog owners and breeders. OFA reviews hip X-rays provided by an owner to evaluate the dog's conformation and, when normal, certifies that fact.

With the newer PennHip technique, veterinarians can pick up the degree of joint looseness even before arthritic changes take place. Whatever laxity or looseness they have at four months, they'll have for the rest of their life.

The PennHip method, developed by Dr. Gail Smith, also positions the pet on his back, but then fits a metal and acrylic form, called a "distracter," between the rear legs. It brings their knees up kind of like a frog so their legs mimic what happens when they stand. That X-ray view plus others are used to gauge the pet's laxity score or "distraction index."

It takes training to take correct OFA or PennHip X-rays, but can be done by experienced general practitioners. Dogs can be certified free of hip dysplasia by sending appropriate X-rays to either the OFA registry or the PennHip registry. OFA costs less because there's only one X-ray taken. This is evaluated by three radiologists who score the hips fair, good or excellent. PennHip evaluation uses computer analysis to compare the X-rays to all the other dogs of that breed in the registry.

There is no cure for hip dysplasia. Treatment is aimed at relieving pain and improving joint function. How well treatment works depends on the severity of the problem.

There are three levels of treatment. The vast majority of dogs do well with medical management to control discomfort. They may be real painful in that first year of life, but they get over that, and 76 percent of them do well with conservative management. Weight control and moderate exercise can help keep dogs flexible. The pain medication Rimadyl is one of the best option now available for control of discomfort of the dog that has severe or moderate osteoarthritis.

Encourage your dysplastic dog to take short walks with you; swimming is ideal, but jumping and prolonged running should be discouraged. Keep him lean; obesity increases joint strain and exacerbates the condition (see OBESITY).

Holistic veterinarians may recommend herbal relief such as boswellia to help relieve joint discomfort. Providing heat pads under the dog's bed also can provide relief, as well as regular gentle massage to keep the dog active.

Limited studies have shown that cartilage-enhancing medications like chondroitin sulfate and glucosamineglycan, used at a very high dose early on, and the for the rest of the pet's life, can slow the development of hip dysplasia. Cartilage never heals itself once it's damaged; the cells do not replicate, so these agents just help the body keep existing cartilage as healthy as possible.

Development of the condition is delayed and the severity is lessened when the growth rate of puppies (during the first four months) is restricted; conversely, the condition in predisposed puppies can be brought on more quickly when the growth rate is accelerated. Feeding a high-quality puppy ration that provides a moderate and healthy growth rate is important, particularly in high-risk large breeds.

Severe cases of hip dysplasia may benefit from surgery that rebuilds or removes bone, or alters the muscles and tendons to reduce pain. Such procedures may not fully restore joint function, but can give the dog improved movement.

TPO. When hip dysplasia can be diagnosed early before arthritis develops (for dogs age seven to 12 months old), the state-of-the-art treatment is a triple pelvic osteotomy (TPO). Osteotomy means cutting the bone.

A TPO cuts the pelvis in three places with a surgical saw in order to rotate the socket to any angle. Wire and a plate hold the reconfigured pelvis in position with the pelvis socket over the head of the femur, and the plate allows the pet to bear weight during the six weeks needed for the fractures to heal. The surgery kind of fools Mother Nature, so the hip won't develop arthritis. The pet remains hospitalized for 24 to 48 hours and can then walk out the door.

Most surgeons perform TPO on one hip at a time, with a four to five week period between procedures to allow for healing and rehab. It requires intensive care to manage patients post-surgery.

FHO. Once arthritis has developed, other surgical options offer better results. A femoral head ostectomy (FHO) removes the femoral head, or "ball" of the joint, and prompts the pet's body to create a new "false" joint from fibrous scar tissue. This procedure works best for pets that weigh less than 40 pounds.

TOTAL HIP REPLACEMENT. Total hip replacement surgery replaces the dog's hip with prosthetic joints, and is recommended in the most severe cases. Hip replacement mirrors the procedure done in people. The dog prosthetics are based on prototypes for human hip replacement but today there are companies that specialize in hip replacements for dogs of various weights, typically from 40 to 150 pounds. Human artificial hips, of course, are all nearly the same size.

The orthopedic surgeon removes the socket portion of the pelvis and replaces it with a plastic cup fixed in place with screws or cement. The ball portion of the femur is removed, and the end of the bone is hollowed to accept the titanium stem-and-ball inserted into the opening.

The prosthetic is usually cemented or press fitted in place. When finished, the dog has a new hip with no cartilage, no pain, and no chance of arthritis. They'll bear weight very quickly, often the very next day, because they're suddenly free of pain.

Rehab for two months following surgery brings the new hip to full function, at which time surgery on the second hip may be done. But for 90 percent of patients, only one hip replacement provides all they need, because the dog learns to transfer weight to the artificial hip and compensate. The cost varies across the country, averaging $2,000 to $3,000 per hip.

There is no way to prevent hip dysplasia in dogs, although acquiring your puppy from parents certified to have normal hips will reduce his chances of having the condition. Reputable breeders should be able to tell you about their dogs' history. Most dogs with hip dysplasia can lead happy, otherwise healthy lives when owners remain vigilant regarding their special needs.

HOLISTIC MEDICINE

While traditional "western" medicine can't be beat for addressing emergencies like broken legs and acute or critical health issues, holistic medical approaches may work better to prevent and treat chronic health challenges. The word *holistic* refers to a whole-body approach that addresses the health of the pet's physical and emotional being. This type of treatment may also be called "natural" or "alternative" medicine.

Rather that treating the "symptom" of disease, the holistic practitioner looks at the entire animal: diet, exercise, behavior, emotions, and even the environment. Conventional "western" medicine tends to focus on the disease, while holistic medicine focuses on the patient. Holistic veterinarians would rather try to prevent problems and to support the body's immune system to keep pets healthy rather than scramble to fix diseases or conditions after they happen. They believe once chronic problems develop they continue to get worse even with ongoing conventional treatment.

Veterinary holistic therapies encompass a wide range of old fashioned to cutting edge modalities. Some of these have been successfully used in human medicine for centuries (see MASSAGE and ACUPUNCTURE). Although veterinary supports believe treatments like homeopathic remedies work exceedingly well, the way they work cannot always be satisfactorily explained by science. Holistic modalities also may include herbal remedies, flower essences, magnetic and light therapy, chiropractic care, nutritional supplements, and home prepared foods.

An integrated approach offers your pets the ideal care specific to his needs. Alternative/holistic veterinary medicine works great alongside much of mainstream medicine.

Conventional medicine can't be beat when it comes to diagnosing problems, so X-rays or blood analysis can reveal a tumor or fracture before the veterinary chiropractor provides a treatment. If your dog chews through an electrical cord and stops breathing, acupuncture resuscitation can start his heartbeat again until you can reach conventional trauma medicine help. Homeopathy can't perform surgery, but may help a traumatized pet survive surgery and heal more quickly afterwards.

Be sure to evaluate the claims of different holistic treatments before rushing into therapy. Sadly, when the term "natural" became very popular, some companies simply slapped on the label to increase sales. Just because something is "natural" doesn't mean it's safe or effective—poisonous mushrooms and a venomous snake bite are natural, too.

It's difficult sometimes to figure out odd-sounding therapies that work from quackery, so ask questions and do your research. Look for studies that back up the claims of a treatment's effectiveness. Your holistic vet will provide proven science when it's available. In fact, the National Institutes of Health (NIH) studies alternative care options for people and many of these apply to pets as well. Veterinary journals also publish studies and measure the effects of different techniques.

When a technique or product is very new there may not be scientific studies available. Because some of these therapies are "natural" there's not much money to be made and so costly evaluations may not be embraced by drug companies. In these cases, testimonials from other pet owners and veterinarians may provide convincing "anecdotal" evidence. Just take some claims with a grain of salt depending on who makes the claims—someone with a monetary gain could be suspect. But other pet owners and animal health professionals able to recognize true health improvements are more credible.

When choosing a holistic veterinarian, look for doctors that have training in natural and alternative treatments. Professional veterinary associations or holistic organizations offer study and accreditation (see APPENDIX B).

HOMEOPATHY Homeopathy is a holistic modality embraced by some alternative medicine veterinarians. It is based on the concept that "like cures like." This sounds similar to the way that vaccinations are made using a part of the disease they are intended to cure, in order to "teach" the immune system to recognize and defend against the dangerous intruder, be that a virus or other pathogen.

Homeopathic remedies have become quite popular because giving the "wrong" remedy generally causes no harm, and owners like to try to treat dog problems at home. Homeopathic veterinarians, though, are in the best position to recommend homeopathic remedies.

Rather than using viruses, homeopathy treatment gives a pet miniscule amounts of substances that in larger doses would cause the same symptoms as the disease. For instance, the homeopathic treatment for vomiting would be to use a tiny amount of a substance that in its full strength would cause vomiting. Theoretically, this amplifies the original symptom and "wakes up" the body's defenses, causing the immune system to recognize the problem and gear up for the attack.

In order to identify substances that can cause certain symptoms, homeopathic practitioners test or "prove" the substances in healthy people. These folks are given the substance and describe what symptoms they feel. Pets aren't used in provings because they can't describe their symptoms. As a result, more than 2,000 homeopathic remedies have been proven, and homeopathic veterinarians say they work just as well in pets as in people.

Not everyone believes homeopathy works, and some attribute cures to the placebo effect. In other words, doubters suggest that the patient expects to get well by taking medicine so that even sugar pills work to a degree. Pets also can have a sort of placebo effect when the owner believes so strongly in the treatment they react differently around the pet and that influences symptoms and behavior.

But supporters argue that some studies support the effectiveness of homeopathy. When researchers from the University of Washington and the University of Guadalajara looked at 81 children with diarrhea, children treated with homeopathy got better 20 percent faster than those given a placebo drug. Scientists in the Netherlands reviewed 107 smaller studies and found that 75 percent of the studies showed homeopathy to be effective. It may sound like magic, but something happens to get pets well.

Homeopathic remedies are labeled according to strength. A designation of "1X" means the remedy contains one part of the active ingredient and 10 parts distilled water or alcohol. A dose of 3X means a 1X solution has been diluted three times, a pretty concentrated dose. Many remedies are "1C" and have been diluted 100 times, or "1M" and diluted 1,000 times. It's not uncommon in homeopathy for a remedy to be diluted so much that not a single molecule of the active ingredient remains. That's yet another reason homeopathy seems like magic.

The remedies are prepared in a process of diluting and shaking, termed "sucussion." They are prepared in the same way flower remedies are diluted and succussed. Sucussion is thought to encode the liquid with a memory, or "vibrational energy" of the original substance, and the more it's diluted and succussed, the more powerful it becomes.

How can this be? We are used to thinking in terms of dilutions becoming weaker, but the opposite is true with homeopathy. The homeopathic X potencies (10-times dilutions) are weaker than the M potencies (1,000-times dilutions). Homeopathic remedies made for home use usually contain the lower potency X-strength remedies, while C- and M-strength remedies are typically prescribed by veterinarians.

Nobody knows how homeopathy works. Some researchers speculate the active ingredients become so minute they pass through the body's blood-brain barrier and influence the nervous system in ways we can't measure.

It takes great skill to properly prescribe the appropriate homeopathic remedy. They work best when matched to the individual pet's situation, and a one-size-fits-all approach may not work. While a conventional drug given to two puppies to address the same problem generally work the same way, the homeopathic veterinarian must figure out the cause of the symptom, too. For instance, the remedy Nux vomica treats diarrhea due to eating rich food (maybe the pet raided the garbage). But if the diarrhea was caused by something else, a different homeopathic diarrhea remedy might work better. So there can be some frustrating trial and error before you find the proper remedy.

Homeopathic medicines don't always work quickly, either, and the longer the condition has been a problem, the longer the treatment may be required. Acute conditions like diarrhea tend to get better more quickly, though. For simple problems, homeopathic veterinarians say it's fine to try homeopathy at home, because giving the wrong remedy won't cause any problems.

Health food stores and pet supply companies often carry homeopathic remedies. The size of the patient makes no difference so you can use human products for your pets. It's the frequency of dosing that influences how strong the remedy becomes.

The remedies last nearly forever, so even though they can be expensive, it's a good investment. Sometimes you can find a pre-packaged home kit with a variety of remedies for the most common issues your dog may face.

Because they're energetic medicines, homeopathic remedies can lose their power when they're exposed to electromagnetic fields. TV sets or contact with your body's natural energy can reduce potency of a remedy. You might even absorb the effect through your hands.

That's why it can be tricky to administer homeopathic remedies to pets. You don't want to hide homeopathic remedies inside treats, either. They'll often come with dispensers able to shake out single tiny pills without you needing to touch them, so just open up the pet's mouth and shake one in, without touching. Don't feed your pet within 15 minutes of giving a remedy.

Homeopathic remedies also lose their effectiveness when they're exposed to heat or sunlight, or if they're stored near strong-smelling substances like coffee or perfume. When stored carefully, preferably in a dark, cool place, they'll last just about forever.

Be selective and try only one remedy at a time. Too many at once can interfere with healing. While homeopathy won't interfere with other medications or cause overdoses, the other conventional treatments may interfere with the effectiveness of the remedy. So check with your veterinarian before mixing and matching.

Most acute problems like diarrhea or a swollen paw go away quickly. But if you don't see results in three days, you've likely picked the wrong remedy, so try a different one. While drugs work to eliminate symptoms altogether, homeopathic remedies just jump-start the body to heal itself—and that can take some time. Usually holistic vets suggest you give the remedy for a couple of days and then stop, and watch to see if it works.

HOOKWORMS

Hookworms are a common intestinal parasite of puppies, and grow to less than half an inch long. Depending on the species, they suck blood and/or take bites out of the wall of the dog's small intestine, which can result in severe bleeding. All dogs are susceptible, but puppies are at highest risk.

That's because puppies may not have the immunity to the worms that adult dogs usually develop. Dogs typically become immune to the worms after several bouts of infection; however, immunity doesn't necessarily clear all the parasites, but does help diminish their effects.

Several kinds of hookworms affect dogs. *Ancylostoma caninum* is the most important, and along with *Ancylostoma braziliense* it is found in warm climates. *Uncinaria stenocephala* also occasionally affects dogs, and is found in cool climates. The highest incidence of disease is found in southern states where higher humidity and temperature conditions provide an ideal environment for the parasite.

HOOKWORMS

SYMPTOMS: Anemia; bloody to black tarlike diarrhea; weight loss; low energy; sometimes vomiting; painful, swollen, cracked feet
HOME CARE: None
VET CARE: Hookworm medication; supportive care, such as fluid therapy or blood transfusion; treatment to relieve enteritis
PREVENTION: Keep yard clean; disinfect kennels; certain heartworm preventatives also deworm the dog

The adult hookworms mate inside the pup's intestine, and females lay eggs which are passed with the stool. The eggs hatch in about a week, then develop further in the environment into infective larvae. In warm and wet conditions, larvae may live for two months. They prefer sandy soil, but may crawl onto grass seeking a host.

Dogs can be infected in several ways. Swallowing the parasite after sniffing or licking is a common route of infection. Puppies can pick up larvae from soil or feces. Larvae are also able to penetrate the skin directly, most usually the dog's footpads. Infective hookworm larvae are capable of penetrating human skin, causing *Cutaneous Larval Migrans* in which migrating larvae in the skin cause small, red itchy trails.

Puppies often contract hookworms through trans-mammary infection—by drinking infested mother's milk—or less often, before birth while in the uterus. Dogs also may be infected by eating an infected mouse or cockroach.

After being swallowed or penetrating the skin, it takes about two weeks for the immature worms to migrate into the bloodstream, through the lungs, and into the intestine where they mature. When the dog is older and has an established immunity to the parasite, the larvae may never reach the lungs, and instead remain in arrested development in various tissues throughout the body.

When a dog becomes pregnant, the worms migrate to the mammary glands or, less commonly, the uterus, and subsequently infect puppies before or shortly after birth. In males and non-pregnant females, tissue-infesting larvae may "leak" back into circulation, mature, and become reproducing adults.

298 *DOG FACTS*

The most common clinical sign of infection is blood loss resulting in anemia. When young puppies are exposed to hookworms for the first time, they have no natural defense and can quickly become overwhelmed by a massive infestation. Acute hookworm disease arises suddenly, and in addition to signs of profound anemia, these pups may have a bloody to black tarlike diarrhea. A severe infestation can cause sudden collapse and death.

Adult dogs more typically develop chronic, or ongoing, disease. Dogs that are stressed, malnourished, or in an endemic region are at highest risk, and chronic infection is characterized by mild diarrhea or vomiting. But if the dog's immunity fully breaks down, chronic hookworm disease can turn deadly even in adults; signs are similar to the acute infection. This is an emergency situation, which may require hospitalization, a blood transfusion, and supportive care (see BLOOD).

Hookworms are diagnosed by finding eggs during microscopic examination of the stool. However, young puppies may suffer acute disease without any eggs being present if the worms are too young to reproduce. Medications are given in doses timed to kill adult worms and maturing larva, but may not clear larvae in arrested development in other tissues. It's important to follow your veterinarian's instructions in treating your puppy to be sure all the worms are eliminated.

Sometimes older dogs with ongoing exposure to the parasite develop a hookworm dermatitis at the site of skin penetration. This most commonly affects the footpads, and is referred to as pododermatitis. The dog's feet become painful, swell, feel hot, and become soft and spongy. Without treatment, the footpads may separate, nails become deformed, and the pads turn dry, thick and cracked. Treatment is the same as for intestinal infestation, but in addition, a medication is applied to affected skin to kill the larvae.

Preventing hookworm infection can be easily done simply by giving a heartworm preventative that also prevents hookworms. Female dogs that are to be bred should receive worm medication given prior to the birth to help kill the larvae that may infect her puppies.

The best prevention is to practice good hygiene. Clean up stools promptly from the yard, because it takes six days for larvae to leave the stool. Outdoor exposure has the greatest risk in damp, shaded areas so keep kennel areas dry and clean.

Direct sunlight will help curb the worm population in the environment. Gravel or sandy runs may benefit from applications of rock salt or borax, which will kill the larvae; however, these substances also kill grass. Concrete runs should be washed down with a one percent solution of bleach.

HOT SPOTS

Also referred to as acute moist dermatitis, a hot spot is a localized area of self-induced trauma that becomes infected. Dogs suffering from atopy are at highest risk (see ALLERGY), but all dogs can develop these sores. Dog breeds with heavy double coats like Chow Chows and German Shepherd Dogs seem most prone to developing hot spots immediately prior to shedding, when dead hair may be trapped next to the skin. For unknown reasons, Golden Retrievers tend to develop deeply infected hot spots.

HOT SPOTS

SYMPTOMS: Quickly growing round circle of itchy hair loss; moist, painful, inflamed skin
FIRST AID: Clip fur surrounding area; cleanse with diluted hydrogen peroxide or benzoyl peroxide cleanser; apply medication like Burrow's solution to dry lesion
HOLISTIC HELP: Herbal remedies; tea poultice
VET CARE: Same as home care; often sedation is necessary; prescription ointments or injections that soothe the itch; sometimes antibiotics and corticosteroids; address underlying cause
PREVENTION: Groom dogs to prevent mats; provide proper flea and tick control; treat wounds promptly

Hot spots can appear anywhere on the dog's body, but the rump, tail, back, and flanks are common sites. Usually, the hot spot appears suddenly as an initially small circular area of hair loss, but they can spread rapidly. Sores can grow to several inches in diameter within a few hours. The infection often smells bad and secretes pus, and hot spots typically are moist due to licking and/or the weeping of the wound, and hot because of infection and inflammation.

No one is certain what causes a hot spot to form, but it's thought to be prompted by some minor irritation, like a flea bite. Itchiness and discomfort prompts licking and nibbling, and when the dog can't leave the wound alone, a hot spot erupts.

Treatment consists of getting air to the infection so it will heal and dry, and preventing further self-mutilation. A collar restraint prevents him from licking or nibbling the sore (see ELIZABETHAN COLLAR).

Hot spots are both itchy and painful, and often require a veterinarian to sedate the dog before treatment can begin. The fur surrounding the area is clipped away, the skin is cleansed with an antibacterial preparation like diluted hydrogen peroxide, Nolvasan, Betadine,

Oxydex or pHisoHex. Pet-formulations of benzoyl peroxide-containing cleansers help reduce the itchiness, dry the lesion, and flush out hair follicles, as well as kill certain bacteria.

Once cleansed, a medication like Burrow's solution, available at most drug stores or pet stores, may be applied and seems to work quite well to dry the sore. Holistic veterinarians recommend using calendula to soothe the sore. Witch hazel can help cool down the heat of hot spots because it evaporates as quickly as alcohol but without the sting. You can use that two or three times a day.

Another natural remedy for hot spots is the tannic acid found in black tea. This astringent helps dry out the sores so they heal more quickly. Soak a tea bag in hot water, let it cool, and apply the bag directly to the sore for five minutes. You can do this three or four times a day.

The veterinarian may prescribe ointments like Panalog or Neocort, or short-acting corticosteroids like prednisone that reduce the irritation. Occasionally, antibiotics are required to clear up deep infection. The underlying problem, fleas, allergy, or whatever, must also be addressed.

Since dogs aren't able to adequately groom themselves, owners must take great responsibility for seeing that coat care is provided. Grooming during shedding season is particularly important, and can help prevent problems like hot spots from developing (see GROOMING and SHEDDING).

HOUSE TRAINING

House training refers to teaching dogs proper bathroom etiquette. Dogs that share house privileges with you must learn where appropriate facilities are located, and how to alert you to their need.

"Accidents" that occur in the house can indicate a health or behavior problem. Leg-lifting in the house is a dominance display (see MARKING) and defecating on an owner's property such as the bed or shoes can be an expression of stress. Dogs and especially puppies may urinate to show deference, or out of fear (see SUBMISSIVE URINATION). Many times, however, inappropriate elimination habits are due to deficient house training. Puppies require specific instruction, and adult dogs often need refresher courses to enforce good habits.

For effective house training, four things are required: patience, consistency, timing and confinement. A plain cardboard box or dog crate is the ideal teaching tool. Given a choice, both adult dogs and puppies will eliminate far away from where they eat and sleep. The most effective house training methods use the dog's natural inclination toward cleanliness to prompt proper elimination.

Puppies aren't physically able to control elimination until they reach about five weeks of age, and complete bladder control develops later. However, it's important to institute the rules of the house as soon as you bring your puppy home.

During house-training, whenever the dog or puppy is not under your direct supervision (your eyes on her at all times!), she should be confined in a small space only large enough for bedding and a bowl of water. Use a crate or cardboard box, which the dog will readily identify as her "den." She'll do her best to wait until released from confinement, so she won't have to live with her own waste. A small area like the powder room or laundry room won't work, because your dog will simply use one corner as a toilet, and sleep in the other "den" end. The idea is that she must live with the consequences of her mistake should she produce a puddle or pile.

Offer your dog plenty of opportunities to eliminate in the right location. This is where timing is important. Puppies have a limited capacity to control their bowels and bladder, and need frequent potty breaks. Two-month-old pups need a break about every two hours; three-month-old pups can hold it for four hours; four-month-old pups can wait five hours; five-month-olds can wait about six hours; and seven-month-old pups should be able to wait about eight hours.

A good rule of thumb is after each nap, meal, and play session, and the first thing every morning and last thing at night. Adult dogs can hold out for longer at a time, but offer more opportunities for good behavior rather than less.

Consistency is extremely important in training. Feed your dog at the same times each day, so her body establishes an internal clock that you can anticipate. Designate the dog's toilet area from the beginning, and always take her to the same place so that she'll associate the sight and scent with what's expected. There's no need to first "paper-train" your dog if she's to use the yard as an adult; that simply adds an extra step, and she'll have to un-learn using the house and switch bathroom allegiance to outdoors. From the beginning, physically take her to a specific corner of the yard and wait for her to "do her duty," then praise the dickens out of her so she knows she's been a good girl. Wait until she's consistent and knows what's expected before simply letting her out the back door into your fenced yard.

High-rise apartments or other housing that offers no yard privileges require you to designate an area of your home as the dog's bathroom. Older dogs may eventually develop the control to be able to "hold it" until they can reach the neighborhood park or nearest fire hydrant; in most cases, you'll need to address any pooper-scooper requirements. Training is identical; timing, consistency, and confinement are still required, but instead of taking your puppy outside you take her to your indoor facility.

Traditionally, paper-training has involved layering newspaper on an area of easily cleaned floor, such as the linoleum of a bathroom. However, some hardheaded dogs have trouble distinguishing between the newspapers in the potty area, and the ones you've left beside your chair after reading them. A better and probably more hygienic alternative is to use jumbo-size absorbable pads available from pet supply stores—or use disposable diapers. Some small dogs will accept using a cat litter box with a dog litter filler. Dogs won't cover their waste, though.

To avoid accidents on the way from confinement to the doggy toilet, either carry the dog if she's small enough, or put her on leash so she's under your command. Dogs are less likely to eliminate when they're "working."

Confine her until she's reliable; that means, whenever you're talking on the phone, eating dinner, watching television, or otherwise do not have your eyes glued to the fuzzy puddle-

maker, she should be in the box or crate. This ensures that if a mistake is made, you catch her in the act and can correct her appropriately.

Dogs have a short-term memory regarding inappropriate behavior. Unless a correction is made during or immediately following the infraction (within 30 to 60 seconds), your dog won't understand why she's being reprimanded and the correction won't have any effect. If you discover a puddle or pile under the dining room table after you left her unsupervised to answer the door, all you can do is clean it up and resolve to watch her closer next time.

Incidentally, rubbing your dog's nose in her mess--even when caught in the act--is not helpful, and even counterproductive. It confuses the dog and can make her think you object to any elimination when in fact it's the location that's the problem. Some dogs may simply think you've lost your mind. Making the dog fear eliminating around you may make her hide messes more effectively and avoid "going" when you can see.

A more effective method is to say "no" when she begins to pose, and immediately remove her to the designated area. Offer extravagant praise when she's productive in the right place. Link a command to the action by saying, "hurry up, hurry up" as she squats, then praise her when she's done. Soon, she'll understand what's expected when she hears the "hurry up" command.

Eliminate opportunities for mistakes by confining her when she cannot be watched. Alternatively, clip her leash to your belt so she can't sneak away and hide her deposit.

Dogs respond more readily to positive reinforcement (praise) than chastisement, so give her every chance to be a good dog. Try "paying" your dog for eliminating in the right spot when you ask, with praise or treats. Keep the pup on a leash until she's been productive, and only then reward with an off-leash game. She'll soon learn to let someone know when she needs to go out, in order to avoid messing her bed.

Dogs and puppies typically are eager to please, and most learn the concept within the first several days. Even hard-case adult dogs can be housetrained within two or three weeks with consistent confinement. Puppies may understand the concept, but be physically incapable of reliable control until they're about six months old. However, confinement needn't continue the whole time, as she should learn to notify you of her needs whether in confinement or not. Once your dog has proved able to keep the box or crate clean, expand her territory by degrees (every two weeks) until she considers the entire house a den and treats it appropriately (see TRAINING).

HUMAN-ANIMAL BOND Once a pet becomes a "family member," she is no longer a nameless, faceless piece of property that can be easily replaced if care becomes too expensive or time-consuming. One of the characteristics of domestication is the ability to have relationships with species other than your own.

Studies on the human-animal bond have shown that children who learn empathy toward animals tend to feel it toward people, too. They recognize that "different" isn't "wrong." Learning to treat a dog like a dog and a cat like a cat, recognizing each species has its own physical and behavioral needs and are not little fur-covered humanoids, goes a long way toward developing a recognition and tolerance for all creatures that are different, including different people.

Behaviorists speculate that just as puppies have a socialization period during which they "learn" to accept other species, humans also have a similar window of opportunity. The pathways in the brain for various functions are forged early in life. Exposure to music, for instance, prompts the biochemical connections that embrace mathematical concepts, and hearing builds the routes necessary to develop language skills. Early positive contact with pets forms the necessary brain circuitry to "turn on" the switch that makes it possible for a special connection with an animal. Miss that window of opportunity, and the door slams shut.

The "pet potential" probably exists in everyone, but not everybody develops the ability to connect with animals. In domestic dogs, the socialization period is seven to 12 weeks (see SOCIALIZATION), and it's likely very early in children, too. People who miss that opportunity as young children can learn as they grow older, but may never quite understand the process or have that deep sense of "one-ness" with the animals in their lives.

Dr. Leo K. Bustad was one of the earliest to recognize the benefits of the human-animal bond. More than 20 years ago, he helped establish the Delta Society, an organization dedicated to celebrating and promoting pet-people partnerships, including training and certification of a variety of service animals that benefit human health.

Due in large part to these efforts, federal laws have been passed protecting the relationship between pets and their elderly or disabled owners or families residing in public housing. Additionally, state regulations barring animals from health-care facilities are being loosened to allow animal-assisted activity and therapy programs. Wonderful work done by dogs that act as surrogate eyes, ears, or hands for their disabled human partners has long been recognized. Dogs have always worked for people in a wide range of capacities, from herders and guardians, to hunters and protectors. Today's service animals are following that tradition, with a newer kind of work assignment. But modern pet partnerships go beyond traditional ones because to be effective, the "job" requires an emotional attachment between the animal and human.

For example, modern dogs learn to "alert" their owners—that is, give a warning of impending medical events such as seizures and migraines—so they have time to seek help. Pets can detect changes in their owner's breathing or heart rate, so they can help head off blackouts, and even heart attacks. Some dogs have "diagnosed" skin cancer—cancer apparently smells different than other kinds of skin sores—when fanatical sniffing pestered their owners into seeking medical care. In the past decade, medicine has acknowledged the benefits that a positive pet relationship can have on our health, especially for stress-related conditions including blood pressure.

Petting a dog, or simply having them in the same room, lowers blood pressure. People living with pets visit the doctor less often, and recover more quickly when they are ill. Heart attack victims living with pets statistically survive longer than those without pets. People who are partnered with service animals, senior citizens living with dogs, and children suffering from a variety of problems who have a pet all benefit both physically and mentally from this "pet effect."

Pets help people connect with other people. An elderly person stays more connected to life in order to care for a beloved pet, when she might not make the effort for herself.

Pets help normalize relationships. Disabled children who withdraw from peers interact with others when a "social" pet becomes the focus and bridge between them and other kids. Injury victims reluctant to endure painful rehabilitation will push themselves, when it means, for instance, throwing a ball for a dog. For many people, a connection with pets is vital. It's what we need to feel whole.

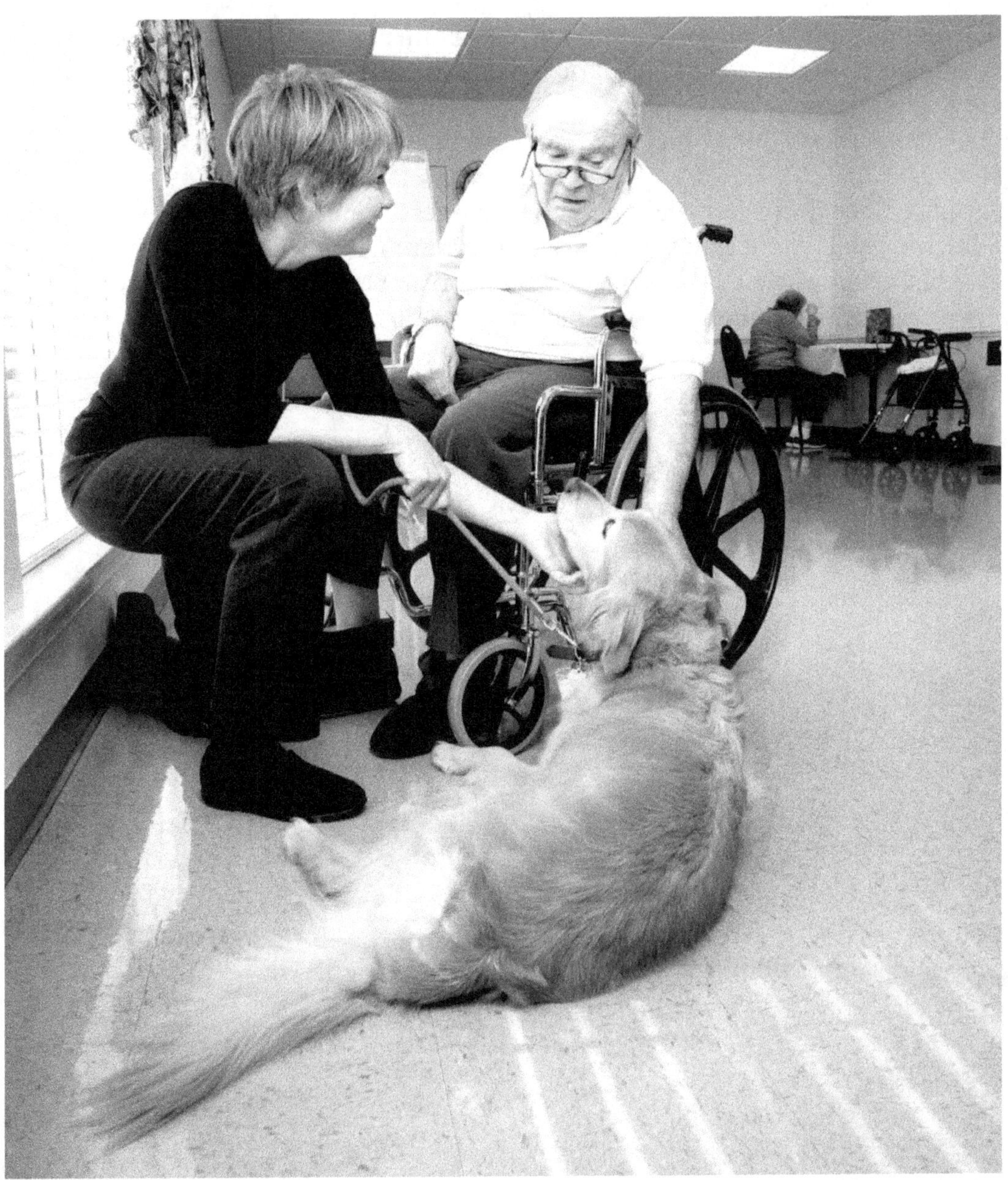

HUNTING BEHAVIOR This refers to behaviors that allow the dog to detect and capture prey. Dogs evolved as hunters in order to survive, and all modern dogs are born with innate predatory skills specific to hunting prey. This applies whether the dog is a free-living feral animal who relies on these behaviors to eat, or a pampered house dog that never wants for food. Many play behaviors use the same techniques as those used for hunting (see PLAY).

But instinct alone does not make every dog a successful hunter. Not all dogs have the same abilities to hunt, and technique is only learned through practice. Each puppy hones technical skill through play and sometimes an adult's example. Dogs never exposed to prey as puppies can learn to become successful hunters as adults.

Dogs do not necessarily hunt to eat. Hunger does not trigger the behavior, it is the sound, scent, or sight of moving prey that provides the stimulus. Even a pampered lap dog reacts to a leaping squirrel, the rustle of leaves, or the scent of the bunny frozen in the shrubs. The urge to track and chase prey is ingrained in the canine psyche.

For most dogs, scent drives hunting behavior, and is used to both identify and locate prey (see NOSE). Sight and sound also play a role. A number of refined behaviors used singly or together compose the dog's hunting repertoire.

Typically, the dog's smell sense alerts him to the presence of prey, and he tracks game by following the scent-trail. This may be done with head held high and reading scent-cues from the air, or with a nose-to-ground posture. As he nears the target, he slows his gait and lowers his head in the classic stalking pose. His eyes remain glued to the prey, and he may pause and freeze in position with his body pointed at the target. Once within striking range, the dog flushes the bird or bunny from hiding. The prey's attempt to escape prompts the hunter's chase impulse. He drives the animal mercilessly, using his stamina to run it to exhaustion. When working with a pack, individual canines may run large prey in relays until it gives up, or may herd it into the waiting jaws of compatriots.

Dogs use powerful jaws and sharp canine teeth for a slashing attack. But it's neck and shoulder muscles that usually provide the lethal blow when the dog grasps the animal and shakes it furiously to break its neck. Larger prey requires a different technique, but are rarely hunted by domestic dogs. The dog's wolf cousins may first cripple very large prey like caribou by slashing their legs, and then the torso; the animal simply weakens from blood loss, and is easily brought down. Canines eat prey on the spot, but may carry small animals home when they have puppies to be fed.

Not all hunting behaviors are seen in all dogs, though. One or more of the tracking, stalking, pointing, herding/driving, attacking, killing and retrieving behaviors have been selectively augmented or even eliminated in certain dog breeds through the domestication process. These changes better fit specific breeds to their roles in the service of humans. In most breeds, the attack and kill sequence behaviors have been inhibited, while others enhanced.

For instance, the Bloodhound has been selectively bred to be an expert tracker, and lives for scent. He cares about little else. Sighthounds like the Afghan Hound and Greyhound, and many of the terriers, trigger more to movement than scent and rely on sight to track prey and run it down. The former are racers that love the chase, while the latter react similarly to cats in their stalk-and-pounce techniques.

Sheepdogs like Border Collies employ the stalk, stare and chase to herd their wooly charges, but the final attack/kill sequence has been bred out. The behaviors of "hunting" breeds have been refined to those that only locate prey for the human hunter (pointers and setters), and those that bring it back once killed (retrievers and spaniels). Some dogs have been breed with an exceptionally inhibited bite which promotes a "soft mouth" to keep the

dog from damaging the game as it is retrieved. Conversely, some hunters like the Foxhound even today remain adept at attacking and killing prey.

Eating wild game exposes dogs to the risk of parasites (see TAPEWORMS and HOOKWORMS). In farming communities, the indiscriminate hunter can become a menace to livestock and poultry. The only way to prevent unacceptable hunting is by keeping the dog under your direct supervision. Confine him to a fenced yard, or keep him on a leash when outside. It's best to offer dogs the opportunity to use their skills by actually hunting, herding, or tracking with their owner, or participating in mock exercises like field trials, lure coursing, herding exhibitions, or other outlets (see TRIALS). Some pets may be satisfied with alternative outlets for hunting behavior during play.

HYPERPARATHYROIDISM This condition refers to the excessive production of parathyroid hormone (PTH or parathormone). PTH is produced by two pairs of parathyroid glands located adjacent to each globe of the thyroid gland in the dog's neck. PTH normally acts to pull calcium out of the bones and into the blood, which lowers blood phosphorus levels. It also increases intestinal calcium absorption and kidney calcium retention.

When too much PTH is produced, bone formation in young dogs is impaired due to increased losses of calcium. Adult dogs with this condition suffer a softening and weakening of the bone that makes them highly prone to fracture.

The most common cause of hyperparathyroidism is a non-cancerous tumor involving one or more of the parathyroid glands. Another cause is long-standing kidney disease, which results in retention of phosphorus in the blood that in turn stimulates excessive production of PTH to counter the resulting low calcium serum level. A third cause is a dietary deficiency of calcium or vitamin D, or an excess of phosphorus (see NUTRITION and FOOD SUPPLEMENTS).

HYPERPARATHYROIDISM

SYMPTOMS: Increased thirst and urination; loss of appetite; lethargy and weakness; vomiting
HOME CARE: Nutritional support
VET CARE: Surgery; sometimes vitamin supplementation
PREVENTION: Feed complete and balanced dog food

Most affected dogs are ten years or older. It appears most commonly in the Keeshond, German Shepherd Dog and Norwegian Elkhound, which indicates there may be a genetic predisposition.

Mild forms of the disease may not cause obvious signs, but usually the dog exhibits increased thirst and urination, loss of appetite, lethargy and weakness, and vomiting. Unless treated, the dog will ultimately suffer kidney failure.

Diagnosis is based on signs, and on laboratory analysis of the blood levels of calcium, phosphorus, and PTH.

Surgical removal of the abnormal parathyroid tissue is the treatment of choice. When the condition is a result of nutritional inadequacy, feed a complete and balanced diet with appropriate calcium or vitamin D supplementation as advised by your veterinarian.

In most cases, the chance of recovery is good. However, when the condition involves kidney failure, the prognosis is guarded and treatment must address renal disease.

HEATSTROKE

SYMPTOMS: Panting; drooling; vomiting; muscle tremors; temperature to 106 degrees; rapid pulse; staring; diarrhea; bright red gums; bloody nose; severe weakness; coma
FIRST AID: EMERGENCY! Wrap dog in cool, wet towel, or immerse in cool water until temperature drops to 103; SEE VET IMMEDIATELY!
VET CARE: Cool-water enemas; oxygen therapy; fluid therapy to fight dehydration; medications to treat bleeding tendency; possibly blood transfusion
PREVENTION: Keep cool water and shade available at all times; provide good ventilation; never shut dog in closed car; keep fur well groomed; restrict exercise during hottest times of the day

HYPERTHERMIA Also referred to as heatstroke, hyperthermia is body temperature above normal that cannot be reduced through natural means. The condition occurs when the body's cooling system is unable to lose heat as fast as it is gained.

The most common causes of hyperthermia are fever, excessive exertion, and confinement in a hot and/or humid area. Poor ventilation and direct sunlight are predisposing factors, and dogs are most often afflicted during the warm summer months. Dogs usually are able to lose excessive body temperature by elevating or "fluffing" their fur to allow ventilation next to the skin, and by panting. When the outside temperature is close to or exceeds the dog's normal temperature (about 102 degrees), this cooling mechanism becomes much less effective.

Most cases of canine heatstroke result when the dog is left in a poorly ventilated car parked in the hot sun. Other times, dogs don't know when to call it quits and over exercise during hot, humid weather. Being confined on a concrete shade-less run can also raise body temperature. Hot apartments, rooms or dog crates that have poor circulation can also be dangerous. And dogs being groomed that are muzzled while exposed to a hot-air drier can also suffer problems. Dogs with preexisting respiratory problems (see ASTHMA and OBESITY) and short-nose dogs like Pugs and Bulldogs are highly susceptible to the condition.

Dogs suffering heat exhaustion may simply collapse, exhibit vomiting, muscle tremors, rapid heart rate, and pant very rapidly. Sometimes they'll faint, but more commonly the dog remains alert, and has only a slightly elevated temperature. In heat exhaustion, the dog's body still works and tries to cool herself.

In the more serious heatstroke, the body's temperature regulating mechanism shuts off. All the signs are similar, except the body gets hotter faster. A rectal temperature over 106 degrees is diagnostic for heat stroke. In severe cases, the dog's gums become bright red, and she may develop a bloody nose. At temperatures over 108 degrees, the cells begin to die as they are literally cooked from the inside out. Among other things, the kidneys and liver stop working, the heart fails, and the brain is irreparably damaged. Without prompt treatment, the dog becomes comatose and will die.

Heatstroke is a medical emergency that must be treated immediately. Treatment consists of cooling the dog as quickly as possible. When the dog's rectal temperature is 104 to 108 degrees, simply soak the dog's fur in cool (not ice) water, and turn on a fan to aid evaporative cooling. If the dog's temperature exceeds 108 degrees, immerse her in ice water. A cold water enema may be required to cool her from the inside out. Check her temperature every ten minutes, and continue cooling until the temperature drops to at least 103 degrees. If she loses consciousness—and even if she doesn't—get your dog veterinary attention as soon as possible. Some cases may require hospitalization to counter damage.

Cases of severe hyperthermia will also require treatment for shock, including fluid therapy to combat dehydration. Oxygen therapy helps prevent brain damage. Sometimes, heatstroke may cause the dog's throat to swell, further compromising the situation and requiring a cortisone injection to counter the inflammation.

Prevent heatstroke by restricting your dog's activity during the hottest times of day, particularly in humid summer weather. A matted coat keeps heat from escaping; keep your full-coated dogs properly groomed and mat-free, or clip the coat short during summer months. Pay particular attention if your dog already suffers respiratory problems, or is a high-risk flat-faced breed. Always provide access to plenty of fresh drinking water, and when she must be confined, be sure she has proper ventilation and adequate shade. NEVER LEAVE YOUR PET in a parked car, not even with the window cracked. Even shaded cars reach 120 degrees in less than ten minutes.

HYPERTHYROIDISM The term hyperthyroidism refers to overactivity of the thyroid gland. The condition is considered rare in dogs, and most commonly affects dogs older than ten years old. Any dog can be affected, but Beagles, Boxers, Golden Retrievers and German Shepherd Dogs appear to have the highest risk.

The thyroid gland has two lobes, and is located at the base of the dog's neck. It secretes hormones called thyroxine and triiodothyronine which help regulate metabolism, the rate at which food and oxygen are turned into energy by the body. Canine hyperthyroidism occurs when a tumor forms on the thyroid gland and secretes excess hormones into the blood, speeding up the dog's metabolism.

The tumor may be benign, but more commonly is a large malignant mass that encroaches into the dog's esophagus and trachea and surrounding tissues. These tumors frequently spread to the lungs or lymph nodes throughout the body.

HYPERTHYROIDISM

SYMPTOMS: Ravenous appetite; increased thirst and urination; weight loss; hyperactivity; increased aggression
HOME CARE: None
VET CARE: Surgery; radiation; chemotherapy; radioactive iodine therapy
PREVENTION: None; remain vigilant for signs; seek prompt treatment

Signs of hyperthyroidism include a ravenous appetite, increased thirst and urination, weight loss, hyperactivity, and increased aggression. Diagnosis is based on clinical signs, on tests that measure levels of thyroid hormones (T3 and T4) in the circulating blood, and on the evaluation of a sample of tumor tissue. Treatment depends on the individual dog's age, anesthetic risk, and health status.

Removal of the tumor has a good chance of curing the dog. Benign tumors and small cancerous tumors that have not yet spread are treated surgically. If all of the thyroid gland must be removed, a daily thyroid supplement provides the necessary hormone.

Tumors that are large and invasive and/or have spread can be treated with therapies that may combine radiation therapy, surgery, and chemotherapy (see CANCER). Radioactive iodine, which selectively destroys thyroid tissue, may also be used. However, dogs suffering from such tumors have a very poor prognosis.

HYPOGLYCEMIA (LOW BLOOD SUGAR) Low blood sugar affects puppies much more often than adult dogs, even when your puppy is healthy, so it's important to learn about low blood sugar symptoms and what to do. The technical term is hypoglycemia. Sugar moves into the cells with the help of insulin, and too much insulin can cause hypoglycemia.

Puppies can develop low blood sugar due to intestinal parasites that compromise digestion. Very small puppies, especially Toy breeds like the Chihuahua or Pomeranian, are so tiny, they have very few fat stores. Fat is body fuel, and when there's not enough, the blood sugar levels fall. Adult pets can make up this difference when their liver churns out the necessary sugar. But immature livers can't manufacture enough necessary sugar and as a result, these tiny pups develop hypoglycemia.

The signs of low blood sugar can be vague. Without enough sugar, the heartbeat rate and breathing slows down and that triggers a cascade effect of other symptoms. Be alert for any one or combination of the following signs: The dog acts weak; becomes sleepy; seems disoriented; develops a wobbly "drunk" gait; eyes look 'glassy' and unfocussed; starts to twitch, shake or tremble/shiver; head tilts to one side; develops seizures; falls unconscious and can't be wakened.

Without prompt help and first aid, your dog could die. When you recognize the signs early in the process, low blood sugar is easy to treat and reverse at home.

In almost all cases, dogs respond very quickly to treatment, within five or ten minutes. However, it treatment doesn't reverse the symptoms within this time frame take your dog to the veterinarian immediately as something else could have caused the signs. Even when your dog responds quickly it's a good idea to have a veterinarian check sometime that day to be sure everything is as it should be.

Without prompt help puppies can fall into a coma, and their breathing and/or heartbeat may stop (see ARTIFICIAL RESPIRATION and CPR).

HYPOGLYCEMIA

SYMPTOMS: Acts weak, sleepy or unfocussed; seems disoriented or drunk; starts to twitch, shake, tremble; head tilts to one side; seizures
FIRST AID: Offer a meal, or sugar source
VET CARE: Same.
PREVENTION: Feed small dogs and puppies several meals daily; add sugar source to water

For All Symptoms. When the blood sugar drops, young puppies can't regulate their body temperature. It's important to keep him warm until the glucose level rises enough to burn for energy. Wrap your puppy in a blanket, and snuggle him with a hot water bottle or heating pad. This can also slow down the effects of shock.

For Sleepy/Woozy Behavior. Getting sugar into the dog counteracts all these symptoms. Often, you'll notice the wooziness when it's been a while since the dog's last meal. As soon as you notice woozy behavior, offer something to eat. Make it something smelly and yummy that you know he'll eagerly snarf up, like a tablespoon or two of canned food.

For Drunk/Shivery Behavior. A highly concentrated sugar source like Karo syrup, pancake syrup or honey can work even more quickly. Just be sure your dog is still able to swallow before giving him about a teaspoonful of the sugar source. If he's very groggy, offer a bit of water first and if he won't lap it up, give some with a syringe. Check to be sure he swallows, and then offer the syrup. He should be able to lap it up from the spoon.

For Seizures/Unconscious. Refer to the tips outlined in section on EPILEPSY. Once the seizure has finished, or when the dog has fallen unconscious, you can still administer a sugar source. He doesn't need to swallow. It will be absorbed directly through the mucus membranes in the mouth and transferred into the bloodstream. Honey works best for this. Rub the honey on the inside of his lips and gums, and watch for recovery in five to 15 minutes. You can drive your puppy to the vet clinic during this period.

When your puppy has suffered from a bout of hypoglycemia, you'll know to be alert for the signs of low blood sugar in the future. You can also take steps to prevent the problem, especially if your puppy is a high-risk Toy breed.

Add two tablespoons Karo syrup to your dog's water for all day sipping. Be sure to dump out and add fresh each day or the sugar water could grow bacteria.

Schedule several meals every day. Toy breed adults and any young puppy have trouble eating enough food at one setting. So a small meal several times a day helps keep the blood sugar levels normal.

Provide dry food out all the time, in a puzzle toy ball, for intermittent snacking. You can measure this amount, too, and regulate how much the pup gets to help keep him slim, while you provide healthy blood sugar levels.

Most adult dogs won't have problems with hypoglycemia. However, playing and running too hard without rest can cause low blood sugar even in adults that are not Toy breed dogs. It's up to pet parents to stay watchful and make sure the puppy and maturing dog eat right and maintain healthy food habits.

HYPOPARATHYROIDISM

SYMPTOMS: Seizures; muscle twitching; spasms; nervousness; weakness; drunken behavior; loss of appetite; excessive panting; face rubbing
HOME CARE: None
VET CARE: Calcium and vitamin D supplements
PREVENTION: None; remain vigilant for signs; seek prompt treatment

HYPOPARATHYROIDISM

This condition refers to the deficiency of parathyroid hormone (PTH or parathormone). PTH is produced by two pairs of parathyroid glands located adjacent to each globe of the thyroid gland in the dog's neck. Normally, PTH maintains the blood calcium and phosphorus levels (see HYPERPARATHYROIDISM).

A lack of PTH results in a deficiency of blood calcium levels, with a corresponding excess of blood phosphorus levels. The cause of the condition isn't known, but is commonly thought to result from an abnormal immune reaction that destroys parathyroid tissue.

Most affected dogs are females less than six years old, but there is no apparent breed prevalence. Signs are severe, and due to lack of calcium (hypocalcemia). They tend to appear without warning, often during periods of exercise or stress. Signs include seizures (see EPILEPSY), muscle twitching or spasms, nervousness, weakness, and uncoordinated drunken gait. Dogs tend to lose their appetite, have no energy, pant excessively, and may exhibit intense facial rubbing.

Diagnosis is based on signs, along with laboratory analysis of calcium and PTH in the blood. Normal blood levels can usually be maintained by calcium and vitamin D food supplements as prescribed by the veterinarian. A maintenance dose of vitamin D supplements may be required for the rest of the dog's life, but in most cases, a full recovery can be expected.

HYPOTHERMIA

Hypothermia is the opposite of hyperthermia, and results when body temperature falls below normal. Dogs have many protective mechanisms for regulating body heat. Their fur insulates by trapping air next to the skin, which is warmed by the body. Dogs conserve heat by curling up in protected areas sheltered from wind and wet and their own body heat the area to keep warm.

When they feel cold, dogs burn more calories at the cellular level, a kind of furnace that increases body temperature and helps keep them warm. Shivering is a spontaneous action of the body designed to generate heat. Cold weather also prompts the body to divert blood circulation from the ears, toes, and tail and pour more into the trunk to protect and keep warm the important internal organs. Failure of any one or several of these protective mechanisms can predispose to loss of heat, and may result in hypothermia. In fact, the very action that protects organs from the cold actually promotes damage to the extremities (see FROSTBITE).

Outdoor dogs are at highest risk for hypothermia. It's seen most often in Toy breeds and dogs with short fur. Very young puppies are unable to regulate their own body temperature, and are at high risk for hypothermia. Body heat is produced by burning muscle and fat, which are less available in very young and very old dogs (see GERIATRIC DOG). However, any dog that is exposed to extreme or long-term cold, a long anesthetic procedure, or that becomes wet or that suffers shock risks hypothermia.

The severity of the hypothermia is designated mild, moderate, or severe, depending on the dog's body temperature. Mild hypothermia results in lethargy, excessive shivering, and sometimes muscle tremors, and the dog will feel cold to your touch. Rectal temperatures down to about 96 degrees are categorized as mild, and can be treated using passive rewarming techniques. If your dog is dry, simply cover him loosely with a blanket, and allow his own body to rewarm itself. When the dog is wet, a warm bath will help rewarm him. Dry him thoroughly with towels. Warm a blanket or towel in the drier, and keep him covered until he's no longer wet.

Dogs are designated moderately hypothermic when their rectal temperature falls between 96 and 82 degrees. At this point, the dog's shivering response will stop, and natural metabolic warming is no longer possible.

Severe hypothermia occurs at body temperatures below 82 degrees; typically, the dog loses consciousness and the heart and respiration becomes so slow he may be mistaken for dead. Veterinarians have special thermometers able to record these low body temperatures, but standard rectal thermometers only measure as low as 93 degrees. If your dog feels cold to the touch but has stopped shivering, and/or loses consciousness, veterinary attention is necessary if he is to survive.

Moderate to severe hypothermia requires aggressive rewarming techniques to reduce further heat loss, prevent organ damage, and keep vital organs working. Moderate hypothermia calls for rewarming with hot water bottles, electric blankets, recirculating water blankets, heating pads, heat lamps, or other heat sources. Extreme care must be taken, though, because too rapid surface warming can cause a drop in blood pressure when the outside returns to normal more quickly than the depressed heart can handle. Heating sources are applied only to the trunk of the body, keeping the extremities cool to prevent shock that may kill the dog. Even then, the heat sources must be buffered and not in direct contact with the skin; hypothermia prevents the body from conducting excessive heat away, so the dog can be easily burned. A heat lamp should ideally be placed about 30 inches away for optimum impact without burning the dog.

Core warming is reserved for cases of severe hypothermia, and in these cases the dog is literally reheated from the inside out. A veterinarian's help is usually required. Treatment can involve warm water enemas, warm intravenous fluid therapy, airway rewarming with oxygen, even heart/lung bypass machines to warm the blood. Fluids may be repeatedly flushed into the abdomen to warm the organs and tissues, then drawn back out until body temperature returns to normal. Sadly, chance for full recovery from severe hypothermia is small, because often the organs and tissues are severely damaged.

If you suspect your dog is suffering from moderate to severe hypothermia but are unable to reach veterinary help, treat the dog using external warming techniques described above. Fill hot water bottles with warm (not burning) water that's about 100 degrees, and wrap them in a towel. Place the buffered water bottle, heating pad, or other re-warming device on the dog's chest and abdomen, and in the armpit areas beneath his legs. Monitor the dog's

temperature—don't try to rewarm too quickly, a degree or two each hour is about right—until it reaches 100 degrees. If the dog begins to stir and move, when he's conscious offer him one to two tablespoons of honey or Karo syrup. Get your dog veterinary evaluation as soon as possible.

Prevent hypothermia by protecting your dog from inclement weather. Most cases occur during cold winter months, but a brisk wind and damp weather raises the risk of hypothermia. Wet fur compounds the effects of cold, and wind strips away the protective warm air layer caught in the dog's fur.

Provide outdoor dogs with shelter from the wet, wind, and the cold. Bedding such as loose straw makes a fine nest that holds pockets of warmer air. Heat lamps, warming pads, or simply a standard light bulb is helpful; however, they should be situated so the dog can escape direct warmth to avoid burns.

Outdoor dogs require a higher calorie and energy-dense ration during cold weather, because the body burns more energy to generate heat. Increase both the amount and frequency of feedings. Your veterinarian can recommend a good product; a high quality adult ration or a high calorie puppy food is appropriate. The best way to prevent hypothermia in dogs is to keep the dog inside (see OUTDOOR SHELTER).

HYPOTHERMIA

SYMPTOMS: Lethargy; shivering; loss of shivering impulse; body temperature less than 98 degrees; loss of consciousness; slowed body function; dog appears dead
FIRST AID: If still shivering, wrap in blanket or give warm bath when already wet; when dog stops shivering and/or has subnormal temperature it's an EMERGENCY! SEE VET IMMEDIATELY!
VET CARE: Aggressive rewarming with heating pads, water bottles, warm-water enemas, heated oxygen, and/or heated intravenous fluids
PREVENTION: Confine dogs indoors during cold weather, and provide outdoor shelter; feed outdoor dogs a higher-calorie food during cold weather

HYPOTHYROIDISM This disease condition results from an inadequate production of the hormones thyroxine (T4) and triiodothyronine (T3) from the thyroid gland. Hypothyroidism is the most common hormonal disease condition of dogs, and is caused by destruction of thyroid tissue due to immune-mediated disease, inexplicable atrophy, and rarely, cancer.

All dogs are susceptible, but certain breeds appear to have an increased risk. Mid- to large-size breeds are most commonly affected, and the condition is rare in toy and miniature breeds. Some researchers report that the Afghan Hound, Airedale, Alaskan Malamute, Beagle, Boxer, Brittany Spaniel, Chow Chow, Cocker Spaniel, Dachshund, Doberman Pinscher, Bulldog, Golden Retriever, Great Dane, Irish Setter, Irish Wolfhound, Miniature Schnauzer, Newfoundland, Pomeranian, Poodle and Shetland Sheepdog are most likely to develop hypothyroidism. Spayed females are also at higher risk.

Hormones excreted by the thyroid gland, located in the base of the dog's neck, regulate the body's metabolism. When not enough hormones are produced, energy levels fall and body processes (even at the cellular level) slow down.

HYPOTHYROIDISM

SYMPTOMS: Lethargy; reluctance to exercise; dullness; weight gain and obesity; seeks warm places; thick and rough skin; symmetrically thinning fur; sometimes puffy face
HOME CARE: None
VET CARE: Blood tests to diagnose and monitor; hormone replacement therapy
PREVENTION: None; remain vigilant for signs; seek prompt treatment

Clinical signs of disease begin to appear between two to six years of age, and can be mild to severe. The onset of symptoms can be very gradual, and mild disease may not be noted for some time. Typically, the dog becomes lethargic, reluctant to exercise, and loses mental focus and acts dull. Some dogs gain weight and may become obese, even though appetite and food intake remain the same. The dog suffering from hypothyroidism has trouble regulating body temperature and is more prone to hypothermia; such dogs are heat-seekers, and will search out warm places to rest. Hormone deficiency also causes changes in the skin and hair coat, but the dog does not act itchy. Skin thickens, becomes rough and dark, sometimes is oily and scaly, and is prone to bacterial infections. The hair becomes brittle and is easily pulled out, and the affected dog exhibits excessive shedding. Symmetrically thinning fur is particularly apparent on the dog's trunk and tail. In moderate to severe cases, dogs develop puffiness to the skin, which is particularly apparent in the face, with thickened droopy eyelids and skin folds on the forehead.

Intact dogs, both male and female, will also experience fertility problems. Female difficulties include irregularity of or failure to cycle, abortion, poor litter survival, and infertility, while males may suffer testicular atrophy, low sperm count, lack of libido, and infertility.

Diagnosis is based on signs, and on laboratory tests including blood analysis that measure levels of circulating hormone. The dog is conclusively diagnosed with hypothyroidism if she responds to therapy; with appropriate treatment, clinical signs usually can be reversed. Improvement in the skin and hair coat condition may be seen after one to two months of therapy.

Treatment consists of replacing the missing hormone with a daily oral synthetic thyroid hormone called Thyroxine. Dogs will require this replacement therapy thereafter. Most recover, and can lead an otherwise normal life.

IBUPROFEN TOXICITY Ibuprofen (propionic acid) is a common human pain reliever found in products like Motrin and Advil, and is one of a group of nonsteroidal anti-inflammatory drugs (NSAIDs) that includes naproxen (Aleve). Dogs benefit from pain-relieving medication (see ARTHRITIS). However, a dog's body metabolizes, or breaks down, NSAIDs at a different rate than humans.

For example, naproxen takes about fourteen hours to be eliminated from the human body, but requires up to 92 hours in dogs. Consequently, the equivalent of a human dose of naproxen can kill a dog. Ibuprofen and other NSAIDs should never be given to your dog without a veterinarian's specific direction.

Use of these pain relievers can cause ulcers, gastrointestinal bleeding, kidney damage or stomach perforation. Vomiting is the most frequent sign, with the digested blood making the vomitus look like old coffee grounds; occasionally, bright red fresh blood is seen. Ongoing bleeding will cause weight loss over time, and anemia can result.

IBUPROFEN POISONING

SYMPTOMS: Vomiting bloody or coffee-ground-like material; weight loss; anemia
HOME CARE: EMERGENCY! SEE VET IMMEDIATELY; stop administering the NSAID medication immediately
VET CARE: Stop administration of the NSAID drug; ulcer medication; sometimes fluid therapy or other support
PREVENTION: Don't give your dog medication without a vet's advice

Diagnosis is based on history of the drug used, X-ray evaluation, and/or by gastroscopy—visual examination of the gastrointestinal tract using a special instrument (see ENDOSCOPE) fed down the dog's throat. Treatment includes stopping use of the NSAID, and prescribing ulcer medication similar to what is used in humans. Veterinary supervision is necessary.

If you suspect that your pet has ingested Ibuprofen, induce vomiting (see ADMINISTER MEDICATIONS) using 3 percent hydrogen peroxide, one tablespoon per 10 pounds of pet, and immediately contact your veterinarian.

IDENTIFICATION All dogs should wear identification. This protects them from being stolen, and ensures their safe return should they become lost (see STRAY). 70 percent of pets that arrive at shelters have no identification, and so cannot be reunited with owners. Most of these animals are euthanized.

Although every dog is unique, it's hard for an outsider to tell the difference between like-colored dogs of the same breed. To the uninitiated, one Golden Retriever may be indistinguishable from other Goldens. For that reason, it's a good idea to record your dog's appearance with photographs.

Include a close-up of the face, full body shots from both sides and the back, and document any distinguishing marks. Perhaps your Dachshund has a thumb-size birth mark on her tummy, or your Dalmatian has three dark spots on his left hip that look like Mickey Mouse. Your description should include the pet's color, breed, sex, age, weight, height at shoulder, length of tail, ear set, and any other distinctive markings.

Should the worst happen and the dog become lost, have photos and a description ready so that you can make posters and advertise the loss. Leave copies at area shelters to alert them; sometimes, people will call shelters after finding a dog, but be hesitant to turn him in. Remember that it may not be particularly helpful to describe your hybrid dog as a Labrador/Poodle or "whatever" cross when the combination can be so varied; rather, describe exactly what the dog looks like—curly chocolate fur, 45 pound neutered male, drop ears, docked tail—and attach pictures.

Other identification is even more important, and several systems are available. The most common and easiest to use is a plastic or metal tag that attaches to the dog's collar. Tag identification may contain a variety of information, such as the owner's contact information, dog license number, rabies vaccination verification, or contact information for the dog's veterinarian. The dog must wear a collar to benefit from this form of identification, though, and some pets are notorious for slipping out of collars. Be sure your dog's collar fits correctly, not too tight or too loose; you should be able to easily slip two fingers beneath a snug-fitting collar.

Tattoos are a more permanent means of identifying your pet. Often, the owner's social security number or the dog's registration number is tattooed onto the skin inside of the thigh or the ear. The tattoo number can then be registered in a local or national database able to access owner contact information should the dog become lost. However, over time a tattoo may fade, or be obscured by fur. Whoever finds your lost dog must know to look for the tattoo, and also know what to do with that information to reunite you with your pet.

Microchip identification is one of the best forms of pet identification. A tiny silicon chip no larger than a grain of rice is encoded with an identification number, encased in surgical glass, and implanted beneath the loose skin of the dog's shoulders. A specialized scanner (similar to equipment used by grocery stores to read prices) retrieves the microchip information. Owner and pet information is kept current by a data base service, which can then match the identifying microchip code on the found animal to the owner so that the lost dog can be returned. Many veterinary clinics and shelters are now equipped with microchip technology.

IMAGING, CT AND MRI

In neurology and neurosurgery, which involves the brain, spinal cord, and nervous system, the biggest advances in the past several years have all stemmed from using computed tomography (CT) and magnetic resonance imaging (MRI) to better “see” your dog’s brain.

CT and MRI are more sensitive than X-rays for identifying abnormalities in complex parts of the body. The main advantage is the ability to remove bones from the picture, which otherwise obscure a clear view of the target.

Brain studies using CT are done with or without contrast, while spinal contrast and thoracic (chest) and abdominal CT usually use contrast medium— that is, injecting a dye like iodine to help tell different structures apart. Iodine has a high atomic number, so it absorbs lots of radiation, which shows up in the test by making the vessels opaque.

In small animals, CT or MRI are most commonly used to diagnose diseases of the brain, spine, nasal and sinus cavities, and middle ear. Less commonly, they are used to detect muscle or skeletal diseases, respiratory problems, and masses on the heart.

CT and MRI imaging are mostly available in veterinary schools and secondary private referral centers. CT uses an X-ray source and detector to take pictures of an object’s internal structure from 180 to 360 different directions, and then “reconstructs” that object through computer projections. Because it takes only two seconds to scan each “slice,” CT offers a more accurate picture of moving portions of the anatomy (i.e., in the chest/abdomen region moved by breathing and heartbeats) than MRI.

Magnetic Resonance Imaging (MRI) was first used to scan a human wrist in 1977, and the first human brain MRI followed in 1979. Veterinary MRIs weren’t used experimentally until the late 1980s. Today, the technology has become increasingly available, and more and more applications are being discovered. MRI images are similar to CT, but unlike using X-rays, no radiation is involved. The image comes from recording radio-frequency signals given off by the tissue.

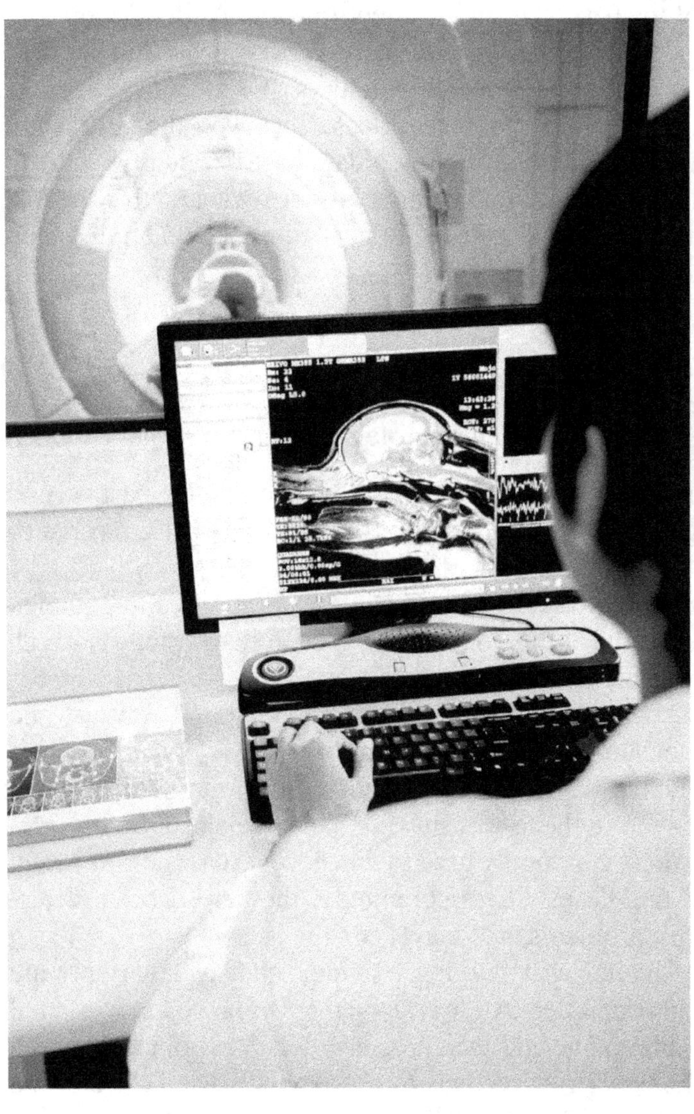

While CT and X-ray imaging refer to "density" of tissues—bone shows up white on the images because it's denser than muscle tissue—that does not apply with MRI. Instead, body structures are defined by degrees of signal intensity. Each part of the body, from bone to skin or lungs, gives off a different amount of radio- frequency. On a MRI image, areas that are bright or white have increased signal intensity, and those that are dark or black have decreased intensity. The MRI offers unsurpassed soft-tissue detail. However, while CT takes seconds to scan a "slice," the MRI takes three to seven minutes per imaging sequence, and may take a total of 45 to 60 minutes for a complete scan (see X-RAY).

INCONTINENCE URINARY Incontinence refers to a loss of bladder control due to a physical condition. This condition typically affects elderly spayed dogs that develop a problem similar to post-menopausal women, as a result of a lack of estrogen.

In most cases, these dogs are only incontinent when they're sleeping, and are unaware of the leakage. The decline in the hormone causes a decrease in the muscle tone that controls the urethra.

More rarely, castrated males have a similar problem. Large and giant-breed dogs, obese dogs, and dogs with docked tails (especially Old English Sheepdogs, Rottweilers, Dobermans, and Weimaraners) are affected most often.

Accidents increase when the dog drinks too much before bedtime and can't "hold it" until the morning bathroom break. Pick up the water bowl two hours before bedtime, and make sure the dog uses the bathroom before you turn in for the night.

Your veterinarian often prescribes medicine to help control the incontinence by improving the strength of the bladder sphincter. Hormone replacement therapy—testosterone for male dogs, and more commonly estrogen—diethylstilbestrol (brand names DES and Premarin)—helps some female dogs. It must be given in tiny doses calculated by the veterinarian for your individual dog's needs. The medication is needed for the rest of the dog's life.

Holistic veterinarians may recommend raw-gland concentrates or multiple-glandular dietary supplements like Symplex F that help the body produce more natural estrogen. These are combinations of extracts from the ovaries and adrenal, thyroid and pituitary glands.

One homeopathic remedy called Urinary Incontinence combines Gelsemium, Alumina, Plantago, Causticum and Cantharsis to help change the dog's hormonal balance. Ask your veterinarian for appropriate recommendations.

INCONTINENCE

SYMPTOMS: Wetting with relaxed or resting; wetting when asleep; urine scald
HOME CARE: Management; keeping dog clean; offering extra bathroom breaks
HOLISTIC HELP: Acupuncture; glandular supplements; massage
VET CARE: Possibly drug therapy
PREVENTION: None

Acupuncture may be effective for some dogs. If back or spinal issues influence the condition by putting pressure on nerves that control urination, motion palpation (a type of massage) may help. Simply hold your index finger and thumb together, and locate the dip between the vertebras on each side of the dog's backbone. Begin at the shoulders and move to the hips, gently pressing between each vertebra only enough to slightly move the spine.

The most effective and commonly prescribed drug to improve bladder sphincter control and treat incontinence is phenylpropanolamine (PPA). PPA was taken off the market when people developed problems from taking it as an ingredient in common diet medications, but dogs don't have those problems, and they still benefit from PPA. They've now made a veterinary version of it that's chewable.

If your dog develops urinary incontinence, it's more than an inconvenience. It can also be a health problem that requires ongoing nursing care. Watch for urine scald—red, irritated, burned-looking skin around the genitals—vulva on female dogs and the prepuce that covers the male's penis. Keep the area clean with Baby Wipes or other mild cleansers. Protect the skin with Desitin or a triple antibiotic ointment to help prevent infection.

Save yourself frustration and aggravation by confining the incontinent dog to an easy-to-clean area. Or you can protect carpet and furniture by putting down sheets of plastic and spreading disposable diapers or products like Depend Undergarments to catch the urine.

Some pet product stores carry diaper-like products made for dogs. Toddler "pull up" pants or premie diapers for human babies work for some dogs, when used in conjunction with a belly band to hold them in place. Caution: the absorbable material, if eaten, can cause upset tummies and diarrhea.

IMMUNE SYSTEM

This refers to the body's complex defense system that protects your dog from microscopic organic invaders that cause injury or disease. The immune system patrols the body seeking foreign substances (antigens), then tries to either neutralize or destroy them.

Antigens include viruses, bacteria, toxins, and abnormal cells like cancer. The immune system is composed of both primary and secondary lines of defense. The bone marrow and thymus gland are part of the primary immune system. They produce protective disease-fighting cells and molecules that patrol the blood and lymphatic system for anything that doesn't belong. The secondary immune system includes the lymph nodes and spleen, which are a part of an intricate body-wide filter that removes antigens from circulation.

There are also two types of immune responses. A humoral immune response refers to the custom-creation of a kind of protein called an antibody. Antibodies are made in response to a specific antigen, and are designed to attach themselves to that single kind of antigen. This marks the antigen as dangerous, so that other specialized cells can destroy it. The

second type of immune response is cell-mediated immunity. Specialized cells like macrophages and lymphocytes attack and destroy virus-infected cells or tumor cells without the aid of antibodies.

The dog's body also has a kind of immunity memory, referred to as active immunity. Once an antigen is marked by antibodies and then destroyed, the remaining antibodies still programmed to recognize the disease continue to circulate. They can immediately react to the antigen should it ever return. In this way, active immunity prompts an early immune response before damage can be done. How long active immunity lasts depends on the particular antigen involved. It is artificially created by stimulating the dog's immune system with vaccinations to protect him from various diseases.

Puppies receive a transient passive immunity from their mother when they nurse her antibody-rich first milk, called colostrum. A puppy's passive immunity lasts only about four months (see VACCINATIONS).

INFECTIOUS CANINE HEPATITIS (ICH)

Also referred to as Rubarth's Disease, ICH is a contagious viral disease of dogs caused by the canine adenovirus 1 (CAV-1). It was first described in the 1920s in foxes, and also affects wolves, coyotes, skunks and bears. It is not contagious to people. The virus is related to CAV-2, one of the causative agents of kennel cough, but the disease primarily affects the dog's liver.

Any dog can be affected, but young dogs and especially puppies are at highest risk. The disease varies from mild fever to fatal illness, and signs may be confused with canine distemper.

The virus is spread by direct dog-to-dog contact by ingesting infected urine, feces or saliva. Incubation—the time it takes for signs to appear—is four to nine days following exposure. Virus first infects the tonsils, spreads to lymph nodes and then the blood. The bloodstream carries virus everywhere, but CAV-1 particularly likes and targets the liver, eyes, kidneys, and cell lining of the blood vessels.

The first symptom is fever up to 106 degrees, which may come and go and lasts one to six days. Shortly after the initial fever appears, dogs develop leukopenia (a low white blood cell count). This is important because white cells act as part of the immune system's defense team. The degree of leukopenia directly correlates with the seriousness of the illness. When fever only lasts one day, leukopenia may be the only sign that develops. But if fever continues longer than that, severe illness develops.

The most severe cases affect puppies less than four months old, and especially aged two to six weeks. In the fatal fulminating form of the disease, the dog suddenly develops bloody diarrhea, collapses and dies in a single day. Some puppies die without any warning. To the owner, it may appear the puppy has succumbed to poison.

The acute form most commonly affects puppies aged six to ten weeks, but can afflict dogs of any age. Signs include anorexia, thirst, lethargy, conjunctivitis (inflammation of mucus membranes of eyes), and mucoid congestion of the nose and eyes. Sometimes, the dog will exhibit a "hunching" posture indicating abdominal pain resulting from a swollen liver, and may suffer bouts of bloody vomiting and diarrhea. Edema—swelling of tissues with fluid—can develop in the neck, head and body.

HEPATITIS

SYMPTOMS: High fever to 106 degrees; bloody diarrhea; anorexia; thirst; lethargy; eye inflammation; eye and nasal congestion; "hunching" from painful abdomen; swelling of body, head, and neck; bleeding from mouth, nose, urinary tract, or rectum; sometimes corneal opacity
HOME CARE: EMERGENCY, SEE VET IMMEDIATELY!
VET CARE: Supportive therapy; blood transfusions; fluid therapy; antibiotics
PREVENTION: Vaccinate as recommended by your vet

Dogs with healthy immune systems are able to produce an antibody response in about a week, and tend to recover. Other dogs develop bleeding disorders between the second and fifth day of infection. Hemorrhage is caused by infection of the blood vessels, and results in bleeding gums, hematomas, and sometimes bleeding from the mouth, nose, urinary tract or rectum (see BLEEDING). Bleeding is particularly dangerous because clotting ability is also compromised by this disease.

Diagnosis is based on the abrupt onset of signs, especially the prolonged bleeding. Virus isolation techniques and other laboratory tests including analysis of a tissue sample from the liver (biopsy) may be necessary to distinguish ICH from distemper.

There is no cure for ICH. Rather, treatment is aimed at stabilizing the dog's condition and offering support until hopefully his immune system takes over and eliminates the virus. Treatment may require blood transfusion in severely ill dogs, along with intravenous fluid therapy to combat shock, anemia and dehydration. Subcutaneous administration of fluids (beneath the skin) can prove dangerous to dogs, because of the potential for excessive bleeding. Antibiotics are also administered; tetracycline is effective for adults, but can cause tooth discoloration in puppies and shouldn't be used unless the dog already has permanent teeth.

Seven to ten days following the disappearance of signs, about a quarter of infected dogs develop a transient opacity of the cornea (see EYES), referred to as blue eye. In mild cases of ICH, this may be the only indication of disease. Treatment for the opacity is rarely required; it usually resolves on its own.

Recovering dogs continue to shed virus in their urine for up to six months, and should be isolated during this period. CAV-1 in the environment can be killed using iodine, sodium hydroxide, or bleach at a 1:32 dilution in water (see QUARANTINE). Highly effective preventative vaccinations are available to protect your dog against ICH.

INFLAMMATORY BOWEL DISEASE

This syndrome refers to a group of disorders characterized by chronic inflammation of the intestine. Nobody knows what causes the disease, but several theories have been proposed. Symptoms may result from any one or a combination of an inappropriate response of the immune system, food allergy, infection or parasites, or even drug reactions.

Inflammatory bowel disease includes the damage or malfunction of the normal barrier protection in the gut. Damage can allow a kind of leakage of large protein particles, and give them contact with the immune system. Whatever the cause, the result is inflammation that clogs the microscopic filaments lining the intestinal tract which transfer nutrients into the bloodstream.

Affected dogs suffer ongoing bouts of colitis. Chronic diarrhea is the most common sign, with frequent straining but minimal passage of stool, which may be streaked with blood. Episodes may be sporadic and occur during times of stress, or can be continuous.

Any dog may be affected at any age, but the condition most frequently occurs in middle-aged dogs. The Basenji, Boxer, Chinese Shar-Pei, German Shepherd Dog, and Rottweiler breeds appear to be more prone to inflammatory bowel diseases than others.

Diagnosis usually is made only after ruling out other causes for diarrhea (see WHIPWORMS and SWALLOWED OBJECT). Conclusive evidence requires a biopsy of the intestine in which a sample of tissue is removed surgically from the anesthetized dog for microscopic evaluation. Sometimes a special instrument called a colonoscope is inserted into the dog's rectum to view the tissue. Visualization and biopsy help determine the specific type of disease by the kind of inflammation and location in the intestinal tract that's affected.

Affected dogs cannot be cured, but their symptoms may be relieved through treatment. The homeopathic remedies Nux vomica and Arsenicum are helpful to stop both diarrhea and vomiting.

IBD

SYMPTOMS: Chronic diarrhea sometimes streaked with blood; straining to defecate with minimal results
HOME CARE: Vet diagnosis and treatment required; feed and medicate as recommended
HOLISTIC HELP: Digestive enzymes; herbal therapy; supplements; homeopathy
VET CARE: Treat underlying cause; antibiotics; immune-suppressing drugs; limited-antigen diet; high-fiber diet
PREVENTION: None

Holistic veterinarians may recommend giving glutamine supplements. Inflammatory bowel disease often damages the intestinal lining, and glutamine can help rebuild these cells. A recommended dose is 500 milligrams of L-glutamine, available from health food stores, twice a day.

Because signs of disease most likely are prompted by some type of allergic response, treatment is aimed at identifying and eliminating the offending substance (if possible), and attempting to block or suppress the hypersensitive reaction. If it's determined that a food allergy is causing problems, then a limited antigen diet may prove helpful. Immune-suppressing drugs and medications to calm inflammation, such as corticosteroids, are often prescribed. Drugs to treat bacterial overgrowth or giardia infection may be necessary. Occasionally, feeding a diet higher in fiber is recommended.

Medical marijuana (or cannabis) today is also available for pets, but must be formulated so that pets receive the medical benefits of the cannabis (hemp) plant while reducing potential toxic concentrations of the herb. Hemp can be used to control pain and inflammation. Ask your veterinarian if this supplement may benefit your pet.

INSECT BITES & STINGS

SYMPTOMS: Local irritation; swelling or itching at site; drooling; difficulty eating; difficulty breathing; swelling of face; drunken behavior; collapse
FIRST AID: Apply ice packs; dab ammonia on spots; apply baking soda wash or paste; anytime dog has trouble breathing, SEE VET IMMEDIATELY!
HOLISTIC HELP: Herbal therapy; aromatherapy
VET CARE: Epinephrine (adrenaline) counteracts life-threatening reactions; more commonly, antihistamines; steroids
PREVENTION: Avoid contract with dangerous insects by supervising outdoor activities

INSECT BITES AND STINGS Dogs are afflicted by the same bugs that pester people. Stings and bites potentially spread disease and often result in allergic reactions that make the dog itch. More often, a single sting from a bee, wasp, spider or fly causes local irritation, but multiple stings–and sometimes even a single bite or sting–potentially may result in life-threatening reactions.

Dogs don't routinely hunt bugs the way cats do. However, puppies enjoy chasing insects and terriers may carry the urge into adulthood. Common insects like crickets and butterflies are harmless, but catching a bee, spider, or other biting or stinging insect can have severe consequences.

The dog's body is usually protected by fur. Most insect bites and stings are located on the less-protected lips or inside the mouth when your dog tries to catch the bug. A puppy may suffer massive bites on the tummy and inner flanks if she walks into a fire ant mound.

Insect bites and stings typically cause painful localized swelling and/or itching. When the mouth is the target, the dog may drool and be reluctant to eat. If a stinger can be seen (bees leave them behind), remove it with tweezers or scrape it free with a credit card.

A paste of baking soda and water is an effective home remedy that eases the sting, and calamine lotion relieves itching; however, both are messy when applied to fur, and would only be appropriate on the sparsely furred areas like the belly. Ice packs reduce swelling, and a dab of ammonia directly on the bites (use a cotton ball or swab) helps soothe the pain and itch. For multiple stings, as from a fire ant mound, giving your dog an oatmeal bath may help reduce the all over itch. You can use a commercial product like Aveeno, or simply run cool water through a sock filled with oatmeal to create a soothing rinse in the tub.

Black tea contains ingredients that help draw out toxins. Dip the tea bag in warm water, squeeze it out, and then hold against the sting for ten to 15 minutes. Chamomile tea will reduce the irritation and help prevent potential infection. Soak a cotton ball in room temperature tea and apply to the sting as a compress for 15 to 30 minutes. Do this three times on the first day, and for a few minutes three times a day for the next two days.

A homeopathic remedy can help prevent swelling by giving two or three tablets of Ledum 30C immediately after the sting. The essential oils lavender or thyme also relieve irritation and itching. Mix three drops of either oil in a teaspoon of apple cider vinegar and dab on the bites.

Injuries inside the mouth are more difficult to address. When the dog is amenable, flush the area with a teaspoon of baking soda mixed in a pint of water. A turkey baster or squirt gun works well to aim the fluid onto the area, but take care the dog doesn't inhale the liquid.

A sting is often painful, and only occasionally dangerous. However, dogs can have a life-threatening reaction to a single bite or sting, and multiple stings tend to cause the worst reactions. The mouth, nose or throat can swell until it's difficult for the dog to breathe. An allergic reaction called anaphylactic shock results in the airways closing down. The affected dog struggles to breathe, drools, become uncoordinated, and finally collapses. These signs appear almost immediately following the bite or sting. Anaphylactic shock is an emergency that must be immediately addressed by a veterinarian if your pet's life is to be saved.

Some spiders like the black widow, Missouri brown spider and tarantulas inject a venom with their bite that cause pain at the site, followed by chills, fever, labored breathing, and shock. Centipede and scorpion stings can also cause severe illness, and slow-healing wounds. The bite of ticks can cause a variety of life-threatening diseases (see BABESIOSIS, EHRLICHIOSIS, LYME DISEASE, ROCKY MOUNTAIN SPOTTED FEVER, TICK FEVER and TICK PARALYSIS).

INTRODUCTIONS Dogs are inherently social creatures who develop strong emotional family ties. To your dog, his family group includes human owners, as well as other pets. However, dogs are also territorial by nature, and a new family member upsets the status quo. For that reason, introduction of a new pet into the household must be done gradually, with attention to the resident dog's feelings.

Many dogs enjoy meeting new pets and people. Dogs tend to get bored, and a new playmate—human or otherwise—can be a welcome diversion. Other dogs, though, may be shy of new experiences, and fear can result in either withdrawal or hostility. Excessively dominant dogs may be possessive of space or an owner's attention. How well your dog accepts another pet (cat or dog) or new family members (spouse or baby) depends the most on the dog's own personality and sense of self.

The degree to which your dog has been socialized (see PUPPY) has a great deal to do with how well he accepts new family members. Obedience training also impacts the situation. Confident dogs are more readily accepting than shy dogs. The dog that has been trained to obey your directives is more confident, less stressed, and more willing to accept new situations.

The finesse of initial introductions can tip the scales. Unless care is taken, a dominant dog may become aggressive to the interloper, while fearful insecure dogs can become depressed. Dogs typically are more accepting of kittens or puppies that don't threaten an adult's status. Introducing an adult resident dog (R.D.) to a new adult cat or dog can be done, too. However, the pair must sort out who is to be in charge, and it may not be the resident dog.

Before anything else, consider these key factors. When there is a large size difference between the two, care must be taken that the bigger pet doesn't injure (accidentally or otherwise) the smaller. After all, the gentlest St. Bernard can cause damage simply by sitting on a Chihuahua or kitten.

Also consider the breeds, because predatory nature can to a degree be predicted by this (see HUNTING). A highly predatory dog may have difficulty stemming his impulse to chase and injure the new dog or cat. Be particularly careful when introducing a resident terrier dog to a prey-size newcomer pet, or a resident prey-size dog to a newcomer terrier or jumbo-size cat.

When possible, let R.D. learn about the newcomer ahead of time by introducing the new pet's scent on a sock or handkerchief. Simply stroke the new animal with the cloth item, then leave the scented item in your house for R.D. to find, sniff and investigate.

One room of the house should be made temporarily off-limits to R.D., and function as the new pet's home base. That way, your dog doesn't feel all of his territory has been invaded by the new pet, only a portion. Further, the newbie has a private place to become used to the new situation.

There are a few differences between introducing a cat or a dog to your R.D. When introducing two dogs, it's helpful to make first meetings on neutral territory—in the park, a friend's house, or your neighbor's yard. That way, R.D. doesn't feel defensive about his property, and can let his natural curiosity prompt more amenable introductions. Both dogs should be under leash control. A new puppy typically will lick R.D.'s face, and roll on her back in deference to the adult. Adult dogs may posture a bit (see COMMUNICATION). Allow sniffing and playing, but excessive growling or escalating aggression are your cue to take a break.

When introductions are to be made at home (which is necessary when introducing a kitten or cat), R.D. and the new pet should first get to know each other by sniffing under the door. Some cats will posture, hiss and growl; others will ignore the entire venture until they think you're not watching. Either behavior is normal. Be encouraged if the pair begin poking and playing with each other's paws under the door.

Make every effort to make the introductions seem like a part of normal life. Don't pay too much attention to the new pet, or you risk putting R.D.'s nose out of joint. If anything, give your old friend more attention, so he'll associate the new pet with good things for him. If he's a shy, retiring dog, he may feel threatened and begin to withdraw if he feels he's losing your attention.

With dog-to-cat introductions, keep the pair separated by the private room for a week or longer, allowing interaction only beneath the door. Then have them switch places for half an hour or so. This gives the pair an opportunity to investigate each other's smells, and to become comfortable with the rest of the house.

When the new pet is a puppy, kitten or a cat, R.D. should be on a leash for the first nose-to-nose meeting. When the newcomer is small, it can be placed in a pet carrier and initial sniffs can occur through the grill.

When both parties appear friendly and eager, simply open the door to the room, or the carrier, and allow the pets to meet at their own pace. R.D. should still be on a leash. New puppies typically race to meet adult dogs, but kittens and cats may be more circumspect. Don't force things; you're there to keep R.D. from becoming too excited and losing control. Safety of the pets is your number one goal. Ensure smaller dogs and cats have safe places, rooms, or elevated perches to get out of reach and control the interaction. Never force face-to-face meetings; the pets should take the lead in how fast introductions progress.

When introducing two adult dogs, both should be on a leash. Get your spouse, an older child or a friend to hold R.D.'s leash while you handle the newbie; that sends an unmistakable message to R.D. that this newcomer is welcome by you, and that he should follow your example. Ideally, make the introductions on neutral territory that neither dog "owns" such as the park. That reduces the chance R.D. will want to defend or protect territory form this interloper.

Every case is different. Initial introductions can prompt love at first sight, or the opposite. Typically, female dogs concentrate on sniffing the newcomer's neck and face, while a male dog's interest is the genital region. Both male and female dogs try to prevent themselves being sniffed in the anal region, and they may turn circles trying to sniff each other while blocking themselves from being investigated.

Usually, it's the resident dog that takes charge, but that's not always the case. There may be some whining or growling, but unless the situation escalates to imminent attack, let the pets sort things out (see AGGRESSION). Interrupting too soon may actually delay the determination of who's to be top dog, and force a replay of the display at a later date.

Remember, it's not always the smaller pet that's at a disadvantage. A big but shy dog may be buffaloed by an intimidating puppy or kitten, particularly if he's never before experienced another pet. Always provide an escape route for both R.D. and the newbie so they can have some privacy when they've had enough. A crate works well for dogs, while cats typically can get out of reach on a tabletop. Until the pair have accepted each other, keep them separated when you are not there to supervise.

A baby gate is a great tool for introductions. It keeps pets separated while allowing them limited interaction through the grillwork. Once you are satisfied R.D. understands Newbie is a part of his family (and vice versa), you can take down the gate. In some instances, the baby gate will allow the smaller pet to regulate interaction by coming and going through the grill, while keeping out the larger pet. Use the leash until you're satisfied no fur will fly.

The same principles apply when introducing new human family members to your resident dog. When he's still a puppy, introducing him to a variety of people of all ages will prepare him for such changes as an adult, and make both your lives easier. An adult dog who has had you to himself can become difficult if you later decide to marry. A new baby can turn the most benevolent dog into an excitable yapper.

Use the scented sock to familiarize R.D. to the new family member ahead of time, just the same as with a new pet. Tape your fiancé's voice and play it while you pet your dog, or have the fiancé bring special treats or new toys. Your dog should associate a new family member's presence with only good things.

When your family is expecting an infant, record baby sounds for the dog to hear. Don't shut out the dog—your first baby—when the new one arrives; let him be a part of your happy event. If you don't want him in the nursery, set up a baby gate so he can at least observe as you paint, change wallpaper, set up the crib, and get things ready. Wear baby powder so he associates baby smells with good things—you. Excluding the dog from this important event makes him feel left out, confused, and even scared he's losing you.

Dogs have a built-in inhibition to injuring infants, including human babies. That's why the typical dog puts up with puppy and baby antics that would prompt mayhem if it came from an adult. In fact, many dogs are delighted by babies, as long as they're made to feel a part of things. You want R.D. to recognize your baby as a part of his family, to be cherished and protected by him.

When you bring home your new baby, act like it's no big deal, even though it is. You want your dog to believe this is an expected part of dog life. Introductions shouldn't be forced; most dogs will be interested and will approach by themselves. If R.D. is calm, let him sniff the baby's foot or hand. He should know what smells so different and sounds so interesting, so he knows it's nothing to fear.

Praise your dog when he acts well. Most dogs follow your lead; be sure to continue giving your dog plenty of quality time, so his nose won't get out of joint. Play a special game with your dog that's associated only when the baby is present; that way, R.D. will welcome the baby rather than resent the baby as an interloper. If you like, your dog can be allowed in the nursery when you are there to supervise. Be aware, though, that some dogs become solicitous and protective quite early; this can be good, but can be taken to extremes. You want to be the parent, not the dog, so make it clear who is responsible for cleaning up the baby's messy face (and other areas) or you may have competition.

As the child grows, be sure she understands R.D. is not a toy. Dogs often have great patience with young children, but it's the dog's home, too. And, the dog could lose self-control if hurt by the child, and cause injury.

Always supervise resident pets with new comers, especially children and dogs. Accidents happen even with friendly loving dogs. Prevent tragedies from happening, by teaching your children to respect pets from an early age. Teach your baby how to pet and hold the dog, and how to care for R.D. Love of dogs begins during childhood, and can only be based on mutual respect. Such love can last a pet's lifetime, and beyond.

JACOBSON'S ORGAN Dogs have a secondary scenting mechanism, called the vomeronasal or Jacobson's organ. The organ is situated in the roof of the dog's mouth, between the hard palate and nasal septum. It's connected to a nasopalatine canal, or incisive duct, which opens behind the upper incisor teeth in the mouth and allows communication with the nasal cavity.

Theoretically, the scent particle is captured on the tongue, then transferred to the incisive duct in the mouth. Fluid in the organ-sacs is pumped into the ducts, then drawn back up once it captures the chemical scent, and the scented fluid is read by the organ.

Although all dogs have these specialized scent organs, experts disagree whether or not they actually use them. Cats exhibit a distinctive facial grimace, called flehmen, when using the organ to detect sexually-specific scents, called pheromones. Dogs do not display this behavior (although coyotes do). Some studies conclude the organ has become non-functional in domestic dogs, based on the fact that no chemical receptors can be found in the sacs.

JUMPING UP Dogs tend to jump up toward people to compensate for their size. It is normal greeting behavior for dogs to nuzzle and lick each other's faces; a submissive dog aims attention at a dominant individual's eyes and mouth. Therefore, licking the owner's face is a canine "howdy!"--a way to solicit attention.

Since most dogs cannot reach us any other way, they jump up to aim their attention at our faces, particularly during greetings. Perhaps this doesn't bother you. Many people consider jumping up cute when the dog's a puppy, but the attraction tends to fade as the dog matures. Jumping up then becomes obnoxious or even dangerous, depending on the size of the dog and the attitude of his target. There are some people in the world that dislike or are even frightened by dogs and will not appreciate your dog jumping up on them.

Even a small dog can prove annoying, while a St. Bernard can pose quite a risk. At best, clothes may be ruined, and at worst, people may be knocked down, frightened or even injured during exuberant doggy greetings. Habitual jumping up can become a behavior problem.

As in all problem behaviors, your dog can be trained to an acceptable alternative. Obedience training is the best way to teach appropriate canine manners. It promotes canine confidence—because after all, she is rewarded and praised for doing well—and more importantly, establishes you as the boss.

Canine jumping up is a way for your dog to adore you with an appropriate greeting. Once she realizes her behavior offends you, she'll strive to find another way to say hello. Wanting to please the leader—you—is simply part of being a dog. The difficult part for the owner is explaining to the dog what you want in terms she understands.

Your goal is to give your dog every opportunity for good behavior; don't wait for her to do something wrong, and then shame her. Instead, anticipate problems and structure the situation to avoid the problem.

Does your dog always jump up when you arrive home? when the doorbell rings to announce guests? when the neighbors' kid walks by? Then anticipate her behavior, and be ready with an alternative.

Don't step on her toes, and don't knee her in the chest. Either action can be painful, which can prompt avoidance behavior or even aggression. Instead of teaching your dog to greet you appropriately, such actions tell her to avoid greeting you altogether--and that's no fun for anybody.

Adolescent jumping up can be the greatest challenge. The behavior can turn into "nose boinking" which can lead to broken glasses or even a bloody nose. Jumping up often combines with mouthing where the dog bites and grabs at your hands, clothing or even your buttocks in a grab-tag game. In most cases, this isn't aggression but just out-of-control play.

Homecomings and departures are a prime time for jumping-up because dogs want to greet or stop you from leaving. Turning your back on some of these dogs actually revs them up even more, so instead, try ignoring the bad behavior. "Ignore" means you make no eye contact, say nothing, and stand still like a boring zombie and offer no reaction for idiot behavior.

Teach your dog a conflicting behavior such as "fetch your ball." She can't jump up if she's running to bring you her ball or other favorite toy. Just the name of a special game or toy—"go get your bear!"—can change the dog's focus and redirect the behavior long enough for you to evade the jumping. With enough repetitions, your dog will begin to associate your home-coming with "go find" instead of jumping up.

A conflicting behavior—like "sit" when you come home—helps enormously. You'll need to practice your puppy's "sit" during calm moments first, and then ask for this polite behavior before you leave and when you arrive home. Guests will appreciate a polite "sit" when they arrive, too, and won't appreciate your puppy leaping around and mugging them for attention.

Many young dogs don't know their own strength. When they jump up and you wave your arms and try to push them off, they may think it's a game and grab and bite harder. Tell them it hurts the same way another puppy would, with a YELP! Lay it on thick, over act, and cry and sob like the pup has done major damage. Some tough dogs really get the message using this. For the out-of-control grabby ambush-type of dog play, give him a taste of his own medicine and SCREAM (very loud but very short), and fall over "dead." Don't move, don't say anything. Play dead for at least 15-20 seconds. The shock value may be enough to send a permanent message that such games stop all interaction, plus they hurt you—and playing dogs really aren't interested in hurting you and won't want you to cry.

An anxious or playful dog may leap high and very rapidly and suddenly "poke" at your face with their nose. That can be triggered by leaning over top of them especially when they're in a high-arousal situation like a homecoming or around other dogs. It may be a way for stressed pups to relieve their anxiety so be aware of situations that cause these behaviors. Dogs control each other's movement with their body language. Think how a Border Collie makes sheep move just by getting close. You can stop your pup's jumps by stepping close to him just before he leaps. Cross your arms, and step into the pup's personal space before he crouches to leap.

Use a drag line to enforce good manners. This is a long leash that the dog can "drag" along the ground. When the dog approaches, before he can jump, you simply step on the line. That prevents him from jumping up. While you step on the line, don't make eye contact or give attention until he stops trying to jump.

With a tie-down, you simply attach your drag-line to a fixed object like a fence, stair rail or other immovable object like an eye-bolt into the wall. That keeps you safe from mouthing and claws, and prevents the dog from jumping up and grabbing. Practice sits and downs, while you stay out of range. The dog only gets rewarded with contact from you when he stays calm with all four feet on the floor.

Practice the tie-down exercise with several friends. Have them approach, one after another, and the pup only gets to be petted if he doesn't jump. If he tries to leap, back out of range and say, "You blew it! Whoops! Too bad!" or something similar. Repeat the exercise ten to twenty times in a row, and the pup will learn the lesson.

If a wet slurp across the mouth doesn't offend you, then you kneel down on your dog's level to put yourself in range of her kiss so she doesn't have to leap. And remember, there's nothing to stop you from training your extremely well-behaved dog to jump up—but only on your command.

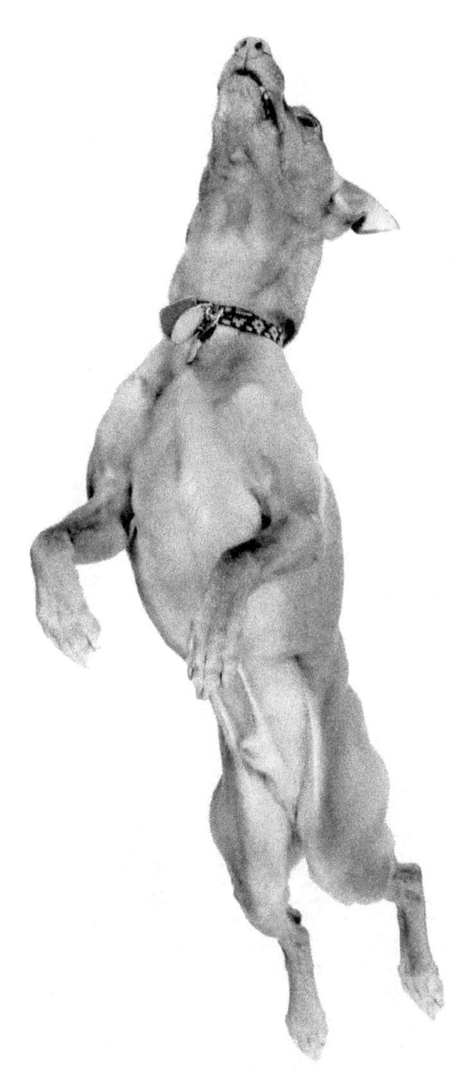

352
DOG FACTS

KENNEL COUGH Canine infectious tracheobronchitis, generically referred to as kennel cough, is a highly contagious and common condition affecting dogs. The disease causes an inflammation of the dog's larynx, trachea, and bronchi (tubes leading to the lungs).

All dogs are susceptible, but the disease is most common in dogs exposed to crowded conditions, such as kennels (hence, the name), shows, or other stressful conditions. Most cases cause only mild disease with signs that tend to be more aggravating to owners than dangerous to the dog. But kennel cough in puppies can cause stunted lung development, and/or develop into life-threatening pneumonia.

KENNEL COUGH

SYMPTOMS: Chronic, high-pitched honking cough; eye or nasal discharge; slight fever; loss of appetite
HOME CARE: None
HOLISTIC HELP: Herbal remedies
VET CARE: Cough suppressants; antibiotics, sometimes anti-inflammatory drugs or bronchodilators
PREVENTION: Reduce exposure to other dogs; vaccinate when dog will be kenneled

The disease can be caused by any one or combination of several different infectious agents. The most common culprits are bacteria called *Bordetella bronchiseptica*, the canine parainfluenza virus, and the canine adenovirus-2 (CAV-2). These agents attach themselves to the delicate hair-like cilia in the dog's trachea, or actually cause the removal of the cilia. Cilia normally protect the tracheobronchial tract by clearing away irritants like bacteria and other microorganisms with wave-like motions similar to wind moving a grassy field. When they are destroyed, or the agent can't be dislodged from remaining cilia--the protective mechanism breaks down, resulting in further irritation to the dog's respiratory tract.

The typical sign of kennel cough is, in fact, a chronic high-pitched honking cough. It can easily be prompted by excitement, drinking, or gentle pressure applied to the base of the dog's neck. The dog tugging at his leash may result in a paroxysm. Rarely there is also a nasal or eye discharge, and dogs may suffer a slight fever or loss of appetite. The signs can last from a few days to several weeks.

Infection is spread through the saliva and nasal secretions, and may occur by direct nose-to-nose contact. However, coughing also transmits the agents through the air from one dog to another. Signs develop four to six days following exposure.

Diagnosis is based on the dog's recent history and clinical signs. Because the disease results in a vicious cycle of irritation causing the cough, and cough causing further irritation, cough suppressants to relieve persistent coughing are very important.

Holistic veterinarians may recommend herbal remedies to help soothe the discomfort and speed recovery. A Chinese herbal liquid called loquat is very sweet, and dogs may lick this willingly off the spoon. Ask your vet about the dosage. You can also make your own remedy by combining lemon and honey. Mix two tablespoons of honey and a teaspoon of lemon juice in one-half cup of water and give to the dog a couple of times a day. For congestion, the herb mullein is available in capsule form and helps break up congestion that may accompany kennel cough.

Antibiotics may be required when bacterial infections are involved. Anti-inflammatory drugs and bronchodilators that open breathing passages to help the dog breathe may also be prescribed.

Preventative vaccinations are available. However, protecting a dog from kennel cough is complicated by the fact that many different infectious agents may be involved. Some vaccinations are given by injection, while others are given as drops in the nose to stimulate a local immunity in the nasal passages (see IMMUNE SYSTEM). However, local immunity is relatively short-lived and may only protect the dog for six months or so.

Dogs at high risk may benefit from annual or oftener vaccinations. These vaccinations may be given alone or in combination, and are often recommended when you anticipate your dog will be placed at risk for exposure, such as boarding at a kennel over the holidays.

KERATITIS

SYMPTOMS: Squinting; dull, hazy, or cloudy cornea; sore on eye surface
HOME CARE: Keep eye clean
VET CARE: Treat underlying cause; topical antibiotics; anti-inflammatory medications; pain-relieving drugs; possibly surgery
PREVENTION: Routine eye care; keep eyes clean; clip hair away from eyes

KERATITIS Keratitis is the inflammation of the cornea (see EYE). The inflammation may include an ulcer, or hole, in the cornea, or affect the surface only. Keratitis can be caused by an injury to the eye surface, such as a scratch or other trauma. It can also occur as a result of disease caused by bacteria or virus.

Any dog may develop keratitis, but breeds with prominent eyes like Pekingese and Boston Terriers are particularly prone to injury. Dogs suffering from eyelid anomalies (see ECTROPION and DRY EYE) may also develop keratitis.

The cause of German Shepherd Pannus, a noninfectious non-ulcerative progressive keratitis, remains unknown. It can affect other breeds as well, and result in blindness if not aggressively treated. Radiation therapy and sometimes surgery is required.

Signs are squinting from pain, and a loss of the transparency of the cornea. It will at first look dull, then hazy or cloudy, and finally completely opaque.

Left untreated, keratitis may result in perforation of the cornea with damage to or complete loss of sight. Deep ulcers may heal and form vision-impairing scars. Treatment depends on the underlying cause, which must also be addressed. Topical antibiotics, anti-inflammatory solutions and pain-relieving medications are often necessary, and surgery may be required.

Most cases of keratitis can be prevented by routine eye care (see GROOMING/EYES). Anytime you suspect injury to your dog's eye, prompt veterinary attention is important to prevent superficial injury from becoming serious (see BLINDNESS).

KIDNEY DISEASE

Kidney disease refers to any condition that damages or impairs the function of these organs. Kidneys screen organic waste and toxins or infectious agents from blood, and excrete them in urine that's voided from the body. These living filters also govern the fluid composition of the dog's body, as well as the nutrient content of the blood. Kidneys also manufacture hormones that control red blood cell production and blood pressure.

Failure of the kidneys to do their job causes devastating illness. Kidney failure may come on suddenly due to toxins or injury, but chronic kidney disease creeps up on the dog. It's most common in older dogs, probably as a result of normal wear and tear over a lifetime of use. About 10 percent of all dogs over the age of fifteen develop some degree of kidney disease.

Kidney disease is characterized as acute (of recent origination) or chronic (of long duration). Acute kidney disease affects dogs at any age and is caused by trauma, disease or poison which damages the kidney. Common causes of acute kidney disease include chemical toxins (see ANTIFREEZE), certain prescription drugs, infectious agents (see LEPTOSPIROSIS), or periods of inadequate blood flow to the kidneys. If the blood pressure falls below a certain level, which may be due to dehydration, blood loss, shock or heart disease, the kidneys aren't able to function adequately.

Dogs suffering from acute kidney failure often benefit from IV fluids, which may bring the dog back into normal. Other times, dogs suffering acute kidney failure require dialysis on a temporary basis, in the hope that once the underlying condition is treated, kidneys will begin working again. However, the machines used to clean the blood in human medicine are rarely available, or are prohibitively expensive for veterinary applications. Peritoneal dialysis is a more commonly used option. It is a procedure whereby fluid is pumped into the dog's abdominal cavity, where it absorbs waste products, then is drawn back out.

KIDNEY DISEASE

SYMPTOMS: Increased thirst and urination; loss of appetite; weight loss; depression and weakness; hunching posture from pain; break in house-training; dehydration; brown-colored tongue; sores in the mouth; ammonia breath
HOME CARE: Supportive care; good nutrition
VET CARE: Supportive care; peritoneal dialysis; drugs to normalize blood; therapeutic diets
PREVENTION: Avoid toxins like antifreeze and NSAID: provide regular dental care

Signs of kidney disease appear abruptly in the acute form, but develop slowly over time when the condition is chronic. The organs are able to compensate and continue to work even when severely damaged; dogs rarely show signs of illness until up to 75 percent of kidney function is gone. An owner may not notice signs of chronic kidney disease until the condition is quite advanced. Without treatment, kidneys will fail; the dog ultimately dies, either suddenly or after first falling into a coma.

Signs of kidney disease vary depending on the cause. The earliest signs include increased thirst and urination due to the inability of the kidneys to concentrate urine. Your dog drinks more water to counteract the water loss from increased urination, and the increased water intake also increases urine volume so he must urinate more often; a vicious cycle is born.

A dog suffering kidney failure tends to drink his bowl dry and may slake his thirst by drinking from toilet bowls, fish tanks or other unusual locations. He may suffer "accidents" in the house when he can't contain himself to reach the yard in time.

As the disease progresses, other signs develop including anorexia and weight loss, weakness and depression, vomiting, diarrhea and constipation. Infections may cause pain, with the dog exhibiting a hunched posture. Sores appear on the tongue and in the mouth, along with a brownish discoloration on the tongue and breath that is foul, and may smell like ammonia.

The diagnosis is based on signs, along with blood and urine tests. Special examination of the kidneys with X-rays or ultrasound may be necessary. The prognosis depends on how much damage has been done. Dogs may be able to live with mild to moderate kidney disease for months or even years following diagnosis and treatment.

A new test from IDEXX Laboratories screens for symmetric dimethyl arginine (SDMA), which is a new biomarker for kidney function. SDMA is a methylated form of the amino acid arginine, which is produced in every cell and released into the body's circulation during protein degradation. SDMA is excreted almost exclusively by the kidneys. This test offers a good estimate of glomerular filtration rate (GFR), an indicator of how well the kidneys are working. Research has shown that SDMA can identify chronic kidney disease an average of nine months earlier in dogs and 17 months sooner in cats. The SDMA biomarker test is recommended as a screening test for cats age six and older.

Chronic renal disease is irreversible. It cannot be cured. Treatment, however, is aimed at stopping or delaying the progression of the disease, and alleviating the symptoms to keep the dog comfortable as long as possible.

Because of the damage, the dog isn't able to effectively filter all waste products from blood which result from normal metabolism of protein. Dogs suffering kidney failure also have trouble excreting phosphorus, and the excess can result in secondary problems.

Reducing the stress on the kidneys will help slow the progression of the disease. This is accomplished by feeding a high quality therapeutic diet that reduces or adjusts the levels of waste products produced. Reduced phosphorus helps lessen the strain on the kidneys, and restriction of salt helps manage arterial hypertension associated with canine kidney disease.

Reduced protein is also important in dogs suffering uremia – that is, excessive levels of waste products such as urea in the blood. The level of protein in a therapeutic diet is typically going to be lower, but of a very high quality and very high digestibility. Protein and phosphorus are linked together, so when you try to control dietary phosphorus you also reduce dietary protein. Protein restriction in these dogs helps minimize signs such as mouth sores and foul breath.

Drugs like sodium bicarbonate help normalize the blood if it becomes too acidic, and potassium supplementation can help even out the blood potassium level. ACE inhibitors (angiotensin converting enzymes) such as Enalapril and Lisinopril, often used to treat heart disease, also help control blood pressure that causes damage to the kidneys. Omega-3 fatty acids (found in fish oil) also reduce the blood pressure within each tiny filter unit. Omega 3 fatty acids are available in health food stores. Lots of fresh water should be available at all times.

Although kidney transplant is now a reality in the treatment of feline kidney failure, the procedure is more complicated and rarely successful when applied to dogs. Dogs must leap an extra hurdle because their body will reject a donated kidney that doesn't closely match their own tissue. Littermates are the best chance of a match. The canine immune system does not tolerate foreign proteins, be they viruses or transplanted organs.

Early detection by using blood and urine tests is the best prevention. Laboratory screening techniques can identify kidney problems before they become severe. All middle aged and older dogs should undergo periodic examinations. Routine checks, whether they're showing signs or not, can keep your dog healthy as he enters his golden years.

KNEECAP, SLIPPING Technically termed patellar luxation, this condition refers to the patella (kneecap) becoming dislocated due to trauma or inherited conditions. The condition is considered common in Toy breed dogs, but can affect any size or breed of dog.

In a normal position, the small bone sits on top of and protects the stifle joint of the hind leg, where the femur and tibia (thigh bones) meet. The patella is held in place by ligaments, and slides over the head of the femur in grooves.

A shallow groove, weak or lax ligaments, or poor muscle tone and alignment predispose the dog to a slipped kneecap. Any one or combination of these conditions may occur due to injury, or the dog may simply be born with the condition. Rather than staying in place, the patella slips to the inside or outside of the knee. When this happens, the dog isn't able to fully straighten the knee.

Dogs may show no signs at all, or may suffer intermittent lameness and limping as the kneecap slips in and out of place. Some dogs may lose all use of the limb. Keeping your dog slim and preventing excessive jumping can reduce the risk of repeat injury.

Your veterinarian diagnoses the condition by palpating, or feeling, the joint and being able to manipulate the patella in and out of place. When the condition is painful and/or causes loss of leg use, surgery to deepen the groove or re-align the tendons is recommended (see KNEE INJURY)

KNEECAP SLIPPING

SYMPTOMS: Intermittent lameness; limping; holding leg up
HOME CARE: None
VET CARE: Surgery
PREVENTION: None

KNEE INJURY The knee contains two crossed ligaments called cruciates that stabilize the joint. All joints are composed of two or more bones that are positioned end to end. Smooth cartilage covers the bones where they meet to provide easy movement, while the ligaments—tough bands of tissue—hold the bones of the joint together. Muscles, specialized tissue able to expand and contract to move the joint, are attached to the bones above and below the joint with other tough bands of tissue called tendons.

Dogs, especially Toy breeds, often tear one or both cruciate ligaments as a result of injury or even routine exercise. The dog suddenly starts limping from pain. It's a major problem in canine athletes, as it is in humans. There are a couple of different kinds of procedures used in animals, but there isn't a very good way to manage the treatment.

Surgeons have used a variety of natural and synthetic materials placed around or near the joint to replace the ruptured ligament and stabilize the joint. These procedures help a great deal, and the persistent lameness is often eliminated, but dogs typically end up with lameness that comes and goes, that's associated with their arthritis.

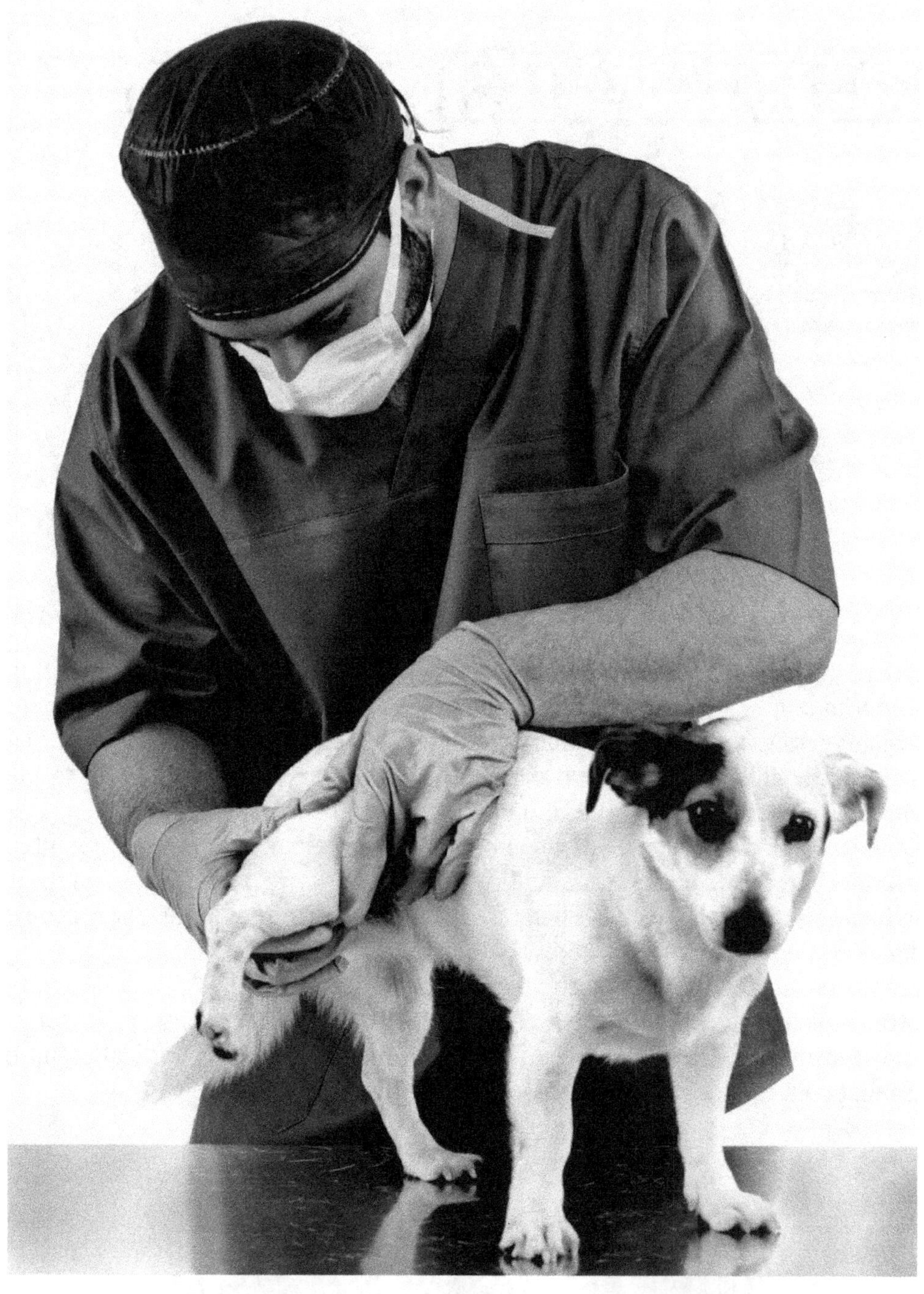

Emerging technology for cruciate ligament repair includes tendon transplants, used as a substitute for the ligament. These surgeries are performed arthroscopically. A major difficulty in using donor tendons, occurs during rehab, because dogs are not as sensitive to pain in the joints and tend to overdo too quickly.

Tibial Plateau Leveling Osteotomy or the TPLO, offers a paradigm shift in treatment options. The technique changes the dynamics of the knee joint. The surgery cuts the end of the tibia and rotates it so the flat part stays level and the femur can't slide off when the dog stands. Surgery reconfigures the joint so it no longer requires the anterior cruciate ligament for stability. After the surgery, the knee functions normally.

The progress of arthritis appears to be slowed greatly as a result. The procedure is used only for pets. There is nothing like it in human knee surgery repair.

Canine hips that suffer crippling pain can be replaced by artificial hips. The knee (stifle joint) suffers from arthritis even more often than the hips, but knee replacement surgery is not as readily available. That's because the ball and socket joint of the hip is relatively easy to duplicate and is held together simply by the dog's body weight.

But the knee joint (like the elbow) is fashioned more like a hinge, and must be held together by ligaments. Dogs would greatly benefit from an artificial knee, because arthritis in this joint often causes severe pain as they age even after repairing ruptured ligaments. Any human knee prosthetic joint is about the same size. But in veterinary medicine, size must range to fit everything from a two-pound Chihuahua to a 180-pound Great Dane.

Ask your veterinarian about options, if interested in total knee replacement (TKR). BioMedrix (http://www.biomedtrix.com) makes these prosthetics and includes a "locator" tool to find practitioners able to perform the procedure.

LARYNGEAL PARALYSIS This common condition is the abnormal movement of the vocal folds, the structures which shape the dog's voice. Movement of vocal folds normally is tied to respiration, and timed to open during inhalation and partially close with exhalation. When the timing is out of sync, or the folds don't move at all, the airway may become blocked.

Laryngeal paralysis is a rare congenital defect in the Bouvier des Flanders, Dalmatian, and Siberian Husky, but can affect any breed or age dog. It is most common in elderly hunting dogs, but is also a problem in large and giant breeds like the Labrador Retriever and Great Dane.

The cause of the syndrome remains uncertain. In the past, it was considered due to hypothyroidism, but recent studies indicate the condition is likely due to muscular and/or neurological inflammation.

LARYNGEAL PARALYSIS

SYMPTOMS: Dry cough; change in voice; noisy inhalation; excessive panting; difficulty breathing; sensitivity to heat and exercise; blue gums; collapse
HOME CARE: Restrict exercise; reduce stress
VET CARE: Tranquilizers; corticosteroids; sometimes surgery
PREVENTION: None; once diagnosed, avoid excess stress and heat, and prevent obesity

Signs include a dry cough, change in voice sounds (i.e., the bark sounds different), and noisy breathing especially during inhalation. Dogs tend to pant excessively, may be sensitive to heat, and often suffer labored breathing or collapse prompted by exercise or stress.

Diagnosis is based on the signs, and confirmed by examination of the larynx using a laryngoscope while the dog is sedated.

Treatment depends on the severity of the signs, and is aimed at relieving airway obstruction. Mild cases respond to tranquilizers and anti-inflammatory drugs like corticosteroids. Severe obstruction may require surgical correction to enlarge the opening.

LARYNGITIS

SYMPTOMS: Harsh, dry cough; gagging; voice changes or loss of voice; sometimes noisy inhalation and difficulty breathing; head-hanging posture to ease respiration; blue gums
HOME CARE: Reduce barking opportunities; humidify air; feed soft foods; breathing difficulties (blue gums, labored breathing) are an EMERGENCY! SEE VET IMMEDIATELY!
VET CARE: Treat underlying cause; often resolves without treatment; sometimes antibiotics and cough suppressants
PREVENTION: Reduce excessive barking

LARYNGITIS This is the inflammation of the larynx, the upper portion of the trachea which contains the sound-producing vocal chords. Laryngitis more commonly refers to the condition of losing one's voice, which often results from such inflammation. But the condition can become dangerous if inflammation and localized swelling interfere with breathing.

In dogs, laryngitis typically results from irritation. This may occur secondarily to an upper respiratory tract infection (see KENNEL COUGH and CANINE DISTEMPER). Inhalation of an irritant like smoke or dust or the presence of a foreign body may also cause the dog to temporarily lose his voice. Trauma can also be a cause, and may result from surgery that requires the placement of an endotracheal tube to administer oxygen or anesthesia. Dogs may also suffer laryngitis as a result of simply barking too much.

The most common signs are a harsh, dry cough, gagging, and/or changes in the sound of the dog's voice. Some dogs may be unable to produce any sound at all. Diagnosis is based on clinical signs, and sometimes on visual examination of the tissues using a laryngoscope while the dog is sedated.

Most cases of canine laryngitis are self-limiting. That means, no treatment is necessary because the dog will get better on his own simply by resting his voice. Try to avoid exposing your dog to situations that prompt excessive barking.

However, sometimes the condition can turn more serious if the inflammation proceeds to swelling. Then the dog may exhibit noisy breathing, particularly on inhalation, as breathing becomes more difficult. The dog may stand with his head hanging between his braced front legs, and mouth open.

As the larynx swells, oxygen is blocked and the dog's gums and tongue may turn blue, while temperature and pulse rate increase Obstruction of the airways, characterized by labored breathing and/or blue gums, is an emergency that must be seen by a veterinarian immediately; it may require surgical tracheotomy to open a passage in the dog's throat so he can breathe.

When laryngitis is not due to excessive barking or the placement of a breathing tube for surgery, treatment depends on the underlying cause. Infections are treated with appropriate antibacterial medications. Cough-suppressants, inhalation of humidified air, and feeding soft foods help speed the dog's recovery.

LASER TECHNOLOGY Medical lasers have been commonly used only since the early 1980s. The laser advantage, basically, is that it will seal blood vessels, lymphatics and nerve endings, so you don't have as much hemorrhage or as much inflammation or pain. However, because surgical lasers use photo thermal energy (heat) healing takes longer than an incision with a scalpel. But lasers are able to vaporize tissue in a very controlled and gentle way that offers a strong advantage.

Lasers are often used in dermatology and skin cancer therapies. Veterinary ophthalmologists have developed ways to treat glaucoma, or to use lasers to spot-weld retinal detachments back in place. In addition, laser energy can be shot through special fibers to reach deep within the body without requiring invasive surgery. Although the carbon dioxide laser is quite common, a variety of special lasers such as the diode laser and the Nd:YAG laser (neodidium yutridium aluminum garnet laser) are available. Each type uses a different wave length of energy, which is absorbed by tissue in different ways and offers specific benefits. Today, the price has come down, and the lasers themselves are better suited to veterinary practice.

LEAD POISONING

SYMPTOMS: Loss of appetite; vomiting; hunching posture from stomach pain; diarrhea or constipation; depression; hyperactivity with excessive barking, teeth grinding, and seizures
HOME CARE: EMERGENCY! SEE VET IMMEDIATELY!
VET CARE: Stomach lavage; treat with chelating agents; supportive care
PREVENTION: Monitor dog's activities; prevent her swallowing or chewing dangerous items

LEAD POISONING Lead poisoning, though less common than in the past, is still a frequently diagnosed poisoning in veterinary medicine. It affects dogs most often because of their less-than-discriminatory eating habits and high susceptibility to the poison.

Dogs like to mouth, bite and chew non-food objects. They may be exposed from swallowing the lead weight from a curtain, or a shotgun slug; when the metal remains in the stomach, ongoing exposure builds over time. Dogs may also suffer ongoing exposure by eating peeling paint, crumbling plaster, or linoleum.

Any dog is susceptible, but puppies are more severely affected because of their smaller size. Most signs stem from gastrointestinal and/or neurologic systems. Initial signs in dogs are anorexia, vomiting, hunching posture from stomach pain, and diarrhea or constipation. Neurological signs may be either depression, or more commonly are sudden hyperactivity with hysterical barking, teeth-grinding, seizures and muscle spasms. Without treatment, the dog will die.

Diagnosis is based on signs of illness, and lead poisoning should be suspected any time a dog exhibits acute neurological signs but has no previous history of neurological problems. Blood tests or analysis of tissue samples from the kidneys or liver confirms the diagnosis.

Prognosis depends on the extent of injury to the nervous system, which is irreversible. In severe cases, treatment will not help and euthanasia is the kindest choice. However, in some instances, flushing the dog's gastrointestinal tract will help clear out any remaining lead.

Mild to moderate toxicities may respond favorably to treatment. Edetate calcium disodium (CaEDTA) mixed with saline or dextrose solution can be administered to the poisoned dog in several doses given every other day for three days. CaEDTA helps move lead out of the tissues, and enhances its excretion through the urine. A repeat of the treatment may be necessary, after giving the dog a week of rest. Dogs may also benefit from an oral chelating agent called D-penicillamine, given daily for a two-week period. Close veterinary supervision during treatment is required.

It's much easier to prevent lead intoxication than to treat its devastating effects. Monitor your dog's investigatory behavior, and prevent the dog from chewing or swallowing dangerous items. NOTE: Whenever lead poisoning is diagnosed in a dog, any young children in the home should also be examined by a pediatrician, as they likely have also been exposed to the risk.

LEPTOSPIROSIS

This disease is caused by a *spirochete*, a type of spiral-shaped bacteria. Several varieties can cause leptospirosis in dogs: *Canicola, Icterohemorrhagiae, Grippotyphosa*, and *Pomona*. Dogs may be infected when livestock or wild animals pass the agents in their urine, contaminating food, soil or water. Most infections are mild and cause no problem. However, leptospirosis is extremely contagious and can be transmitted from infected dogs to people. Fortunately, canine leptospirosis is relatively uncommon.

The bacterium infects the dog by entering through a break in the skin, or when the dog swallows contaminated water or food. Drinking from standing water in cattle pens or from mud puddles are common routes of infection.

Owners probably won't notice signs of mild disease. But following recovery, untreated dogs can become carriers, and they'll shed bacteria in their urine for as much as a year.

Common symptoms include low-grade fever with mild to moderate listlessness, loss of appetite, and increased thirst and increased urination. Pain in the kidneys causes the dog to walk in a hunched posture. In severe disease, diarrhea and vomiting develop, and mouth ulcers can make eating painful. The dog may have blood-shot eyes or reddened gums, and a brownish coating on the tongue may be seen. Diagnosis can usually be made by the signs themselves, and the disease is confirmed by finding the bacteria in the dog's urine or blood. When diagnosed early and treated aggressively, most dogs recover.

To reduce the chance for human infection, dogs usually must be hospitalized. When the dog returns home, owners should wash their hands thoroughly with soapy warm water after handling the dog. Confine the dog away from where you prepare and eat your meals.

The bacteria are killed and further organ damage arrested using a combination of antibiotic therapies, such as penicillin and streptomycin. Antibiotics may be required for several weeks to ensure all the bacteria are eliminated. Diuretic drugs that promote urination help with the kidney failure. Supportive care such as fluid therapy to control dehydration, along with medication to help minimize vomiting and diarrhea, are often required. If hemorrhage is present, the dog may need blood transfusion.

Vaccinations are available, but they do not combine all agents and it can be difficult to recommend based on geographic region. Only dogs at risk for infection are recommended to receive this *noncore* vaccination. In addition, puppies less than 12 weeks of age may suffer mild-to-severe vaccination reactions, so vaccination is not recommended until after this age.

The best way to prevent leptospirosis in your dog is to prevent her opportunity for infection. Don't allow her to roam unsupervised, and provide fresh drinking water so she's less tempted to drink from contaminated puddles.

LEPTOSPIROSIS

SYMPTOMS: Low-grade fever; listlessness; loss of appetite; increased thirst and urination; hunched posture due to kidney pain; diarrhea; vomiting; reluctance to eat from mouth pain; bloodshot eyes; reddened gums; brown coating on tongue; jaundice; sometimes bleeding
HOME CARE: Supportive nursing care; soft food; usually, dog must be hospitalized and treated under quarantine
VET CARE: Antibiotics; diuretic drugs to promote urination; fluid therapy; medication to control vomiting and diarrhea; sometimes blood transfusion
PREVENTION: Vaccinate your dog; provide ample fresh water; prevent exposure to contaminated water

LICE Lice are wingless flat insects that parasitize the skin using either biting or sucking mouth parts to feed. There are countless varieties, but each species prefers a specific host and tends to remain on one animal for its entire life. Dogs in North America may be afflicted with the sucking louse *Linognathus setosus* which feeds on blood, or the biting varieties *Trichodectes canis* and *Heterodoxus spiniger* which feed on skin debris.

Louse infestation, called pediculosis, is rare in dogs. This may be because flea treatment also kills lice. When it does occur, dogs contract the bugs from direct contact with an infected animal. Typically, they infest skin beneath areas of matted fur, around the head and neck, and near the anal area. Itching and poor hair coat and/or loss of fur are common signs. Severe infestations can result in life threatening anemia, particularly in small dogs or puppies.

LICE

SYMPTOMS: Scaling or scabby skin; itchiness; poor hair coat (often matted); hair loss; visible bugs or eggs stuck to hairs; sometimes anemia
HOME CARE: Treat weekly with a topical flea product; destroy infected bedding; thoroughly vacuum premises; provide high-quality nutrition
VET CARE: Rarely necessary
PREVENTION: Keep dog well groomed; avoid contact with other dogs; provide good nutrition

Diagnosis is based on signs; usually, owners will see the parasite or the eggs (nits) glued to the individual hairs. Nits look like white sand, and are hard to brush off. Sucking lice move quite slowly, while biting lice are quicker. They are pale and small, about two or three millimeters long.

Pediculosis is treated using an appropriate insecticide; most flea preparations also kill adult lice. However, the immature nits are very resistant, and so ongoing treatment is necessary to kill these babies as they hatch. Weekly topical treatment of a dog-safe flea product is necessary for up to five weeks. Anemic dogs may require fluid replacement therapy or blood transfusions.

The bugs can't survive for long when off the host. Destroy the dog's bedding, and thoroughly vacuum carpets to help eliminate the parasite from the environment. Most affected dogs are run down, poorly kept, and undernourished. Prevent lice infestation by regularly grooming your dog, and keeping her skin and fur coat healthy and clean, and providing optimum nutrition.

LICK SORES

More correctly termed acral lick granuloma, this is a common condition thought to be associated with canine boredom. The affected dog incessantly licks a selected area, usually on a lower leg, which creates a raised, hairless ulcerative plaque, almost a callus that surrounds the never-healing sore. The constant licking makes the area itch and can cause secondary bacterial infection. This prompts further licking to relieve the itch, and a vicious cycle is created.

Any dog can be affected, but the condition most commonly affects males older than three years. The syndrome is often seen in large active-breed dogs that demand a lot of owner interaction, such as Golden Retrievers, Labrador Retrievers, Doberman Pinchers, Great Danes, and German Shepherd Dogs.

Diagnosis is based on the clinical signs, history, and microscopic examination of the lesion (biopsy). Treatment is difficult, and some dogs may never be completely cured. Infections may respond to antibiotics after several months, and steroid injections may temporarily soothe itchiness. The best treatment is to alleviate the dog's boredom, and give him something better to do with his time.

Your veterinarian may recommend PEMF therapy, which stimulate the electrical and chemical processes in the tissues to relieve inflammation and pain, and encourage healing. Devices may be designed for whole body treatment or targeted areas of the body. Some of these devices have successfully completed efficacy studies and are FDA-approved. Therapeutic products may be available in mats, wraps or other devices from your veterinarian or over the counter (see PULSED ELECTROMAGNETIC FIELD).

374 DOG FACTS

An owner's interaction—spending more one-on-one time with the dog playing games, walking, or training—is beneficial. Dogs that are confined alone for long periods of time tend to have more problems with boredom, and so avoiding extended confinement can help. Some dogs respond favorably when another pet is adopted into the home (see INTRODUCTIONS).

The habit may be interrupted in some dogs through the use of veterinary prescribed tranquilizers. Anti-depressant drugs such as Prozac (fluoxetine) and Anafranil (clomipramine) used in treating obsessive/compulsive disorders may be effective in certain instances.

LICK SORES

SYMPTOMS: Raised, hairless ulcer; calluslike plaque on lower leg; incessant licking of sore
HOME CARE: Apply Elizabethan collar
VET CARE: Treat underlying cause; antibiotics; immune-suppressing drugs; tranquilizers; antidepressant medication
PREVENTION: Reduce dog's boredom

LIVER DISEASE The liver acts as an organic processing plant that removes toxins, metabolizes drugs, and manufactures and processes nutrients and enzymes. Liver disease refers to any condition that interferes with one or more of the organ's functions. That can happen to dogs of any age. Because older dogs are more prone to other health challenges, the liver may be more susceptible to stress, damage, or disease in senior canines.

Even when a large percentage of the liver stops working, the remainder is able to handle the job. After some insults, it's fully capable of regenerating to its original size but it takes lots of medical support to buy the necessary time for recovery. And in some disease states, the liver's regenerative capacity becomes limited, and it can't repair itself.

Food in the intestine is absorbed into the blood, which then ferries specific components to the liver. There, sugars and fats are processed, amino acids are produced, and certain vitamins and minerals are stored. The liver also manufactures hormones, important blood-clotting enzymes, and a substance called bile that allows fats to be absorbed. These stored products are later delivered throughout the body as needed by the blood.

Other substances such as drugs that are carried by the blood are metabolized, or altered by the liver into other forms. Foreign matter including viruses and bacteria or poisons are filtered out in an effort to protect the rest of the body from damage. For that reason, the dog's liver is exposed to disease and injury more than any other part of the body.

Because the liver interacts with so many other body systems, it can be affected by other conditions (see CUSHING'S DISEASE). The excessive production of cortisol associated with Cushing's disease stimulates the liver to make a lot of glycogen—carbohydrate storage material—and so the liver gets really big. Liver tests fall into the abnormal range. In this case, though, the liver is actually absolutely fine, and it's just the cortisol inducing all these changes. Once you get Cushing's disease under control, the liver's size returns to normal.

LIVER DISEASE

SYMPTOMS: Refusal to eat; vomiting; diarrhea; weight loss; lethargy; jaundice; swollen abdomen; bloody urine or stool
HOME CARE: EMERGENCY! SEE VET IMMEDIATELY! Once diagnosed, supportive nutrition
HOLISTIC HELP: Herbal therapy; massage; supplements; aromatherapy
VET CARE: Treat the specific cause; supportive care; steroid-type drugs; prescription diet; sometimes drugs to kill parasites; congenital defects are surgically corrected
PREVENTION: Keep poisons out of reach of the dog

A congenital defect may result in a **portosystemic shunt**, an abnormal connection of a vein into the liver that should normally close off shortly after the puppy is born. When the vein remains open, blood is shunted through this opening instead of passing through the liver. Small dog breeds like Yorkshire Terriers and Miniature Schnauzers are most commonly affected, although all dogs are at risk. Any dog with this defect will usually show signs of liver disease before reaching a year old; occasionally, dogs will not show any signs until they are older. Diagnosis can be confirmed by a combination of blood tests, ultrasound, special X-rays and/or exploratory surgery. Surgical correction is the treatment of choice for some types of shunts, and a reduced protein diet in the interim relieves the clinical signs of the condition

Other conditions affecting liver function include parasites, and cancer. In particular, a tumor called hemangiosarcoma, which usually originates in the spleen, often spreads to the liver.

Drug-induced liver problems are also common, and any drug could cause problems. Rimadyl used to treat canine arthritis is a common culprit, as is long-term use of the antiseizure medication Phenobarbital.

Nonspecific inflammation of the liver—referred to as hepatitis—may also flare up. Degenerative changes in the liver may occur due to anorexia, diabetes mellitus, pancreatitis, gastrointestinal disease or cancer. When the cause can be controlled, it's expected the liver can return to normal function.

The signs of liver diseases are remarkably similar, whatever their cause. Commonly, liver dysfunction results in anorexia, vomiting, diarrhea, weight loss and lethargy. When bile backs up in the circulation, it can turn light-colored areas of the dog's body pale yellow or tea-colored. This is called jaundice and is most easily seen in the whites of the eyes, gums, or inner surfaces of the ear flap. Increased pressure of the veins that drain into the liver may result in ascites, which is an accumulation of fluid into the abdomen. The dog's abdomen will appear swollen or bloated. Hemorrhage is another sign of advanced canine liver disease, with bleeding into the stomach, intestines and urinary tract; blood in the stool or urine is the sign.

Sophisticated tests are required to diagnose liver disease. A biochemical profile of the blood is the first step toward diagnosis. Liver enzymes may be elevated for a number of reasons, though, and elevated enzyme values do not automatically mean the dog has liver disease. Blood tests may be followed by ultrasound and possibly a biopsy. Diagnosis can be complicated by the presence of nodular regeneration, a poorly understood mechanism whereby the liver develops little nodules as a result of decreased blood flow. The bumpy liver is simply a sign of aging, and usually doesn't indicate any disease.

Together, blood tests, imaging techniques (ultrasound) and symptoms can point to liver disease. However, a definitive diagnosis can only be made by a biopsy—examining tissue beneath the microscope. An ultrasound-guided needle allows cells to be collected through the abdominal wall, often without invasive surgery.

Chronic hepatitis, or inflammation of the liver, is the most common liver disease of dogs. All dogs are at risk, but mature dogs six to eight years old (especially Doberman Pinschers) are at highest risk. Most cases are idiopathic, which means no cause can be determined. Treatment consists primarily of supportive care, and removal of the cause, if known. Prognosis depends on the cause, but usually isn't too good. About 30 percent of dogs suffering from hepatitis will die within one week of diagnosis, despite treatment. The remaining dogs, when treated with immune-suppressing drugs like corticosteroids and fed a veterinarian prescribed therapeutic diet, tend to live longer.

When diagnosed and treated very early, liver damage in some instances may be reversible. Budesonide (used to treat human liver ailments) may be an option in some dogs. Azathioprine is an effective immunosuppressant drug that may also be beneficial in dogs by increasing the immunosuppressive response while reducing the amount of steroid dose and side effects. Cyclosporine also has shown good response in chronic cases.

Hepatitis is usually treated with medicines to try and suppress the inflammation. An oral ursodeoxycholic acid (UDCA, Actigall, or Ursodiol) is a naturally occurring bile acid that helps protect the liver from further damage. S-Adenosylmethionine (SAMe) is a kind of nutraceutical that can increase the antioxidant glutathione levels in liver cells of both dogs and cats. Glutathione is a potent antioxidant that protects liver cells from toxins and death. Some studies indicate that up to 45 percent of dogs with severe liver problems are deficient in glutathione. Taking S-Adenosylmethionine (brand name Denosyl SD4) has been demonstrated to improve liver function in these pets.

Dogs with liver disease typically feel so sick they don't want to eat. Refusing to eat makes sick dogs even sicker and delays recovery. Anorexia and weight loss occur commonly in patients with liver disease, and therefore one of the most important aspects in liver disease therapy is ensuring the patient has appropriate energy intake.

Dogs with liver disease generally tolerate fat in the diet very well. Fat improves palatability and provides energy. In the past, restricting protein was thought to reduce the liver's workload, but many veterinary nutritionists and gastroenterologists now believe protein restriction in liver patients could be detrimental. Feeding small yet frequent meals throughout each day seems to help. Occasionally force-feeding is necessary to get the dog over the hump. A feeding tube may be placed down the nose into the stomach, or surgically through the dog's side, to allow him to be fed a soft diet, either while in the hospital, or after going home.

Holistic veterinarians recommend a number of herbs and supplements to help cleanse and support the liver. Dandelion helps remove toxins, and milk thistle has been shown to help the liver generate new cells and protect it from toxins. Nutritional supplements such as raw beets contain natural chemicals that also work very well to support the liver. Dogs under fifteen pounds shouldn't have more than a few slivers of raw beet, as it's quite powerful, so offer once a day for five days, and then give the body a rest. Dogs that weigh fifteen to 50 pounds can have one-half teaspoon, and larger dogs can have one to two teaspoons.

When dogs refuse to eat anything else, some holistic vets recommend creating a raw liver formula by combining raw egg yolk, raw sheep or beef liver, a teaspoon of honey, two tablespoons of plain yogurt and a cup of water in a blender. Offer as much as he wants every hour or two for up to a week or so, until his appetite for regular food returns.

Once the dog begins eating again on his own, the right diet helps maintain sick dogs and helps them recover. The nutrient profiles of therapeutic diets provides highly digestible protein, zinc, and other ingredients designed to reduce the workload of the liver, support liver repair and regeneration, and help regulate the metabolism of blood sugar (see COPPER POISONING, FLUKES, and INFECTIOUS CANINE HEPATITIS).

LUNG WORMS

SYMPTOMS: Harsh, dry cough; labored breathing; refusal to eat; weight loss
HOME CARE: None
VET CARE: Antibiotics; medication to kill the parasite
PREVENTION: Prevent the dog from eating earthworms; limit contact with other dogs

LUNGWORMS Lungworms are slender, hair like worms that parasitize the branches of the respiratory tract. Two kinds of lungworms affect dogs: *Filaroides osleri* are contracted when the dog swallows the eggs or larvae found in infected feces or saliva; *Capillaria aerophila* are contracted by a dog eating infected earthworms.

Adult worms live in the lung tissue where they lay eggs. The hatched larvae are coughed up and usually swallowed by the dog. Puppies may be infected by contact with their mother when she licks them. Finding larvae or eggs in a stool sample during microscopic examination is diagnostic; sometimes a sample is taken directly from the trachea and brochials using needle aspiration.

The two types of lungworms cause different kinds of disease. *Capillaria aerophila* live in the nasal cavities and upper airways, and rarely causes symptoms. It takes about thirty days from the time the dog swallows the infective earthworm for adult lungworms to emerge. At most, dogs may suffer a chronic cough and harsh sneezing. The egg found in the stool sample closely resemble those of whipworms, and misdiagnosis is common.

Infestation of *Filaroides osleri* are more dangerous, and are largely a problem in kennels where they can affect entire litters of puppies. It takes about ten weeks for worms to develop in the dog. The parasites are isolated in encapsulated grayish wart-like growths up to ¾ inches in diameter within the trachea. These nodules can result in bronchitis causing a harsh, dry coughing spells. Anorexia and weight loss may result, and in severe cases, up to 75 percent of affected puppies in a litter may die. Bronchitis may be treated with antibiotics, and requires a veterinarian's care.

Worm medications such as fenbendazole, Ivermectin and doramectin are commonly used to treat infections. Some heartworm preventives that contain milbemycin or selamectin may also be helpful. Check with your veterinarian for best choices for your dog.

Routinely picking up feces and practicing good hygiene in the kennel, as well as preventing dogs from eating earthworms, will help prevent infection.

LUPUS ERYTHEMATOSUS (SLE)

Lupus, more accurately termed systemic lupus erythematosus (SLE) refers to a rare autoimmune disease complex of disorders which may affect only the skin (usually of the face), or the entire body. Essentially, instead of acting in a normal fashion to protect the body from outside invaders, the dog's immune system goes haywire and attacks itself.

Discoid lupus erythematosus can affect any dog at any age, but is most common in Collies, Shetland Sheepdogs, German Shepherd Dogs (white German Shepherds at particularly high risk) and Siberian Huskies. Because of the high incidence of the condition in Collies, and the possible influence of sunlight, the condition has in the past been referred to as "Collie Nose" or nasal solar dermatitis. Whether or not there is a direct causal relationship between exposure to ultraviolet radiation and development of discoid lupus erythematosus isn't known, but sun exposure does aggravate an existing condition. Lesions are more severe during the summer months and in high-exposure geographic regions such as high altitudes.

The first signs are loss of skin color and reddened scaly skin particularly on the bridge of the nose. The dog loses hair in the affected regions, which develop crusting sores. The leather of the nose (the tip) is also affected, and seems to erode. Sores and ulcerations grow progressively worse, and may also involve the muzzle, lips, around the eyes and ear margins.

Diagnosis is based on clinical signs, and on skin biopsy in which a sample of the affected tissue is examined for characteristic changes. Treatment is similar to that for sunburn. Affected dogs should be kept away from direct sunlight and owners should apply sunscreen to the dog's nose, ears or other high-risk areas. The veterinarian may prescribe anti-inflammatory creams or ointments for affected tissues; anti-inflammatory pills or injections are only rarely used.

LUPUS

SYMPTOMS: Loss of nose pigment; red scaly bridge of nose; eroding nose tip; ulcers and crusting sores around mouth and eyes; sometimes footpad ulcers and joint disease
HOME CARE: Protect dogs from direct exposure to sunlight; use sunscreens on high-risk areas
VET CARE: Same as home care; also, anti-inflammatory creams; immune-suppressing drugs
PREVENTION: Protect dogs from sunburn; keep dogs inside during high sun-exposure hours; use sunblock

SLE is considered quite rare in dogs, and appears to be similar to the condition in people. Skin sores similar to the discoid lupus condition also appear in this disease, and dogs may also develop footpad ulcers; however, SLE affects the whole body, attacking blood, joints, kidneys, heart and other organs, often at the cellular level.

Signs of disease depend upon the organ affected, and the severity of disease. Diagnosis is similar to that of discoid lupus erythematosus, in that skin biopsy and clinical signs are evaluated. In addition, a blood test can detect the antibodies that attack DNA; their presence provides definitive diagnosis in both dogs and people. Immune suppressing drugs such as corticosteroids offer the best treatment hope for dogs suffering SLE. Such dogs should also be protected from exposure to the sun. Prognosis is guarded.

LYME DISEASE

Lyme disease is one of the most common tick-borne diseases in dogs and puppies. Youngsters appear to be more susceptible so it's important to protect your puppies from Lyme disease especially if you live in a region known to harbor the Lyme disease tick.

Lyme disease was first identified in 1975 when a cluster of childhood arthritis cases were reported in Lyme, Connecticut. It's caused by a spirochete, a type of bacteria named *Borrelia burgdorferi,* which occurs naturally in white-footed mice and deer. The organism is transmitted to people and dogs by deer ticks.

A number of tick species are able to carry *B. Burgdorferi*, but the deer tick, *Ixodes scapularis* is the most effective transmitter of the Lyme bacterium. It's found most commonly in the northeastern, north central, and Pacific Coast states.

Deer ticks mature in a two-year cycle, progressing from egg to larvae, nymph and then adult. Adult ticks prefer to feed on deer, but immature stages feed on white-footed mice and sometimes other warm-blooded animals.

The Lyme bacterium makes its home in deer and mice, which don't become sick, but spread the disease to ticks at any stage when they feed on infected blood. Both the nymph and adult tick are able to transmit the disease to people and dogs, and will make do with such victims when a preferred host isn't available.

Human symptoms include a red rash around the tick bite in a kind of "bullseye" pattern. Other early signs involve flu-like symptoms, including fever, headache, stiff joints and swollen lymph nodes. The disease can ultimately cause arthritis, lethargy, heart disorders and damage to the nervous system.

The most common sign of Lyme disease in dogs is a sudden (acute) lameness characterized by limping from painful swollen joints of one or more leg. Other times there may be "shifting leg lameness" where the dog limps on different legs as the discomfort comes and goes.

Affected dogs may walk with a hunched back from pain, limp, be sensitive to touch, have difficulty breathing, run a fever, refuse to eat, and act depressed. More serious problems happen with some dogs and include kidney damage, heart issues or even neurological problems. Labrador Retrievers, Golden Retrievers and Bernese Mountain Dogs seem to be affected more often by kidney complications.

LYME DISEASE

SYMPTOMS: Sudden lameness with limping; painful, swollen joints; sometimes fever; history of tick infestation
HOME CARE: Remove ticks; requires vet treatment
VET CARE: Antibiotics; sometimes supportive care
PREVENTION: Tick repellents and on dog and environment; prompt removal of ticks; vaccination when recommended by vet

Diagnosis is based on the presence of these signs, a history of being in an endemic region, and blood tests as well as urinalysis to look for bacteria, parasites and/or fungi. The fluid in swollen joints may also be tested and X-rays may be needed.

Since arthritis most commonly affects older dogs, a puppy with lameness may be suspected to have Lyme disease. However, some blood tests simply indicate that exposure has taken place and are not a definitive diagnoses because in endemic regions, up to fifty percent of tested dogs will show they have been exposed to the bacterium, yet may show no signs of disease.

A positive reaction to antibiotic therapy is a better confirmation of diagnosis. Dogs may refuse to walk, yet within 24 hours of antibiotic treatment appear to be fully recovered. Most dogs show signs of pain relief within three to five days of therapy, and antibiotics are most effective when given soon after onset of the symptoms. Typically the treatment is given for about four weeks. Sadly, some dogs continue to show signs of joint pain even after the disease is eliminated, and may require ongoing treatment.

There is a preventative vaccine available for dogs; ask your veterinarian if it is appropriate for your situation. Deer ticks are found in high grass and weeds between the lawn and the woods, and pets and people that roam these areas are more likely to pick up ticks. Use veterinarian-approved tick repellents or insecticides which kills both fleas and ticks.

Prevention also includes removing ticks promptly. The tick must feed 18 to 24 hours before the organisms will be transmitted into the host. When your dog comes inside, immediately inspect him for ticks, and remove them with tweezers to avoid exposing yourself. People don't become infected from their pets, but you can become sick by touching infected ticks, so wear gloves.

Application of insecticide directly to tick-infested environment is another method of control. However, since the tick's life cycle is two years, one application isn't enough.

People living in endemic areas should wear light-colored clothing, tape socks over pants cuffs, and use insect repellents on clothing and exposed skin when in tick-infested areas. For further information, please refer to the Lyme Disease Association (http://www.lymediseaseassociation.org).

MALABSORPTION SYNDROME This uncommon condition refers to the inability of the dog's body to digest and/or to absorb food that is eaten. Any dog may be affected, but German Shepherd Dogs appear to have the highest incidence.

Dogs with this condition may have a healthy appetite, but appear malnourished, thin, and have a poor hair coat despite eating well. The dog produces a large volume of stool that typically contains a great deal of fat, giving it a characteristic rancid odor. The fur surrounding the anus is often greasy or oily.

The most common cause of malabsorption syndrome is pancreatic insufficiency, when the pancreas fails to produce the necessary digestive enzymes (see PANCREATITIS). This syndrome is most common in dogs two to three years old.

MALABSORPTION SYNDROME

SYMPTOMS: Malnourished appearance; healthy appetite; poor hair coat; large stool volume; fatty, rancid-smelling stool; oily fur surrounding anus
HOME CARE: Feed a highly digestible diet, as directed by vet
VET CARE: Treat underlying cause; supplement diet with pancreatic enzymes; sometimes antibiotic therapy; therapeutic diet
PREVENTION: None

Liver disease is another cause, which results in a lack of bile, the substances that allows fats to be absorbed. Parasites or viral or bacterial infections that cause intestinal damage may also result in malabsorption. A more recently identified cause of the syndrome is bacterial overgrowth of the small intestine, in which normal bacteria proliferate to excess levels.

Treatment depends on the cause of the condition, and a variety of specialized laboratory tests may be required for diagnosis. Analysis of the stool reveals the presence of undigested dietary fats, starches and/or muscle fibers. A blood test may confirm pancreatic insufficiency. A biopsy of the intestinal tissue may be necessary.

Depending on the cause, treatment may include replacing the missing components necessary for digestion of the dog's diet. For instance, the missing pancreatic enzymes may be added as a powder to the food. When bacterial overgrowth is the cause, antibiotic therapy is the treatment of choice. Other times, feeding a diet that is more easily digested may be required for the rest of the dog's life; a combination of cottage cheese or tofu with boiled rice along with a balanced vitamin and mineral supplement may be recommended. Always consult with your veterinarian to ensure your dog receives the best treatment and diet for his situation (see INFLAMMATORY BOWEL DISEASE).

MAMMARY GLANDS Also called breasts, mammary glands are modified sebaceous glands of adult mammals that provide nourishment to offspring by secreting milk through nipples. Both male and female dogs typically have eight breasts located in four pairs along the abdomen, but most male dogs do not produce milk.

When not producing milk, mammary glands remain nearly flush with the abdomen, and are apparent only by slightly elevated light pink nipples. Milk production causes swelling of the breast tissue and darkening of the nipples, and the fur surrounding the nipples may thin. The breasts nearest the flanks tend to produce the most milk, and so are often favored by puppies.

A lump, bump or swelling of the breast not associated with milk production requires immediate veterinary evaluation to rule out cancer. If a mother dog suffers a high fever during nursing, this may indicate trouble; stop the pups from nursing and take the dam to see a veterinarian (see ECLAMPSIA and MASTITIS).

MARKING Marking is a behavior used by dogs to identify territory. Dogs primarily use urine, and possibly scratching, to leave visual and scent cues. These signals not only indicate ownership, but also act as a canine bulletin board to tell other dogs who has been there before them, how long ago the mark was left, the sexual status of that dog, and other important information. However, because the scent of urine tends to fade as soon as it contacts the air, markings must be constantly freshened with new markings on top or nearby the original.

Marking is different than elimination behavior. When the purpose is to simply void a full bladder, female dogs usually urinate downward in a crouched position over a flat surface like the ground; males may also squat to urinate. In contrast, marking is done from a standing position by cocking a rear leg and aiming the urine stream at a (usually) vertical object. This places the scent at a convenient sniffing level, just as people would place a Post-It Note at eye level to attract the most attention.

Both male and female dogs urine mark, but typically it is the male that is most enthusiastic. And, it is the intact dog able to produce puppies that exhibit the most prominent behavior. Females may leg-cock to announce their breeding availability to male dogs.

It takes very little urine to send the intended message. During walks with your dog, he may stop you every five yards or so to leg-cock against a tuft of grass, telephone pole, or other obvious landmark. By the end of the walk, he may run out of urine but continue to leg-cock, in effect simply going through the motions. This is thought to be a visual signal to any watching dogs.

Urine marking is a sign of dominance which has great social and sexual significance to dogs. However, they sometimes get carried away and mark inappropriate targets. Extremely dominant dogs may even urinate against a person's leg, and intact indoor dogs often feel compelled to scent their household top to bottom. Neutering greatly reduces leg-cocking behavior, curtailing the baptism of bedroom walls, tires, and furniture.

Altered dogs of either sex that excessively mark with urine usually are experiencing stress. When feeling insecure, a dog attempts to assert control over his or her environment by aggressively marking territory with the comforting familiarity of personal scent. Soiling may also be due to medical problems.

One theory says that scratching or kicking the ground following elimination helps spread the scent; however, dogs may move after splashing urine on the side of a building, and kick up grass some distance away. Others believe there may be scent left during the scratching or kicking behavior from glands in the dog's feet, similar to what cats use when scratching objects. The scarred ground could also be a visual sign of territorial marking (see HOUSE TRAINING and SUBMISSIVE URINATION).

MASSAGE Massage is a hands-on therapy that addresses the tendons, muscles and other soft tissues by gently manipulating these areas with your hands and flexing the joints. Massage increases blood flow to sore spots and removes lactic acid that collects in tissues and makes the dog stiff and painful. That helps speed recovery from muscle pain or strain, and can also loosen tight tendons and scar tissue from old injuries.

Massage is a good way to relax with your dog after high energy play. Very young pups shouldn't exercise too much anyway or can risk injuring themselves. Adolescent dogs, though, can be hard to contain and sometimes get sore just from growing so fast. Dogs that are active in canine sports like agility and flyball can become stiff, and a massage before and after these fun sessions can be helpful. A massage can ease the discomfort, and get the dog ready to rumble all over again.

The hands-on treatment has added benefits, too. It reduces stress and even helps strengthen the immune system. Since contact with pets also benefits human health, massaging your dog has benefits for you both.

Range of motion exercises where the DOG's joints are moved probably are best left in the hands of a professional—or have your veterinarian show you how to safely do this. But simple massage techniques can be safely done by you at home and your dog will tell you where he wants the attention most, by backing his butt-end near your hands, or moaning with pleasure when you rub his shoulders. Here are some massage techniques for you to try.

Effleurage is a gentle long, slow strokes with your palm, starting at the pet's head and continuing down to the tail and feet. This technique helps move the blood through the body but also is a stroke that encourages relaxation. Start with a soft touch, and then slowly increase the pressure of your palms.

Fingertip massage uses the tips of your fingers in small, circular patterns to move the muscles beneath the skin. Don't press directly over the bone. Instead, use fingertip massage on each side of the spine, for example, to ease stiff muscles and tissues.

Petrissage is sort of a combination of effleurage and fingertip massage, and uses a kneading technique. Your DOG may not need this intense type of massage, or may object since it can be a bit painful on sore areas. But petrissage done correctly can move waste products out of the sore muscles.

TTouch ("tee-touch") is a specialized massage developed by Linda Tellington-Jones that works particularly well to address fear and aggression issues in pets. Tests show that TTouch changes the electrical activity in pets' brains. This helps them relax so they're open to learning new ways of coping, rather than just reacting out of fear. TTouch uses very specific circular stroke patterns on the surface of the skin all over the pet's body, with extra attention paid to the ears. The basic circle technique is called the Clouded Leopard TTouch because the strokes follow the circle shape of leopard spots. For large dogs, use your thumb and for smaller dogs, use one or two fingers to push the skin in a clockwise direction by "drawing" a complete circle with your fingers. Completing the circle changes the brain waves. After completing each circle, slide your hand on the pet's body an inch or two, and form another circle. Never lose contact with the body. Continue making "chains" of circles all over, as long as the pet allows. A ten-to-twenty-minute session is a good target. Let your pet be your guide, whether he wants a light touch or stronger pressure.

Many of the same rehab techniques created for human athletes have been adapted to dogs. Massage and muscle stretching, muscle stimulation with E-Stim (electrostimulation), or treadmills and whirlpools are available. Swimming is often used to rehab dogs and specialized heated pools with adjustable jets create a resistance against which the pet swims help speed recovery.

One of the most effective rehab techniques employs an underwater treadmill. Many dogs feel severe pain for several weeks following surgery and refuse to swim because it hurts too much. Even water-loving dogs tend to be fearful of water in the veterinarian's office. They thrash so much they're in danger of hurting themselves.

But with the underwater treadmill, you just open up the door, and they walk into an empty holding tank that looks kind of like an aquarium. The door seals, and the water is pumped into the chamber very slowly, underneath their paws, so they don't get as scared. These specialized treadmills gives buoyancy so he can use his legs and move the joints without painful weight bearing issues.

The water, warmed to 85 to 90 degrees, soothes sore muscles, and walking on the underwater treadmill doesn't force them to stay afloat. The walking in water offers lower impact exercise compared to swimming, and the dog slowly builds up speed and stamina over time. The therapist controls the amount of water—up to four feet deep—and the speed at which the treadmill runs.

There are windows on all sides so the therapist can watch the dog's body in action—and so the dog can see where he's going. For some dogs, the underwater treadmill treatment may reduce the need for pain medication or surgery, and helps dogs recover more quickly after surgery.

MASTITIS

Mastitis is an inflammation of the milk glands in the breast. Infection most commonly develops in one of two ways: either bacteria is introduced by a scratch or puncture wound from the puppies' claws during nursing, or not enough milk is evacuated from the breasts and they become blocked or caked (galactostasis).

Caked breasts are more uncomfortable than dangerous, but can lead to infection if not addressed. It's usually the two hindmost breasts that are affected. The condition may result when too much milk is produced, puppies don't suckle adequate amounts to relieve the pressure, or a deformed nipple prevents milk from being expressed. Sometimes dogs suffering from false pregnancy produce milk, and develop caked breasts when there are no puppies to suckle.

Breasts that are caked will be swollen, hard, warm to the touch, and very sensitive and painful. When the condition progresses to infection, the mother dog also loses her appetite and refuses to eat, is listless and/or restless, and develops a high fever.

Both the tissue and the milk produced are affected. The milk may appear normal, but often is tinged with blood or a yellowish cast, or is thick or stringy. Normal bitches' milk has a pH from 6.0 to 6.5, and you can test the acidity of the milk using litmus paper. Milk from caked breasts should be evaluated by your vet or tested with litmus paper before letting puppies nurse. If the litmus paper tests the milk at a pH of seven or higher, the milk is infected and dangerous for the babies.

Puppies that ingest toxic milk become ill and can die. Signs of toxic milk syndrome in puppies may include depression and lethargy, diarrhea, fever, and bloating.

MASTITIS

SYMPTOMS: Swollen, hard, hot, and painful breasts; high fever; anorexia; yellow or blood-streaked milk; stringy or thick milk
HOME CARE: EMERGENCY! Remove puppies and hand-feed, and SEE VET IMMEDIATELY! Once diagnosed, massage affected breast several times daily; apply warm wet compresses; medicate as directed
VET CARE: Culture milk to diagnose; administer appropriate antibiotics; sometimes surgical drainage
PREVENTION: Clip puppies' claws; spay dog to prevent future pregnancies

Puppies should be prevented from nursing from infected breasts. It is possible to tape over the nipples of the infected breasts to prevent puppies from suckling; however, it's safer to bottle feed the babies using a canned commercial canine milk replacer available from your veterinarian (see MILK, AS FOOD).

In the meantime, get the bitch to a veterinarian immediately. Infected milk must be cultured to discover the type of bacteria involved, so the appropriate antibiotic may be administered. If an abscess develops, surgical drainage of infected glands may be necessary.

Caked breasts may be resolved using gentle massage of the affected gland twice a day. Application of cold packs helps relieve the pain, and also reduces milk production, but warm wet compresses may help keep the milk ducts clear.

MEGAESOPHAGUS

SYMPTOMS: Dog is always hungry but underweight; suffers chronic regurgitation
HOME CARE: Feed dog from a table so she stands on her hind legs; offer semiliquid food
VET CARE: Treat underlying cause when possible
PREVENTION: Be vigilant to swallowed objects or poisons

MEGAESOPHAGUS This condition refers to an enlargement of the esophagus, the tube which moves food down the throat and into the stomach. Megaesophagus results in a partial or complete paralysis of the esophagus. The nerves that tell the tube to move food simply don't work, and the food when swallowed must fall downward to get to the stomach. Unfortunately, food comes back up even more easily.

In some instances, adult dogs can develop the condition. However, most cases are congenital; puppies are born with the defect. Congenital megaesophagus appears to primarily affect larger breed dogs, such as German Shepherd Dogs and Great Danes.

Affected dogs typically have a voracious appetite, but are underweight because of difficulty holding food down. Often, the puppy or dog suffers chronic regurgitation in which food comes back up immediately after eating, or hours thereafter. Rather than immediately passing into the stomach, the food may sit in the esophageal passage, ballooning and enlarging the tube even more.

Diagnosis is based on clinical signs and X-rays and/or endoscope examination. Unfortunately, there is no effective treatment for congenital megaesophagus but it may resolve by six months of age in youngsters. Feeding the affected dog in an elevated position—having him stand on his hind legs while he eats from a table, chair, or elevated box—may help keep food down. Semi-liquid diets may pass more easily into the stomach than solid foods. However, the condition makes puppies and dogs prone to pneumonia if vomitus is inhaled on the way up. Prognosis is poor, and often the puppy is humanely euthanized.

Cases of acquired megaesophagus may be surgically reversible (see SWALLOWED OBJECTS, CANCER, LEAD POISONING and LARYNGEAL PARALYSIS).

METRITIS

SYMPTOMS: Fever following the birth of puppies
HOME CARE: None
VET CARE: Antibiotics
PREVENTION: Veterinary injection of oxytocin after whelping to clean out uterus; spay the dog to prevent future pregnancy

METRITIS Metritis is the inflammation and/or infection of the uterus, and typically occurs shortly after giving birth. Some cases are caused when not all the placenta and birth materials are expelled from the uterus. Others result from contamination of the birth canal when unsterile fingers or instruments are used to help during whelping.

The most common sign is fever, and bitches should be examined by a veterinarian immediately after they have whelped. An injection of oxytocin may be administered to induce the uterus to expel the placenta. Antibiotics are usually prescribed to treat metritis. The condition can be prevented by spaying the dog and preventing pregnancy.

MILK, AS FOOD As soon as they're born, puppies begin suckling, and thrive on their mother's milk. If a puppy is orphaned or the mother can't feed the baby, milk is the obvious substitute.

However, the composition of bitch's milk and cow's milk is quite different; cow's milk only provides half the necessary nutrients for a growing puppy. Also, the lactose content of cow's milk is three times higher than bitch's milk. Lactose is a kind of sugar in the milk, and many puppies and adult dogs have inadequate amounts of the enzyme lactase in their intestinal tract that's necessary to break it down. Feeding cow's milk to puppies or adult dogs often results in diarrhea.

In addition, on a calorie basis, cow's milk has fifteen percent less protein than bitch's milk, which makes it inappropriate as a substitute for puppies. Human baby formula is similar in composition to cow's milk, and so isn't a good substitute. An interim option (emergency only) is using canned evaporated milk; dilute three parts milk in one part water.

The best choice for long term supplemental or replacement feeding of puppies is commercial puppy milk replacers. These are formulated to closely resemble the nutrient composition of bitch's milk. Several brands are available from your veterinarian and pet products store.

Many adult dogs may like the taste of milk, but treat your dog with caution until you determine whether or not an upset tummy will result. There are a few commercial lactose-free milk drinks made for pets for owners who want to treat the dog without tummy upset (see DIARRHEA).

MISMATING

Mismating is the application of medications designed to terminate an unwanted canine pregnancy. Bitches that are in heat are notoriously difficult to protect from the attentions of amorous males (see REPRODUCTION). A couple of options are available, depending on the specific circumstances.

One option is veterinary administration of an estrogen (hormone) compound, which usually has no adverse effect on the dog's future fertility. The drug prevents normal implantation of the fertilized eggs into the wall of the uterus. Repeated use may redispose bitches to dangerous infections of the uterus (see PYOMETRA), or prolonged heat cycles. If you choose this method, the dog must receive the drug shortly after copulation to be effective.

Yet another choice is clinical abortion, which can be induced for up to 40 days into gestation. Injections of prostaglandin are used, which stop the normal production of the hormone progesterone. The lack of progesterone prompts the uterus to contract, resulting in an abortion of the developing puppies. Hospitalization is required to monitor side effects. These can include panting, drooling, vomiting and diarrhea, but are typically not life-threatening.

When the bitch is not to be used in a professional breeding program, the best choice is spaying. It is an economical, permanent solution that can be safely performed during early pregnancy with almost no risk to the dog. Later-stage surgery is also possible, but is more involved and does pose some risk.

MUSIC THERAPY

Sound therapy is still considered pretty new. One of the best known applications of sound therapy is ultrasound that uses the "echo" of high frequency sound waves to take diagnostic pictures inside the body. Doctors even use it to break up kidney stones with vibration instead of surgery. Over the last 20 years, music therapy has become a staple of the human mental health profession, and is often used with troubled children and brain-disordered patients.

Music therapy works as well in dogs as in people, not only blocking out scary sounds but actually changing the way the brain processes emotion. Music therapy and therapeutic sound techniques are particularly effective when dealing with behavior issues such as noise phobias, separation anxiety and fear. It can also energize a lethargic or depressed pet by influence the body's natural rhythms, and speed them up or slow them down to calm your dog. Because dog ears and hearing is so sensitive to sound, the music doesn't have to be loud to have an effect.

Sound causes physical changes in the body. Brain waves change with different kinds of sounds. Music with a pulse of about 60 beats per minute slows the brain waves so the listener feels more relaxed and peaceful and shifts the consciousness into a more alert state. This rhythm also slows breathing, which calms the mind and improves the metabolism.

Even the heart wants to follow the pulse of the music. Faster rhythms energize the listener as his heartbeat increases and blood pressure rises, while slower tempos calm. Listening to music releases endorphins—natural painkillers that are produced by the brain—and reduces the levels of "stress hormones" in the blood.

Therapeutic harp music helps relieve pain that drugs don't help, soothes emotional upset, and has become of particular help in hospice situations for human patients. The sound of harp music also calms fractious pets and offers almost a natural sedative effect so that the upset animals become quiet, lay down and go to sleep.

The simplest way to treat dogs with music is to put on a CD or turn on the radio. Choose music you like—pets seem to respond best to music their owners enjoy because of the bond you share. If you have favorite music you often play, your pet will associate the sound with your presence—so playing that same music when he's alone will remind him of you and help ease anxiety (see SEPARATION ANXIETY).

Soft music with a slow, steady rhythm helps calm agitated dogs and rambunctious puppies. It can help arthritic pets relax their muscles and increase their range of motion. It takes about 10 or 15 minutes for the music to take effect. Many pets enjoy Mozart or other classical music. New Age, soft jazz, southwest music with flutes and nature sounds, or even ballad-type country music can be soothing. The music should be melodic (not dissonant) and the tempo even and slow. You can play calming music anytime your pet feels stressed—even all day long as a background to help keep him calm.

Turn up the volume to energize your pet. Moderate to loud music with a more driving beat energizes can encourage lethargic pets to exercise and lift depression. Rock music, even the driving energy of Rap may get a pet's tail moving, but any up-tempo music from classical to contemporary has the power to energize. Again, play the music for at least 10 to 15 minutes at a time to get your pet in the right mood.

Any music that you play on a regular basis helps your puppy identify that sound with your comforting presence. Even if your puppy doesn't suffer from separation anxiety, familiar music can help if you need to be away from home, because you can play your favorite music to help the baby dog feel better about your absence.

MUZZLE The muzzle is the front part of a dog's face that includes the nose, mouth and jaw. The term also refers to confining or enclosing this part of the dog's anatomy, to prevent him from using his teeth and/or mouth and protecting handlers from injury.

Commercial muzzles are available from veterinarians or pet supply stores. Most are designed to fit over the dog's face, and are secured behind his ears. You can teach dogs to readily accept muzzles by putting a treat like peanut butter inside, and introducing the concept gradually. Homemade muzzles are also effective (see RESTRAINT).

NAVIGATION Navigation refers to the dog's ability to find his way home. Canines allowed to roam may claim territory of several square miles. The homing mechanism for feral or free-roaming dogs is a survival tool that guides them to familiar territory after distant exploration.

Dogs "map" their territory using marking behavior that leaves scented signposts along the way. The scent-oriented breeds are particularly adept at simply backtracking by sniffing their own paw-steps. Also, dogs may note visual landmarks or familiar sounds, such as a stream or a noisy highway. By reading these signals, most dogs can easily retrace the route home.

The roaming canine is equally familiar with the smells of other dogs in adjacent or overlapping territories, which tell him how far and in which direction from home he may be. Should he become separated from his owner—say he leaps the fence chasing a squirrel from Grandma's yard during your out-of-town visit—some dogs are able to use this knowledge to return home. Behaviorists believe dogs travel in a kind of ever-increasing spiral until they run across a familiar scent, like a neighboring dog's scented signpost. This gives them their bearings, so they can from that point head directly home.

What of the tales of amazing journeys in which dogs traveled hundreds of miles to be reunited with loved ones? Again, when returning to familiar territory, it's believed that displaced dogs may be stimulated to travel in a certain direction to make the relationship between the sun's position and his own internal clock "feel" normal again. Dogs may be able to use the position of the sun or setting stars to point them in the right direction, just as migrating birds use a kind of internal compass.

In fact, microscopic deposits of iron have been found in the front part of the brain of cats and some other animals, like homing pigeons, and it's possible that dogs may have this as well. Scientist believe the substance acts like a neurological compass that responds with geomagnetic sensitivity to the earth's magnetic field.

Nobody knows whether a mysterious compass or inexplicable psychic ability accounts for the extraordinary homing ability of some dogs. However, there are many more dogs lost each year than ever find their way home. Few dogs are blessed with an infallible homing ability; some can become lost only a block away from home, while others may be fatally injured or killed during their ramblings.

The best way to ensure your dog's safety is to confine him in the house or an enclosed yard whenever not under your direct supervision. Your pet should also always carry some form of identification so that should you become separated, you can be reunited (see IDENTIFICATION).

NEUTERING Neutering, also called altering or sterilizing, refers to the surgical removal of an animal's reproductive organs (see SPAYING). In pets, neutering usually refers to males while spaying refers to females. A male's testicles are removed in surgery called a gonadectomy or castration.

The University of Georgia looked at a sample of 40,139 canine death records from the Veterinary Medical Database from 1984-2004 and concluded that neutered dogs could be expected to live a year and a half longer (on average) than intact dogs. Animal welfare organizations such as the Humane Society of the United States provide statistics that show over 80 percent of owned dogs in the United States are sterilized.

Neutering not only prevents the births of unwanted puppies, it reduces and in some cases eliminates certain health and behavioral problems. Excessive roaming and aggression which can result in abscesses, excessive marking behavior, and embarrassing "mounting" behavior are all greatly reduced in neutered dogs, making them better pets.

Castration during development decreases your pup's sexual interest, but even castrated dogs often continue mounting behavior. Mounting can be used as a challenge display, or a way to try and intimidate and achieve social status. In addition, dogs that discover masturbation feels good may continue the practice, have erections and ejaculate even though they've been castrated. This can become a default response to stress or excitement, too, in which case you can try to control and anticipate situations that could prompt stress.

Castration also eliminates any chance of testicular cancer, which accounts for up to 7 percent of all canine tumors. Prostate problems are suffered by more than 60 percent of sexually intact male dogs over the age of five (see PROSTATE INFECTION). Neutering drastically reduces the chance of your dog every having these problems.

Is there any good reason to NOT neuter your puppy? Surgical castration permanently removes 100 percent of the dog's testosterone, and that can cause consequences some new studies indicate may pose problems, depending on the timing and the breed.

People with puppies they hope to develop into hunting, herding or other athletic-intensive activities may be reluctant to castrate their male dogs. The sexual hormones generated by the male dog's testis give him that "male" look, and impact bone, joint and musculature development important for performance. Also, some cancers--like prostate cancer--once thought to be preventable through neutering may in fact increase in incidence.

Studies indicate that large breed dogs that are neutered are at increased risk for bone and spleen cancers. Another study of 759 Golden Retrievers at the University of California/Davis showed a doubling in the incidence of hip dysplasia in male dogs neutered before their first birthday. This early neutering also showed an increase in the occurrence of cranial cruciate ligament tear and lymphosarcoma in males and of cranial cruciate ligament tear in females. Older age sterilization was associated with the later development of mast cell tumors and hemangiosarcoma in females. Different breeds may have different results, but this information may be helpful in choosing when to time neutering your puppy.

Finally, in some areas around the world (including the southern states in the US), the stray or feral population can account for a significant number of unwanted dog pregnancies. Surgical sterilization of stray and feral population is both labor and cost prohibitive. Currently, many veterinarians say they perform pet sterilizations at a loss, simply as a service to owners, yet the economic climate makes even these opportunities out of financial range for many people.

To reap the greatest benefits, avoid behavior problems, and prevent unplanned puppies, dogs should ideally be neutered before reaching sexual maturity. Timing varies from dog to dog and from breed to breed, but most male dogs are able to reproduce by five or six months of age. Healthy dogs may be castrated at any time, and the procedure can be done safely on puppies as early as eight weeks of age. The American Veterinary Medical Association currently endorses four months of age to be an ideal time for the surgery especially for shelter pups.

Neutering is performed while the dog is under a general anesthesia. A combination of injectable drugs and/or inhalant anesthetics may be used. Depending on the pet, pre-anesthetic blood work may determine which anesthetic is best for the animal. Your dog's stomach should be empty during the procedure so that the danger of aspiration is reduced. Inhaling foreign material such as food or vomitus into the lungs can cause life-threatening complications, including pneumonia. For this reason, it's usually recommended that food and water be withheld for a period of time prior to the surgery. Should your dog sneak an unauthorized snack, tell the veterinarian so that appropriate precautions can be made or the surgery can be delayed.

Once the dog is comfortably anesthetized, the surgical site is prepared. Sterile procedures include removing the hair and disinfecting the area with solutions like betadine and alcohol, or chlorhexidine and alcohol. The dog is placed on a towel or heating pad positioned on the surgery table to keep his temperature constant. The surgeon wears sterile gloves and uses sterile surgical instruments, and the dog is draped with sterile cloth or towels to keep the site clean.

The two fur-covered spheres seen between the male dog's rear legs are the scrotum, skin sacs which contain the sperm-producing testicles. Each testicle is joined to a spermatic cord that contains an artery and the spermatic duct.

The surgical procedure to neuter your dog is typically done in one of two ways. When the dog is very small, as in tiny breeds or young puppies, each testicle is expressed through a separate incision made in each scrotal sac. With older or larger dogs, a single one to two inch incision is made in front of the scrotum at the base of the dog's penis, and then each testicle in turn is pushed out of the scrotum through that single incision.

The attached spermatic cords are tied with suture material to prevent bleeding, then the testicles are cut free. The stub of the spermatic cord recedes back into the surgical opening, leaving the scrotal sac empty. An antibiotic may be sprayed into the scrotal cavity, and scrotal incisions may be closed with internal stitches or skin glue. Male dogs that lick at the site may need a collar restraint (see ELIZABETHAN COLLAR) that prevents them bothering the incision until it heals. Other times, absorbable stitches close the incision from the underside and won't need to be removed. A routine castration takes ten to twenty-five minutes of actual surgical time.

In rare cases, there's a failure of testicles to descend into the scrotal sac as the dog matures. This inherited condition (a testicle is retained in the abdomen) is called cryptorchid. Dogs with this condition have a thirteen times greater incidence of tumors in that retained testicle. Because both testicles must be removed to prevent unwanted sexual behaviors, a veterinarian must go into the abdomen to castrate a cryptorchid dog. Your veterinarian should check for this condition prior to performing a castration surgery.

Following the surgery, dogs may be held for only a few hours, or overnight for monitoring by the veterinarian. Until the anesthesia wears off, a dog often acts drunk or disoriented, but typically is fully awake and functional within an hour or so of the surgery.

The dog's activities should be restricted for two or three days following the surgery. Outdoor dogs should be kept inside for several days, and prevented from laying in the dirt until the incision has healed. The neutered dog doesn't need to see the veterinarian again unless there's a problem.

Post-neutering difficulties are rare, but monitor the incision site for inflammation or swelling. See the veterinarian if there is a discharge or puffiness at the surgery site. Most problems are minor and involve the dog licking the incision.

NEUTERING, NON-SURGICAL

Zeuterin™, an FDA-approved nonsurgical sterilization technique for male dogs from Ark Sciences, is now available in the US for all puppies three to ten months old. Termed "Zeutering," the injectable treatment offers an alternative to the traditional surgical castration methods.

Zeuterin neuters with less pain, no anesthesia (usually only sedation is necessary), he recovers more quickly, and it costs less than surgical techniques. Because it requires less time, that's a cost savings to the veterinarian, too.

Ark Sciences that owns the drug and procedure says its initial offer to nonprofits in the United States was 1/5th the average cost of surgical castration. That makes Zeuterin a good candidate for shelters and those dealing with stray and feral populations. Savings to the pet owner may potentially reduce the cost of sterilization by 30-50 percent compared to surgical castration.

DOG FACTS

Zeuterin is an injectable spermicide composed of Zinc Gluconate (a trace element), neutralized with L-Arginine (an amino acid), two natural and essential substances for the dog's body. It's actually been around since 2003 when it was called Neutersol. Ark Sciences bought the rights to the product in 2007, and renamed it. The company has since conducted clinical trials starting in 1999 on 270 dogs. They have followed 40 of these dogs for over two years, and collected information on many of the study cases for over five years. Since 1999, the company has not received any reports of long-term side effects.

In addition, Ark Sciences has embarked on a veterinary education and training program targeted primarily to shelter medicine practices. Veterinarians or vet techs (under supervision of a licensed veterinarian) must be trained and certified to qualify to perform the procedure. Only those trained by Ark Sciences may administer Zeuterin, and by doing this, errors and adverse reactions are uncommon. That protects your puppy to ensure the best possible outcome.

Esterilsol™ is Ark Sciences' product for international markets and is registered in four countries, and pending approval in several others around the world. It is approved for all dogs over three months of age in Mexico.

Zeuterin is injected in the testicles. Your pup or older dog isn't likely to notice at all. There are no pain sensors inside the testes, only pressure sensors. So when properly administered by your trained veterinarian, little to no sensation will be experienced by your sedated dog.

When injected into the testicles, the compound diffuses throughout the testis, and the Zinc acts as a spermicide and destroys all stages of sperm maturation. The tubules that were filled with sperm are emptied, and collapse.

In response, blood flow increases to the testicles to heal, and this causes inflammation resulting in scar tissue (fibrosis) within days. These block the "feeder" conduits permanently, and causes irreversible sterility. The Zinc Gluconate and Arginine are ultimately absorbed and metabolized by the dog's body.

Sperm stops being manufactured within three days, but sperm may reside in the organ for up to 30 days. Because sperm maturation lasts 60 days, the company recommends keeping your Zinc-neutered adult dog away from a female for at least that period. Over time the interior structures of the testicles including the prostate all atrophy, and shrink in size.

Unlike castration that removes 100 percent of testosterone from the body, "Zeutering" removes only about 50 percent. Leydig cells that are responsible for the endocrine function of the testis are not affected and in test dogs, overall testosterone levels were reduced by 41-52 percent. The testis continue to produce the hormones at a level that recent research shows is protective and beneficial.

There's a low incidence of severe side effects in surgical castrations, with discomfort and swelling, licking and occasional infection noted. Similar adverse reactions may occur with Zeuterin, and most do not require medical care.

Minor local reactions include testicular swelling, which is a normal reaction to the inflammation from the injection. Pain may be demonstrated by the dog not wanting to sit, or sitting with hind legs open, or licking/biting the area. More rarely, systemic reactions include vomiting, anorexia, lethargy and diarrhea.

Most reactions in the clinical trial group of 270 dogs were seen with the first week after the injection treatment, and more than 93 percent didn't show any painful signs. When discomfort was noted, it usually happened within the first two days and then went away.

Long-term observations have shown no increase in risk for testicular cancer in dogs neutered with Zeuterin. But to date, no studies have been performed to see if there might be a decreased risk of testicular cancer.

If your puppy has undescended testicles, surgical castration is still the best option. Not all dogs are the best candidates and your veterinarian will know if he has a history of allergic reactions to any of the components in the drug, for example.

Zeutering may or may not eliminate the behaviors associated with mating, although anecdotal reports from owners of dogs indicate the effects are similar to those expected from surgical castration. Of course, surgical castration doesn't guarantee to totally suppress mounting, roaming, marking or aggression, either.

Puppies and dogs sterilized with Zeuterin will still appear to be intact. For dogs and pet parents getting the "hairy eyeball" at dog parks and gatherings, you may want to invest in a bandana or other way to show off your pet's special Zeutered status.

Because he'll still look intact, it's recommended that you document the dog's sterilized status on his microchip and/or a tattoo (a "Z" near the scrotum) be placed. That way if the worst happens and your dog becomes lost, he won't be castrated at a later date if found by a rescue organization.

Ark Sciences continues to conduct training sessions at spay/neuter shelters, animal centers and private practices. Ask your veterinarian about becoming certified. She can contact the folks at Ark Science.

NOISE PHOBIAS

Some behaviorists estimate that nearly 20 percent of dogs suffer from noise phobias such as thunder or fireworks. Thunderstorms are particularly problematic because of the multiple elements that may be frightening—the sound, flash of lightning, and change in barometric pressure. Some dogs likely are born with the tendency to fear loud, unexpected noises and won't outgrow the fear. Instead, noise phobia tends to worsen with age.

Noise phobias, particularly fear of thunderstorms, are among the most difficult behavior problems to resolve. Counter-conditioning or desensitization training works with some but not all dogs. This technique exposes the pet to the trigger situation in controlled settings. For example, recordings of thunder set at an extremely low volume begin the therapy, and the volume is gradually increased to build up the pet's tolerance level. This therapy does not duplicate changes in barometric pressure or lightning flashes, however, and many dogs will still be frightened by the real thing.

Desensitization training also has its difficulties, since rewarding the pet with attention for acting scared more likely perpetuates the fear response. Improper desensitization can make the fear worse.

Other behaviorists recommend a behavior-modification program that uses training to engage the pet's mind during stressful situations. By getting the dog to "think" about and concentrate on a pleasant game (which also rewards him for playing), some dogs become too busy to worry about the scary noise.

Antianxiety medicines, including tranquilizers like Valium, have been helpful in the past, and Buspirone shows great promise in treating pet anxiety disorders. But drugs alone rarely cure the problem, for a couple of reasons. To be effective, antianxiety drugs must be given up to four hours prior to the onset of the trigger. These drugs tend to be eliminated from the body very quickly, so another dose is necessary every three to six hours.

For thunderstorms, you can get a barometer and give the medicine any time the barometric pressure drops, but that won't work for other unexpected noise triggers like a back-firing car. Clorazepate dipotassium, available in a time-release form (Tranxene-SD), may work well with some dogs, but it also tends to interfere with the pet's ability to learn. Most behaviorists and trainers recommend a combination of behavior modification and drugs, when medication is needed.

Flower essences may help some dogs, especially Rescue Remedy. Your dog may also be calmed down with a melatonin supplement, which is similar to a natural chemical that helps regulate sleep. Be sure to ask your vet for the proper dose for your individual dog.

Some dogs benefit from the Storm Defender, a cape the dog wears, that reduces static electricity that prompts some behavior problems. Another option is the Anxiety Wrap that applies even pressure to the dog's body and helps him better manage his stress. A similar product that applies pressure is the Thundershirt. In addition, the Calming Cap which fits over the face and seems to help some dogs through stressful, anxious situations by hiding their eyes. A product called The Rein Coat combines a harness, rain-shedding properties and calming relief for anxiety, fear and aggression and fits dogs from 5 pounds to 250 pounds. Because each Rein Coat is custom fitted, it's a bit pricier than other options (see FEAR).

NOSE The nose contains the scent-detecting organs that provide the dog with olfaction, or sense of smell. More than looks or a name, it is scent that identifies each dog as an individual among other dogs. Smell distinguishes friend from foe, provides sexual information, and is important to communication and social interaction.

The shape and size of the external nose, which is part of the muzzle, varies greatly between dog breeds. The profile of flat-faced dogs like the Pekingese, which have a "break" or indentation at the eyes, may be many inches shorter than that long-muzzled breeds like the Collie, and there are many breeds that fall in between the two extremes.

In fact, the short skulls of certain snub-nosed breed dogs can distort and narrow the nasal passages and airways. Bulldogs and Boston Terriers may have abnormally small nasal openings and excessively long soft palates, which makes them work harder to breathe. When the condition results in breathing problems, it's referred to as brachycephalic upper-airway syndrome. Physical activity, excessive heat, or stress make breathing more difficult, and can prompt wheezing and noisy breathing; affected dogs often snore. Surgery to increase the size of air passages may be necessary.

The hairless end of the nose is called the leather, and is usually dark, but may be brown, pink or spotted to match the coat color. The leather contains the nostrils (nares) through which air-borne scent enters. The leather is typically cool and moist from mucus glands that lubricate the area.

Nostrils open into the nasal cavity that is enclosed in bone and cartilage and runs the length of the muzzle. This cavity empties into the throat behind the soft palate. Open spaces in the bone (sinuses) connecting to the nasal cavity help shape a dog's vocalizations.

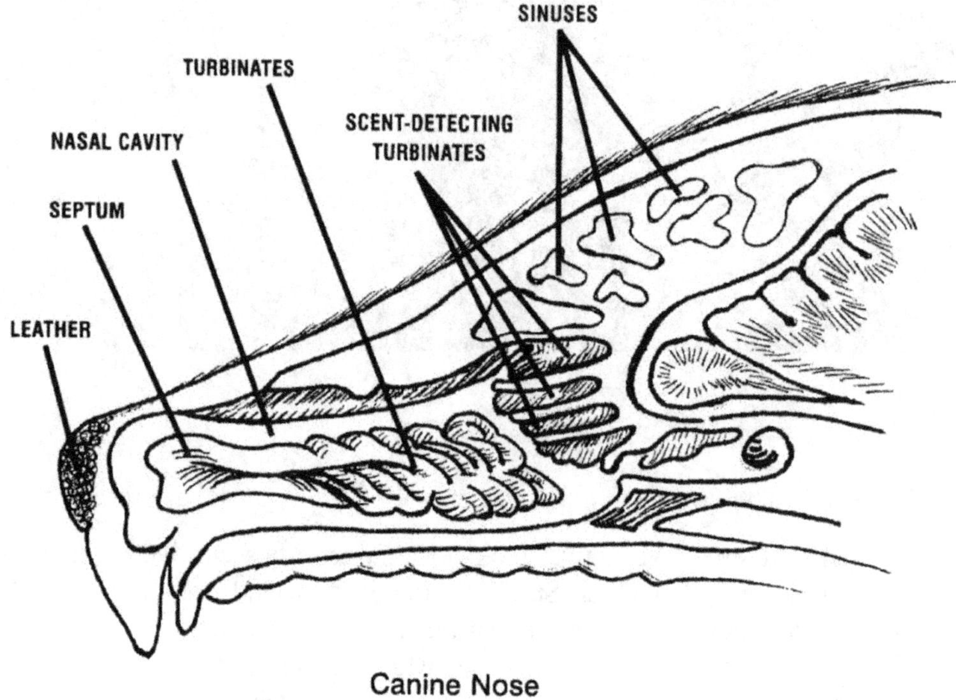

Canine Nose

The nasal septum is a midline partition made of bone and cartilage and lined by mucus membrane. It divides the nasal cavity into two halves, one for each nostril. Within the nasal cavity are a series of scrolled bony plates, called turbinates. Those situated nearest the nostrils clean, warm and humidify air as it's inhaled. This protects the dog's delicate internal nasal structures by screening the air before passing it on to the sensitive scent-detecting portions.

Further inside, additional turbinates are covered by thick, spongy membrane, called the olfactory mucosa. It is this structure which contains the scent-detecting nerves and cells. Depending on the breed and size of the muzzle, dogs have from seven to 60 square inches of olfactory mucosa, compared to the human's one square inch. A long muzzle accommodates more scent-detecting equipment, which is why longer-nosed breeds tend to be better sniffers and hunters than the flat-faced dogs. Humans have between five to 20 million scent analyzing cells, but canine scent sense varies between breeds. For instance, the Dachshund has about 125 million such cells, compared to the German Shepherd Dog's 200 million. The best sniffer of them all, the Bloodhound, is said to have 300 million olfactory cells. The flat-faced breeds have far less, but no matter their conformation, all dogs have an extraordinary ability to detect scent.

The internal structures of the canine nose are also protected by a layer of moisture produced by serous glands and mucus glands throughout the nasal cavity. The muco-ciliary blanket is composed of microscopic cells covered with hair-like filaments called cilia that move the moisture toward the nostrils and throat. This mucus coating protects the body against infection by trapping foreign material.

Odor particles that are inhaled must first be dissolved in the moist layer of mucus that coats the inside of the nose. Millions of microscopic hair-like cilia sprout from the olfactory cells up into this thin layer of mucus. Odor-detecting receptors are found on the cilia. When the dissolved odor particle makes contact, it somehow excites the receptor which in turn feeds the impulse down to the olfactory cell.

Every odor is thought to have a distinctive molecular "shape" which defines the amount of excitement stimulated in a given nerve cell. In turn, these nerves signal the olfactory bulbs, which send the information directly to the brain where the smell is interpreted as a rabbit, or whatever. A second scenting mechanism may play a role in interpreting sexually-related odors (see JACOBSON'S ORGAN).

Because dogs tend to meet the world nose-first, they are often exposed to illnesses and infected through inhaling bacteria or virus. Dogs do not get "colds" the way people do. A nose dripping clear, watery fluid may be due to canine nervousness or excitement, and usually goes away when the dog settles down. If it doesn't, or the discharge is anything other than clear, there may be a problem. Nasal disorders such as thick discharge, sneezing, or bleeding from the nose can indicate a number of different conditions, such as canine distemper, rhinitis, cancer, poisoning or a foreign object in the nose.

BLOCKED NOSE

SYMPTOMS: Head tilt or eye squint on affected side; sudden violent sneezing; pawing at nose; open-mouth breathing; thick discharge or bleeding
FIRST AID: Muzzle dog; remove object, if possible; see veterinarian if the signs don't resolve within twenty-four hours
VET CARE: Sedate or anesthetize dog to remove the foreign body; sometimes surgery or antibiotics
PREVENTION: Supervise sniffing activities to prevent foreign-body inhalation

NOSE, BLOCKED PASSAGES Dogs may tilt the head to one side, or squint the eye on one side when a foreign body lodges in the nasal passages. Sudden symptoms include violent sneezing and pawing at one side of the nose. Dogs with blocked nasal passages may resort to open-mouth breathing, not panting, which is normal.

Foreign matter like grass, an insect, or dust may work its way out by itself; other times, a veterinarian's help is advisable.

If you can see the foreign object, you may try to remove the foreign body yourself. First, muzzle your dog (see RESTRAINT). That helps keep the dog calm and prevents you from being bitten. Have one person hold his head, while another uses fingertips or blunt tweezers to grasp and remove the object.

If the dog won't let you do this, don't struggle. Your dog will best be helped by the vet. The nasal structures are very sensitive and bleed easily, and you could injure the dog without meaning to. The dog likely will need to be sedated or anesthetized to have the object removed or condition diagnosed and treated.

NUTRIGENOMICS A new science called nutrigenomics promises to prevent, slow the progression of, treat, or even reverse disease in dogs and cats. Researchers have identified 619 genetic diseases in dogs, outstripping all other species in this contest. So nutrigenomics potentially could have far reaching benefits.

Nutrigenomics studies how individual nutrients or combinations of nutrients affect health by altering the expression of genes. Nutrigenomics views nutrients or bioactive foods as "dietary signals" that can directly or indirectly alter genomic expression or function. The science combines information from genetics, nutrition, physiology, pathology, molecular biology, bioinformatics, biocomputation, sociology, ethics, and other disciplines.

Experts compare genetic traits to a hand of cards dealt to you by your parents, and notes that no two individuals play identical cards the same way. Environmental factors can change how those cards—genetic traits—get played. Nutrigenomics doesn't look at the cards you're dealt, but how those cards are played (expressed).

Environment influences how genes are turned on and off, or turned up or down—whether the pet suffers severe, slight or no disease at all. Genes load the gun, but environment pulls the trigger, and how genes are expressed changes constantly, sometimes minute-to-minute or day-to-day, and even over longer periods of your lifespan. Genes are critical for determining predilections, while nutrition modifies the extent to which different genes are expressed.

Nutrients influence gene and protein expression, and metabolite production. Resulting patterns (dietary signatures) studied in healthy and diseased groups of animals identifies abnormal versus normal dietary signals so researchers can adjust nutrients to help sick pets.

Commercial pet food companies look toward nutrigenomics to design cutting edge foods for pets. Such foods can turn "fat storer" pets into leaner "fat burner" individuals, reduce the signs of arthritis by "switching off" an enzyme that causes cartilage degradation, "starve" cancer, reverse cognitive brain impairment, or address insulin-receptors in diabetic cats. Even though nutrigenomics may not be able to completely prevent or cure a disease, it could very likely delay the onset of a condition, or at least modulate disease severity so it's manageable.

NUTRITION Nutrition refers to the food your dog eats. Eating a complete and balanced diet is required to maintain optimal health. "Complete" means all essential nutrients are present in the diet, while "balanced" means these components are in the proper proportions as compared to each other.

Nutrients are the elements of food that provide nourishment. It's necessary they be present in the correct amounts, and also in the proper balance because they benefit the dog both individually and also by interacting together. Dogs require six different classes of nutrients for optimum health.

Water is the most important nutrient. Sixty percent of a dog's body weight is water; the ratio is even higher in puppies. Water lubricates the tissue and helps electrolytes like salt to be distributed throughout the body. Moisture is used in digestion and elimination, and helps regulate the body temperature. Even a 15 percent loss of body water (see DEHYDRATION) results in death.

Protein builds and maintains bone, blood, tissue and even the immune system. Proteins are composed 23 different chemical compounds called amino acids. Ten of these amino acids cannot be produced by the body in sufficient amounts and are called essential because they must be supplied by the diet. Dogs require dietary arginine, isoleucine, lysine, phenylalanine, histidine, leucine, methionine, threonine, tryptophan, and valine.

Dogs require much lower levels of dietary protein than do cats, but more than people. A dog's life stage or lifestyle may influence his protein requirement. For example, geriatric dogs need higher levels of protein in their diet compared to young adult dogs.

Proteins are derived from both plant and animal (meat) sources; however, most single protein sources (except for eggs) don't contain an ideal balance of the essential amino acids. A single meat or single vegetable protein source won't provide balanced nutrition for the dog. When chosen properly, combinations of two or more protein sources will complement each other by providing the amino acids the others lack, and so together will provide adequate protein. It is possible to formulate a complete and balanced canine vegetarian diet, but an all meat diet is not balanced. Signs of a protein deficiency may include loss of appetite, weight loss, poor hair coat, poor growth, and impaired reproductive performance.

Carbohydrates are starches, sugars and dietary fiber, and provide ready energy when the body breaks it down into glucose. Carbohydrates are obtained primarily from cereal grains and sugars like lactose (milk sugar). Fiber gives minimal energy, but helps regulate the bowels, assists in normalizing the bacterial populations living in the gut, and may give a full feeling for obese dogs that are dieting. An excess of carbohydrates will be turned to fat. Not enough carbohydrate may cause problems in whelping, and interfere with the development of healthy puppies.

Dogs use protein, carbohydrates and fats as sources of calories, or energy. Fats provide 2¼ times the available energy per unit of weight than carbohydrates or proteins, because up to 95 percent of dietary fats can be digested and used. Fats are particularly important for dogs with high energy requirements, like pregnant or nursing bitches, and hard-working dogs that hunt or herd. However, excess intake of calories from fat or other sources can lead to obesity

Fat also helps make food taste good to the dog. Fats are the only source for linoleic acid, an essential fatty acid that helps in the absorption of fat-soluble vitamins. Dogs are able to efficiently use both animal and vegetable source fats. Fatty acids and fats promote healthy skin and fur, but too much can result in obesity. Fat deficiency is rare, but when it occurs, it produces greasy fur, dandruff, weight loss, and poor healing of wounds.

Minerals are needed in relatively tiny amounts but are essential for nerve conduction, muscle contraction, acid/base balance, fluid stability inside the cells, and many other things. Necessary minerals include calcium, phosphorus, magnesium, potassium, sodium, chloride, sulfur, and the trace minerals copper, iodine, iron, manganese, selenium, and zinc. Minerals work together, and the balance is as important as the amount. Too much can be as dangerous as too little. An imbalance can cause bone deformities, anemia, muscle weakness, heart or kidney disease, and countless other problems.

Vitamins are used in biochemical processes inside the cells, and very small amounts are sufficient. Vitamins are divided into two groups. The fat-soluble vitamins A, D, E, and K are stored in the body. The B-complex vitamins are water-soluble, are not stored in the body, and must be replaced every day in the diet. B vitamins include thiamin, riboflavin, pyrodoxine, vitamin B12, folic acid, niacin, pantothenic acid, biotin, choline, and inositol. Unlike people, dogs don't require vitamin C in their diet, because their bodies produce adequate amounts of this vitamin.

Vitamins must be in proper combinations and amounts, or severe problems may result. Over-supplementation can be toxic to the dog, while insufficiency can cause dangerous diseases. Too much or too little of certain vitamins may result in problems including bone deformities like rickets, anemia, eye disease, anorexia, bleeding, and even death. Nutrient requirements for dogs vary depending on several factors, including the animal's age, health status, activity level, and living conditions. Every dog is different, but most are able to obtain optimum nutrition by eating commercial dog foods that have been properly formulated. Properly formulated homemade diets also are an option that benefit many dogs.

"Staged feeding" refers to your dog's life stage, and generally has been divided into three broad categories: growth (puppies), reproduction and lactation (mother dogs bearing and nursing puppies), and maintenance (adults). Pregnant bitches, those nursing a litter, and growing puppies require much higher levels of energy than do most adult dogs. Among other things, puppies need more protein, fat, and calcium than mature dogs. Adults may gain too much weight if fed on a high-calorie puppy ration. Today, some pet food companies have added a "geriatric" or "senior" life stage for older pets.

Always choose a food that is appropriate to your dog's life stage and life style. High-quality commercial pet foods clearly label their products for growth and reproduction (pregnant or nursing mothers and puppies); maintenance (adult dogs); or all life stages (from puppyhood to motherhood and adult maintenance). Feed only products that have been tested in feeding trials and are proven to be complete and balanced.

Select a diet that contains a calorie or energy level appropriate to the activity level of your dog; higher fat levels usually indicate more calories. Very active dogs, such as working animals, require more calories than sedentary pets. Choose appropriate diets by reading food labels.

Specialty diets are also available that address a number of nutrition-related concerns. Those that help control health problems generally are available only through a veterinarian, and should be used only as prescribed. Many are designed to relieve specific clinical signs of disease by manipulating nutrient profiles, and are not appropriate for routine maintenance in healthy dogs (see EATING, FOOD, FOOD ADDITIVES, FOOD SUPPLEMENTS, GRASS/EATING, MILK AS FOOD, OBESITY, and READING FOOD LABELS).

OBESITY Obesity is an excess of body fat that impairs health or normal body function. Defined as body fat that's 30 percent beyond the ideal, obesity most often affects middle aged and older dogs and is the most common nutritional disorder of dogs. According to 2014 statistics published by Association for Pet Obesity Prevention, 52.7 percent of dogs are overweight or obese.

The incidence of canine obesity has drastically increased in the last decade. Obesity is caused by eating more energy than is expended through exercise. In the past, most dogs lived much of their lives outdoors, which offered them greater opportunity for exercise. Many modern pets are housedogs that are left confined during the day while owners work, and so lead a more sedentary lifestyle. These dogs may also eat more than in the past because modern foods are extremely tasty, and because often there's little else for the bored dog to do. And, the higher the fat and calorie content of food, the greater is the dog's risk for obesity.

All dogs can potentially become overweight, but the incidence is greatest in middle aged dogs between five to ten years of age. The dog's activity levels slow as she ages, and metabolic changes may also occur which promote obesity. The tendency to become overweight can also be inherited; certain breeds or lines of dogs seem to be more prone to obesity than others, suggesting there is a "fat gene" in dogs. Breeds that tend to suffer from obesity more commonly include Labrador Retrievers, Cairn Terriers, Shetland Sheepdogs, Basset Hounds, Beagles, Golden Retrievers, Cocker Spaniels, Dachshunds and Miniature Schnauzers. Certain diseases can cause obesity by changing the dog's metabolism (see HYPOTHYROIDISM).

Neutered and spayed dogs are more prone to obesity than intact ones. Neutering alters the behavior of dogs, and the resulting decline in activity can result in weight gain when the diet isn't adjusted. There is also some evidence that neutering may cause metabolic differences with reduced calorie requirements due to hormonal influences. Owners must adjust diets accordingly or risk weight gain (see NEUTERING and SPAYING).

In humans, excessive weight raises the risk for a number of conditions, including atherosclerosis. However, this is not a problem in dogs. Canine obesity does cause and/or significantly increase the risk for a number of health problems, though.

Obesity can quadruple the dog's risk for diabetes, and is an aggravating factor for dogs with heart problems or arthritis. Long-term studies also indicate that fat dogs don't live as long as thin ones, so obesity becomes a longevity and quality of life issue (see DIABETES MELLITIS and ARTHRITIS).

Obesity can increase your dog's risk for cancer, skin problems, and lameness due to arthritis or hip dysplasia. Severely overweight dogs are more likely to suffer surgical complications from bleeding or anesthesia, heat or exercise intolerance, and complications from cardiovascular diseases.

Weight alone isn't a good measure of the ratio between body fat and muscle/bone mass. A better method is evaluating your dog's body condition by looking at her profile, and feeling her body. You should be able to feel your dog's ribs, but not see them. (Coursing breeds like Greyhounds that have thin coats and light fat cover are the exceptions to this rule. You'll see their ribs! Also stand above your dog and look for an "hour glass" figure. There should be an indentation at the waist beginning at the back of the ribs to just before the hips. Again, the degree of the indentation depends on the breed; a Scottish Terrier will be more level while a Whippet is quite extreme without being underweight. Finally, look at your dog's profile for a tummy tuck beginning just behind the last ribs and going up into the hind legs. Again, there are extremes like the Greyhound, and more moderate tuck-ups like the flatter tummy on a West Highland White Terrier. If you can't feel the dog's ribs, and/or she has a pendulous or bulging tummy, your dog is too pudgy. Overweight dogs often develop rolls of fat on the lower back above the tail.

Before beginning a diet, have a veterinarian examine your dog to rule out hypothyroidism or diabetes mellitus. Controlling hypothyroidism often will help correct the weight problem as well. Then evaluate your current feeding protocol. Your veterinarian can help calculate how much weight your dog needs to lose, and advise you on the best way to proceed. Most diets target losing about a 1-1½ half percent of the dog's starting weight per week.

For some dogs, simply eliminating the treats (see FOOD SUPPLEMENTS) and slightly reducing the amount of their regular ration is adequate. Because of the average 70 percent water content, canned food is less calorie dense than dry foods. Rather than free-feeding dry food, success may be obtained by meal feeding with canned. However, dry food is absorbed more slowly, so may provide a greater feeling of fullness. Divide the food into four or even five small meals a day to help keep your dog from feeling deprived. Multiple small meals also tend to increase the body's metabolic rate, which can help the corpulent canine slim down.

In other cases, switching the dog to a lower calorie/fat diet is a better option. Special "lite" diets are designed to provide complete and balanced nutrition in a reduced calorie/fat formulation that also satisfies the dog's need to feel full. These diets typically replace fat with indigestible fiber, dilute calories with water, or "puff up" the product with air. However, special reducing diets may not work when offered free choice, because dogs that are gorgers simply eat more of the reduced-calorie food. Measuring the amount of food will help with weight loss, and will help to keep it off.

The definition for reducing products historically has varied between pet food companies, so that one company's "lite" product actually might have more calories than the next company's "regular" food. Pet food regulators have recently defined the term to establish an industry-wide standard. For example, the new standard requires dog foods labeled "lite" to contain no more than 3100 calories per kilogram (about 1400 calories per pound). These products can still vary in the calories per cup. Also, other terms like "lean" or "reduced" have different meanings.

In extremely obese dogs, prescribed reducing diets in conjunction with a therapeutic weight loss program supervised by the veterinarian is the safest option. Gradual weight loss is best; she didn't gain it all at once, so give her time to trim it off. If your dog needs to lose a quarter of her current weight, expect her to take at least three months to slim down. Increasing the dog's exercise is encouraged.

Some of the newest weight reducing formulations employ nutrigenomic principles. By combining specific nutrients, experts are able to change the way the dog's inherited genes are expressed, in effect turning a "fat storing" pudgy pooch into a "fat burning" lean and healthy canine (see NUTRIGENOMICS).

To keep your dog in condition, choose a quality complete and balanced diet. Think thin from the moment you get your dog. A fat puppy may be cute, but tends to become a fat adult. Monitor the dog's body condition, and adjust the amount of food offered as needed. Don't feed table scraps and severely limit treats; reward your dog with attention rather than snacks. And play interactive games with your dog like fetch, and take her on walks to promote healthy exercise. Start exercising obese dogs in small increments, and work up to two or three 15 minute sessions a day. Once she's lost the weight, keep her on a regular exercise program. Nearly all dogs require 45 minutes of aerobic exercise every day to stay healthy (see NUTRITION and FOOD).

OTITIS

Otitis means inflammation of the ear, and refers to a condition which may develop suddenly (acute), or be ongoing (chronic). The condition is categorized by the area of the ear affected.

Dogs with drop ears are more prone to developing otitis than breeds with erect ears. In fact, up to 80 percent of canine ear problems treated by veterinarians occur in drop-eared dogs. The infection is typically brought on by poor air circulation that promotes moisture in the ear canal conducive to the growth of bacteria, yeast or fungus.

Anything that throws off the normal balance of the ear secretions can result in otitis. This can be caused by something as simple as getting water or soap in the ears during a bath (see GROOMING). Other common causes include a foreign body (like a grass seed), parasites like mites or ticks, excess hair or mats in or around the ears, allergies, or excess wax production.

Most cases are confined to the external portion of the ear canal and/or the ear flap (pinna), and are termed otitis externa. Otitis externa occasionally advances into the middle ear (otitis media), and even more rarely into the inner ear (otitis interna).

Signs of otitis include painful and sometimes itchy ears that may be red, raw, or even bloody if the dog has scratched them. Dogs typically hold the painful ear down, tipping their heads. Excessive shaking or scratching may result in ear flap swelling (see HEMATOMA). A bad odor from the ear indicates infection, as does any sort of discharge. Normal wax is light amber; an abnormal discharge is anything different.

Red, itchy ears without discharge are probably due to allergy, but may progress to infection due to scratching trauma. An acute bacterial infection is often due to the *staphylococci* organism, and the discharge will be light brown. Chronic bacterial infections may be caused by the *proteus* organism, and will typically result in a yellow discharge; or they may be caused by *pseudomonas* organism characterized by a soupy black discharge. *Pseudomonas* infections are particularly difficult to cure because the organism quickly becomes resistant to antibiotics, and so may require long term treatment.

When the infection is due to parasites, a crumbly brown to black debris will be present (see EAR MITES). A buildup of oily yellow wax may be a sign of ceruminous otitis (see SEBORRHEA and HYPOTHYROIDISM). A thick, dark or waxy discharge characterized by a distinctive musty odor is a sign of yeast or fungal infection.

OTITIS

SYMPTOMS: Itchy or painful ear; red or raw ear; head shaking; scratching ears; ear discharge; bad odor; head tilt; eye squint; circling
HOME CARE: After veterinary diagnosis, gently clean and treat ears with prescribed medication
HOLISTIC HELP: Herbal treatment
VET CARE: Cleaning may require sedation; antibiotics, steroids, antifungal creams and/or ear mite preparations; sometimes surgical reconstruction of ear canal
PREVENTION: Proper ear maintenance; avoid water in ears from bathing or swimming

Otitis media usually results from an ascending infection from the external ear canal, or penetration of the eardrum by a foreign object. From there, the problem can progress into otitis interna, which can cause severe signs and permanent damage.

Signs of nerve involvement, such as head tilt, droopy eyelids or a facial palsy on the affected side, indicate middle to inner ear involvement. Inner ear infections can interfere with balance, and dogs will walk in circles and/or fall toward the affected side. Severe damage from otitis may cause hearing loss (see DEAFNESS).

Treatment depends on identifying and addressing the cause of the inflammation. Sedation is often required when the ears are very sore. An instrument called an otoscope that has a magnifying lens and light allows the veterinarian to examine the horizontal and vertical ear canal to see if the eardrum is intact.

The status of swelling or scarring of the ear canal is evaluated during the exam, and it's determined if a foreign body is involved. The veterinarian also collects a sample of the discharge when present, and examines it under the microscope to identify the type of bacteria, yeast, fungus or parasite that is involved.

Treatment must first begin with thorough cleaning and drying of the ears; general anesthesia may be necessary. Your veterinarian will know which cleaning solutions are most appropriate. If the eardrum is ruptured, some solutions or medications can actually damage the middle ear, and make a bad situation even worse. Wax-dissolving solutions are particularly helpful with dogs suffering from seborrhea.

After the initial cleaning and flushing of the affected ears, most cases can be treated by owners at home (see ADMINISTER MEDICATION). Topical antibiotic ointments and drops, sometimes with steroids to reduce itchiness and inflammation, are generally prescribed for bacterial infections. Medicine is usually administered twice a day for two weeks.

Fungus and yeast infections require antifungal medications such as nystatin and typically take longer to resolve and often recur. Medication generally is applied twice daily for two weeks, then once a day for another week. If the infection is caused by more than one thing, an antifungal/antibacterial cream may be prescribed to address all issues. The herb pau d'arco, also called Inca Gold, is a natural antibiotic that quickly kills fungi and bacteria and may be recommended by your holistic veterinarian.

Treatment usually resolves acute otitis within two or three days, but chronic problems take much longer to cure and often recur. If the eardrum is punctured, six weeks or more of treatment may be required to prevent permanent damage to hearing or balance. Sometimes the veterinarian must lance the eardrum to relieve the pressure of infection that has built up; usually, the eardrum heals quickly.

Chronic infections tend to leave the ear canal swollen. When this is the case, or when infections are deep inside the ear, drops and ointments may not reach the source and surgery may be necessary to clean out these pockets of infection. Long-term oral antibiotics are given to fight the infection, along with steroids to address inflammation and protect nerve involvement.

Surgical restructuring of the ear canal may be required in cases of severe chronic infection. The vertical portion of the canal is removed, and a new opening created to allow better aeration and drainage. When there is severe damage to the middle or inner ear, neurologic signs may continue for the rest of the dog's life even after the infection is cured.

The best way to prevent otitis is to keep your dog's ears clean and dry. Avoid getting water into the ears during baths, and inspect the dog's ears for grass awns or other debris particularly after rambles through brush. Your veterinarian may dispense a drying agent or acidifying solution for use in your dog's ears, particular water-loving dogs that are hard to keep out of the water.

OUTDOOR SHELTER

While many dogs spent a large percentage of their time indoors sharing your sofa, others do well spending a large amount of time outside. Working dogs like guard dogs and shepherds may be required or prefer life outside. Responsible dog owners, however, provide safe outdoor shelter for dogs that protect them from the extremes of temperature and weather.

Commercial dog houses are available at farmer supply stores as well as home product and garden stores. Homemade versions can be built inside the back yard fences, with runs connected to pet doors to allow your dog indoor/outdoor access that's safe.

Dogs don't care what the shelter looks like. Ideally, a dog house offers a dry sanctuary from icy wind chill, and protection from the heat during summer months. The size of the shelter should be just large enough for the dog to stand up and turn around, so that in cold weather, his body heat warms the small area.

Raise the shelter off the ground by placing it securely on bricks or on a wooden pallet. If left on the ground it will retain moisture and will rot. Insulate the shelter with thick plastic or other material to keep out wind and cold. Mylar insulation is made of polyester and aluminum that reflects radiant heat. It is used to keep houses cooler in summer and warmer in winter. This type of insulation is normally used in attics and is a perfect material to use to insulate outdoor pet shelters. Or you can use straw for the bedding, not hay (it mildews) nor fabric.

Blankets, sheets and towels retain moisture and remain damp and should not be used during winter. Bedding should be straw or made of a synthetic fleece material such as that used to make horse saddle covers. Clean shelters each spring and autumn by replacing the bedding with fresh hay (see FENCE, FERAL and HYPOTHERMIA).

PAIN Pain refers to extreme discomfort resulting from injury or illness. It is usually limited to one specific area of the body. Pain is designed to be a protective way to help pets recognize when something isn't right. For instance, the pain of a flame prompts the paw to retract, rather than lingering and receiving a more damaging burn. Pain keeps a dog from making an injury worse so, for instance, they'll favor a sprained leg, which allows the protected area to heal when rested.

Dogs feel pain similarly to their owners, and the unpleasant sensation can arise in the skin, bone, joint or muscle, and even within internal organs. However, the nerves that respond to touch reach a maximum response level before true pain is reached. It's therefore more difficult for a dog to tell the difference between a strong, uncomfortable sensation and one that is dangerous.

Current thinking recognizes that pets do suffer similar levels of pain as people, but just react differently. Some pets are so stoic they may feel pain but not show any signs, while others may be critically ill and seem to be in pain but aren't. And excessive pain increases stress, which causes metabolic changes in the body, which interferes with healing.

SIGNS OF PAIN

- **Hides,** remains very still and quiet
- **Becomes vocal**, whines, whimpers or cries
- **Acts agitated,** can't get comfortable
- **Pants** or drools
- **Refuses food**
- **Flinches,** yelps or snaps when touched in tender place
- **Trembles**
- **Limps** or carries paw, begs for attention
- **Assumes hunched posture**
- **Squints** eyes, or has watering eyes

When tissue is damaged, it releases chemical substances that make nerve endings extra sensitive. That makes the pain "threshold" lower than normal. The same thing happens with a bad sunburn, when the gentlest touch is excruciating because the nerves over-react.

Pain management in veterinary medicine has long been complicated by the fact that analgesic drugs, such as aspirin, also interfere with monitoring the condition. Yet in the past decade great strides have been made in pain management. This has been driven in part by the pet-owner bond. People don't want their furry family members to suffer, and have demanded relief.

Today it has become an ethical obligation to address pain in an effort to reduce suffering. But treatment for pain is complicated by the fact that, just like people, pain tolerances vary from pet to pet.

In the human patient there probably is a five- fold variation in pain tolerance for the same surgical procedure, and experts believe that holds true in dogs as well. Some of that tolerance has to do with experience. The nervous system is plastic and can respond.

For example, a football player at the beginning of the season has a lower pain threshold than he has at the end, when he's used to the pain and the bruises. So you might expect a rough-and-tumble outdoor pet to have a higher pain threshold than a couch-potato spoiled pet.

Response to pain travels through the nervous system, up the spinal cord to the cortex of the brain. Drugs and therapies can be used to control pain at any point along this pathway. A larger variety of medicines today make it possible to take the edge off excruciating pain, but allow the pets to recognize enough discomfort they don't overdo.

Before treatment can begin, the cause of the pain must be determined. Pain is caused by any number of things, including injury due to trauma or surgery, illnesses like canine parvovirus, or conditions such as arthritis, skin allergy, and periodontal disease.

Pain medications, termed analgesics, are appropriate to relieve moderate to severe pain in the dog. However, pain-killers must be used with discretion. Otherwise, removing the discomfort may allow the dog to overdo and further injure himself. Analgesics should never be used without consulting a veterinarian, nor should they take the place of identification and treatment of the cause.

Visceral pain is dull, vague, and achy discomfort located inside the body and organs (i.e., intestines, heart, lungs). Visceral pain is caused by the tissue being crushed, torn or cut, by chemicals like drugs or poisons, or from a lack of blood to the area. **Somatic pain** is a sharp, localized pain in any tissue other than the viscera, such as the skin, muscle, joints, and bones. Somatic pain is caused by extremes of temperature, or by chemical or mechanical (i.e., crushing, cutting) injury. **Neuropathic pain** is a sharp, burning discomfort caused by direct damage to the nerves or spinal cord. This kind of pain often cannot be controlled with drug therapy. **Acute pain** results from a sudden stimulation (you hit your thumb with a hammer) and tends to be the most responsive to pain-relieving medication. **Chronic pain** is a dull, achy discomfort usually due to old injuries. Cancer pain falls into this category. Chronic pain tends to be hard to control.

There are many drugs available to manage pain. The most common ones used for pets are over-the-counter NSAIDs, or non-steroidal anti-inflammatory drugs, which include aspirin. Dogs require different dosages and metabolize drugs differently than people, so human medicines may be dangerous or even lethal when given to pets. For instance, aspirin works well in dogs but can cause bleeding ulcers. Ibuprofen isn't as effective and causes more side effects, and acetaminophen (i.e., Tylenol) will kill a cat. When the pet is critically ill, only a few drugs are safe or can be easily administered.

Traditional pain relief comes in the form of pills, liquids, and injections. But oral medicine isn't ideal for pets that are vomiting or refuse to eat. Intravenous medications, though they work quickly, must be given by the veterinarian and don't tend to last very long.

Instead of a pill, medicines are being formulated in liquids that can be dripped into the pet's mouth or added to the food. Narcotic pain relievers such as morphine, codeine and Demerol are available by prescription only from the veterinarian. Codeine is preferred for dogs because it's well absorbed in the digestive tract and provides effective relief for all but the most severe forms of pain such as cancer pain. Codeine can be compounded into peanut butter to help dogs accept it.

Buprenorphine is said to be twenty-five times more potent than morphine. It takes longer to work, but effects last longer for pets that have severe or chronic pain.

Transdermal treatments can be absorbed through the skin. Fentanyl (Duragesic) is an opioid drug that comes in a transdermal patch that provides prolonged narcotic relief for both dogs and cats. It comes in a variety of strengths and is particularly helpful for pets that are reluctant to take medicine orally. Today, Fentanyl is often used for post- operative pain.

In human medications, the pluronic gel approach—a carrier substance that moves through the skin—allows combining all kinds of different analgesic drugs. For instance, DMSO (Dimethyl Sulfoxide) penetrates the skin within five minutes of application and carries other substances mixed with it into the body. Pain medicine mixed into the gel can be pasted on the skin, the gel carries the drug through the skin into the nerve tissue, and helps lessen the pain at the source.

Veterinary anesthesia has traditionally been conservative because of fears about side effects and respiratory depression. For this reason, pets have been under-anesthetized as a rule. That's particularly important because of something called "pain memory."

Human anesthesiologists routinely administer general anesthesia, followed by a nerve block, which prevents pain in a particular region of the body, such as a fractured leg being set or a joint that's being repaired. But until recently pets were simply given general anesthesia to keep them immobile, and oblivious to any pain during the treatment.

Your veterinarian may recommend PEMF therapy, which stimulate the electrical and chemical processes in the tissues to relieve inflammation and pain. Devices may be designed for whole body treatment or targeted areas of the body. Some of these devices have successfully completed efficacy studies and are FDA-approved. Therapeutic products may be available in mats, wraps or other devices from your veterinarian or over the counter (see PULSED ELECTROMAGNETIC FIELD).

Research has found that pain medication given before the pet undergoes a painful treatment will reduce the amount of pain after the event. Doing this also decreases the total amount of pain medication needed. After surgery, continued pain control can be accomplished with drains that deliver the medicine into the chest and abdominal cavity, the joint, or even intravenously via a catheter.

The biggest difficulty continues to be the lack of feedback. A person can tell the doctor if a given medicine works or doesn't. With pets, their reactions and the doctor's experience and intuition combine to find the drug that works the best.

PANCREATITIS

Pancreatitis is the inflammation and/or infection of the pancreas, an organ situated near the liver that provides digestive enzymes and insulin. The condition is common in dogs, and typically affects adults age two to seven years old.

In about a third of pancreatitis cases, the cause is unknown, but probably a number of factors are involved. Obesity, sudden high levels of dietary fat (such as meat and fat scraps from your dinner plate), trauma, and overuse of corticosteroid drugs are thought to contribute to the condition. Pancreatitis may be related to kidney, liver or cardiovascular disease, or systemic infection.

The inflammation causes the pancreas to swell and release digestive enzymes into the bloodstream and surrounding abdominal cavity, instead of into the small intestines. The misdirected enzymes digest fat and tissues in the abdomen, or even the pancreas itself. Rather than too many enzymes, some dogs may suffer from not having enough. Blood tests that measure the level of the circulating pancreatic enzyme, lipase, confirm the disease in dogs.

Signs of the disease may be mild and easily missed, or acute with sudden illness. Signs of canine pancreatitis include a high fever, hunching posture from abdominal pain, vomiting, weight loss, diarrhea, listlessness and anorexia, or even death.

Treatment varies depending on how severe the disease is, and may include pain relievers and drugs to control vomiting. Fluid therapy is particularly important, and helps restore normal pancreatic circulation and calms the inflammation. Antibiotics to fight the infection may be prescribed, and initially the dog may be fasted (food withheld) for up to five days.

After recovery, the dog is placed on a special low-fat diet such as boiled white chicken and rice. Some cases require dietary enzyme supplementation. Selenium, a trace mineral, is required in the diet in tiny amounts to keep the skin and cell membranes healthy. Supplements with this micro-nutrient have decreased the number of deaths in dogs with pancreatitis.

Medical marijuana (or cannabis) today is also available for pets, but must be formulated so that pets receive the medical benefits of the cannabis (hemp) plant while reducing potential toxic concentrations of the herb. Hemp can be used to control pain and inflammation. Ask your veterinarian if this supplement may benefit your pet.

Dogs that recover from an acute attack may develop chronic disease and have occasional flare-ups the rest of their life. They are at increased risk for developing diabetes mellitus or malabsorption syndrome secondary to the disease.

Your dog's risk of developing pancreatitis can be reduced by watching her weight, encouraging regular exercise, and feeding a healthy diet while avoiding fatty table scraps.

PANCREATITIS

SYMPTOMS: High fever; hunching posture from abdominal pain; vomiting; weight loss; diarrhea; listlessness; anorexia
HOME CARE: Supportive care; special diet recommended by vet
VET CARE: Drugs to control vomiting; sometimes pain medication; fluid therapy; antibiotics; fasting the dog; therapeutic diet
PREVENTION: Keep dog slim; avoid feeding fatty table scraps

PANTING Panting refers to the moderate to rapid open-mouthed respiration dogs use as a means to lower their body temperature. This normal cooling mechanism is necessary because dogs do not have an effective system of sweat glands like people do.

Instead, dogs cool their bodies using the evaporation of moisture from the mouth and tongue, and by exchanging the hot air of their lungs with cooler external air. The panting dog breathes with his mouth open and tongue somewhat protruding.

Dogs also pant when stressed or nervous. A high fever or pain also can cause panting. And a rapid "ha-ha-ha" pant during play may be a dog laugh (see COMMUNICATION).

Panting should not be confused with labored breathing, which is strained and may be accompanied by sounds of distress or whistles due to blockage. Rapid or labored breathing can be a sign of heat stroke (see HYPERTHERMIA) which needs emergency attention.

PARASITES, see EAR MIGHTS, COCCIDIOSIS, CUTEREBRA, DEMODECOSIS, FLEAS, GIARDIA, HEARTWORM DISEASE, HOOKWORMS, LICE, LUNGOWRMS, ROUNDWORMS, SCABIES, TAPEWORMS, and TICKS.

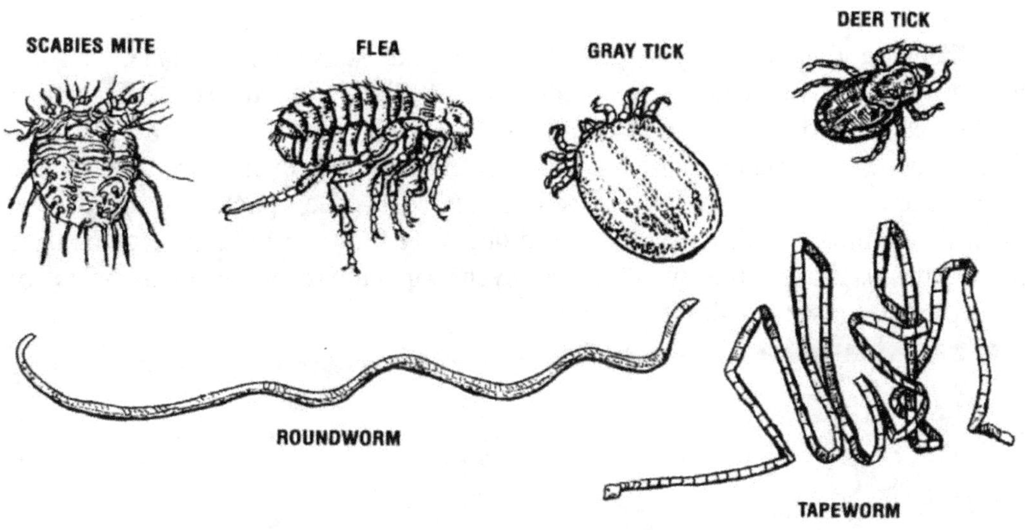

Parasites

434

DOG FACTS

PERIODONTAL DISEASE Periodontal disease refers to disorders that affect the teeth, oral bones and gums. Oral disease is the number one diagnosed health problem in dogs, with 85 percent of dogs developing gum disease by age three. In fact, nearly four out of five dogs over the age of three show signs of oral disease, and breeds with greatest risk include the Toy Poodle, Yorkshire Terrier, Maltese, Papillion, Standard Poodle, Pomeranian, Shetland Sheepdog, Cavalier King Charles Spaniel, Dachshund and Havanese. The condition tends to worsen as the dog ages.

Some dogs are more prone to dental problems than others. Small dog breeds are more likely to develop periodontal disease than large dogs because the teeth of small dogs are often crowded and are too large for their mouths. For instance, although the teeth of the Yorkshire Terrier and Doberman Pinscher are very similar, the Yorkie has much less jaw bone to support the teeth and is affected more severely by gum disease. Breeds like the Pug and Yorkie tend to develop periodontal disease quite early; however, all dogs are at risk.

Bacteria grows readily in food that sticks to the teeth. As the bacteria grows, a soft, sticky colorless film called plaque forms on the tooth surface. Eventually, plaque turns to a chalk-like material that mineralizes and forms hard deposits called calculus or tartar. This is the yellow to brown crusty debris you may see on your dog's teeth. These deposits increase bacterial activity in the mouth, resulting in bad breath which is the earliest warning sign of dental disease.

The bacteria releases enzymes which attack the surrounding tissue, causing gum inflammation (gingivitis) which is another early sign of periodontal disease. The gums at the tooth line become red, tender and swollen, and may easily bleed.

The immune system attacks the bacteria, but this results in even more inflammation and tissue destruction. Chronic infection is characterized by deep pockets of plaque and pus between the gum and tooth root which hold decaying food particles. The gums try to pull away from the resulting toxins, which causes even more gum recession and bone destruction; teeth become so loose they simply fall out.

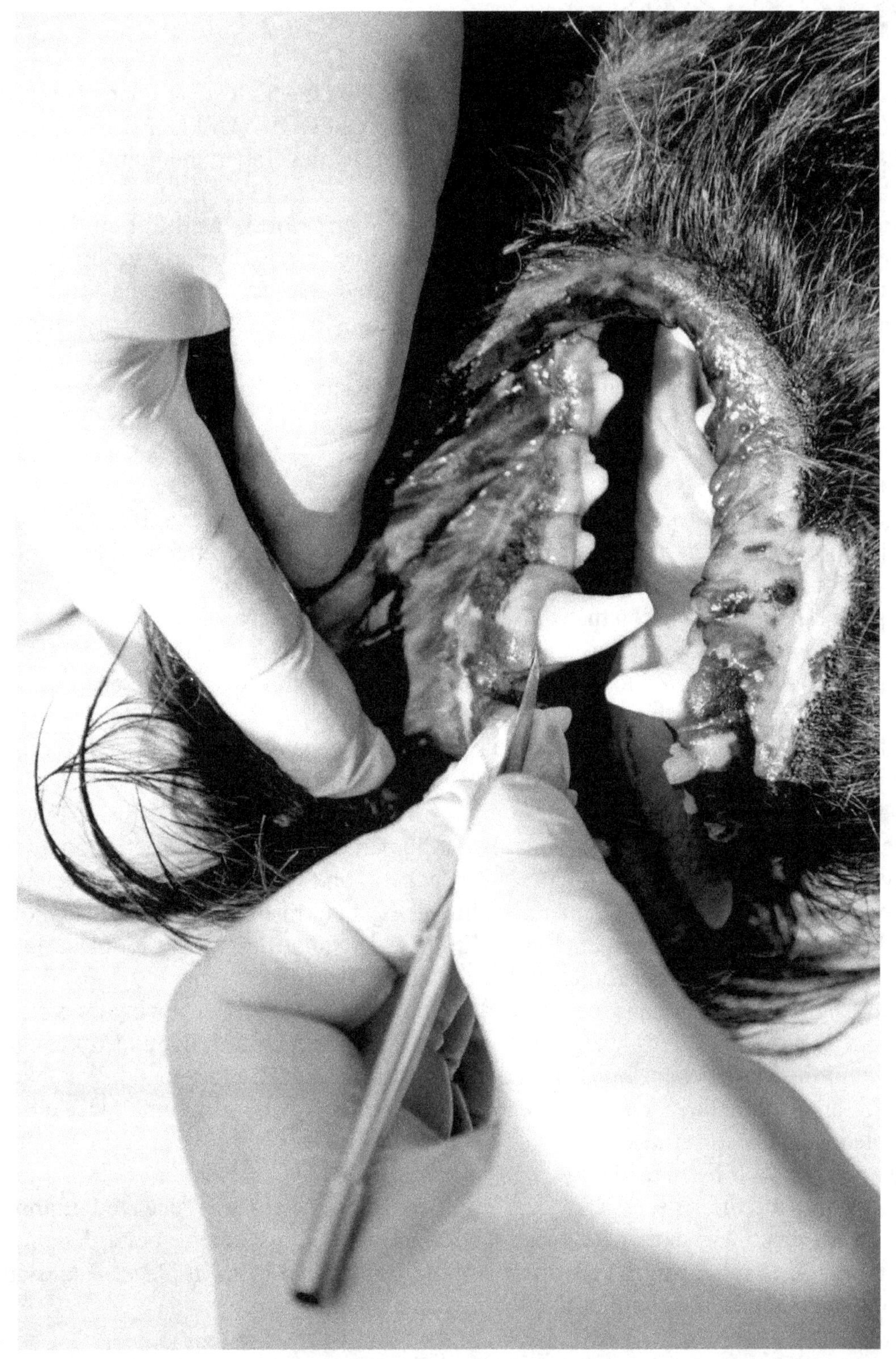

Dogs rarely develop cavities, because their diets lack the high sugar content common in human foods. However, feeding a dog human foods (see FOOD SUPPLEMENTS) increases the risk of cavities. When canine cavities do occur, they develop at the gum line secondary to plaque accumulation.

Because dogs use their mouths to explore their world, teeth often break from overenthusiastic chewing. Hard objects like cow hooves are particularly hazardous. A dog with a broken tooth may chew only on the unaffected side, salivate at the food bowl, or refused to eat at all. Tooth fractures or cracks in the crown that expose the internal pulp can become abscessed if not treated appropriately. An abscessed tooth typically causes sudden severe swelling of the face, and sometimes a pusy discharge from the face, chin, gums, or nose that produces sneezing and nasal discharge. A painful mouth is characterized by a reluctance to chew toys or hard food, pawing the face, sneezing, constant nose licking or nose bleeds.

Mouth infections are not only painful, but also impact the dog's overall health. Chewing literally pumps the bacteria into the bloodstream and can spread infection throughout the body. Periodontal disease may cause sudden lung, heart, liver and/or kidney disease, or a slow, progressive deterioration that shortens the dog's life. Plaque and calculus may contain up to a billion bacteria per gram, and is 1,000 to 1,500 times more resistant to antibiotics than free-living bacteria. Periodontal disease increases insulin resistance, resulting in poor control of diabetes, and the two have an interrelationship where one worsens the other. Periodontal disease can increased inflammatory lipids—a state of overall body inflammation leading to chronic disease processes and an abnormal immune response.

Dentistry is a veterinary specialty which offers teeth cleaning, fillings, crowns, root canals, and even orthodontia work—just like a human dentist. Treating periodontal disease involves a thorough cleaning, which requires general anesthesia. Tartar is scaled from the teeth both above and below the tender gum line using an ultrasonic cleaner. This is followed by polishing to smooth the enamel and eliminate irregularities in the tooth surface that collect plaque. Treatment concludes with a protective fluoride treatment.

Some holistic veterinarians recommend giving dogs a naturally occurring enzyme called coenzyme Q10 to help gums heal. For small dogs weighing up to 20 pounds, you can give up to 10 milligrams of coenzyme Q10 a day. Dogs weighing 21 to 50 pounds can take up to 30 milligrams once a day, and dogs over 50 pounds can take 30 milligrams twice a day. It's available in health food stores but be sure to check with your vet for the specific product and dosage best for your individual dog.

Antibiotics are often necessary when infection is present. Usually, decayed or abscessed teeth are extracted and extremely loose teeth may also be lost due to bone degeneration. Once the tartar is removed, there's often nothing left to hold teeth in place. Removing the painful teeth may offer such relief that the dog acts young again.

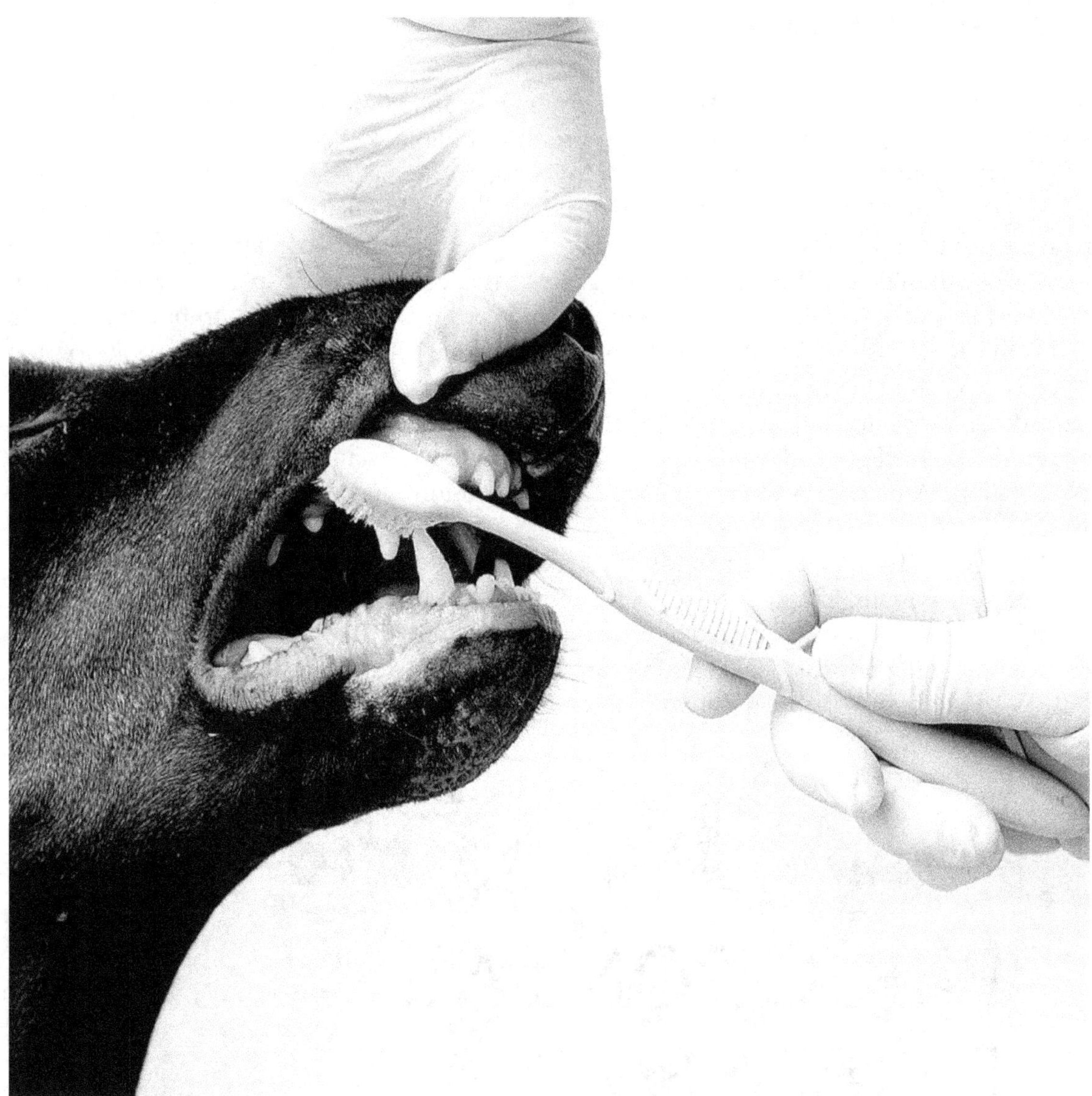

Canine periodontal disease is a completely preventable condition. The development of plaque and tartar depends on several things, particularly food. Although processed commercial canine diets offer complete and balanced nutrition, they aren't particularly helpful when it comes to dental health.

Textures and chemicals in food affect how the ration impacts dental health. Canned diets that stick to teeth stay in the oral cavity longer and offer more opportunity for bacterial growth than dry foods. Be aware, though, that dry food alone does not prevent problems from occurring. Dogs don't tend to chew, but rather gulp their food, so the detergent benefit

is less helpful than in people. Also, canine dental problems tend to occur at or below the gum line, not on the crown of the tooth where the kibble makes contact.

A commercial dental diet may help prevent dental disease. Look for sodium hexametaphosphate (sodium HMP) listed in the food. This helps to prevent plaque from attaching to the tooth surface. More and more "regular" pet diets contain sodium HMP as a part of the formula. Some diets with dental claims include polyphosphate crystals to help prevent the mineralization of plaque into calculus. Other foods offer a scrubbing action to clean the tooth as the dog chews by way of unique fibers in the food. Look for the "Veterinary Oral Health Council (VOHC) Seal of Acceptance." That means the product has passed a rigorous and objective review of effectiveness from representatives from the fields of veterinary dentistry and dental science along with representatives of the American Dental Association, American Veterinary Medical Association, and American Animal Hospital Association.

Veterinary dentists recommend having your dog's teeth professionally cleaned as often as your own—about once a year—as a preventative measure. High-risk breeds like Toy dogs probably benefit from more frequent attention. Cleaning your dog's teeth at home may reduce how often professional cleanings are needed. If you and your dog are lucky, he may only need professional attention two or three times in his lifetime.

PERIODONTAL DISEASE

SYMPTOMS: Bad breath; yellow to brown debris on teeth; red, swollen gums that easily bleed; loose or broken teeth; receding gums; reluctance to eat; sometimes nasal involvement with discharge; pawing at the face; constant nose licking or nosebleeds
HOME CARE: None
HOLISTIC HELP: Supplements
VET CARE: Anesthetize dog to clean and/or extract decayed teeth; sometimes antibiotics are required
PREVENTION: Clean dog's teeth regularly; avoid feeding exclusively soft diets

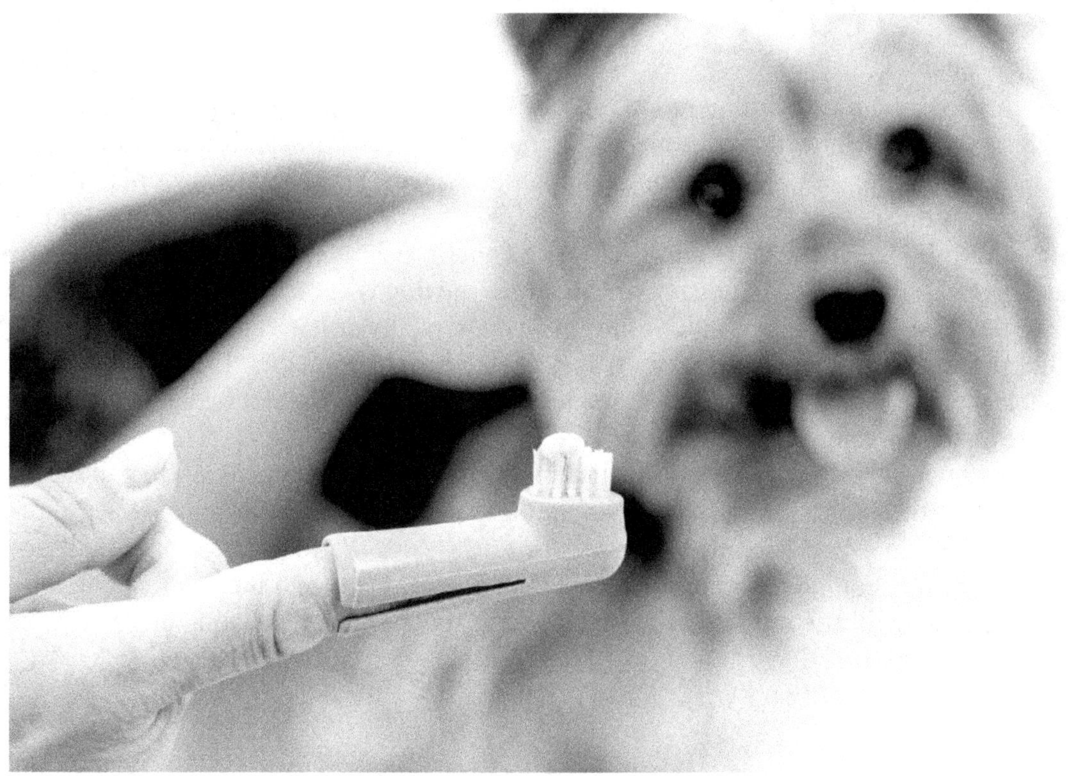

Brush your dog's teeth as frequently as your own. This isn't always possible, but aim for at least two to three times a week; once a week is better than nothing. Toothbrushes and pastes designed for dogs are available from veterinarians and specialty pet stores. Avoid human products; our toothbrushes generally are too stiff and too large for the dog's tender mouth. Dogs can't spit; swallowing human toothpaste can upset their stomachs, and the foaming action is distasteful. Also, our toothpastes contain high fluoride levels that may damage the dog's kidneys when ingested.

Pet toothbrushes or human baby toothbrushes may be appropriate for medium to large dog mouths. Also, finger toothbrushes with tiny rubber bristles that slip over the owner's finger are accepted more readily by some dogs. Canine toothpastes don't foam, and come in beef or poultry flavors that most dogs savor.

Dogs should be introduced to home dental care gradually by making it a natural part of the human/canine interaction. Most dogs are quite mouth-oriented, and often mouth an owner's hands and fingers without prompting. Capitalize on this; stroke your dog's lips and handle his mouth for short times, and reward his acquiescence with a play session or a healthy treat. Then try rubbing the teeth and gums with one finger. There's no need to force open the mouth, just slip your finger through the lips into the cheek. Try flavoring your finger with meat-flavored broth like bouillon or the canine toothpaste.

Progress to using a soft cloth wrapped around your finger. Spread the paste on the cloth, and massage your dog's teeth and gums as long as he allows. Be satisfied if you complete one side, and don't force the dog beyond his tolerance level; you can always finish the rest at the next session.

A toothbrush is the next step, but the cloth or finger brush work fine and often are better tolerated because they are an extension of you. Once the dog is completely comfortable with the idea, put a dog toy in his mouth to prop it open, wrap your hand around his muzzle to hold him steady and keep the toy in place, then brush the teeth. Dental rinses with antibacterial properties that help prevent plaque build-up, promote healing, and control bad breath are also available.

Puppies often tolerate brushing well, but most adult dogs will need gentle persuasion. The trick is to convince the dog that the attention is pleasant and rewarding. Don't expect success the first time you attempt to clean your dog's teeth. Patient consistency will go a long way toward encouraging a dog to accept dental care. It's worth the effort, though, for routine brushing will not only alleviate bad breath, but will extend your dog's life (see TEETH).

PERITONITIS

Peritonitis refers to inflammation and/or infection of the abdominal cavity. The condition is caused by introduction of bacteria, usually as a result of a puncture wound to the stomach, intestines, or uterus. This can happen due to infections like pyometra, or from swallowed objects that puncture or cut.

The dog suffers abdominal pain and may "hunch" her back and tuck up the abdomen to protect the stomach area. Dogs may assume a stiff-legged gait when walking, or may refuse to move at all. A high temperature is characteristic, and typically the dog refuses to eat and acts depressed. Sometimes the abdomen swells.

Prognosis for dogs suffering peritonitis is very poor; sadly, dogs rarely survive the condition. When diagnosed in time, treatment includes supportive care and massive antimicrobial therapy to fight infection and try to stabilize the pet. Surgery is required to repair the damage and clean out the infection (see SWALLOWED OBJECTS).

PERITONITIS

SYMPTOMS: Extreme abdominal pain; hunching posture; stiff-legged walk; refusal to move; anorexia; shock; depression; fever; swollen abdomen
HOME CARE: None; EMERGENCY! SEE VET IMMEDIATELY!
VET CARE: Emergency surgery to clean out infection and repair damage; antimicrobial therapy to fight infection; fluid therapy; possibly blood transfusion
PREVENTION: Keep inedible objects away from the dog

PLAGUE Plague is a deadly bacterial disease historically associated with humans and wild rodents. Although it can cause deadly illness in cats and in people, it rarely affects dogs.

The disease is caused by the bacterial organism *Yersinia pestis*, and most commonly affects rodents and the fleas that live on them. In the United States, prairie dogs and ground squirrels are the primary reservoirs. According to the Centers for Disease Control, the states of New Mexico, Arizona, Colorado and California account for about 90 percent of reported plague cases, with more than half occurring in New Mexico. Plague has also been reported in Texas, Montana, Wyoming and Utah. On average, ten to 15 cases of human plague are reported each year in the United States.

People typically become infected from bites of infected rodent fleas, which are different than the fleas that typically affect pets. Plague fleas prefer rat, squirrel or prairie dog blood, but will readily feed on any available pet or human they encounter. Pets are exposed from the bites of infected fleas, or by eating infected animals. Dogs that roam and hunt endemic regions are at highest risk; although they may not become sick themselves, a dog may carry the dangerous bugs home where they can potentially infect people. Plague can occur anytime, but the incidence appears highest during flea season.

Dogs appear to be resistant to the disease, but when they become ill, signs are usually mild and characterized by a moderate fever and enlarged lymph nodes. Conversely, cats run

a high fever, and usually develop a draining bubo beneath the chin that looks like an abscess (see PLAGUE in CAT FACTS). If you suspect your dog is suffering from plague, alert the veterinarian so appropriate precautions may be taken.

Because plague is a human health risk (see ZOONOSIS), suspect cases must be reported to public health officials. Diagnosis is confirmed by blood tests, and dogs are commonly treated with tetracycline or comparable medications, and usually recover.

Protect your dogs and yourself by preventing exposure to infected rodents and fleas. Keep dogs confined in yards, or under your supervision when outdoors in endemic regions. Use appropriate flea control, and destroy prime rodent habitat to evict plague-carrying varmints. Clean out brush and wood piles, barns and sheds.

PLAGUE

SYMPTOMS: Prairie dog or ground squirrel exposure; mild fever; lethargy; enlarged lymph nodes
HOME CARE: None; HIGHLY CONTAGIOUS TO PEOPLE! SEEK HELP IMMEDIATELY!
VET CARE: Tetracycline-type antibiotics
PREVENTION: Prevent dogs from hunting plague-carrying rodents; clean out rodent habitat; use flea control

PLAY Play refers to a group of canine behaviors that people interpret as recreational in nature, because the activities appear to have no clear function. In the past, it was assumed that puppy play was instinctive behavior designed to develop survival skills necessary for life in the wild. It followed that adult dogs continue to play as a replacement for hunting or defense urges frustrated by domestic life.

However, there have been few studies that specifically examine the role of canine play and how it influences the dog's behavior. In fact, many wild animals continue to play as adults, and domestic dogs that practice these skills through hunting trials still continue to play. Today, many researchers agree that one of the major benefits of play is that participants develop communication skills through these behaviors. In any event, it's obvious that play is great fun for dogs, whether puppy or adult, and that in itself should be enough.

Each dog is different, and all dogs play. But because behaviors and attitudes vary significantly across breed lines, some dogs tend to be more playful than others. For example, in one survey of 56 dog breeds, Airedale Terriers, English Springer Spaniels and Irish Setters scored high in playfulness while Bloodhounds, Bulldogs and Chow Chows scored very low.

Play behavior can be categorized as social, locomotory or object play. Social play is interactive; wrestling, biting, play-fighting, and chase games characterize social play. Locomotory play in adults usually involves a pair or group of dogs, but puppies may indulge in games of running, jumping and rolling about as individuals. Object play describes interaction with some interesting object such as chasing or tossing about a ball, rag or stick.

During play, puppies realize what is and isn't acceptable behavior, learn to inhibit their bites, and discover the limitations of their bodies and the world around them. Puppies of both sexes may exhibit sexual behavior as early as four weeks of age, mounting each other during play games. Prey killing behavior like pouncing and object shaking is also seen, and the language of dominance and submission is learned. Although wolf pups may establish who's to be the dominant "top wolf" at eight weeks of age, most experts today agree that dominance status expressed in play by puppies at these early ages is not a good predictor of future status. Dogs are not wolves.

Puppies begin social play as early as three weeks of age, with play-biting and pawing, and barking. The intensity escalates and becomes more complex as the dog matures. The first play-eliciting gesture seen in puppies is the raised paw. The play bow—butt end up, front down—is the classic invitation for a canine romp and is used by older pups and adults, along with barking, leaping forward to nose-poke and then withdrawing, face pawing or licking. Exaggerated and highly ritualized gestures characterize canine play, in order to avoid misunderstandings which might result in fights.

It appears that dogs, being such social creatures, have an innate need to play. Most dogs continue to play in one form or another throughout their life. Self-directed play, such as tail chasing or pouncing on imaginary objects, is thought to be a replacement for social play when a play-partner isn't available.

Play behavior is also an expression of emotion and seems to characterize an individual dog's personality, and styles vary somewhat across breeds. Some are more athletic and tend to enjoy games of chase, others like to fetch, and retrievers are fascinated by water.

Dogs use exaggerated behaviors, called meta signals, to tell other dogs all action that comes after is not serious but a game. For instance, the play-bow is a butt-in-the-air with front-end down position where the forelegs dance back and forth to invite play. When your dog first play-bows, he's telling you that any growls or wrestling that comes after are meant as fun and games.

Adult dogs often "pretend" to be subordinate to a puppy—with play-bows or rolling on the back—to build up the pup's confidence and invite him to play. This "just kidding" game allows lower-ranking pups to practice being in charge with play bites, mounting behavior, and wrestling games. Once the play is over, the higher-ranking dog again assumes his more "mature" behavior that tells the pup to respect his leadership.

Dogs commonly drop toys on your feet or lap to solicit a game, and offer toys to other dogs in the same way. Play includes inhibited mouth-open bites often aimed at the legs and paws of other dogs. Dogs also paw and bat each other without force to hurt. In appropriate play, all the dogs willingly participate. If you suspect one of the dogs doesn't like the activity (one dog repeatedly tries to escape or hide), gently separate the pair to see if they go back for more. If the play session was too rough, one will sneak away.

Inappropriate play results in one or more dog frightened, hurt, or overwhelmed. Bully dogs always end up on top, while in appropriate play you'll see dogs take turns chasing and pinning each other during wrestling. Mouthing aimed primarily at the head or neck, or uninhibited bites means play has gotten out of hand. You'll hear yelps from the bitten dog.

Consistent play up on hind legs may indicate problems. Ongoing mounting, clasping and thrusting also can lead to problems, as can resting of paws, heads or whole bodies across other dog's shoulders to intimidate or achieve social status.

Growls don't usually indicate problems, but play can be so exciting that the action escalates into aggression. Listen for louder, lower pitched growls, and be prepared to break up the session before dogs get too aroused.

Dog toys like balls and flying disks that prompt the dog to chase, leap and fetch are some of the best interactive dog games available. Some toys even float for those water-loving canines. Dogs also enjoy soft stuffed or fuzzy toys, and most commercial products are available in a variety of colors or sizes to fit your dog's needs. Please be careful, however, of toys containing squeakers; they entice the dog, but if chewed out of the toy they can be swallowed and cause serious problems (see SWALLOWED OBJECTS). A number of "tug" toys are also available; these are not appropriate for aggressive dogs, however, because tug-of-war games can escalate aggression. Tug games can help boost the confidence of shy dogs. Toys don't need to be expensive to be successful; a tennis ball is popular, and even an old stuffed sock will provide hours of fetching fun.

Playing together serves to reinforce social bonds between group members. And because your dog considers you her leader and best friend, playing with your dog brings you closer together. In fact, play is often a particularly effective therapeutic tool for dogs with health or behavior problems. Interactive play encourages dogs to exercise and stimulates healthy weight loss in obese dogs. Aggressive dogs may benefit from play, which allows them to release their energy in a more productive way. And play can boost the confidence of a shy dog, distract the fearful dog, and help relieve stress.

PNEUMONIA Pneumonia is an infection of the lungs caused by virus, bacteria, or parasites. It can also result from aspiration, the inhalation of something which should instead have been swallowed. Aspiration of vomit may occur with chronic regurgitation during surgery when the dog is under anesthesia, or suffers a seizure. Incorrect administration of liquid medications or foods (see MEGAESOPHAGUS) or inhalation of gaseous fumes from a fire or chemical spill may also cause pneumonia.

Usually, pneumonia affects very young or elderly dogs secondary to upper respiratory infections (see KENNEL COUGH and CANINE DISTEMPER) or to tick-borne illnesses (see EHRLICHIOSIS and ROCKY MOUNTAIN SPOTTED FEVER). Pneumonia resulting from fungal infection is rare in dogs, and occurs most commonly in those that are already ill, or that have suppressed immune systems.

Signs usually include a high fever with rapid or strained breathing. Coughing helps clear the lungs, but dogs with pneumonia may have bubbly wheezing or rattling sounds when they breathe. Dogs that aren't able to get enough oxygen develop blue-colored gums. Typically, the breathing-impaired dog will sit with his front "elbows" turned out and head extended to aid breathing, rather than lying down which may restrict expansion of the chest.

Diagnosis is based on examination of the lung secretions and chest X-rays. Pneumonia is often deadly, and requires prompt veterinary intervention, so get your dog to a hospital as soon as possible. Treatment usually consists of antibiotic therapy.

When immediate veterinary attention isn't available, humidify the air to help ease your dog's breathing until you can get expert help. Try running a hot bath or shower so the dog can breathe the steamy air. Offer plenty of water, and ask your veterinarian for an appropriate buffered aspirin dosage for your dog to help bring down his fever.

PNEUMONIA

SYMPTOMS: High fever; rapid or strained rattling breathing; wheezing; bubbly breath sounds; blue-tinged gums; coughing; sitting with "elbows" out to aid breathing
FIRST AID: EMERGENCY! SEE VET IMMEDIATELY! Humidifier (or breathing in steamy bathroom) helps relieve breathing difficulty; offer plenty of water; fever-reducing meds as recommended by vet
VET CARE: Antibiotics; supportive care
PREVENTION: Vaccinate for distemper and kennel cough; prevent tick-borne diseases with insecticides; feed dogs with megaesophagus from elevated bowl

POISON

POISON Poison refers to any substance that through chemical reaction impairs, injures or kills your dog. Poisoning is a life-threatening emergency that requires immediate veterinary help. The sooner your dog is treated, the better is her chance of survival.

Dogs are particularly prone to poisoning because of their less-than-discriminatory eating habits. Often, dogs are exposed when they mouth, chew or even swallow non-edible items, like batteries. They may absorb toxins through their footpads when they wade or walk through toxic substances like fresh tar, paint, or a salted icy sidewalk.

Anytime you suspect poisoning has occurred, immediately call your animal emergency center. Give them as much information as possible so they're prepared, then rush your dog to the hospital for expert treatment. The veterinarian needs to know the type of poison (check the label), how much was administered, time elapsed from exposure, and the symptoms your dog is showing. When available, take the poison package with you to help identify the poison, and if the dog has vomited, bring a sample.

Signs of poisoning vary depending on the chemical agent, the amount of exposure, and the individual animal. A certain antidote or treatment is often specific to the individual poison, which is why identification of the toxin is so important. The wrong treatment may cause more harm than good.

When your dog loses consciousness or seizures, first aid won't help; however, specific home treatments in certain situations will improve potential for survival, especially if immediate veterinary intervention isn't possible. Therapy strives to eliminate or neutralize the toxin, and often includes supportive care of the dog to combat shock and systemic signs.

Never try to give oral medications unless the dog is completely awake and in complete control of her body. Putting liquids into an unconscious dog's mouth risks aspiration into the lungs which can cause pneumonia or even suffocation. Treatment decontaminates the dog's body and/or neutralizes, dilutes or absorbs the poison.

Contact poisons usually are spilled onto the fur, or the dog walks through them; they affect the skin, and the longer they remain in contact, the more poison is absorbed into the body. Therefore, first aid consisting of flushing the affected area with plain water is extremely important. Wash or rinse the entire body (for whole body poisoning) or the affected area for at least ten minutes. Dogs poisoned by natural gas, smoke, or carbon monoxide need fresh air as soon as possible.

When the toxin was ingested within the past two hours, vomiting may help eliminate a good portion of the poison. However, with caustic poisons, do not induce vomiting because the toxin can do as much damage coming back up as it did going down.

Vomiting may be induced using 1/4 to 1 teaspoon of syrup of ipecac (smaller amounts for small dogs. One to two tablespoon of three percent household hydrogen peroxide mixed half and half with water will foam when squirted to the back of the tongue, and may induce vomiting within about five minutes; the dosage can be repeated once, if the first attempt fails. Another effective emetic is dry mustard; use one to two teaspoons or one tablespoon mixed in one cup water (see ADMINISTERING MEDICATION). Your veterinarian has available even more effective emetic drugs, should your first aid attempts prove fruitless.

For caustic poisons like drain cleaner or bleach, DO NOT INDUCE VOMITING; not only will the poison burn on its way back up, but retching could cause the already damaged stomach to rupture. One to five teaspoons of lemon juice or vinegar helps neutralize the effects of caustic alkaline poisons such as drain cleaner. Acids like bleach or battery acid can be neutralized with milk of magnesia; give one teaspoon for every five pounds your dog weighs.

Encourage your dog to drink water or milk, which helps dilute ingested poisons. Milk also coats and soothes the injured stomach, and can prevent certain poisons from being completely absorbed. Activated charcoal also helps absorb toxin. It's available at nutrition or drug stores; mixed one capsule in 10 teaspoons water, and give one teaspoon of this liquid for every ten pounds your dog weighs.

Poisonous Flea Treatments: The most common poison affecting pets is the misapplication of flea products and other insecticides. Toxicities often result from the wrong combination of flea products (alone, they're fine but combined, they become toxic), or misreading label applications and using too much of the substance.

A range of subtle to conspicuous behavior changes may result. Dogs poisoned by flea products may simply act lethargic, and/or drool a lot with bouts of vomiting and diarrhea. Shivering, incoordination, or even staggering gait may be seen.

Flea product poisoning is usually a dermal exposure; the pet absorbs the toxin through the skin when the product is applied. For this reason, signs may not appear until several hours following exposure. Whenever you realize your dog has been poisoned, whether she's sick or not, rinse her thoroughly in plain lukewarm water to speed decontamination. Then see a veterinarian.

Home Medications: The second most common canine poisoning involves the misuse of medications, especially human pain relievers like Tylenol, aspirin, ibuprofen and naproxen (Aleve). Dogs don't metabolizes these drugs at the same speed or in the same ways as people, which means smaller doses remain in the dog's system for much longer periods. Also, safe dosage varies dramatically between dogs, due to the differences in size. The most common effect of toxicity is gastrointestinal bleeding. Give these medications only when advised to do so by your veterinarian.

Dogs may also get into other medication and inadvertently overdose. Often, pills are flavored to make them go down easier, and the scavenging dog may willingly eat a whole bottle of your medicine. The signs and treatments depend on the type of medication, and how much was taken. Induce vomiting or give activated charcoal, then get your dog to the veterinarian. Take a sample of the drug with you.

Houseplants: A wide range of plants are poisonous to pets. The toxin may only be in the seed or leaves; other times, the entire plant is poisonous. In rare instances, simple contact with the plant causes a reaction the way poison ivy affects sensitive people. But the most dangerous plants require chewing and/or swallowing.

The symptoms of plant poisoning depend on the individual toxin, and may be as innocuous as localized contact irritations and rashes, to systemic poisonings. Drooling, vomiting and diarrhea, hallucinations, convulsions and even death may result.

Therapy is aimed at counteracting or preventing the effects of the poison. Depending on the individual plant, the toxin may be addressed either by flushing the area with water, inducing vomiting, or dilution or neutralization of the poison.

Household Products: Pets can be poisoned by almost any cleaning agent; bleach, drain cleaner, or phenol preparations like Lysol disinfectant or coal-tar products are common culprits. Most often, the dog is poisoned when the product is splashed on the dog, or she walks through a spill and/or licks the substance. Ice-melting chemicals and salt on sidewalks or roadways will severely burn your dog's foot pads. Flush the area with lukewarm water to remove the toxin from the skin, and get your dog to a veterinarian (see ANTIFREEZE and CHOCOLATE).

Pest Poisons: Dogs that catch or scavenge wild animals or bugs can be exposed by ingesting a poisoned rodent, roach or snail. In addition, the same cereal grains often used in commercial dog foods are also used in rodent baits, so dogs may willingly seek out and eat the poison.

There are three general groups of rodenticides: anticoagulants, cholecalciferol, and bromethalin. Anticoagulants like warfarin are the most common, and work by preventing blood from clotting, leading to uncontrolled and fatal bleeding from the rectum, nose, and even the skin. Cholecalciferol is a vitamin D analogue that interferes with the body's ability to eliminate calcium, leading to toxicity and death. Bromethalin is a neurotoxin that causes irreversible damage to the nervous system. Strychnine can result in seizures, and arsenic can kill before signs develop (the dog's breath smells of garlic).

The common rodenticides take 24 to 72 hours to induce signs, but once the dog is showing distress, treatment may not be as effective and can be too late. Induce vomiting immediately if you see your dog swallow the poison, then get her to a vet; a specific antidote is available for each of these poisons.

If you are unable to reach a veterinarian, call the Animal Poison Control Center located online at the ASPCA.org website. They can walk you through emergency home remedies appropriate to your circumstance. Call (888) 426-4435 FREE. A consultation fee may be applied to your credit card.

POISONOUS PLANTS

TOXIN	SIGN/SYMPTOMS	TREATMENT
APPLE SEEDS, APRICOT PITS, CHERRY PITS, HYDRANGEA, PEACH PITS	difficulty breathing, muscle tremors, convulsion, death	SEE YOUR VETERINARIAN IMMEDIATELY. Induce vomiting if ingested recently. These contain cyanide, which acts to suffocate the dog. A chemical antidote administered by the veterinarian is usually required to save the dog's life.
AZALEA	salivation, vomiting and diarrhea, muscle weakness, seizures, coma and death	administer lots of water to wash out the stomach, along with activated charcoal to absorb toxin, then see your veterinarian.
BELLADONNA, DATURA, HENBANE, JESSAMINE, JIMPSON WEED	dry mucous membranes, excessive thirst, rapid heartbeat, dilated pupils; can lead to coma or convulsions, and death	SEE A VETERINARIAN IMMEDIATELY. Supportive care along with chemical antidotes are required if the dog is to survive

BIRD OF PARADISE, BOX, CROWN OF THORNS, DAPHNE, ENGLISH IVY, HONEYSUCKLE, IRIS, SNOW-ON-THE-MOUNTAIN	intestinal irritation with nausea and vomiting. Dog exhibits stomach pain, suffers diarrhea immediately upon ingestion	induce vomiting, administer lots of water to dilute toxin, or several tablespoons milk to coat the stomach; giving activated charcoal helps absorb the poison . See a veterinarian as soon as possible.
BLACK LOCUST, CASTOR BEAN, ROSARY PEA	signs can be delayed up to 24 hours after ingestion, then abdominal pain, bloody diarrhea and vomiting. Dogs may suffer fever, act depressed; signs can progress to coma, seizures and death.	HIGHLY POISONOUS: eating a single pea or bean can kill a dog. Induce vomiting, then get the dog to a veterinarian immediately.
CALADIUM, DIEFENBACHIA (DUMB CANE), JACK IN THE PULPIT, PHILODENDRON (HEART-LEAF & SPLIT-LEAF), SKUNK CABBAGE	irritation of the mouth, tongue and throat, increased salivation, with possible ulcers and swelling which may interfere with breathing	DO NOT INDUCE VOMITING. Offer water or milk to cleanse the dog's oral cavity. Rarely fatal; should see veterinarian if breathing becomes difficult or severe oral irritation develops.
CHINABERRY, MARIJUANA, MORNING GLORY, PERIWINKLE,	bizarre or odd behavior, trembling, convulsions	induce vomiting, and get to the veterinarian.
CREEPING FIG, CHRYSANTHEMUM, WEEPING FIG	contact rash affecting skin surrounding and inside the mouth	wash area with cool water to sooth rash, see veterinarian
DAFFODIL, TULIP, WISTERIA (especially the bulbs)	gastric irritation, violent vomiting, possible depression -- death in severe cases	induce vomiting. Administer lots of water to dilute toxin, or several tablespoons milk to coat the stomach; giving activated charcoal helps absorb the poison. See a veterinarian as soon as possible.
ENGLISH HOLLY, EUROPEAN HOLLY	abdominal pain, vomiting and diarrhea when two or more berries are eaten; death reported rarely	SEE YOUR VETERINARIAN IMMEDIATELY. Supportive care is necessary to treat the digitalislike toxin
FOXGLOVE, LARKSPUR, LILY OF THE VALLEY, MONKSHOOD, OLEANDER	slowed heartbeat (this plant contains digitalis) followed by severe abdominal pain and vomiting. Finally, signs of agitation are exhibited, followed shortly by coma and death.	SEE YOUR VETERINARIAN IMMEDIATELY. Induce vomiting if ingested recently. This plant's toxicity can stop your dog's heart.
GOLDEN CHAIN, INDIAN TOBACCO, MESCAL BEAN, POISON HEMLOCK, TOBACCO	salivation, incoordination, muscle twitches, rapid heartbeat; breathing becomes labored and the dog can collapse in minutes to hours following ingestion	SEE YOUR VETERINARIAN IMMEDIATELY. This plant contains nicotine, and requires a chemical antidote to save the dog.
JERUSALEM CHERRY, POTATO (GREEN PARTS & EYES)	signs may not appear until 18-24 hours following ingestion; then the dog exhibits a painful abdomen, bloody diarrhea, vomiting, and dry mouth. Severe cases may proceed to tremors, paralysis, and cardiac arrest.	DO NOT INDUCE VOMITING as this may further damage the gastrointestinal tract. Immediate veterinary attention is imperative.

MOTHER-IN-LAW PLANT	vomiting, salivation, mouth irritation, diarrhea, occasionally staggering or collapse	DO NOT INDUCE VOMITING. Offer water or milk to cleanse the dog's oral cavity. Rarely fatal; should see veterinarian if dog loses coordination or collapses
POINSETTIA	irritates mucous membranes of mouth, may cause excessive salivation or vomiting but not death	Offer water or milk to cleanse the dog's oral cavity. Consult your veterinarian
RHUBARB (upper stem and leaves)	vomiting, excessive salivation, abdominal pain, staggers followed by convulsions	induce vomiting, then get your dog to the veterinarian. Without treatment, the toxin causes extensive damage to the dog's kidneys
YEW (American Yew, English Yew, Japanese Yew, etc.)	irregular heartbeat, dilation of the pupils, shivering, nausea, abdominal pain; but death often occurs without warning signs	SEE VETERINARIAN IMMEDIATELY. Induce vomiting if possible

OTHER TOXINS

TOXIN	SIGN/SYMPTOMS	TREATMENT
ACID POISONS (bleach)	when swallowed, drooling, pawing at mouth, painful abdomen; when spilled on skin, vocalizations, signs of distress, rolling, licking area	DO NOT INDUCE VOMITING! flush the area of contact with plain water for at least ten minutes; if substance was swallowed, administer two teaspoons of milk of magnesia; see a veterinarian ASAP
ALKALINE POISONS (drain cleaner)	when swallowed, drooling , pawing at mouth, painful abdomen; when spilled, vocalizations, signs of distress, rolling, licking area	DO NOT INDUCE VOMITING! flush the area of contact with plain water for at least ten minutes; if substance was swallowed, administer six tablespoons of half water and half lemon juice or vinegar to neutralize, then get dog to veterinarian ASAP
ANTIFREEZE (ETHYLENE GLYCOL)	drunken behavior, excessive thirst, increased urination, diarrhea, vomiting, convulsions, loss of appetite, panting	EMERGENCY! seek veterinary help ASAP. If ingested in last two hours, induce vomiting and/or administer activated charcoal; veterinary treatment administers 100 proof alcohol
CHOCOLATE	drooling, vomiting and/or diarrhea, excessive urination, hyperactivity, muscle tremors, seizures, coma	EMERGENCY! seek veterinary help ASAP. if ingested in last two hours, induce vomiting
COAL-TAR POISONING (phenol disinfectants like Lysol, treated wood, tar paper, heavy oil)	depression, weakness, incoordination, coma, death	get dog to veterinarian ASAP. Lysol is absorbed through skin; wash dog immediately if exposed.

FLEA PRODUCTS (ORGANOPHOSPHATES, CARBAMATES & CHLORINATED HYDROCARBONS)	signs may be delayed due to skin absorption of toxin; a variety of signs possible, including: apprehension, muscle twitches, shivering, seizures, drooling, diarrhea, hyperactivity or depression	wash dog as soon as you realize poisoning has occurred, even if several hours have passed and no signs are yet seen; then get to veterinarian ASAP
GRAPE/RAISIN TOXICITY	abdominal pain, vomiting, diarrhea, lethargy, cessation of urination	induce vomiting; see veterinarian ASAP
LEAD POISONING (insecticides, paint, linoleum, roofing shingles, plumbing materials, solder, batteries, golf balls)	abdominal pain, vomiting, seizures, uncoordinated gait, excitation, continuous barking, hysteria, weakness, blindness, chewing fits	when ingestion is within past two hours, induce vomiting; see veterinarian for specific treatment ASAP
MEDICATIONS, ASPIRIN, IBUPROFEN, TYLENOL, OTHER NSAIDS	blood in vomit that looks like coffee grounds	stop administering the medication, see your vet; if dog ingested more than one tablet in past two hours, induce vomiting then see vet ASAP
MEDICATIONS	various signs dependent upon toxic agent	induce vomiting if ingested within last two hours; seek veterinary help ASAP
PETROLEUM PRODUCTS (gasoline, kerosene, turpentine)	vomiting, difficulty breathing, tremors, seizures, coma, respiratory failure and death	EMERGENCY! DO NOT INDUCE VOMITING; SEE VETERINARIAN IMMEDIATELY; if help is more than thirty minutes away, give the dog 1 to 2 ounces mineral oil, olive oil or vegetable oil by mouth; follow it in 30 minutes with Glauber's salt (sodium sulfate) to stimulate defecation; be prepared to perform artificial respiration
PEST BAITS, ANTICOAGULANT TYPES (warfarin, pindone, Dcon, Mouse Prufe II, Harvoc, Talan)	bleeding in stool and/or urine, from nose, ears, and beneath the skin and gums—symptoms first appear several days after ingestion	EMERGENCY! induce vomiting if ingested within past two hours, then see veterinarian ASAP; blood transfusions and treatment with intravenous vitamin K is a specific antidote
PEST BAITS, ARSENIC (slug/snail bait, ant poisons, weed killers, insecticides)	thirst, vomiting, staggers, drooling, abdominal pain and cramps, diarrhea, paralysis, strong garlic breath	EMERGENCY! induce vomiting if poisoning occurred within last two hours, then see veterinarian ASAP; a specific antidote is available
PEST BAITS, BROMETHALIN (Assault & Vengeance rodenticides)	muscle tremors, staggering gait, high fever, stupor, agitation, seizures	EMERGENCY! induce vomiting if ingested within past two hours, then see veterinarian ASAP
PEST BAITS, CHOLECALCIFEROL	vomiting, diarrhea, seizures, heart/kidney failure	EMERGENCY! induce vomiting if ingested within past two hours, then see veterinarian

(Rampage, vitamin D3)		ASAP
PEST BAITS, METALDEHYDE (rat, snail & slug bait)	drooling, incoordination, excitability, muscle tremors, progressive weakness	EMERGENCY! induce vomiting if ingested within past two hours, then see veterinary ASAP
PEST BAITS, PHOSPHORUS (rat & roach poisons, matches & matchboxes)	vomiting, diarrhea, garlic breath, sometimes symptom-free period, then return of signs with painful abdomen, seizures and coma	EMERGENCY! induce vomiting if ingested within past two hours, then see veterinarian ASAP
PEST BAITS, SODIUM FLUOROACETATE (rat poison)	vomiting, agitation, straining to defecate/urinate, seizures (not triggered by external stimuli), staggering gait, collapse	EMERGENCY! induce vomiting if ingested within past two hours, then get to a veterinary ASAP; a specific antidote is available
PEST BAITS, STRYCHNINE (rat, mouse, mole, coyote poison)	agitation, apprehension, excitement, seizures prompted by noises like clapping hands, drooling, muscle spasms, chewing, collapse	EMERGENCY! Seek veterinary help ASAP; cover dog with towel to prevent stimulation of further seizures; if poisoned within two hours and dog remains alert, induce vomiting
PEST BAITS, ZINC PHOSPHIDE (rat poison)	depression, difficulty breathing, weakness, seizures, vomiting (with blood), seizures, coma	EMERGENCY! induce vomiting if ingested within past two hours, then see veterinarian ASAP
SNAKE BITE (copper head, cotton mouth, rattle snake, coral snake)	restlessness, drooling, panting, weakness, diarrhea, collapse, sometimes seizures, paralysis or coma	EMERGENCY! SEEK VETERINARY HELP ASAP. If help is more than 30 minutes away, apply tight bandages between bite and dog's heart and loosen for five minutes once an hour; keep dog quiet until help is available. Don't wash bite, don't cut bite to suction out poison, and don't apply ice to bite--all could increase venom absorption and/or damage tissue further
TOAD POISONING	slobbering or drooling, pawing at mouth, seizures, coma, collapse	EMERGENCY! flush dog's mouth with plain water for at least 10 minutes, induce vomiting; be prepared to perform artificial respiration; SEE VET ASAP
XYLITOL POIZONING	vomiting, incoordination/drunk behavior, lethargy, seizures, collapse	EMERGENCY! signs appear within 15 minutes so induce vomiting immediately, seek veterinary help ASAP

PORCUPINE QUILLS Curious dogs, especially those living in rural areas, often encounter a porcupine with devastating results. The needle-like barbed quills up to four inches long penetrate flesh and continue moving inward. The quills typically lodge in the dog's face or open mouth.

Porcupine quills are exceptionally painful. A dog typically loses self-control, rolls with pain, and may even reflexively strike out at concerned owners in his attempts to seek relief.

Visible quills may be plucked out using needle-nose pliers; grasp the quill near the skin, and pull straight out. Be aware, though, that the barbed ends can break off. Once beneath the skin, they travel inward and may result in deep infections. Also, a dog's fur may hide small quills that you may miss.

Holistic veterinarians may recommend an antiseptic wash of calendula and St. John's Wort. Put two drops of each tincture in one-half cup of water and use the solution to gently bathe the wounds. Homeopathic Hypericum addresses pain. Give three pellets of Hypericum 30C, and repeat the dose up to three times as needed.

PORCUPINE QUILLS

SYMPTOMS: Needlelike barbs protruding from body, particularly face or mouth; crying with pain; rolling; pawing at injured area
HOME CARE: Grasp quill with needle-nose pliers close to the skin, pull straight out; disinfect wash wound
HOLISTIC HELP: Herbal treatment; homeopathy; flower essences
VET CARE: Anesthetize dog, remove quills, swab each wound with disinfectant; possibly oral antibiotics
PREVENTION: Supervise outdoor excursions

Because a dog in pain is rarely able to hold still even for a beloved owner's ministrations, a veterinarian is usually better equipped to do the plucking. Once anesthetized, a search and seizure of quills hidden by fur—and particularly inside his mouth—is more easily accomplished. The wounds are then treated with a disinfectant, like peroxide or betadine.

The only way to prevent your dog from encountering an irate porcupine is to keep outdoor exploration confined to the yard by a fence, or supervise outside adventures from the end of a leash.

PRA

SYMPTOMS: Loss of night vision; total blindness
HOME CARE: None; maintain familiar surroundings to keep dog comfortable
VET CARE: None
PREVENTION: None

PROGRESSIVE RETINAL ATROPHY (PRA) This is an inherited eye disorder characterized by degeneration of the retina, which ultimately results in blindness. Most dogs are first affected at age five to seven years.

PRA is similar to retinitis pigmentosis in people. The retina degenerates a little at a time. In late stage disease, the widely dilated pupil makes the eye look very dark.

PRA can be inherited and can affect most breeds but historically has affected Irish Setters, Labradors, Golden Retrievers, Border Collies, Shetland Sheepdogs, Norwegian Elkhounds and Poodles. Genetic tests can now detect PRA. DNA analysis allows dogs to be diagnosed before they lose their vision. Breeders are able to avoid perpetuating the disease once they know which dogs are affected, and owners can plan to better care for their dog as he loses his sight.

There are two forms, referred to as central and generalized. The generalized form is most common, in which the light-detecting cells on the surface of the retina gradually stop working. This results in an overall loss of sight. Generalized PRA is recognized in many breeds.

The central form is inherited in the Border Collie, Golden Retriever, English Springer Spaniel, Irish Setter, Labrador Retriever, and Shetland Sheepdog, and affects the deepest layer of the retina below the photoreceptor layer. Initially, it is the center-most portion of the retina that is destroyed, with peripheral vision the last to go.

Signs of both forms are similar, and begin with the dog's loss of vision in dim light often characterized by night blindness. Dogs may try to compensate by staying near light sources at night. Others become increasingly dependent on the owner. Affected dogs avoid stairs or jumping on furniture, and dislike unfamiliar environments.

Eventually, PRA progresses to total blindness. There is currently no effective treatment. Owners can make the vision-impaired dog more comfortable by establishing a routine and not rearranging the dog's familiar surroundings (see BLINDNESS).

Because this is an inherited condition, dogs suffering from PRA should not be bred. Conscientious breeders are aware of the potential for congenital eye disease, and high-risk dogs should be examined and certified free of the disorder before being bred. The Canine Eye Registration Foundation issues certification and collects data, in conjunction with the Veterinary Medicine Data Bank at Purdue University.

PROPTOSIS OF EYEBALL

A sharp blow to the head or bite wounds may cause the eyeball to prolapse, or "pop" from the socket. Sometimes tumors or infection may also cause the condition. This is not only disconcerting to the owner, but extremely painful for the dog and will result in permanent vision damage if not replaced within the hour. This is an emergency; see your veterinarian immediately.

Dogs with large prominent eyes such as Boston Terriers, Pekingese and Pugs are most prone. Once the eye has left the socket, the eyelids may try to close behind the organ blocking its return. Subsequent to the prolapse, tissue behind the eye will swell from the trauma, making the condition even more difficult to correct.

To prevent the surface from drying, place a wet gauze sponge or wet cloth over the eye. Don't try to manipulate the eyeball back into place yourself; you could cause even more damage. Hold the covering in place either manually or with tape until you reach veterinary help.

The eyeball will need to be surgically replaced. Medications are prescribed to relieve the trauma and reduce and/or prevent further injury. It may take several weeks after the eyeball is replaced before the extent of the damage can be determined.

EYE OUT OF SOCKET

SYMPTOMS: Eye bulges out of socket
FIRST AID: EMERGENCY! Place saline-soaked gauze pad over eyeball until you can get veterinary care
VET CARE: Mechanical replacement of eye; medications to reduce swelling and pain and prevent infection
PREVENTION: Avoid trauma especially in flat-faced breeds

PROSTATE INFECTION The prostate gland is located at the base of the bladder in male dogs, and aids in reproduction. Bacterial infection of the prostate gland is quite common in dogs, and the agents involved are often similar to those causing urinary tract infections.

Signs include lethargy, loss of appetite, bloody or pus-like discharge from the penis, and a hunching posture indicative of abdominal pain. The condition is diagnosed based on these signs, and on culture of the prostatic fluid, urine or semen. The culture identifies the bacteria involved, so that a specific antibiotic is prescribed. Usually, at least three weeks of medication is required to ensure the infection has resolved.

Prostate infection, referred to as prostatitis, can become chronic if the infection cannot be resolved. This may prompt ongoing urinary tract infections or even sterility in an otherwise healthy dog.

Holistic veterinarians suggest using the herbal remedy palmetto to help shrink swollen prostate tissue. Ask your vet if this is an option for your dog.

In chronic cases, antibiotics are indicated for at least three months, and sometimes for the life of the dog to control the infection. When there is no response to treatment, your veterinarian may recommend neutering.

PROSTATE INFECTION

SYMPTOMS: Lethargy; loss of appetite; bloody or puslike discharge from penis; hunching posture from pain; constipation
HOME CARE: None
HOLISTIC HELP: Herbal remedy
VET CARE: Antibiotic therapy; sometimes neutering
PREVENTION: Neuter the dog

PULSE Pulse refers to the rhythmic movement of blood by the heart. The pulse rates of individual dogs vary depending on their age and size. The average-size adult dog's resting pulse rate ranges from 60 to 150 beats per minute; large dogs fall in the slower end, while small dogs' pulse rate is up to 180 and a puppy's may be 220 beats per minute. And just like athletic people, the working dog's pulse rate may be slower than a couch-potato dog of the same size.

Your dog's pulse should be strong and steady. A rapid pulse rate indicates anything from excitement or exertion, to anemia, infection or heart disease; a slow pulse can indicate illness.

You can calculate your dog's pulse rate by counting the number of beats in a minute. The drum-beat can be felt by placing the flat of your fingers against the femoral artery in the groin, at the juncture of thigh and body. Or, place your palm over the ribs on your dog's left side directly behind his front elbow, to feel his heartbeat.

PULSED ELECTROMAGNETIC FIELD (PEMF)

Pulsed electromagnetic field therapy influences the body's natural bioelectromagnetic fields. Every organ in the body produces its own signature bioelectromagnetic field. Disruption of electromagnetic energy in the cells causes impaired cell function, and PEMFs seek to address this impaired chemistry to improve cell function and positively impact health.

Holistic veterinarians may advocate the use of magnets, for instance, thought to positively influence these fields to effect health benefits. As a general rule, magnets produce stationary or "static" nonvarying magnetic fields that have a fixed strength and only penetrate the tissue a shallow distance. Magnets may be fastened against one or more acupuncture points to stimulate the point in a gentle but prolonged way. More commonly, magnets are found in mats for the pet to sleep on, or wraps and patches to place on specific parts of the body.

Low frequency PEMFs work more effectively because they penetrate every cell, tissue, organ and even bone, and stimulate the electrical and chemical processes in the tissues. Therapeutic PEMFs are specifically designed to positively support cellular energy, and vary in frequency, waveform, strength, and types of stimulators. These resonating magnetic fields can create currents without heating to alter cell signaling, and studies now show that the proper frequency and intensity can relieve pain, stimulate bone and wound healing, and provide other health benefits.

Devices that produce these benefits may be designed for whole body treatment or targeted areas of the body. Some of these devices have successfully completed efficacy studies and are FDA-approved.

Today, mainstream veterinary medicine also uses PEMF technology to help pets heal, and relieve inflammatory responses responsible for pain, among other things. Therapeutic products may be available in mats, wraps or other devices from your veterinarian or over the counter.

For example, the Assisi Loop® is an FDA-cleared Non-Pharmaceutical Anti-Inflammatory Device (NPAID®) that has undergone clinical evaluation with results published in peer-reviewed journals. It's used as both a first-line and adjunct therapy for managing persistent pain and inflammatory conditions that impact canine health. The Assisi Loop® is a light weight battery powered non-invasive therapy that employ targeted EMFs to reduce inflammation, promote healing of wounds and surgical sites, reduce arthritis discomfort, and ameliorate pain as well as aid in stroke recovery or back problems. It comes in two sizes (10 cm and 20 cm diameter coil), and has an auto-shut off as well as a cycling therapy version. It is available from your veterinarian, or from the company (with a prescription from your vet) and is easy to use at home. Ask your vet if PEMF therapy may benefit your pet.

PUPPY

PUPPY A puppy is an immature dog. Dogs are considered puppies from birth to one year of age. However, each dog develops differently, with smaller dogs tending to mature earlier and some large breeds not physically mature before they are two years old.

Newborn puppies vary in size depending on the breed; tiny dogs like the Chihuahua produce puppies sized about four inches long, while giant breed newborns like Great Dane puppies may be twice that size. Rate of puppy development also varies from breed to breed. For instance, Cocker Spaniel puppies open their eyes sooner than Fox Terrier puppies, and Basenji puppies develop teeth earlier than Shetland Sheepdog puppies. However, no matter the breed, all puppies are born totally dependent on the bitch.

At birth, puppies are blind, deaf and toothless, unable to regulate body temperature, or even urinate or defecate on their own. Puppies depend on their mother and littermates for warmth, huddling in cozy piles to conserve body temperature. A puppy separated from this warm furry nest can quickly die, and cold, lonely puppies cry loudly to alert Mom to their predicament.

Puppies first experience the sensation of being petted when washed by their mother's stroking tongue. The bitch licks her babies all over to keep them and the nest clean, and also to stimulate them to defecate and urinate.

From birth, puppies are able to use their sense of smell and touch, which helps them root about the nest to find their mother's scent-marked breasts. The first milk the mother produces, called colostrum, is rich in antibodies that provide passive immunity and help protect the babies from disease during these early weeks of life (see IMMUNE SYSTEM and VACCINATIONS).

For the first two weeks of life, puppies sleep nearly 90 percent of the time, spending their awake time nursing. All their energy is funneled into growing, and birth weight doubles the first week. Newborns aren't able to support their weight, and crawl about with paddling motions of their front legs. The limited locomotion provides the exercise that develops muscles and coordination, and soon the puppies are crawling over and around each other and their mother.

The second week of life brings great changes for the puppy. Ears and eyes sealed since birth begin to open during this period, ears at about two weeks and eyelids between ten to 16 days. This gives the furry babies a new sense of their world. They learn what their mother and other dogs look and sound like, and begin to expand their own vocabulary from grunts and mews to yelps, whines and barks. Puppies generally stand by day 15 and take their first wobbly walk by day 21.

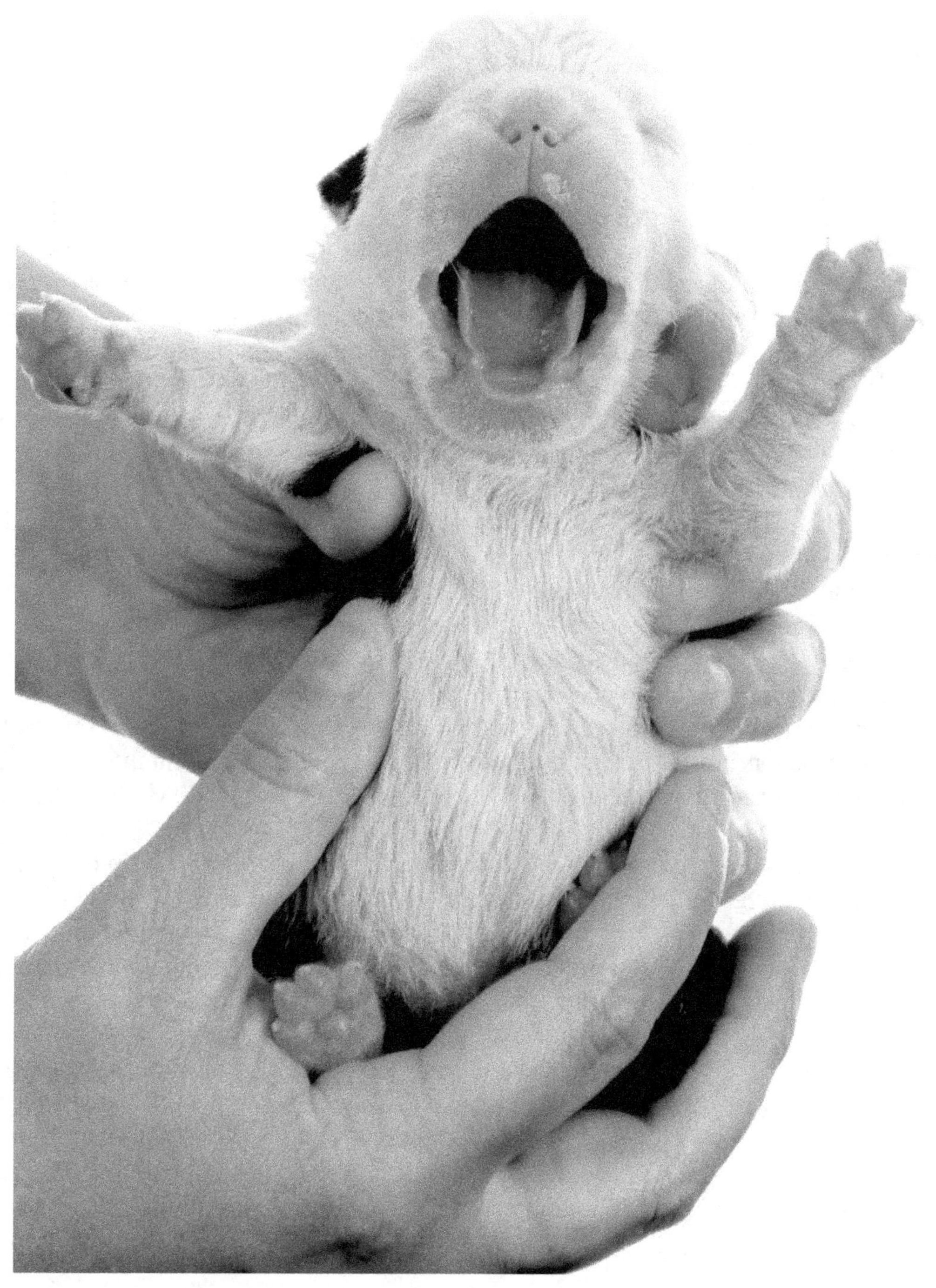

By age three weeks, puppy development advances from the neonatal period to the transitional period. This is a time of rapid physical and sensory development, during which the puppies go from total dependence on Mom to a bit of independence. They begin to play with their littermates, learn about their environment and canine society, and begin sampling food from Mom's bowl. Puppy teeth begin to erupt until all the baby teeth are in by about five to six weeks of age. Puppies can control their need to use the bathroom by this age, and begin moving away from sleeping quarters to eliminate.

Following the transitional phase, puppies enter the socialization period at the end of the third week of life; it lasts until about week ten. It is during this socialization period that interaction with others increases, and puppies form attachments they will remember the rest of their life. The most critical period—age six to eight weeks—is when puppies most easily learn to accept others as a part of their family.

The puppies learn to identify friend and foe during this time. Those exposed to friendly people like babies, children, and strange adults, and other animals like cats and dogs during this impressionable period will more readily recognize them as safe and accept them as family members later in life. Puppies that miss out on these vital introductions will be fearful of strangers, and have a more difficult time adjusting. Studies show that puppies handled daily by friendly people during this period learn more quickly and are more easily trained (see SOCIALIZATION).

Beginning at four weeks of age, the bitch's milk production begins to slow down just as the puppies' energy needs increase. As the mother dog slowly weans her babies from nursing, they begin sampling solid food in earnest. Weaning typically is complete by week eight.

Nearly every waking moment is spent in play, which is not only great fun for the babies, but is great practice for canine life (see PLAY). Puppies learn how to do important dog activities like chasing and running, pawing, biting and fighting. Social skills and canine etiquette are learned by interaction with littermates and Mom. Puppies learn to inhibit their bite when they are bitten by each other, and learn canine language (see COMMUNICATION). Through play, they practice dominant and submissive postures, and prepare for life in the world.

The juvenile puppy period generally begins at age ten weeks, and lasts until puberty and the onset of sexual maturity (see REPRODUCTION). It is during this period that puppies begin to learn the consequences of behavior, and determine what is most appropriate to certain circumstances. Puppies at this age have boundless curiosity, exasperating stubbornness, and enthusiastic affection. Expect your puppy to get into everything, and you won't be disappointed. This is an ideal time to begin training.

Puppies may be placed in new homes once they are eating well on their own; however, they will be better adjusted and make better pets by staying and interacting with littermates and the bitch until they are twelve weeks old. Puppies tend to make transitions from one environment to another more easily at this age.

A healthy puppy has bright, clear eyes and clean, soft fur. Her ears, eyes, nose and anus should have no discharge. Well socialized puppies are curious and friendly, will readily come to you with wagging tail, and are easily engaged in a game. Proper health care includes preventative vaccinations, screening for intestinal parasites, and a nutritionally complete and balanced puppy diet.

Temperament tests may be used by breeders or shelters to measure a puppy's stability, shyness, aggressiveness, and friendliness. There's no one-size-fits-all test. Some are used by breeders to assess Schutzhund performance or tracking ability, for example. Shelters use temperament tests to measure general temperament and suitability for adoption. Still others test dogs for their therapy or assistance dog potential. Most also test for aggression.

Ask your breeder or shelter what temperament tests, if any, have been performed and the result. They may use these to choose your puppy for you, based on what you're looking for or your experience level/home environment you're able to provide. For instance, an experienced owner would do better handling a pushy puppy, and a fenced yard might be required for a "nosy" breed obsessed with running off after scents.

Personality and temperament aren't cast in stone at birth. Early experience, socialization, development and the consequences of learning all impact your puppy's future behavior. Resistance to handling, possessive aggression, territorial vocalization, excessive reactivity and many forms of fear might not emerge until the dog is older. Testing puppies as late as possible—at three to four months—may be more accurate. If you can recognize the potential for negative behaviors, you can diminish the impact.

Shelter pups (especially older ones) may test with fearfulness or aggression in the shelter, and behave very differently once out of the stress of an overwhelming environment. Socialization and training can overcome many potential problems so what's predicted doesn't always HAVE to happen (see TEMPERAMENT TESTS).

PUPPY MILLS

This derogatory term refers to the factory-like production of puppies by unscrupulous "back-yard breeders" who care nothing for the health of the animals. Dogs of questionable parentage are constantly bred to produce supposedly "purebred" puppies, which are then sold for profit typically in pet stores. To make more money, proper care, socialization and housing are neglected. The result is sickly, emotionally bankrupt puppies which, if they live, make poor pets for the gullible soft-hearted souls tricked into buying them for exorbitant prices.

In recent years, the horrors of puppy mills have been exposed by the national media, leading to a better awareness by the pet-loving public. Sadly, there are undoubtedly still some unscrupulous breeders making a buck at the expense of the innocent.

Most reputable pet stores no longer traffic in puppies and kittens, and often instead promote adoptions from animal welfare organizations. If you are interested in a pup of a particular breed, ask the registering organization for a breed club referral in your area. Then, insist on viewing the breeder's accommodations for the dogs, and ask questions. A reputable breeder is more interested in finding an appropriate home for the puppies than making money, and will be happy to satisfy your curiosity. You may need to convince the breeder that you've got what it takes to provide the best home!

PYOMETRA

Pyometra is a bacterial infection of the uterus that can spill into the bloodstream. This is a life-threatening condition, and requires a veterinarian's immediate attention.

The condition is most common in bitches over seven years of age, and is thought to be due to hormone exposure. High levels of the hormones progesterone or estrogen can result in pyometra. Over a lifetime, the intact female dog cycling in and out of heat is exposed to these hormones, and with age, her risk of developing pyometra increases. Younger dogs may develop pyometra from exposure to estrogen used to interrupt pregnancy (see

MISMATING). One of the earliest canine birth control drugs used high levels of the hormone progesterone; because it often resulted in pyometra, it was taken off the market.

Signs typically develop four to eight weeks after the dog goes out of heat. Symptoms include loss of appetite, lethargy, increased thirst and urination. When pus collects in the uterus, a painful swelling in the lower abdomen develops. Other times, the infection is termed "open" and will drain from the cervix; the discharge smells and looks like pus. The dog may have a low-grade or even sub-normal fever, but sometimes the temperature remains normal.

Diagnosis is based on the signs, and may be confirmed with an X-ray or ultrasound. The treatment of choice is spaying the dog to remove the infected reproductive organs and prevent the condition from recurring (see METRITIS).

PYOMETRA

SYMPTOMS: Loss of appetite; lethargy; increased thirst and urination; swollen abdomen; sometimes a creamy to greenish smelly discharge from the vagina; low to subnormal temperature
HOME CARE: EMERGENCY! SEE VET IMMEDIATELY!
VET CARE: Spay surgery removes infected uterus; antibiotic therapy
PREVENTION: Spay dogs that aren't in a professional breeding program or show career

470
DOG FACTS

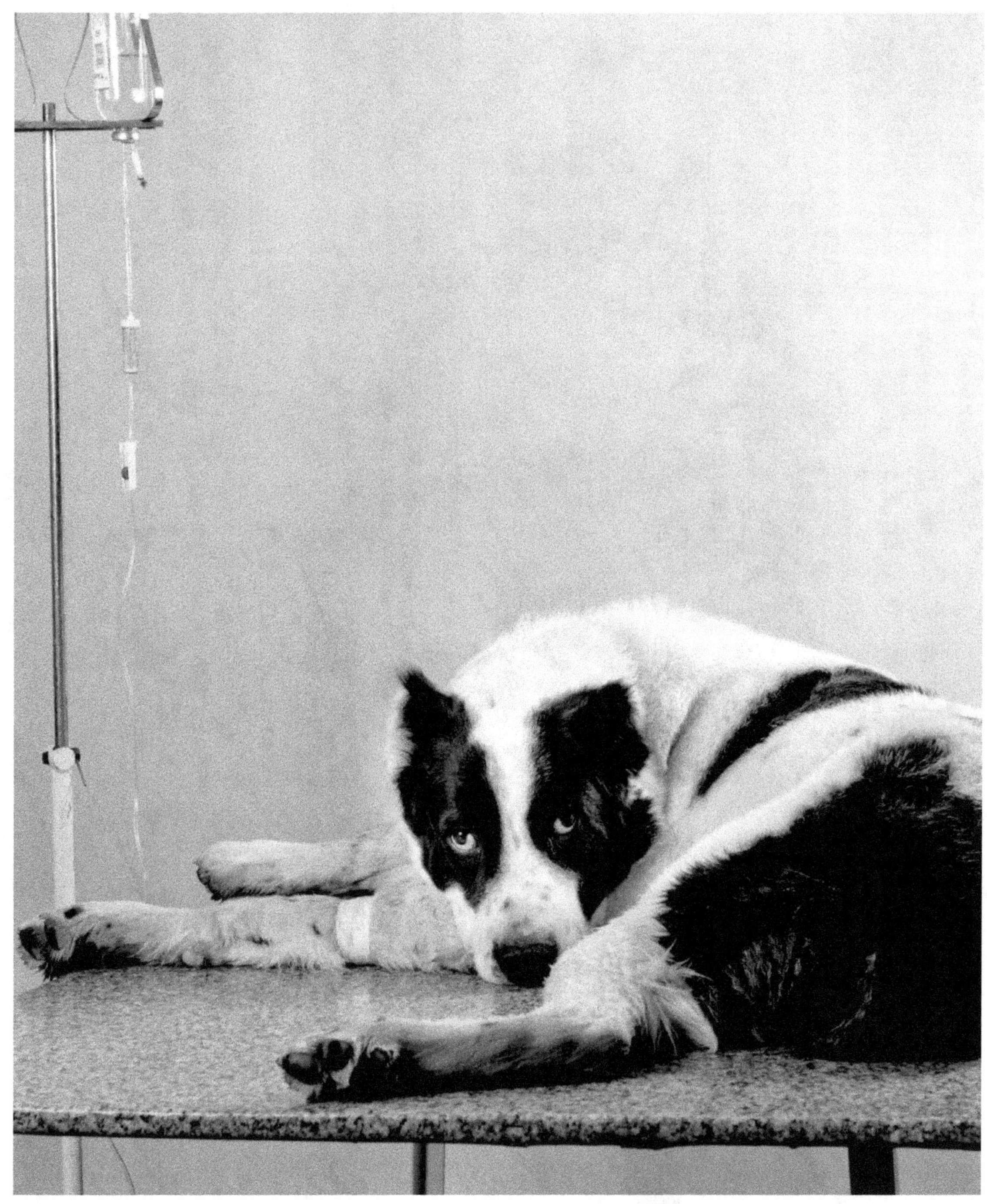

QUARANTINE Quarantine is the isolation of a dog for a period of time to prevent the potential spread of disease or pests to other pets or people. New dogs and puppies should undergo a veterinary examination and be given appropriate treatment before or shortly following adoption. But it's prudent to isolate even healthy-appearing newcomers when they are to be introduced into a home that already has pets.

Any animal showing signs of illness should be isolated from healthy animals. However, it's possible for a new pet to expose resident animals to illness before they become sick themselves. That's because the incubation period—the amount of time between exposure to disease and the development of symptoms of illness—varies depending on the causative agent. For instance, the incubation period for canine parvovirus is five to eleven days, while rabies can be months or even years. It is for this reason that some countries like the United Kingdom and states like Hawaii impose a quarantine on pets imported into these areas.

In most cases, dogs incubating a highly contagious disease becomes sick within two to three weeks of exposure. If unsure of your new dog's recent health, quarantine him for at least two weeks (a month is better) to reduce risk of exposure for your other pets. If the newcomer remains healthy during the quarantine period, he can then be safely introduced to your home and other pets. Segregate an area like the laundry room or enclosed porch, and furnish it with necessary food and water dishes, toys and bed. The new dog and your resident pets should have no direct contact, not even sniffing through the screen or beneath the door, as even this risks disease transmission.

Use a disinfectant to keep the quarantine area and canine necessities clean. A good all-purpose disinfectant is Clorox at a dilution of one cup bleach to two gallons of water. Remember to also disinfect yourself following interaction with the new dog, particularly after cleaning up any accidental puddles or piles. Thoroughly clean your hands and even wipe down your shoes to prevent carrying something nasty out of the room that could infect your other pets.

DOG FACTS

RABIES Rabies is caused by a bullet-shaped virus that belongs to the family *Rhabdoviridae.* It causes a devastating neurological disease that affects the brain, causing symptoms that are similar to meningitis. Once symptoms develop, the disease is always fatal.

Rabies is an ancient scourge that has been around for centuries, and continues to appear throughout the world. The disease affects all mammals, most commonly wild animal populations, but also afflicts dogs, cats, and people. However, since 1884 when Louis Pasteur developed the first vaccine, rabies has been preventable. Some areas such as Hawaii and Great Britain eliminated the disease using strict quarantine protocols.

Rabies still appears today in pets or people as a result of disease "spillover" from wild animals, and parallels the incidence of rabies in these feral reservoirs. Animals most often associated with the disease include raccoons in the north eastern United States (New York, Connecticut, New Jersey, Maryland and spreading), coyotes and gray foxes in Texas and the southwest, foxes in Alaska and skunks in Kansas. Bats are also often associated with rabies. Pets allowed to roam in these regions are at highest risk for encountering a rabid animal, and getting sick. Consequently, such high-risk pets place owners in danger as well.

Infection requires direct contact with an infected animal. The usual transmission is through a bite that introduces infective saliva into the wound. There, the virus proliferates until it reaches the nerves, which carry the infection to the spinal cord. Ultimately the virus reaches the brain, whereupon symptoms develop.

Puppies allowed outside risk wildlife encounters. It's not just the aggravation of having to remove skunk smell, but could prove deadly. Even puppies confined to yards or the house could be exposed to "high risk" wildlife, which includes the skunk, coyote, fox, raccoon and bat. When sick, animals lose all fear and may wander into fenced yards, through pet doors, down chimneys, or attack litters of puppies or kittens.

Finding the dead animal where pets have access qualifies as exposure. Even when the skunk can't be tested for the disease (too badly decomposed, or too damaged for brain analysis), the law requires it be treated as though rabid. That's because pets can also be exposed by playing with the dead body, or coming in contact with infective material.

Rabies has three recognized states of clinical disease: 1) incubation, 2) clinical signs, and 3) paralysis terminating in death. The incubation period- the time from exposure (bite) to development of symptoms—takes 14 days to 24 months, with an average of three to eight weeks for most species. From the brain, the virus spreads to other tissues, like the salivary glands.

Clinical signs are mild to severe behavior changes. The first symptoms are refusal to eat or drink, and the stricken dog typically seeks solitude. The disease then progresses to one of two forms; paralytic (dumb) rabies, and furious rabies.

In the dumb form, dogs act depressed, become insensitive to pain, and develop paralysis of the throat and jaw muscles. It may look like they are choking or have something stuck in their throat as they salivate and drool. Pets with dumb rabies usually fall into a coma and die within three to ten days of initial signs.

Furious rabies is the classic presentation of "mad dog" symptoms. Dogs become extremely vicious and violent, and any noise prompts attack. Such dogs snap and bite at real or imaginary objects, and may roam for miles attacking anything in their path. They lose all fear of natural enemies, and commonly chew or swallow inedible objects like stones or wood. Death occurs four to seven days after onset of clinical signs as a result of progressive paralysis.

The signs and course of rabies in people are similar to animals, and incubation ranges from two weeks to twelve months. There is no cure for rabies. Once signs appear, the mortality rate for the animal or person is virtually 100 percent.

Diagnosis of rabies can only be accomplished by microscopic examination of brain tissue from the suspect animal; this cannot be done while the animal is alive. Wild animals that act suspiciously or attack humans or pets should be euthanized immediately, and the brain examined for evidence of rabies. Any pet that is bitten by an animal that cannot be tested for the disease should be considered exposed to rabies.

The Law and Rabies: Pets must be protected with rabies vaccination by state law, because they come in such close contact with people and may transmit the virus to humans after being infected by a rabid animal. But each state has established its own rules regarding rabies exposure in pets.

Animals are thought to be infectious only shortly before and during the time they show symptoms. Therefore, a biting animal capable of transmitting disease at the time of the bite will typically develop signs within a ten-day period. For that reason, ten days is the recommended period of quarantine in such cases.

The human risk is so high when handling suspect animals that it's safest that unvaccinated pets exposed to rabies be euthanized, and then tested for the disease. However, some local or state laws may allow an exposed pet to live under stringent quarantine for six months and, if no signs develop, be vaccinated prior to release. Recommendations for pets current on rabies vaccination that are exposed to the disease include immediate revaccination and strict owner control/observation for not less than 45 days.

Prevent exposure and protect your dog and yourself by restricting roaming. Keeping his rabies vaccination current also protects your dog from the risk of being euthanized for testing, if he's ever exposed. Any contact with wild animals acting in an abnormal behavior, including stray or feral cats or dogs, increases the risk.

The rabies virus is sensitive to many household detergents and soaps. Should you or your puppy suffer a bite, thoroughly wash the wounds with soap and hot water to kill as much virus as possible, and then consult a doctor and/or veterinarian immediately. The post-exposure vaccine available for people is virtually 100 percent effective when administered in the right period of time.

RABIES

SYMPTOMS: Refusal to eat or drink; hiding; depression; drooling; throat paralysis and inability to swallow; vicious, violent behavior; excessive vocalizing; chewing or eating wood, rocks or other inedible objects
HOME CARE: None; EXTREMELY CONTAGIOUS TO PEOPLE
VET CARE: None; euthanasia; test brain tissue to confirm diagnosis
PREVENTION: Vaccinate dog; prevent contact with wild animals

READING FOOD LABELS Pet food labels are governed by regulations established and enforced by Feed Control Officials in each state; however, most states based their regulations on those developed by the Association of American Feed Control Officials (AFFCO). Among other things, the AAFCO Model Regulations detail what and how information is presented on the label. Virtually all pet food manufacturers with interstate distribution follow AAFCO label guidelines. Label information on pet foods must also follow rules and regulations established by the Food and Drug Administration (FDA), the U.S. Dept. of Agriculture (USDA), and the Federal Trade Commission (FTC). These national, state and local rules regulate how pet food is distributed, what goes into the food, how it's sold, and even the way it's labeled. By reading and understanding food labels, dog owners are able to choose the best products for their pets.

All pet foods involved in interstate commerce must, by law, disclose on their labels a guaranteed analysis, list of ingredients, and a statement and validation of adequacy. The dog's nutritional needs continue to be studied and better defined as time goes on. After eight years of deliberation, the revised AAFCO Dog Food Nutrient Profiles (along with some amendments to accommodate different maximum allowed calcium levels for large-sized puppies) were accepted by the full membership and will be published in the 2016 Official Publication. One notable inclusion in the update has to do with the term "human grade" being used in relation to pet foods. It is now solely left up to individual states to determine acceptability of "human grade" claims and whether they are properly substantiated. Reputable dog food manufacturers follow the AAFCO nutrient profiles or nutritional standards based on extensive nutrition research to formulate their foods.

The label includes the principle display panel which identifies the product by brand and/or product name. Many times, a picture identifying the species (dog) is on the display panel along with the words dog food or a similar designation. The principle display panel must also disclose the total amount of food in the package, and can also include a nutritional claim.

Even the name of the food is regulated by certain rules. A flavor may be used in the food name—Beef Flavor Dog Food—only if the product contains enough of that flavor to be recognized by the dog. Ingredients from animals, poultry or fish must make up at least 25 percent of a product before that ingredient may be included as part of the product name, but a modifier, like beef "cakes" or liver "dinner," must also be used. For instance, a food called "Moochie Poochie's Beef Dinner" indicates that beef makes up at least 25 percent of the product. When the name includes an animal, fish or poultry product without the modifier, the food must contain at least 95 percent of the named ingredient. "Moochie Poochie's Chicken" indicates that chicken comprises at least 95 percent of the product. "All" or "100 percent" means the product contains only the named ingredient, with only water, preservatives and flavorings, vitamins and minerals added.

The information panel contains a guaranteed analysis statement listing minimum levels of crude protein and fat, and maximum levels of crude fiber and moisture. "Crude" refers to the amount measurable by laboratory equipment, not the amount that can be used by the dog.

If the nutritional claim isn't on the Display Panel, it's on the Informational Panel. Dog-food manufacturers may label the food "nutritionally complete and balanced" only if they meet AAFCO standards. These standards can be validated in one of two ways:

1. By laboratory chemical analysis or calculation of nutritional values. Products tested this way say "(name of product) is formulated to meet the nutritional levels established by the AAFCO Dog Food Nutrient Profile for (lifestage)."

However, calculation methods don't include feeding the food to dogs to ensure it's usable by their bodies. This method costs less because long-term nutritional adequacy tests (i.e., digestibility and other trials) are not conducted.

2. Feeding trials that determine whether dogs benefit from food. Products tested in this way will be labeled "Animal feeding tests using AAFCO procedures substantiate that (name of product) provides complete and balanced nutrition for (life stage)."

Feeding trials are expensive and time-consuming, but are the only way to ensure the nutrition is adequate for the dog's needs. The best commercial foods for your dog are complete and balanced products validated through feeding trials that determine whether the nutrients are truly usable by the dog's body.

If the food doesn't say it's complete and balanced, choose a product that does. Some foods are formulated as gourmet treats designed as supplements to a complete and balanced diet. When research hasn't proven nutritional adequacy, the label must state that the product is "Not Intended for Sole Feeding Purposes."

Reputable pet food manufactures determine nutritional adequacy using long-term feeding trials that test for support of growth, adult maintenance or reproduction. Reproduction trials must maintain the dam through gestation and lactation, and the puppies through six weeks of age. Growth tests determine if a diet will support normal growth of puppies; they begin at weaning, and run approximately ten weeks. Adult maintenance trials run for about six months with dogs at least one year old. An "all life stages" claim is validated by testing the same animals through all stages of reproduction and growth.

Dog-food manufacturers also conduct short-term tests to determine digestibility and palatability of diets. Palatability refers to how tasty the dog considers a diet, and is determined by offering test dogs more than one choice in foods and measuring the quantity and how fast the food is eaten. Digestibility describes how well the dog's body is able to utilize the food, and is measured by comparing the difference between what's eaten and what comes out in the feces.

Some labels will include a statement of caloric content in the food. A calorie is a measure of energy produced by eating a specific food. A single calorie is such a small unit of measure, that often a unit of 1000 calories, termed a "kilocalorie" (or interchangeably as a Calorie) is a more useful measure. Disclosure of Calories is not required on the label, except in diets making "lite" claims, but when it appears, it must be stated as "kilocalories per Kg of food." For convenience sake, it's also often labeled as "Calories per cup" or "per unit" of food.

Dry rations generally contain 1400 to 2000 metabolizable kilocalories per pound of diet (3080 to 4400 Kcal/Kg); semi-moist have 1200 to 1350 metabolized kilocalories per pound of diet (2640 to 2970 Kcal/Kg); and canned rations only provide 375 to 950 metabolized kilocalories per pound of diet (825 to 2090 Kcal/Kg). That's why dogs must eat more canned foods than dry diets to obtain the same energy intake.

The amount of calories a dog requires varies widely from dog to dog; the animal's size, metabolism, age, and energy expended determines each dog's need. On average, large dog breeds need less food per pound of body weight than do small breed dogs. For purposes of this discussion, small breed dogs are those whose adult body weight is less than 20 pounds; they require about 50 kilocalories per pound of body weight each day. Medium breed adult dogs are those weighing 20 to 50 pounds, which need approximately 30-40 kilocalories per pound of body weight each day. Large breed dogs weigh 50 to 100 pounds, while the giant breeds exceed 100 pounds as adults; they need 20 to 30 kilocalories per pound of body weight each day, or less. Individual dogs can vary greatly from these averages due to differences in activity, lifestyle or metabolism.

Growing puppies and reproducing female dogs require as much as two to four times more energy per pound of body weight than an adult dog. Working dogs like hunting or herding animals, those under stress, and outdoor dogs exposed to cold weather have much higher energy requirements. Inactive couch-potato dogs, and outdoor dogs exposed to hot weather require much less. Feeding guidelines are on the label only as a starting point for the amount to feed your dog. Be sure to decrease or increase the amount fed to keep your dog in ideal body condition.

The dog food label must also list ingredients in the food in decreasing order of the amount present by weight. Therefore, ingredients listed first are present in the greatest amounts, while smallest amounts are listed last. Although the quality of individual ingredients may vary from very poor to excellent, pet-food manufacturers aren't allowed to cite the quality of their ingredients.

In general, the dog food ingredient list should have:

1.ONE OR MORE PROTEIN SOURCES, which should be one of the first two ingredients in canned dog food, and one of the first three in dry dog food;

2. CARBOHYDRATE SOURCE, such as cereals;

3. FAT SOURCE; and

4. LARGE NUMBERS OF TRACE MINERALS AND VITAMIN SUPPLEMENTS, which will be toward the bottom of the list.

Water content varies depending on the form of food: dry foods contain 6 to 12 percent moisture, soft-moist foods contain 23 to 40 percent moisture, and canned foods contain 68 to 82 percent moisture.

Pet owners understandably are concerned about what goes into pet food, and AAFCO attempts to clear any misunderstanding with labeling definitions that manufacturers must meet. Definitions of terms can be very complicated, and may not mean exactly what everyone assumes. Some pet food terms have become associated with "good" compared to "bad" ingredients, so it's important to understand what exactly is meant by these terms.

Byproducts is one such label, and according to AAFCO definitions, a byproduct is what is left over after the intended product has been made. Those left-overs potentially are a great source of additional nutrients, depending on what they are. Here's an example: harvesting a common weed's flowers to make dandelion wine or an herbal remedy means the dandelion greens are byproducts. But harvesting that same plant for only the greens makes the bloom a byproduct. In fact, many "byproducts" do not include that term in the ingredient name at all.

Organic claims abound today, but these labels do not mean the food is any better than those not so labeled The organic label on pet foods mean the ingredients meet production and handling requirements of the USDA National Organic Program (NOP), which says these products are "produced through approved methods that integrate cultural, biological and mechanical practices that foster cycling of resources, promote ecological balance and conserve biodiversity. Synthetic fertilizers, sewage sludge, irradiation and genetic engineering may not be used." Certified organic foods display a USDA organic seal and must be made of at least 95 percent organic ingredients.

Natural is a descriptive term that until recently, was not even defined by AAFCO. It was used mostly by marketers to promote one type of food over another. In answer to consumer concerns, definitions have been created to create equal footing between any foods with this label claim. The current AAFCO definition says "natural" refers to "a feed or feed ingredient derived solely from plant, animal or mined sources, either in its unprocessed state or having been subject to physical processing, heat processing, rendering, purification, extraction, hydrolysis, enzymolysis or fermentation, but not having been produced by or subject to a chemically synthetic process and not containing any additives or processing aids that are chemically synthetic except in amounts as might occur in good manufacturing practices." Sound confusing? It is. This definition is very liberal and allows nearly all pet foods to carry some form of the "natural" label, because most pet food ingredients are 1) derived from plant, animal or mined sources; 2) can still undergo common manufacturing processes and retain the "natural" label; and 3) contain "trace" amounts of chemically synthetic compounds and still be called "natural."

Human-grade is a notable inclusion in the 2016 update. While the term "edible" is a standard in relation to food, "human-grade" is not, and the term isn't just about the ingredients. The U.S. Department of Agriculture (USDA) defines products fit for human consumption to be officially "edible" which requires them to have been processed, inspected and passed manufacturing regulations designed to assure safety for consumption by humans. This term's use has become so complicated and contentious that in the updated profiles, it will be left up to individual states to determine acceptability of "human grade" claims and whether they are properly substantiated.

Any questions concerning a dog food product should be directed to the manufacturer. Reputable manufacturers include an address or toll-free telephone number on the label.

Dog food labels will not tell you everything about the food. There's no easy way to judge the overall quality of a dog food, but usually better foods cost a bit more because feeding trials and high quality ingredients are more expensive than lower-quality generic food brands. It's also important to judge food quality by the manufacturer's reputation, including its history in nutritional research.

And although you may choose the finest ration available, it's worthless if your dog refuses to eat it. Smell, texture and taste define whether your dog will like a food or not. Ultimately, it's the dog's sense of taste, not the label, which decides palatability.

REPRODUCTION

Reproduction is the biological mechanism that allows dogs to create puppies. Dogs become sexually mature and able to breed at various ages, depending on the individual animal's health and breed. By four months of age, male dogs show interest in a sexually receptive female, but males typically aren't able to successfully breed until seven to eight months of age. Female dogs typically experience their first breeding cycle at about six months of age. Onset of sexual maturity varies between individuals as well as breeds, however. Large breeds of both sexes tend to mature more slowly, and may take 18 to 24 months to become sexually mature.

Ideally, females should not be bred until their second heat cycle to allow them to fully mature first. A healthy bitch will continue to cycle and be able to produce puppies all her life, but beyond the age of about eight, reproduction problems are more likely to develop. Males are able to sire puppies throughout their life. Size of the litter depends on the mother, with tiny dog breeds usually producing one to four babies and large breed dogs giving birth to litters of eight, ten, and even more puppies. Females generally are able to produce one or two litters a year.

The estrus cycle is the period during which a female becomes sexually receptive to the male and breeding takes place. Nearly all dog breeds experience estrus about every seven months; some cycle more often, while a few (like the Basenji) cycle only once a year.

Canine estrus, also called heat, is categorized by distinct periods of time. Proestrus is the onset, lasts about nine days, and is distinguished by the vulva swelling and a dark bloody discharge. Ovulation, the release of the eggs, occurs during the next "standing heat" phase, which is technically termed estrus and which lasts another seven to nine days. Once the eggs are released, they must mature in the female for 72 hours before they can be fertilized by sperm. The vaginal discharge lightens to a faint pink color during this receptive period, during which the bitch will allow breeding to take place. Diestrus is the next stage; it begins at the end of standing heat and lasts about 58 days. Hormone levels increase in response to the body's anticipation of developing puppies and birth. Anestrus is the final stage, and lasts about four and a half months, beginning with whelping of the puppies, and ending with the beginning of a new cycle when proestrus returns. It may be difficult to tell exactly when one stage ends and the next begins in dogs that don't become pregnant.

The breeding period is also announced with subtle behavioral signals. The female may become more active or nervous during estrus. Her body gives off scented cues that males readily detect, and canine suitors are attracted from miles away. They mark territory by leaving urine advertising their status as breeding males, and defend that territory from other dogs with raucous and often violent fights.

Canine breeding is a science that requires a comprehensive knowledge of canine health, anatomy and genetics. It's also an expensive proposition, and only professional breeders, or those under the direct supervision of a professional, should attempt canine matchmaking. All too often, puppies are produced with little to no thought which ultimately results in their deaths because, frankly, there simply aren't enough good homes to go around. Unless your dog is in a professional breeding program or is being shown in competition that precludes this option, surgically sterilize your dogs. Neutering males and spaying females prevents accidental breeding.

Before breeding, both the male and female dogs should be in optimal health. Males should be tested for brucellosis, and females should receive any necessary medication, worming and vaccinations prior to pregnancy. This not only protects the health of the bitch, but also helps protect her puppies during development and for a period after birth. The preliminaries to mating include a great deal of exploratory sniffing of the anal regions. Once she's ready and interested, the bitch presents her rear quarters to the male, and flags her tail to one side in invitation. The male mounts, clasping her with his forelegs while thrusting forward. Insertion of the penis takes place prior to erection. Following penetration, he treads with his rear legs as erection begins.

His penis swells inside the bitch's vagina. Muscles in her vagina constrict, tying the pair together. The first ejaculate (within the first minute of intromission) is sperm-free prostatic fluid, followed by a sperm-rich ejaculation within the next five minutes. Usually, the male lifts one rear leg over his penis after dismounting, and turns around so the breeding pair stand tail to tail. The genital tie last five to 60 minutes, during which prostatic fluid will continue to be produced. This tie is thought to have evolved to better ensure fertilization. Sperm survives in the female for up to seven days (see ARTIFICIAL INSEMINATION).

The female may immediately initiate another breeding, or subsequent encounters may be delayed for several hours or even a day or more. It's also possible for a single litter to be fathered by more than one male. The dog's uterus is a Y-shaped organ; puppies develop within each arm of the Y. Gestation, the length of time between conception and birth, varies somewhat. The average is 63 to 65 days; however, it's not unusual for puppies to be born between days 56 through 72.

The first signs of pregnancy are the dog's nipples swelling and darkening from light to rosy pink at about 40 days into gestation; some dogs may suffer morning sickness between the third and fourth week. By day 27 a veterinarian can detect individual babies by palpating, or feeling, the pregnant dog's abdomen which won't noticeably swell until about the fifth or sixth week of pregnancy. Large dogs that carry babies high beneath their rib cage may not show at all.

The health of the bitch and her unborn puppies requires high-quality nutrition. Most pregnant dogs eat more during this time, but overfeeding and excessive weight gain should be avoided. Offer her an appropriate commercial reproduction ration like an energy dense puppy food as recommended by your veterinarian. Food supplements are rarely required.

Within a few days prior to birth, the mothers' breasts swell and further develop. Long fur should be clipped away from the breasts and genitals before the puppies are born. Nesting behavior becomes apparent 12 to 24 hours before whelping, or giving birth. Typically, canine mothers-to-be seek hidden, cozy spots, dig in the laundry, or rearrange the bedspread. A whelping box for dogs should be provided to dissuade Mom from giving birth on your cashmere sweater.

The dog's rectal temperature drops from the normal range to 98 or 99 degrees eight to 12 hours prior to onset of labor. The first stage of labor lasts six to 12 and sometimes 24 hours. During this time the bitch appears restless, may pant and shiver, vomit or pace and scratch at the floor. She either seeks seclusion or looks for an appropriate nest. Leave her alone; give her some privacy to get ready.

Dogs with more than one puppy will alternate between the second and third stages of labor. Stage two consists of the birth of the baby, and stage three is the expulsion of the placenta; combined, they usually last only ten to 30 minutes, and rarely longer than 90 minutes. Placentas usually pass within five to 15 minutes of each puppy birth.

Vaginal discharge signals imminent birth. Involuntary contractions begin until the bitch is fully involved and bearing down to deliver. If the first puppy isn't born within an hour following these strong contractions, take Mom to a veterinarian. Normally, a dark green-gray bubble which is the placental sack containing the puppy will emerge from the vagina, and should be fully passed within 30 minutes. Normal presentation can be either tail or face first. Puppies are expelled from alternating arms of the Y-shaped uterus.

After each baby is born, the bitch cleans herself, may consume the placenta that follows, and bites through the umbilical cord. She licks her baby to clean away fetal membranes so it can breathe. Often, the mother dog may give birth to several puppies, and then rest for several hours before resuming labor and delivering the rest of the litter. Seek a veterinarian's help if labor does not resume within four hours, if Mom acts restless or feverish, ignores her puppies, or there's a white or foul-smelling discharge from the vulva. An odorless green, dark red or brown fluid discharge is usually normal.

The distinctive configuration of some dog breeds may interfere with a normal birth, or make it more difficult. Those that are tiny, or that have a proportionally large head and a narrow pelvis may require help. The Bulldog, Boston Terrier, Pekingese, Toy Poodle and Chihuahua are prone to whelping problems, and may require a cesarean to deliver healthy puppies.

The mother dog remains with their newborns for the first day or so following the birth, leaving only to relieve herself or grab a quick bite to eat. Attention is focused on cleaning and feeding the babies. Mom's first milk, called colostrum, provides puppies with important nutrients and protective antibodies (see IMMUNE SYSTEM). Licking their anal region stimulates puppies to eliminate, and the bitch consumes the feces and urine to keep the nest clean.

A healthy puppy actively squirms and cries aggressively if moved away from his mother. Puppies which feel cold to the touch, move sluggishly or make only weak sounds may be stimulated by massaging them with a dry, warm towel. Very cold puppies may be warmed by dipping them up to their neck in 100 degree water until they squirm. Then dry them off, and give them back to Mom.

If Mom fails to remove fetal membranes from the face within a minute or two of birth, do it for her so the puppy can breathe. Babies that fail to breathe need immediate help, and may need their airways cleared. Wrap the puppy in a dry, warm cloth, cup him in both hands keeping his head secure, and swing him in a downward motion to help clear fluid from his lungs. When the baby begins breathing, give him back to the mother.

Nursing continues for up to eight weeks, and during this time the bitch also protects and teaches her babies how to be dogs. If Mom isn't able to feed her puppies, supplemental feeding may be necessary. Newborn puppies require feeding four or more times a day with an appropriate bitch's milk replacer (see MILK, AS FOOD).

RESPIRATORY DISTRESS

SYMPTOMS: Gasping; coughing; excessive panting; slowed or shallow breathing; whistling or strained breathing sounds; pale or blue color to lips, gums or tongue; standing with front legs braced and head hanging, or sitting with "elbows" outward to aid breathing; loss of consciousness
HOME CARE: Remove blockage from mouth (if present) and/or give artificial respiration; EMERGENCY! SEE VET IMMEDIATELY!
VET CARE: Address the underlying cause; possibly oxygen therapy
PREVENTION: Prevent poisoning, electrical shock, or other traumas that can cause breathing problems; avoid overheating and obesity

RESPIRATION Respiration is the act of breathing. Dogs on average breathe at a rate of about 12 to 30 respirations each minute when at rest; smaller dogs tend to breathe more quickly than larger breeds. The respiratory system includes the nasal passages of the nose, the throat, voice box, windpipe, bronchial tubes and lungs.

The bronchial tubes repeatedly branch in a series of progressively smaller passageways, like a tree. They terminate in tiny air sacs deep inside the lung; it's here that the blood/oxygen exchange takes place. Muscles of the chest, including the diaphragm, pump air in and out of the lungs.

Breathing is normally rhythmic and even. Changes in the sound or rate of respiration may indicate a wide variety of illnesses and should be addressed by a veterinarian. Excitement, fear, pain or fever may prompt heavy breathing in the dog. Typically, the dog suffering breathing problems is reluctant to lie down, and may sit with his front "elbows" held away from his body to make respiration easier.

Upper respiratory infections (see CANINE DISTEMPER and KENNEL COUGH) can cause obstruction of air and result in noisy breathing. Slowed respiration may indicate poison. Increased respiration, or panting, is normal during exertion or hot weather, and is a way for the dog to cool off. But prolonged labored panting can be a sign of heatstroke (see HYPERTHERMIA).

When air must be forced through narrowed, constricted airways, the dog makes whistling wheezing sound during respiration. This sound is typical of dogs suffering from asthma, but may also indicate laryngitis, collapsed trachea, or even growths in the airways.

Painful breathing due to rib fracture or other painful conditions cause the dog to breathe in shallow, quick breaths to keep from moving too much. A punctured lung or ruptured diaphragm also compromise normal respiration. Fluid in the chest, called pleural effusion, also results in shallow breathing.

Coughing may be the dog's attempt to a clear swallowed object like a piece of bone from his throat. It can also be an indication of bronchitis, congested heart failure (see HEART DISEASE), or heartworm disease.

RESTRAINT This refers to restriction of the dog's movement so she can be safely and efficiently medicated or transported, while preventing injury to the person handling the dog. A dog suffering pain or fear may often become frantic or even violent and may injure herself or the person that comes to her aid.

The degree of restraint required depends on the individual circumstances, the competence of the handler, and the personality of the dog. A good rule is to restrict your dog only as much and as long as required to accomplish what needs to be done. Slow, gentle and confident movements are best. Dogs that have obedience training are more easily handled, and may require less restraint than others.

Avoid sudden movements, which can be frightening to a pet. When possible, gather your equipment and medication ahead of time so that you're prepared and don't feel rushed. The aim is to avoid the dog's teeth, while keeping her from escaping. A two-person team is most effective; one restrains while the other attends the dog. A couple of restraint techniques are appropriate.

For small dogs, use one hand to firmly grasp the loose skin at the back of her neck (the scruff) while your other hand captures both of the hind legs above the hock. Simply stretch the dog gently on her side. A similar approach is to again lay the dog on her side, capturing the hind legs with one hand as before. But rather than grasping the scruff with your other hand, lay your forearm across the dog's shoulders and press her down to hold her in place; that hand captures the forelegs.

For medium and large dogs, the hugging technique works well. Place the dog in a sitting, standing, or reclining position, whichever is best for your treatment. Then, one arm goes under her neck and chin, and snugs her head to your chest, while the other arm goes across her back and around her tummy and hugs her body close. Whoever is restraining the dog should be well known and hopefully liked or at least respected by the dog. Talk soothingly to the dog during the restraint, then reward her afterwards with praise and petting or a game.

It may become necessary to restrain and medicate your dog all by yourself. For some dogs, simply grasping the scruff and gently pressing her down with one hand while you medicate with the other may be sufficient. Other times, a muzzle may be helpful; it negates the dog's teeth, so you can maneuver better with both hands. Placing the dog on a leash and tethering her to a table leg may also give you the necessary advantage.

Another highly effective method is to wrap your dog in a blanket or large towel while leaving the treatment area on her body uncovered. Drop the fabric over the dog (get her head end with all the teeth!), then wrap her up to immobilize her legs so she can't escape. Be sure to give her adequate breathing room, though. Often, the blanket trick helps calm the excited dog long enough for treatment to take place.

RINGWORM Ringworm is a fungal parasite (dermatophyte) that causes skin disease in pets and people. The dermatophyte feeds on keratin, the outer dead surface of growing fur, skin and nails. There are many types of dermatophytes, but most cases of canine ringworm are caused by *Microsporum canis.* Another type of ringworm, carried by rodents, may infect dogs that dig through rodent burrows. A third kind of ringworm lives in the soil.

Ringworm easily spreads to humans, too. Very young children, older folks, or those with a depressed immune system are most susceptible. In people, ringworm infections spread outward from a central spot. As the inside central sore heals, the "ring" of reddened inflammation surrounding the area gives it a characteristic look and name.

Dogs suffering from ringworm infection won't necessarily show this distinct pattern, though. Sores expand but not in rings, and can look like a variety of other pet skin diseases such as skin allergies.

RINGWORM

SYMPTOMS: Hair loss; skin inflammation in patchy areas and/or ever-increasing circles
HOME CARE: After veterinary diagnosis, miconazole preparations or lime sulfur dips; vacuum; clean surfaces daily with bleach and water solutions (CONTAGIOUS TO PEOPLE)
VET CARE: Culture hairs to diagnose; prescribe antifungal medication
PREVENTION: Avoid contact with contagious pets; bring dog only to reputable groomers

Typically there is scaling and crusting at the margins of bald patches, with broken or stubbled hair in these areas along with variable itchiness. The dermatophyte lives only on hairs that actively grow. The infected hairs break off, and leave a stubby patchwork fur pattern, and mild to severe crusty sores also can develop.

Some pets become itchy, others do not. The inner hairless regions appear clear as they start to heal. The face, head and forelimbs are the first areas affected, but the fungus potentially can spread and affect the dog's whole body.

All dogs are at risk for ringworm, but the condition is most common in puppies less than a year old, and in older dogs with compromised immune systems. Healthy adult dogs often resist infection because their immune system squelches any exposure. Some healthy pets become "typhoid Mary" carriers, with no health problem themselves, but spread infection to other animals. Once a pet becomes infected, spores contaminate the environment and can remain infective for months.

The condition is transmitted by direct animal-to-animal contact usually from infected hair or skin debris. However, ringworm is also transmissible from contaminated grooming equipment, and can even be picked up from dermatophytes in the environment. If one pet in the house is diagnosed, all should be treated whether showing signs or not. Infected pets should be quarantined from those not showing signs.

Canine ringworm is diagnosed by identification of the fungus. The veterinarian may use a Wood's Lamp to screen suspect cases; about half of *M. canis* cases will "glow" when exposed to its ultraviolet light.

Other times, a skin scraping collects debris from the lesions, which is then examined microscopically. Many cases are identified using a culture test that grows the ringworm fungus. A sample from the lesion is placed in a special medium designed to grow ringworm. It may take up to three weeks before the test indicates a positive result.

In most cases, otherwise healthy dogs self-cure in 60 to 100 days without any treatment at all. However, in severe cases and when the infected pet may expose humans to infection, specific topical or oral antifungal treatment may be recommended. Be cautious about medicating sores with anything prior to veterinary examination. That may interfere with an accurate diagnosis. Treat only after your veterinarian diagnoses the condition, and follow his or her recommendation.

Ringworm fungus is difficult to eradicate. Human products like athlete's foot preparations aren't effective. Neither are captan, or ketoconazole shampoos. The only topical treatment proven to be effective in controlled studies is lime sulfur dip, but it smells like rotten eggs.

Dog with long fur must be clipped first to reduce the amount of contaminated hair (remember to disinfect the clipper blades afterwards!). Avoid shampooing or scrubbing the pet when you bathe your dog because that can make the infection worse by breaking off infected hairs and spreading the spores over the body.

A variety of drugs have been used. Ketoconazole is probably the most common. The drug griseofulvin (Fulvacin) is also very effective in treating ringworm. Once swallowed, it is incorporated into the growing hair where it slows the growth of the fungus. Your veterinarian will recommend the best choice for your situation.

In addition to treating your puppy, you must clean the environment. That's easier said than done because the ringworm spores are nearly indestructible. Contaminated hairs and skin debris shed into the environment remain infective for over a year, and act as a reservoir for reinfection. Treating the environment helps reduce the numbers of fungal spores, and helps prevent reinfection.

Only concentrated bleach, cancer-causing chemicals, and enilconazole (toxic to cats) have been shown to effectively kill ringworm spores, and none of those options work well in your home. Currently, experts recommend environmental control by daily cleaning of all surfaces using a diluted bleach solution (one part bleach to ten parts water), along with thorough vacuuming.

Get rid of spore reservoirs such as carpet, drapes, pet bedding, and the like. Repeatedly bleach all surfaces with a 1:10 bleach and water solution. High temperature steam also may be effective. Vacuum repeatedly, but remember to toss out the bag every time, or you'll simply spread the spores. Disinfect the vacuum, too, with the bleach and water spray.

Sunlight also kills ringworm spores. Anything that can't be thrown away or bleached can be left outside in the bright sun for a couple of weeks.

You must treat the puppy and continue disinfecting the environment until follow up cultures of the pet are negative. In a single pet home, treatment may be needed three to eight weeks and longer in multipet households. When an otherwise healthy pet develops ringworm and is not re-exposed, the lesions typically will self-heal in about three weeks even without medication.

ROCKY MOUNTAIN SPOTTED FEVER

Rocky Mountain spotted fever is a rickettsial disease caused by the organism *Rickettsia rickettsii*. *Rickettsiae* are tiny bacteria-sized parasites that live inside cells, and most spend a portion of their life cycle in an insect vector which then transmits them to an animal host, or reservoir. People and dogs are not the natural host for most of these agents, but can become ill when infected.

Rocky Mountain spotted fever can be transmitted by several different kinds of ticks, particularly the wood tick and the American dog tick. The illness affects both people and dogs.

The disease is seasonal, with most cases occurring from spring to early fall. It has been reported in nearly every state, but is most prevalent in the central states from Colorado west to the coast. Most infected dogs may not show any signs at all, but others can suffer severe illness and rapid death. For unknown reasons, Siberian Huskies appear to be most severely affected.

The agent is transmitted to the dog from the bite of an infected tick, and the rickettsiae travel from the tissues to the lymphatic system. They proliferate in the cells found in the walls of small blood vessels throughout the body. This prompts an inflammatory response that results in blood clotting and bleeding disorders, and organ damage.

Signs begin with fever of up to 105 degrees, loss of appetite, signs of arthritis, coughing or labored breathing, abdominal pain, vomiting and diarrhea, and swelling of the face or extremities. A thick mucoid discharge may be seen from the eyes and nose. Neurologic signs are also common, and may include altered mental states, poor balance, and a rigid neck. Many of these acute signs are similar to canine distemper.

A week or two following initial signs, the dog develops bleeding disorders similar to ehrlichiosis. Nosebleeds, bleeding beneath the skin, or in the urine or feces may result in shock and multiple organ failure. Loss of blood circulation may lead to gangrene and death of affected tissue. Ultimately, kidney failure causes death.

Diagnosis is sometimes difficult to make, but Rocky Mountain spotted fever should be suspected when these signs appear in a tick-infested dog during spring to fall. The diagnosis is best confirmed with tests, which are available in veterinary laboratories or schools.

ROCKY MOUNTAIN SPOTTED FEVER

SYMPTOMS: Fever; loss of appetite; lameness; coughing or labored breathing; hunching from abdominal pain; vomiting; diarrhea; swelling of face and legs; thick discharge from eyes and nose; poor balance; rigid neck; altered mental state; nosebleeds; bloody urine or feces; shock
HOME CARE: None
VET CARE: Treat with doxycycline or tetracycline; supportive care, including fluid therapy
PREVENTION: Use tick control, including insecticides and/or mechanical removal of ticks from your dog

When the disease is suspected, dogs should be treated immediately with tetracycline even before blood tests confirm the diagnosis. Dogs suffering from acute disease will respond with a reversal of symptoms within only a day or two of antibiotic therapy, which should be continued for two to three weeks. Dogs may also require other supportive therapy, such as fluid replacement to combat shock and clotting disorders. Dogs that recover from infection appear to become resistant to reinfection.

To prevent the disease, practice tick control with appropriate insecticides. In most instances, the tick vector must be attached and feeding for 12 to 48 hours before a rickettsial agent can be transmitted. Therefore, prompt removal of any ticks found on your dog will virtually eliminate chance of the disease.

However, the crushed tick that contaminates your skin may result in infection, so wear gloves and/or use tweezers to remove ticks from your pet, to protect yourself from exposure. Human signs of the disease include flu-like symptoms, and a rash on the hands, wrists, ankles and feet. See your doctor immediately if you suspect you've been exposed, because the disease causes death in 15 to 20 percent of untreated human cases (see ZOONOSIS and TICKS).

ROLLING

ROLLING Dogs tend to live through their noses, and certain pungent scents prompt rolling behavior in dogs. This scent ecstasy is similar to what cats experience when exposed to catnip; however, the canine indulgence is a good bit more noxious, and tends toward offal.

When a dog finds what he considers an attractive odor, he rolls to rub his shoulders, back and neck into the offering. He spreads the scent over himself as though it's doggy cologne. Nobody knows for sure why dogs roll in nasty things like rotting garbage, dead animals, or feces. Experts theorize that perfuming themselves with such scents may allow the dog to carry the smelly message home, so other dogs can "read" all about it.

ROUNDWORMS Roundworms are one the most common intestinal parasites of puppies. Even puppies that come from pristine kennels and environments often develop roundworms because it is found in almost all puppies at birth. There are several types of roundworms, technically called nematodes, but the species *Toxocara canis* most commonly affects dogs. Roundworms are passed in the stool or vomited, and look like masses of spaghetti.

Dogs can become infected in four different ways. Puppies may be infected before they are born when immature worms the mom-dog harbors migrate to the uterus. Puppies may also contract roundworms from nursing the mother's infected milk. The parasite can also be contracted when a puppy or adult dog swallows infective larvae found in the environment, or by eating an infected host like a mouse or bird.

When a puppy swallows infective eggs, the larvae that hatch in the intestines later migrate to the liver and lungs. They are coughed up, and swallowed again, and then mature once they return to the intestines.

The parasites grow into one to seven inch long adult worms. Mature females can lay 200,000 hard-shelled eggs in a single day, which pass with the stool and can live in the environment for months to years. Eggs hatch into infective larvae, completing the cycle.

Older dogs that swallow infective larvae are more resistant to the worms, and their immune system tends to arrest the worm's development. Such larvae simply stop developing, and remain wherever they happen to alight. In other words, they can lodge in the pet's muscles, kidneys, brain, or even the eyes. In male dogs, and females that are spayed or never bred, the larvae remain permanently frozen in time.

But when a female dog becomes pregnant, the same hormones that promote the unborn puppies' development also stimulate the worms to grow. Immature roundworms begin again to migrate and typically cross into the placenta or the mammary glands to infect the puppies before or shortly after birth.

ROUNDWORMS

SYMPTOMS: Potbellied appearance in puppies; dull coat; diarrhea; mucus in the stool; "spaghetti worms" in the stool or vomit; adult dogs rarely show signs when infected
HOME CARE: None (CONTAGIOUS TO PEOPLE IF STOOL IS INGESTED—USE CAUTION WITH SMALL CHILDREN)
VET CARE: Oral worm medication
PREVENTION: Preventative worm medication; pick up feces from yard

Roundworms are rarely life-threatening, but massive infestations may cause intestinal damage, or rarely bowel obstruction or even rupture. More commonly, roundworms interfere with absorption of puppy food.

Puppies with roundworms often have a potbellied appearance. They may also develop a dull coat since the worms take away nutrients that keep the coat looking healthy. Heavy worm loads can cause diarrhea, or mucus in the stool. Puppy owners typically diagnose the worms themselves when they see the spaghetti-like masses passed in the stool or vomited. Your veterinarian also can diagnose roundworms by examining a sample of the puppy's stool under the microscope and finding the eggs, which confirms adult worms are present in the intestines.

Veterinarians usually prescribe medication for roundworms as a matter of course. These treatments are considered safe even in quite young puppies. Many heartworm preventatives also protect against roundworms, since heartworm is a kind of nematode as well. This is important because roundworms can also affect children.

Children may be at risk for infection with *Toxocara canis*, primarily from accidentally ingesting infective stages of the worm. Ewww! But actually, this most commonly occurs when the kids taste or eat contaminated dirt.

The parasite causes a disease in humans called *visceral larva migrans* in which immature worms never reach maturity, but simply migrate throughout the body. Symptoms include fever, anemia, liver enlargement, pneumonia, and other problems. Because of this human risk, the Centers for Disease Control (CDC) recommends that all puppies and their mothers undergo deworming treatments, whether diagnosed with the parasite or not.

These precautions, along with simple sanitation procedures, will protect both puppies and human family members from roundworms. Clean up feces from the puppy's yard at least once a week, and prevent young children from playing in the dog's "toilet area."

498
DOG FACTS

SALMONELLA Salmonella is a bacteria which can cause illness in people and pets. Salmonella can contaminate homemade as well as commercial pet foods, and leads to some pet food recalls. There are nearly 2000 kinds of salmonella bacteria. Most are found naturally in the environment, and can remain alive for months or years in manure or soil. Some types are normal inhabitants of animals, and don't cause problems. Others prompt a variety of illnesses from diarrheal disease to life-threatening illness that cause a variety of salmonella symptoms you need to watch for.

Puppies and young dogs, and those that are stressed by other illness, poor kenneling conditions, or inadequate nutrition are most commonly affected. Dogs contract the bacteria by drinking infected water, eating food contaminated with infected droppings, or by eating manure.

SALMONELLA

SYMPTOMS: Bloody, foul-smelling diarrhea; fever; vomiting; loss of appetite; hunching posture from pain; depression
HOME CARE: None
VET CARE: Fluid therapy; antibiotics
PREVENTION: Don't feed contaminated raw or undercooked meats; prevent dog from eating wildlife; keep yard clean by promptly picking up feces

Most infected pets never show signs of illness, but may harbor the bacteria and spread the disease to other animals and people. When illness develops, signs include bloody, foul-smelling diarrhea, fever, vomiting, appetite loss, a hunching position due to stomach pain, and depression.

The bacteria may be carried in the bloodstream to the liver, lungs, kidneys or uterus. Signs of disease typically last four to ten days, but diarrhea may continue for a month or longer.

The condition is diagnosed from signs of illness, and from finding the bacteria in the blood or tissues of the affected dog. When enteritis is the primary problem, treatment usually consists of fluid therapy (see DEHYDRATION).

A culture of the stool sample will identify the strain of salmonella, so that the most effective antibiotic can be given. However, antibiotic therapy is only indicated in instances of severe systemic disease, to avoid the possibility of prompting the development of a drug-resistant strain of the bacteria.

Protect pets from salmonella by curtailing hunting. Dogs that eat rodents or other wildlife are at much greater risk. If you choose to provide a raw food diet, take extra precautions to ensure the food is safe for your dogs and humans handling the food.

Protect yourself by religiously washing your hands after dealing with feces or handling an ill dog. Use a dilute bleach and water solution (1 to 32 ratio) to disinfect your hands, dog bowls, toys, and areas where the dog sleeps.

SALMON POISONING

This disease is an acute, frequently fatal gastrointestinal disease contracted from eating raw salmon or trout infected with the rickettsial bacteria *Neorickettsia helminthoeca*. This disease is limited to the Pacific Northwest region of the United States.

The prevalence of the disease corresponds to the natural home range of a snail that lives in the streams of Washington, Oregon and northern California. These snails are host to a fluke called *Nanophyetus salmincola* which later leaves the snail to parasitize salmon and trout. When a dog eats the raw fish, he in turn is parasitized by the fluke. The fluke rarely causes problems by itself. (Humans may also contract the fluke by eating infested raw fish, but aren't affected by salmon poisoning.) However, when a dog eats a fish that is infested with flukes carrying *Neorickettsia helminthoeca*, salmon poisoning is the result.

Dogs typically become ill within five days of eating the tainted fish. The agent infects the lymphatic system, and spreads throughout the body, causing a persistent high fever. The signs of illness resemble those of canine parvovirus, and include loss of appetite, depression, runny eyes and nose, weight loss, and severe vomiting and bloody diarrhea. After several days, the fever drops to subnormal levels. Untreated dogs die within five to seven days of infection.

SALMON POISONING

SYMPTOMS: Loss of appetite; depression; runny eyes and nose; weight loss; severe vomiting; bloody diarrhea; subnormal temperature
HOME CARE: VET CARE NEEDED IF DOG IS TO SURVIVE
VET CARE: Supportive therapy; fluids; blood transfusion; antibiotics
PREVENTION: Keep dog from eating raw or undercooked fish

Diagnosis is based on signs of illness, and confirmed by finding either fluke eggs in the stool, or the rickettsiae in a blood sample. Treatment is supportive, and similar to that of parvovirus. Fluid therapy to combat dehydration is extremely important. Blood transfusions may also be required. Antibiotics like tetracycline eliminate the parasite.

Dogs in endemic regions should be prevented from eating any raw fish. Keep dogs under your direct supervision when they are outside, or confine them to a safe area. Feed only cooked fish, or fish that has been frozen for at least twenty-four hours.

SEBORRHEA This term is commonly used to describe symptoms of scaling, flaking skin (dandruff) which may be characterized by dry waxy skin and fur (*seborrhea sicca*), or greasy, oily skin and fur (*seborrhea oleosa*). Most commonly, seborrhea is a sign of any number of unrelated disorders of the skin (see MANGE, FLEA ALLERGY and HYPOTHYROIDISM). The skin condition is treated appropriate to the underlying cause.

However, a condition called primary seborrhea is used to describe inherited skin disorders which interfere with the normal processes of skin cell generation and development.

Dogs suffering from the condition will, in addition to skin crusting and dandruff, develop a waxy otitis along with a rancid body odor. Weeping sores and hair loss develop in some cases, in part due to itchiness and trauma from scratching. Dogs may suffer secondary bacterial infections of the skin. There is a genetic predisposition to primary seborrhea in the Basset Hound, Chinese Shar-Pei, Cocker and Springer Spaniel, Doberman Pinscher, German Shepherd Dog, and Irish Setter.

Diagnosis is based on symptoms, breed risk, and microscopic examination of a skin sample (biopsy) that shows characteristic changes. Treatment may involve a combination of medications to manage the symptoms, including anti-seborrheic shampoos.

SEBORRHEA

SYMPTOMS: Dandruff; dry, waxy skin; greasy, oily skin; waxy ear discharge; rancid body odor; weeping sores; hair loss over the body
HOME CARE: Medicated shampoos as prescribed by vet
VET CARE: Treat underlying cause; antibiotics; steroid-type drugs to control itching; antiseborrheic shampoos
PREVENTION: Control fleas

SEPARATION ANXIETY This is a common problem with dogs, accounting for 20 to 40 percent of the patients seen by veterinarians. These dogs are anxious and distressed when left alone and become extremely vocal, "forget" house training, and destroy property either as a means to escape confinement or a way to relieve tension. Property destruction is one of the common reasons dogs are put to sleep.

To make up for their dog's upset feelings, owners over-do good-byes, making over the dog extravagantly just before departure. This can accentuate your dog's feeling of abandonment once you leave the house.

Separation anxiety is most commonly seen in dogs that have been abandoned young and then rescued from a shelter, street or lab setting. Pups that leave their mother earlier than eight weeks of age are also more likely to develop the problem. Older dogs may develop separation anxiety when household circumstances drastically change, such as children leaving for college, or a new work schedule that leaves the dog alone more often.

SEPARATION ANXIETY

SYMPTOMS: Cries when you leave; refuses to eat; soils; destroys property; seeks to escape
HOME CARE: Desensitize and counter condition to departures; distract with puzzle toys; pheromone-type products
HOLISTIC HELP: Music therapy; flower essences; massage and TTouch
VET CARE: Antianxiety medications if severe
PREVENTION: None

Separation behaviors encompass a whole range of activities that might take place as a result of the dog being left alone. Animal behaviorists now use different terms to describe the condition because not all dogs become anxious when left alone, although they do act out.

Separation distress doesn't necessarily mean the dog feels anxious and probably is a more accurate description of dogs displaying separation behaviors.

Many times, dogs act out because they're stressed or anxious at the owner's absence. These behaviors may also arise from boredom, and could be compared to a teenager left alone by parents, and throwing a party. About the only way you can tell the difference is to set up a video camera while you are gone, and have it looked at by a behavior expert to see if the dog shows anxious behavior or simply appears to have a good time disemboweling the sofa cushions.

Typical signs include the dog following owners around the house with increasing distress during preparation for departures. When left alone, affected dogs act anxious or distressed, often become extremely vocal and sometimes forget house training. Dogs destroy property out of boredom, or to relieve stress, and sometimes in an attempt to escape the confinement.

The acting out is most intense during the first twenty to thirty minutes after the owner has left, and the length of absence doesn't seem to matter. As with other fearful behaviors, punishment usually makes the problem worse. It gives dogs another reason to fear being left alone.

In the most severe examples, full-blown panic takes over once the owner is gone. This is truly a panic response. The dog isn't acting or thinking rationally and is abnormal during the episodes. Recent research in human panic attacks indicates it's not the event or circumstances that cause continuing or escalating attacks, but the memory of how awful the person felt during the attacks. If similar in dogs, an anti-anxiety drug would help control the condition in dogs, and offer a crucial step in breaking the cycle to teach dogs more appropriate ways to react.

Clomicalm (clomipramine hydrochloride, Novartis Animal Health) has been approved to treat dogs who suffer from separation anxiety. The drug prevents the metabolism of serotonin, a natural hormone produced by the brain that affects behavior. The pet version of Prozac ™ has been released by Eli Lilly under the brand name Reconcile™. The drug fluoxetine has been used in many animal behavior issues: separation anxiety, compulsive chewing, circling, self-mutilation, and even aggression.

Drug therapy isn't a magic wand, however. It merely is a tool to help dogs learn better ways to deal with fear. Programs for separation anxiety are designed to desensitize the dog to the triggers of departure—like rattling keys, picking up the coat, or opening the garage door. Staged absences of one minute, three minutes, five minutes and so on in incremental "doses" help build the dog's tolerance.

Pets should never be punished for any anxiety-based behavior because punishment makes it worse. If you can distract the dog during the critical twenty to thirty minute period right after you leave, much of his upset feelings will be relieved, and destructiveness may be eliminated.

Desensitize the dog to the triggers of departure. Pick up your car keys fifty times—but then don't leave. Put on your coat or open the door a dozen times, then stay inside. Repetition of these cues makes them lose meaning so the dog doesn't get upset, and remains calmer when you actually do leave.

Make sure the dog gets lots of exercise before you leave, and after you return home. A tired pet is a better behaved dog. If he's worn out, he'll snooze rather than chew up the cushions.

Soothing music can also help calm anxiety. Harp music acts like a natural sedative and keeps anxious dogs peaceful (see MUSIC THERAPY). Flower essences such as Rescue Remedy also can help dogs with anxieties. You can add the drops to the puppy's water bowl for all day sipping (see FLOWER ESSENCES). Use TTouch to help reduce the dog's fear. This not only soothes fear at the moment, but can help the dog be more calm and relaxed in the future (see MASSAGE).

You can also offer puzzle toys filled with tasty treats, and hide them around the house for the puppy to find. When he's thinking and hunting for treats, he can't worry or develop a full-blown panic attack.

An extremely fearful dog, especially one who reacts with aggressiveness, may need more help that you can offer. Consult a professional animal behaviorist for advice; some dogs may benefit from antianxiety medications (see FEAR).

When choosing a new puppy, some behaviors may be predictive of separation anxiety in the future. Puppy reactions fall into three broad categories when left alone in a room with toys.

Couldn't care less when owners left or came back perhaps indicating a tendency toward more independent, willful behavior or improper bonding

Super needy who whined and ignored toys when owners left and clung to owners when present, suggesting over attachment predictive of future separation anxiety

Middle of the road paid attention to owners' coming and goings, but not traumatized and enjoyed toys, suggesting a healthy attachment and easygoing personality without need of either firmness or coddling.

Choose the middle of the road pup. These dogs have the best chance for maturing into emotionally healthy canines (see TEMPERAMENT TESTS).

SHEDDING

Shedding refers to the seasonal loss of hair that is a normal function of dog fur. Hair does not grow all the time, but is continuously renewed in a cycle of growth, rest, and loss. New hair pushes out the old resting ones, and this fur loss is called shedding.

Light exposure, either to sun or artificial light, determines the amount and timetable of canine shedding. Environmental temperature has a lesser influence. More hair is shed during the greatest exposure to light, which typically coincides with the summer months. In fact, house dogs under constant exposure to artificial light may shed all year long. Outdoor dogs living in the northeastern United States tend to experience seasonal sheds, with the most fur flying in late spring for the several weeks during which daylight increases.

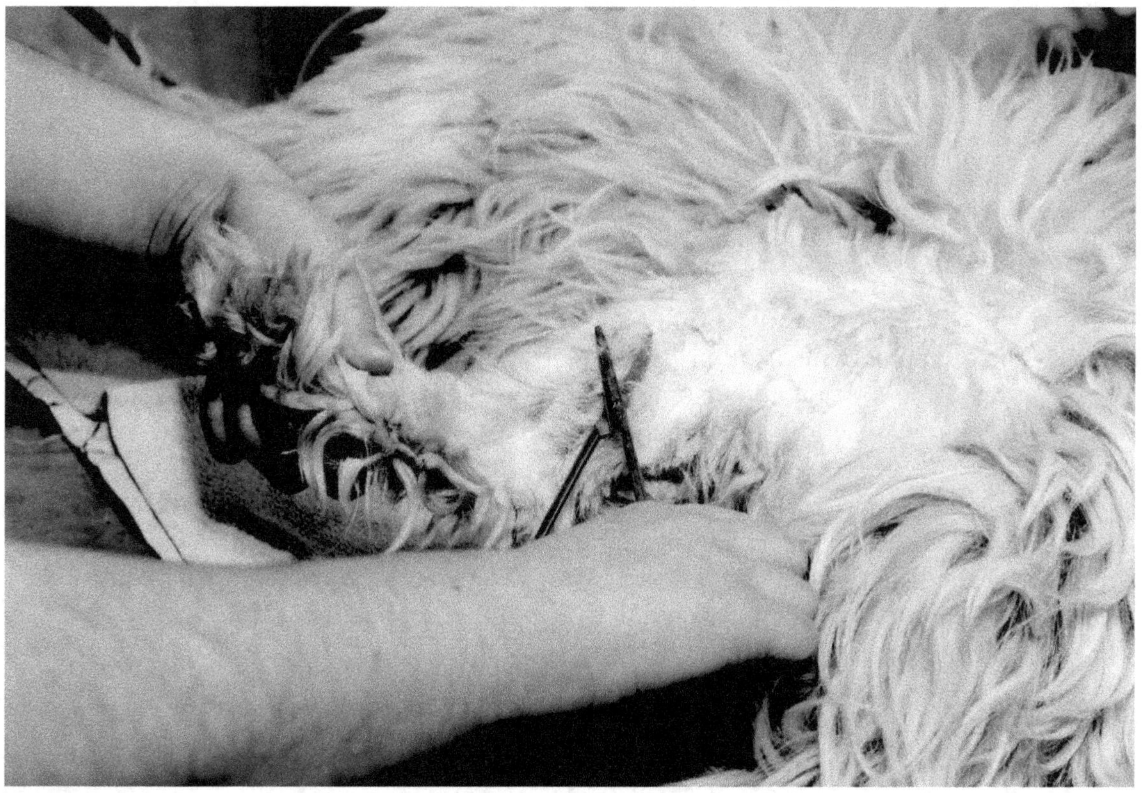

In North America, the furry growing season begins in the early spring, heralded by shedding when the new incoming growth pushes out the old dead hairs. Fur grows unevenly, and is shed in an irregular pattern which leaves double-coated dogs looking decidedly ragged.

The fur continues to grow throughout the summer, then rests during the winter months when the least amount of daylight is present. During this resting phase, fur tends to be most easily pulled out, because the hair root loosens in preparation for the spring shed.

All dogs shed, but some breeds shed more than others. In general, breeds with curly coats like Poodles and Soft-Coated Wheaten Terriers have much longer fur-growing seasons in which hair continuously grows for years at a time; they tend not to lose huge amounts of hair all at once. These "non-shedding" breeds also tend to have curly coats, so that any lost hairs are caught and held in the coat and are not more obviously left on the furniture.

Breeds that have heavy double coats, like German Shepherd Dogs and Chow Chows, are more obvious in their fur loss. The hair reaches a certain length, stops growing, and is shed all at once, with dogs typically leaving clumps of undercoat in their path during seasonal sheds.

Thickly-furred and curly-coated dogs may also suffer from painful mats when shed fur is trapped by fur next to the skin. To help prevent skin problems (see HOT SPOTS), pay particular attention to grooming your dog during shedding season.

SHOCK

Shock is a common condition that results from injury or illness. It is defined as a collapse of the circulatory system often secondary to trauma associated with burns, crushing injuries, or profound dehydration. Common causes of shock include hit-by-car injuries, hyperthermia, severe vomiting or diarrhea, bleeding disorders, and heart disease.

A decrease in blood volume, compromised heart function, or a collapse of the vessels means blood can't adequately be distributed to oxygenate the body; tissues become starved for oxygen. The body attempts to compensate by shutting down normal blood flow to non-vital areas. The compensation mechanism also produces toxic byproducts that further compromise circulation. And as the organs become more and more oxygen starved, they start to fail. This vicious cycle intensifies the shock, and without treatment, the dog will die.

Signs include mental depression or loss of consciousness, body temperature that feels cold to the touch, weakness, shivering, pale gums, shallow rapid breathing, and faint weak pulse. Shock is an emergency that must be treated as soon as possible by the veterinarian.

First aid involves keeping your dog warm and calm as possible. Wrap her in a blanket, and if she's conscious, allow her to find a comfortable position. If she's unconscious, place her head below her body to improve circulation to the brain. Determine whether she's breathing, and pull her tongue clear to keep the airway open.

When the dog has no heartbeat or is not breathing, begin artificial respiration or cardiopulmonary resuscitation. When possible, immobilize obvious fractures, apply pressure to stop copious bleeding, and then get your dog veterinary attention as soon as possible. The ideal treatment is efficiently and quickly rehydrating the dog using intravenous fluids and/or blood transfusions.

SHOCK

SYMPTOMS: Depression; loss of consciousness; below-normal temperature (feels cold to touch); weakness; shivering; pale gums; shallow, rapid breathing; faint, rapid pulse
FIRST AID: Warm dog in blanket; if unconscious, place head lower than body; when not breathing, provide artificial respiration; SEE VET IMMEDIATELY!
VET CARE: Intravenous fluid therapy; other supportive care
PREVENTION: Avoid trauma; treat illness promptly

SINUSITIS

Sinusitis is the inflammation of one or more of the sinus cavities. A sinus is an open area in the skull that communicates with the nasal passage. Human sinusitis typically results from an allergy.

However, the most common cause of acute sinusitis in dogs is a viral infection such as canine distemper or fungal infections. Sometimes a foreign body such as a grass awn may be sniffed up inside the nose and cause inflammation. Dogs may also develop sinusitis secondary to a tooth abscess, or to a tumor.

Signs include a nasal discharge that initially is clear and later becomes thick and cloudy as infection sets in. When the cause is due to systemic disease, both nostrils are affected; foreign bodies or tooth abscesses more typically affect only one side, in which case the dog may paw at that side of his nose. In addition, dogs suffering sinusitis may breathe with the mouth open, or exhibit a "reverse sneeze" in an attempt to clear breathing passages.

Diagnosis is based on physical signs and sometimes X-rays. Treatment attempts to address the underlying cause. Because a runny nose may be a sign of viral infection, a veterinarian's expertise is particularly important in these instances. Symptoms may be relieved by keeping the dog's nose clean using a damp cloth, and by using a vaporizer to open up swollen sinuses. Try running the shower with hot water, then placing your stopped-up dog in the steamy bathroom to help him breathe.

SINUSITIS

SYMPTOMS: Clear nasal discharge that turns thick and cloudy; mouth-breathing (not panting); reverse sneeze
HOME CARE: Keep dog's nose clean; use vaporizer or humidifier (or steamy shower) to help dog breathe
VET CARE: Treat underlying cause
PREVENTION: Vaccinate dog against systemic illnesses

SKIN

The skin is the largest organ of the body, and serves as a protective barrier between the dog and the outside world. Skin insulates the dog from extremes of temperature, controls moisture loss, and shields the body from foreign agents like toxins or bacteria.

Dogs have three primary layers of skin. The outermost is called the epidermis and provides external protection. It contains special pigment-producing cells that color your dog's body and fur, and screens her from the harmful rays of the sun.

The dermis is the middle, thickest layer found immediately beneath the epidermis. The dermis defines the skin's shape, and also contains the elastic connective tissue that gives skin flexibility. The nerves are also found here, along with specialized cells of the immune system. Hair follicles which produce the root of each hair are found in this layer, along with sweat glands. Hair grows from the follicles, and each follicle is adjacent to a pressure-sensitive pad which responds to touch.

The subcutis is the final and innermost layer. It's composed of fat cells and connective tissues which divide the outer surface of the body from the inside open cavities that contain the organs.

SKUNK ENCOUNTERS Curious dogs allowed outdoors in rural areas may stick their noses where they don't belong, and end up on the receiving end of a skunk. The skunk is simply telling the dog to "back off!" the only way it knows how, and consequently sprays its pungent defense on the nosy canine.

A skunked dog needs a bath—usually several baths, in fact. Perseverance is the key to eliminate the odor; a single dunking rarely does the job. A regular pet grooming shampoo may do the trick, but there are other more effective options.

Commercial products available from pet stores are designed to help neutralize skunk odor. A tried and true home remedy is a tomato juice soak; wash the dog first with pet shampoo, towel him dry, then douse him with the juice and let it soak for ten or fifteen minutes. Then rinse him off and suds again with the regular shampoo. Alternate the tomato juice soak with the shampoo bath until he's less pungent. Be aware that tomato juice soaks will dye white dogs pink.

Massengill brand douche is recommended by some professional groomers as an effective odor-absorbing soak. Mix two ounces of the douche to a gallon of water, pour over the washed dog, and let soak for at least fifteen minutes. Then bathe with normal shampoo once more.

You can also use chemistry to neutralize the thiols. Mix one quart of 3 percent hydrogen peroxide with ¼ cup of baking soda, and one teaspoon of pet shampoo (any kind will work). Apply to the pet's wet fur, allow the mix to bubble for three or four minutes, then rinse thoroughly. This recipe, created by chemist Paul Krebaum, works better than anything on the market. You can't buy it, though, because the formula can't be bottled. It explodes if left in a closed container. So if your pet is skunked, mix only one application at a time. Otherwise you'll be cleaning up more than just the pet.

Avoid the problem altogether by preventing skunk encounters. Confine your dog to a fenced yard that's secure against critters, or supervise outdoor excursions. Skunks tend to be nocturnal, so try not to let your dog roam your farm at night. If you have a pet door, investigate those that only allow your dog access so that varmints don't come into your home. These feature a coded collar that "keys" access to the door.

SKUNK ENCOUNTERS

SYMPTOMS: Pungent odor; dog rolling/rubbing against ground, floor or furniture
HOME CARE: Bathe; alternate pet shampoo with commercial product or homemade deodorizer
VET CARE: Same; sometimes ointment to soothe eyes
PREVENTION: Keep dogs indoors at night; supervise outdoor treks; make pet doors inaccessible to wildlife

SNAKEBITE Dogs living in rural areas may encounter snakes in their outdoor exploration. When the dog is too curious, or too hardheaded, to leave a snake alone, she may be bitten.

Most snakes in the United States are not poisonous, and such bites may at most be painful and risk secondary infection. Thick fur helps protect the dog from body injuries, and bites most often occur on the face or neck when the dog tries to catch the snake. A non-poisonous snake bite will leave tiny horseshoe-shaped teeth marks. Clean the wound with soapy warm water, and see a veterinarian if you notice any swelling. An antibiotic is usually sufficient.

There are four poisonous snakes endemic to the United States: copperheads, cottonmouths (water moccasins), and rattlesnakes are pit vipers, and the fourth is the tiny coral snake. Pit vipers have slit-eyed pupils like a cat (compared to round pupils in non-poisonous snakes), pits beneath their eyes, big arrow-shaped heads, rough scales, and a pair of fangs in the upper jaw. The coral snake is recognized by its small black-nosed head, and vivid banded body colored red, yellow, white and black (red and yellow bands are always next to each other).

SNAKEBITE

SYMPTOMS: Profound pain and swelling at bite site; agitation; excessive panting and drooling; weakness; vomiting; diarrhea; collapse; seizures; shock; sometimes paralysis and coma
FIRST AID: EMERGENCY! SEE VET IMMEDIATELY! Apply ice; if help is more than half an hour away, apply a tight bandage between dog's heart and wound (not around neck!) and loosen for five minutes once an hour; keep dog quiet
VET CARE: Supportive care; sometimes antivenin; medications to counter symptoms
PREVENTION: Discourage dog's interest in snakes; supervise outdoor exploration in snake habitat

If you suspect your dog has been bitten by a poisonous snake, kill it if possible and bring it to your veterinarian for positive identification. Get veterinary help immediately, as this is an emergency. Snake bites are diagnosed by identification of the snake, characteristics of the wound, and behavior of the dog.

A poisonous snakebite results in fang marks, and usually rapid and severe swelling of the wound, which is extremely painful. There may be redness or bleeding. The dog's behavior varies depending on the size of the dog and snake, species of snake, and location of the wound. First signs usually include agitation, excessive panting and drooling, and weakness. Vomiting, diarrhea, collapse, seizures, shock, and sometimes paralysis (with coral snake bites), leading to coma and potentially death may follow.

Check for signs of shock, and keep the dog still to reduce the circulation of the poison. Most dogs get bitten on the face or neck so remove the collar to avoid choking when the area swells. Keep the bite below the leave of the heart. Apply a cold pack to the bite to reduce pain and slow the blood circulation. If help is more than a half hour away, wrap a small towel around the leg, then cover with an elastic bandage like an Ace bandage to slow the spread of the poison.

Most dogs that die from snakebite pass away within only an hour or two. Pets that survive that period usually recover, but it can take support and treatment. Usually the vet gives antibiotics and a tetanus shot, and depending on the wound, treatment may go on for several weeks to protect against tissue damage.

SOCIAL STRUCTURE

The social structure of dogs is similar to people but there are enough differences that cause confusion. Human social system is based on a "group" mentality and held together by vocal communication. Dog ancestors—wolves—evolved to live in social groups, too, but dogs are not wolves and mistakes are made when we think of them in terms of their ancestors. Also, dog communication relies on a combination of vocalizations, and silent communication through body posture and scent signals. Each system works well for that particular group, but when you put the two together, there are bound to be misunderstandings.

To understand dog culture, you must first take a close look at the human equivalent to see how different they are. Social groups provide a greater benefit than one individual could get by themselves. Early people banded together to hunt and bring down big game that one person couldn't tackle alone. They built communities for safety, raised children together, and shared responsibility. Working together offered great rewards in terms of food, safety, and companionship.

In order to work together, people needed to communicate. When disputes arose, people created ways to settle arguments so that the group didn't suffer and fall apart.

In broad terms, human society chooses a leader to arbitrate decisions for the entire group and settles disputes. The followers who bow to the leader's wise council benefit from this situation by gaining the protection of the group. When the leader is absent, a second in command takes over until the boss returns.

A modern-day example happens every day when you report to work. A boss makes the decisions for you and your co-workers. When you follow the rules (i.e., do your job correctly), you receive your colleague's approval and respect, the boss' loyalty, and a paycheck reward. Well, that's the way it's supposed to work, anyway.

In communal animal societies, a single wolf can't easily bring down a deer, but the pack can. The group also offers better protection. Individuals take turns guarding their territory and den, and communally raise the young. A wolf cub that follows the rules gets to eat with the group, and has earned their affection and loyalty and protection.

Social groups are individuals that come together for a common purpose. The ancestors of dogs survived by forming packs that hunted together, communally protected young, and defended territory from outsiders. But as numbers of any group increase, so does the potential for conflict. Understanding each other as well as having a system to resolve conflict is essential if the group is to survive.

Therefore, your dog's social system is based on rules of behavior, a kind of canine etiquette that all dogs understand and obey. To be efficient and harmonious, the doggy social structure depends on a hierarchy of dominant and subordinate individuals. Social ranking decides which dogs get the preferred or prime access to valued resources: resting spots, food pans, water, toys, bones, your attention, and so on. However, dominance has nothing to do with bullying or aggression, nor does submission necessarily correlate with fear or shyness. In years' past, much has been made of the "canine alpha" dominance hierarchy of dogs, whereas today behaviorists describe it as a subordinance hierarchy.

Relentless, active appeasement and deference of subordinate animals allows for harmony in social groups. The canine communication often described as submissive behavior could more accurately be translated as signaling *non-contest*, or *let me be your friend*.

Dog society consists of a linear hierarchy, often with both a male hierarchy and a female hierarchy. Males tend to be more territorial about space (the yard and house), while females are more likely to be territorial about toys, food, and other belongings.

This happens from puppyhood on, with a "top dog" and "bottom dog" usually established in a litter by eight weeks of age. Boys are usually bigger than girls, so the male often is the top dog. The top and bottom pups (and adult dogs) have the easiest time dealing with canine society since everyone is either above or below them, so they know how to act and react.

Middle pups have a harder time establishing rank and won't have a firm sense of social position until about three months or so, when rank usually correlates pretty strongly with sex and weight. But in non-related pups of different ages, once they all socialize to each other, the most important determinant of rank is age and sex. Pups that grow up with other dogs quickly learn that exaggerated appeasement gestures can cut short the harassment with a preemptive apology characterized by a low-slung, wriggly approach with ears back, a submissive grin, and tail and hindquarters wagging.

Older males usually rank higher, and size/strength help determine ranking as pups grow. Once they've grown up, though, and take their places within an already established adult hierarchy, there may be no correlation between rank and weight. Among adult male dogs, an individual's relative rank decides nearly everything in advance, such as who gets the toy, where dogs sleep, and which one gets to greet the owner first. Relationship between males and females can vary from day to day.

Girl dogs have a linear but less rigid hierarchy, with day-to-day success depending on the individual circumstances. The top bitch always gets the preferred toy or treat first, and if she's not there, the second-ranking bitch likely will score the trophy. However, the girls seem to respect ownership a bit more than the boys. While the highest ranking male might challenge a subordinate and take away his bone, the highest ranking female often allows a lower-ranking girl to enjoy the treat when it's already in her possession—dogs signaling possession by keeping a paw or two on the toy or just looking at it. And while a subordinate boy dog typically gives up the bone if a higher-ranking male tells him to, a lower-ranking girl may defend her ownership of the goodies. Think of this as a sort of "finders/keepers" mentality. Once a dog relinquishes possession, though, any lower-ranking dog of either gender can have at it with impunity.

Maintaining the existing social structure relies on the lowest-ranking dogs to express respect for the dogs of higher rank. The major function of the hierarchical structure is to lessen the need for fighting. For example, if two dogs see one toy, but the "owner" is predetermined by rank, there's no need to fight. Fights or noisy disputes are rare because top dogs have no reason to fight, and low-ranking dogs know they'd be foolish to try. Excess growling and repeat fighting are symptoms of insecurity and uncertainty about social rank compared to other dogs, and are the hallmark of middle-ranking males.

How do dogs decide who will be the boss, and who will be the follower in a particular territory? There are several factors that influence positions. There are exceptions to these rules, but basically four categories decide the status of a dog.

Sexual status plays a major role in the canine community. Dogs that have not been spayed or neutered typically rank higher than sterilized ones. The Mom-dog with puppies has the most power of all. Neutering all the dogs helps level the playing field, and eliminates the potential for many squabbles.

Personality impacts the way the puppy perceives herself, the world around her, and other pets. Every puppy is an individual and early socialization—exposing puppies to positive experiences during their formative weeks of life—will prevent many dog hierarchy disputes later in life.

Shy insecure puppies may feel the need to squabble to keep "danger" away out of fear. Brash in-your-face youngsters are more likely to become problem dogs because they like to pester even the boss-dogs, or may not be satisfied with a lower-ranking position. Confident puppies, those with the middle-of-the-road calm personalities, seem destined for leadership and handle it well.

Age defines who rules to a great extent. Puppies almost always bow to the rule of adult dogs. A mature dog usually will be dominant over an elderly pooch.

Health status throws out everything else. A sick dog loses any status she has, and becomes subordinate to healthy ones. Even a young puppy may bully a sickly elder-statesman dog.

Most dogs get along very well together especially when all are spayed and neutered and they have been properly introduced. Puppies raised in litters of four or more and that remain together until they are 12 to 16 weeks old usually get along best with other dogs.

SOCIALIZATION To be good pets, dogs require early-age socialization. That's a fancy way of describing how they learn to interact in a positive way with the world around them.

Dogs can be trained at any age, and continue to learn throughout their lives. But the prime socialization period is a narrow window during babyhood when learning the "wrong" lessons can emotionally cripple the puppy. Dogs not exposed to positive experiences with humans, other pets, important places and situations during this period may become fearful and bite out of fright.

Proper socialization develops canine social and communication skills. Socialization also teaches puppies what's safe, normal and acceptable. Anything the puppy doesn't learn about during socialization could potentially be considered dangerous, to be feared or even attacked.

Puppies are most receptive during a six-to-eight week window, but your dog benefits from socialization exercises for the first year. During the early weeks, mother animals teach many lessons by example. For instance, if Mom-Dog becomes hysterical around men, her pups pay attention and copy her behavior.

People raising litters must begin positive lessons before the babies go to new homes. Consider this kindergarten for pups. Youngsters have an increased capacity for learning when they're young, so it's helpful for new owners to continue these lessons after adopting a pup. Even after your little guy becomes a grown-up dog, regular practice sessions help remind him that the mailman is actually a good guy even if he wears a funny hat.

How do you create kindergarten for pups? Create a checklist of all the experiences your puppy will face during the first several months living with you. And then systematically introduce her to each situation, while associating it with fun benefits for the puppy. For example, handle her paws to help her learn to accept nail trims. Ring the doorbell, and offer a squeaky toy so she associates the sound and guests with rewards. Here are 10 broad categories of situations you can expect your new puppy to deal with.

1. Handling the puppy's paws, ears, mouth, eyes, and tail simply feels good. It's also a great way to prepare your pup to calmly accept exams.

2. Owner's homes are different so add your specifics to the list. In most cases, puppies will live with occasional delivery or repair people entering the house, the phone and doorbell ringing, guests and strangers arriving, sweeping/mopping/vacuuming, the noise of the washer/dryer and dishwasher, and loud TV shows or music.

3. People come in different ages, genders, and ethnicities. Puppies won't necessarily accept all humans in the same way. Those raised in shelters by only women need help accepting men. Children—especially babies and toddlers—look, smell, sound and move differently.

4. What people wear, carry or how they move also changes a puppy's perceptions, so socialize the baby to uniforms, raincoats, hats, sunglasses, bearded men and even people shaved heads, or strong perfume if that's appropriate. What people carry or how they move also can surprise and frighten pups. Those destined for therapy work especially benefit from being socialized to people using canes, crutches, legs in cast, walkers, wheelchairs, baby carriages, back packs, or erratic body movement. Don't neglect athletes and their equipment, including joggers, skate boarders, bicyclists, tricycles, or roller bladers.

5. Animals also can frighten, intrigue, or prompt attacks. Even if your puppy will be an only pet, it's important to socialize him to other puppies and adult dogs, kittens and cats especially if he'll be living with them. Do you live in the country? Socialize to the livestock so you won't have a pestering pup chasing the cows or chickens.

6. Vehicles either enrapture or terrify dogs. Your pup will need to make trips in the car but don't neglect other experiences. Let him get used to trucks backing up, garbage trucks, motorcycles, or any other vehicle he might encounter.

7. Noises and weather can upset many pups. You can counteract much of this with socialization. Associate sirens, thunder/lightening, snow blowers, snow, rain, fireworks, people yelling and other unexpected noises with a favorite treat, toy, or attention.

8. Yard equipment can be scary, too. Pups not used to a garden rake might think you plan to hit with the stick. Get your baby used to shovels, the garden hose, sweeping with broom, wheelbarrows, lawn mowers or other yard equipment.

9. New surfaces can seem scary if a pup has never before seen ice, for instance. Dogs raised in kennels may not know how to pee on grass, or act frightened of dirt or gravel. Be sure your pup has practice walking on all kinds of surfaces including cement, sand, wooden decks, carpet, and learns how to climb up and down stairs.

10. Environments come in all shapes and sizes. Each new place could potentially be scary, so take your time but be sure your pup has experience with the important ones. That may include car rides, the vet clinic, boarding kennel, groomers, gas station, the bank, friend's homes, pet supply store, school grounds, car wash, walks after dark, crossing a bridge or busy intersection, drive-thru, crowd of people, the beach, hiking trails, or the office.

SOILING Soiling is a break in housetraining in which the dog eliminates inappropriately in the house. In some instances, the accidents are simply due to inadequate potty training, which a refresher should cure (see HOUSE TRAINING).

However, dogs that suddenly begin leaving puddles or piles about the house may have an underlying health problem. Inappropriate urination may signal problems like cystitis, diabetes mellitus, kidney disease or urinary tract problems like bladder stones or obstruction. Loss of bowel control is associated with diarrhea which can be a sign of dangerous viral infection like canine parvovirus or distemper, or simply result from raiding the garbage. Elderly dogs may lose control due to age-related problems (see GERIATRIC DOG). Check with your veterinarian to rule out a medical cause.

Soiling is often confused with territorial marking, which is a dominance display usually of intact male dogs. Stress may prompt increased marking behavior. Changes such as the addition of a pet, moving to a new home, or a change in the owner's work schedule may exacerbate the problem. Stress-related marking is a way for the dog to try to bring his world back under control.

Accidents in the house, if not adequately cleaned, can inspire a return to the scene of the crime and repeat offense. Clean soiled areas with a commercial product designed for that purpose. Avoid ammonia-containing cleaners, which tend to intensify the smell of urine.

Be sure to thoroughly clean soiled areas of carpet with a commercial product designed for that purpose. If the scent is not eliminated, the dog may return to the scene of the crime and repeat the offense. Urine soaked into carpet proves particularly difficult to remove. With fresh accidents, pick up the solids and blot up as much liquid as possible. Avoid using ammonia-based cleaning products. Since urine has ammonia in it, such products may mimic the smell and make the area even more attractive as a potty spot.

Once urine dries on carpet or walls your dog's "pee-mail" notes are even more difficult to locate and clean. Turn off all your lights and shine a high-quality black light on suspect areas—that makes urine glow in the dark. Don't forget to check vertical areas marking cats like to target (see MARKING). The best products don't just clean the area or cover up with perfumes, but actually neutralize the chemicals that smell bad.

Urine is composed of sticky urea, urochrome (the yellow color), and uric acid. The first two can be washed away, but uric acid is nearly impossible to dissolve and remove from surfaces. That's why successful products not only clean away the urea and urochrome, they also neutralize the uric acid with enzymes or encapsulate the urine molecules to contain the odor.

Some targets, like your bedspread, benefit from being washed with the product in your washing machine. When the odor cannot be removed, it's best to discard the item if possible rather than fight the dog's instinctive urge to re-baptize the spot.

Dogs dislike eliminating in the same area where they eat, so moving a bowl of food to a canine target area may help dissuade him. Some dogs prefer privacy, and refuse to do their duty when under scrutiny, instead hiding their deposits beneath the piano when you're not looking. A pet door that allows the dog access to a fenced back yard may be the answer for some dogs, particularly if he's having trouble containing himself for scheduled bathroom breaks. It may be necessary to confine the dog when you can't watch his every move. Some hard case dogs will need days to weeks of convincing before they'll become reliable (also see INCONTINENCE).

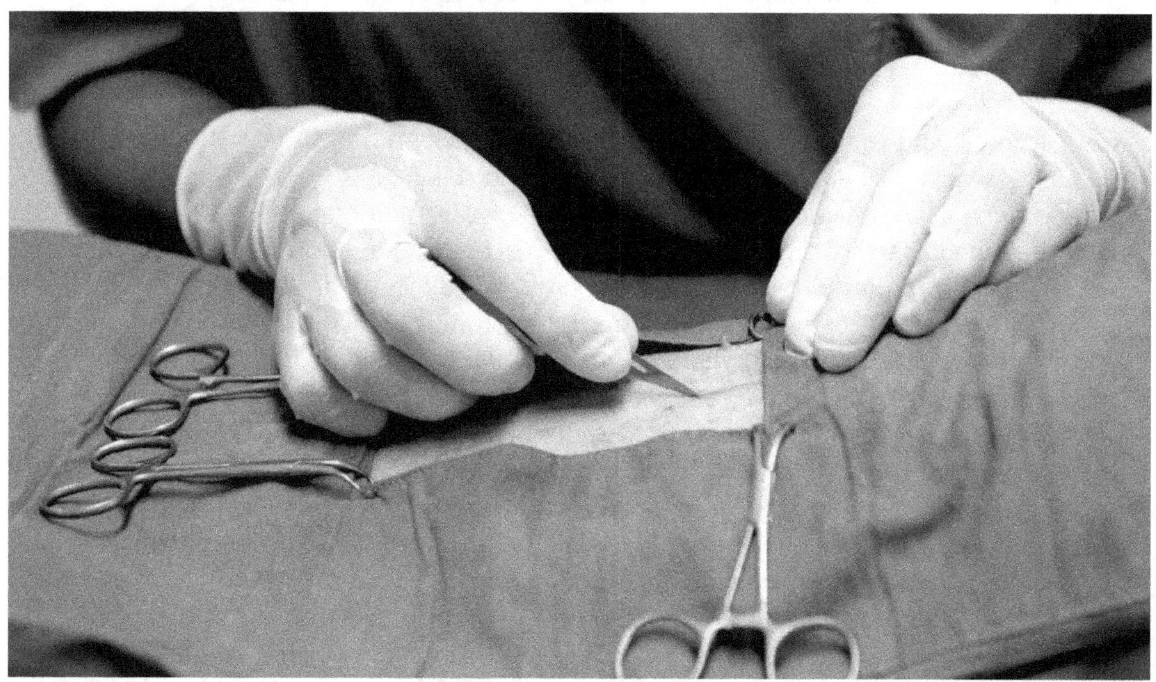

SPAYING

Spaying is the surgical sterilization (ovariohysterectomy) of a female dog in which her uterus and ovaries are removed. This prevents the births of unwanted puppies, and eliminates or reduces the chances of health problems like pyometra and mammary cancer. It also curtails obnoxious heat-related behaviors. When she's in season, your dog's bloody vaginal discharge may stain your carpet and furniture. Spaying also curbs the attentions of doggy Romeos who tend to stake out your front yard.

To gain the greatest benefits, dogs should be spayed before reaching sexual maturity. Individual dogs and breeds mature at different rates, but most are able to become pregnant by six months of age. The American Veterinary Medical Association (AVMA) currently recommends that pet dogs be spayed at four months of age.

It's better to perform the surgery when your dog is not in heat; during estrus, the uterus becomes engorged with blood, and this slightly increases the risk of bleeding. And if accidentally bred, she can still be spayed within about two weeks of pregnancy without increased risk. However, most veterinarians prefer waiting until the mother dog has stopped nursing before spaying, because the milk may interfere with healing of the incision line. Consult with your veterinarian to determine the best schedule for your dog.

The ovariohysterectomy is performed while the dog is under general anesthesia. In most cases, veterinarians recommend you withhold food and water from your dog for a period prior to surgery so the dog's stomach is empty; this reduces the risk of inhaling vomit while she's asleep. Should your dog sneak an unauthorized snack prior to surgery, be sure to inform the veterinarian so that appropriate precautions can be taken.

A variety of anesthetics may be used, alone or in combination. Many times, pre-anesthetic blood analysis is performed to help determine the best anesthetic for a particular dog. The spay procedure is major abdominal surgery and takes a bit longer than castrating a male dog. Often, an injectable sedative is first given, followed by inhalant anesthesia usually administered by an endotracheal tube inserted into the mouth, down the throat and into the lungs. Some practices may use a mask that fits over the dog's face to administer the anesthesia. Inhaled anesthesia is preferred, because the dosage can be adjusted during surgery, and the dog awakens quickly after the anesthesia is stopped.

The sleeping dog is placed on a towel or heating pad to keep her warm during the procedure, then positioned on her back. Her tummy is shaved and disinfected with antiseptic soap solutions to keep the surgical field sterile. For some dogs, respiratory and cardiac monitors may be used.

A small slit in a sterile paper or cloth drape is positioned over the prepared abdomen. Surgery is performed through this shielding drape, which helps keep fur out of the way and the incision sterile.

The surgeon makes an incision in the skin of the dog's tummy, usually just below the belly button and along the midline. Depending on the size of the dog, the incision is an inch to two inches long. The veterinarian uses a scalpel to first incise the skin, then a thin layer of fat, and finally the abdominal wall. Special instruments hold the incision open so the surgeon can see into the abdomen.

The canine uterus is shaped like a "Y" with an ovary attached to the top of each "horn." An ovarian artery, vein and nerve are attached to each ovary. The spay hook, a long smooth metal instrument with a crook on the end, is inserted into the abdomen to retrieve the uterus.

The ovarian ligament that attaches ovaries to the wall of the abdomen is detached to allow ovaries and uterine horns to be brought further out.

Each ovary is ligated, or tied off, with absorbable suture or secured with stainless steel hemoclips to prevent bleeding, and cut free. The stumps containing the artery, vein and nerve recede into the abdomen.

Finally, the uterus is ligated just beyond the cervix, then cut free. The uterus and ovaries are discarded. Once the surgeon ensures there is no bleeding, the uterine stump is allowed to fall back into the abdomen.

The dog's abdomen is stitched closed in three layers, using absorbable suture material or even metal sutures or staples for the internal layers. The surface skin is the last layer stitched closed, using a curved needle and placing individual loops that are separately knotted. A routine spay is completed in about 25 to 45 minutes, depending on the size of the dog and other factors.

The type of anesthesia influences how quickly the dog will awaken. Usually, the dog is moved from the surgery table to a recovery area, and she is kept warm and monitored as she recovers. Typically, the drugs cause drunken behavior until they fully leave the body; your dog may not be steady on her feet for several hours. Sometimes, the dog is kept overnight while other times she's sent home the same afternoon. The veterinarian may prescribe medication for pain.

Dogs generally don't interfere with their stitches, but always keep an eye on the incision to be sure your dog isn't a problem licker. Fitting the dog with a collar restraint will prevent any damage (see ELIZABETHAN COLLAR).

Limit your dog's activities for the first two or three days following the procedure. Stitches are removed in a week to ten days after the surgery, and outdoor dogs should be confined indoors and not allowed to sleep in the dirt or grass until after the stitches are out.

Complications resulting from a spay procedure are rare. Occasionally, dogs develop nominal puffiness or redness at the incision site. See your veterinarian if there's bleeding or severe swelling, or if your dog acts depressed or refuses to eat for more than 24 hours.

STRAY

STRAY A stray refers to an owned dog separated from his home who must fend for himself. Stray dogs that have experienced kindness from former owners may seek out people. But those that have been mistreated, or are suffering from illness, injury or emotional trauma often exhibit extreme shyness.

Dogs may stray when allowed to roam unattended. In particular, hunting breeds like Beagles may become carried away by the chase, and inadvertently become lost. Other times, a dog may leap from a car, or escape a confined yard and wander away. A few dogs may be able to find their way home (see NAVIGATION).

Unfortunately, some strays are purposefully created by owner abandonment. Perhaps the dog has outgrown the cute "puppy stage," or the owner must move and is unable to take the dog along. Some people mistakenly believe that such dogs have a better chance on their own than if they're relinquished to a shelter. However, the vast majority of dogs aren't able to survive for long on the streets. Strays are at high risk for disease and injury from other animals and lethal encounters with traffic.

Although a large percentage of cats are adopted off the street as strays, dogs for the most part tend to be "chosen" from local animal welfare agencies, friends, or reputable breeders. A stray dog can become an excellent pet; the reality is, however, that few do.

Should you undertake the rewarding goal of rehabilitating a stray dog, be aware that he may exhibit aggression, aloofness, or even fearful behavior. If you already have pets, the resident animals' health and feelings must be addressed by providing safe quarantine and proper introductions. Strays that are ill or injured will need special veterinary attention.

Finding a stray should first prompt you to try to find his owner. Friendly strays are the easiest to help, but remember that you don't really know the dog, so be cautious. Look for a collar, tags, or other identification. Decide what you'll do with this furry waif; relinquish him to a shelter, temporarily hold him until you find his old owner or a new one, or adopt him yourself.

FINDING LOST DOGS or STRAY'S OWNER

- **Monitor** local lost-and-found advertisements for not less than a month
- **Contact** area shelters and give them a description of the dog; provide shelters with a photo of the dog
- **Distribute** posters about the dog around the neighborhood (with or without photo)
- **Check** veterinary offices, pet stores, the post office, and community bulletin boards for "lost" notices; leave a "found" notice on each

Shelters may be public or private, but all are essentially warehouses for unwanted pets. They do their best with limited funds to help animals in their care. When the stray is wearing identification, it is held until every effort to find the owner is exhausted. Pets without identification are kept only a day or two, and if not adopted, they are put to sleep, a sad end, but better than a slow death on the street.

Your other choice mean you assume responsibility for the stray's life. The dog should first be evaluated by a veterinarian.

A friendly, healthy stray indicates only recent separation from owners. Advertise your find in the local paper and at the shelter, which are the first places an owner should look for a lost dog. If after diligent search his owner can't be found, seek an adoptive home by advertising his availability in the same places. Promote his handsome looks and affectionate nature, and include he's a healthy neutered animal. Ask friends for names of people who may want a dog.

Don't give him to just anyone; interview prospective owners with pointed questions. You don't want him to be abandoned again, so seek a responsible, loving—and permanent—home for your adoptee. Chances are you will fall in love with the stray before a new owner can be found, and will decide to keep him yourself.

STRESS Stress is a negative emotional state that physically and/or mentally impacts the health of the dog. Dogs most commonly suffer stress as a result of change to the dynamics of their social group, especially as it relates to the owner.

Introduction of a new family member like a pet, baby or spouse, or conversely, the loss of a close family member, often results in stress. Change in work habits that alter the amount or quality of the time spent with the dog is also a common stress inducer. Dogs in overcrowded conditions such as kennels, or with compromised health are subject to stress-related behaviors. Even a stray dog in the neighborhood or moving to a new home may cause stress to some dogs.

The most common signs of stress in dogs are increased behavior problems, such as leg-lifting in the house (see MARKING) or inappropriate elimination. Dogs may demand more attention, whine and stay underfoot, or destroy a loved one's property like shoes or a purse just to feel closer to that person. Separation anxiety may lead the dog to refuse food when the owner is gone any length of time. Stress and insecurity may also result in aggressive behaviors toward other pets or the owner, while submissive dogs may hide.

Stress-related behavior problems are best resolved by identifying and eliminating the cause, when possible. Play therapy is also a great stress-reliever, and offers aggressive dogs an outlet and helps build the shy dog's self-confidence. Interactive games are best, such as fetch and tug-of-war games.

A small percentage of dogs suffering psychological stress react by excessively licking themselves, which can result in hair loss. Excessive licking, biting and pulling at the fur can become a habit and even lead to self-mutilation if the stressful conditions are not addressed. Dogs may worry an isolated area, and cause an ongoing sore usually on one leg, the flank or feet (see LICK SORE).

Removing the cause of the stress is helpful, but often these behaviors develop into habits that are hard to break. Veterinary diagnosis followed by antianxiety drug therapy and/or a behaviorist's intervention is probably necessary to break the cycle.

STROKE A cerebral vascular accident, called a "stroke" in humans, is a disorder of the blood vessels in the cerebrum (front part of the brain) as a result of an impaired blood supply. Common causes of stroke in people include smoking, primary high blood pressure, and atherosclerosis, which are deposits of cholesterol-rich plaques within the arteries. Strokes are not as common in animals because pets don't have those diseases.

Dogs develop plaque from thyroid changes or blood clots from endocrine diseases, and develop vascular changes. As a result, quite a few dogs suffer strokes. The good news is the brain doesn't really feel pain the way that the rest of the body does. So a stroke isn't painful or progressive, and can resolve over time.

STROKE

SYMPTOMS: Seizure; depression; circling and/or dizziness; incoordination; behavior change.
HOME CARE: Soften food; provide nursing care
VET CARE: None
PREVENTION: None

In most cases, a cerebral vascular accident in dogs is associated with hypertension (high blood pressure) as a result of kidney failure, infectious disease, or inflammation of the heart (endocarditis). Endocrine diseases (see CUSHING'S DISEASE and HYPOTHYROIDISM) seem to allow predispositions for vascular accident, but many times an underlying cause can't be found.

Diagnosis can be difficult. Even with an MRI (magnetic resonance imaging), the changes caused by the brain damage may be hard to see. Treatment is aimed at supporting the dog and giving him time to recover. If there's an underlying cause, the disease is also treated. If the dog has hypertension, you want to get that under control. When heart disease, endocrine disorders or other conditions are at the root, the veterinarian may consult with a specialist.

Dogs tend to recover more easily from strokes than people do. Some very badly affected animals walk out of the hospital. That may be because dogs don't feel sorry for themselves, they don't have to drive a car, they don't have to sit down and play piano, they just have to be a pet. Dogs are very good at compensating. If they have a weakness in one or more legs, they adjust and walk more slowly or carefully on stairs, for example.

Also, dogs are much more dependent on their brain stem for their strength and function than people. If they have a stroke in the forebrain they may initially be very weak, but they'll usually get up and get going again with only a few subtle deficits. They're not going to be paralyzed on one side like the human.

The aftermath of a stroke may leave your dog very weak, confused, or unable to walk. Recovery time varies, depending on the severity of the damage. But in almost all cases, dogs slowly improve. In the meantime, you may need to offer extra TLC.

Soften food or hand feed, and carry him to the outdoor "facilities" or provide absorbent pads in his bed to help deal with accidents. Rehabilitation exercises may help strengthen weak muscles. Medicate as indicated to deal with underlying diseases.

STUD The term stud refers to an intact male dog used in arranged breedings to sire, or father, exceptional puppies. A stud dog is generally considered by professional breeders to be of outstanding conformation and quality for his particular breed. Stud dogs are used in the hope that puppies they father will inherited these fine qualities.

SUBMISSION Submission is ritualized behavior that communicates deference to another individual. Low-ranking dogs within a social group are submissive and give way to the more forceful personalities within the family (see DOMINANCE and SOCIAL STRUCTURE).

The canine social system is based on a stair step ranking of individuals, with the most dominant at the top and lesser ranking individuals below. Submissive dogs yield to those in power, be that another dog or pet, or the owner. However, submission is not necessarily expressed as fear, but is more a matter of compliance to those that are perceived to be in authority.

Submissive behavior is expressed in a variety of ways (see COMMUNICATION). Submissive dogs avert their eyes from a dominant dog or owner. They may whine, whimper or yelp, or offer a distinctive doggy grin as a way to appease a more dominant individual. Such vocalizations, as well as licking of the owner's hands or face, or raising a paw, may be directed at a dominant individual to solicit attention, food, or to go in or out. Wide, loose wags of the tail that include the whole body are characteristic of a submissive dog.

A submissive dog both figuratively and literally assumes a low position. He crouches humbly before his superiors, and wags his tail in a low position—even his tail is tucked tightly between the legs—and looks almost apologetic. The ultimate sign of submission is rolling onto the back to expose the throat and belly. The submissive dog will urinate in a crouched position, or while on his back to show his deference.

A submissive dog isn't necessarily tiny, either. A Great Dane may be dominated by an assertive Chihuahua or child. In fact, it's important that within the household the human owner be the most dominant member of the family.

In its best sense, the submissive dog is one that is biddable—that is, willing to follow the directions of, and please the owner. These are the dogs that are most easily trained, and are the best choice for most pet owners (see COMMUNICATION, DOMINANCE, FEAR, INTRODUCTIONS, SOCIAL STRUCTURE and TRAINING).

SUBMISSIVE URINATION

Dogs urinate submissively in an effort to diffuse a threat. Puppies use submissive urination to show deference to older dogs, other pets, and humans they respect.

This should not be confused with a potty training or marking behavior (see HOUSE TRAINING). In youngsters, this normal behavior is a reflexive action to cry "uncle" and declare they are no threat.

That's why raising your voice or physical correction will not stop submissive urination. It will instead escalates this problem; the dog urinates even more to try to block the growing threat of your displeasure.

Most puppies outgrow the behavior and very submissive adult dogs can be taught new ways to declare their undying devotion and deference. It's counter-intuitive, but the best way to stop submissive wetting is to ignore the behavior.

Puppies usually outgrow the wetting behavior, but some very submissive dogs continue as adults. Any actions on your part that communicate you being in charge—yelling, shaming, touching, or even making eye contact—communicates to your dog that he's not yet submissive enough. In dog body language, the top dog put a paw across the puppy's shoulders, or leans his chin across the baby dog's neck to show they're in charge. When you pat your dog on the head, that's sending a similar message.

Instead, teach him better control and more confidence so he doesn't feel the urge to wet. The best way to do this is to ignore the behavior, and simply mop up the mess as you avoid eye contact. Try a softer, gentler voice. Avoid baby talk, and be matter of fact.

Sometimes confident people and especially men with low voices sound gruff without meaning to and that can turn on the puppy pee-works. Rather than standing still and "looming" over the dog, back away while you ask him to COME and then SIT. Keep backing

up, ignore the "wet" sits, and gently praise and offer food rewards for dry sits so your dog learns that NOT wetting prompts the payday.

Or simply walk away when the dog begins to urinate submissively. The behavior is most often triggered during home-comings, so refrain from greeting the dog right away, or direct the dog to a contradictory action—send the dog to find a toy, for example. Do this consistently; clean up any mess in a moment or two after the situation has diffused. The dog will soon learn that urinating results in an absence of attention, and controlling himself prompts positive owner attention (see PUPPY).

SUNBURN

SYMPTOMS: Redness, crusting of ears or nose; hair loss; itchiness
FIRST AID: Apply cool, damp cloth; mist burns with water; apply moisturizing cream
HOLISTIC HELP: Herbal treatments; supplements
VET CARE: Topical steroid preparations; sometimes amputation of damaged skin
PREVENTION: Keep dogs inside during prime sunburn hours; protect white or sparsely furred dogs; apply SPF 15 or higher-rated sunscreen to ears and nose of at-risk dogs

SUNBURN Sunburn refers to an inflammation of the skin caused by exposure to the sun's radiation. Certain breeds are more prone to a condition in the past called solar nasal dermatitis (see SYSTEMIC LUPUS ERYTHEMATOSUS).

Sunburn most commonly affects short haired white or light-colored dogs, especially on the sparsely furred bridge of the nose and tips of the ears. White Bull Terriers and Dalmatians seem particularly prone, and dogs that enjoy lying on their backs risk sun burning their tummies. But any dog that is clipped close for summer loses furry protection, and can suffer a painful burn. Pets living in particularly sunny regions, or in the mountains at higher elevations tend to burn more quickly.

The first signs are redness that leads to hair loss in the affected areas, followed by crustiness and itching. In some cases, the ear margins may curl and turn brittle. The problem tends to go away during cool weather, and returns in sunny summer months. Sunburn is painful for your dog, and can lead to disfiguring loss of tissue, or even sun-induce cancer.

Prevent sunburn by restricting your dog's outside activities during the most dangerous hours of the day—from 10:00 a.m. to 4:00 p.m. When she must endure the sun, apply topical sunscreens containing PABA and a high sun protector factor (SPF) of 15 or higher. Your veterinarian may provide steroid creams or pills to control the inflammation of existing burns. Aloe vera or jojoba moisturizing creams are helpful to rehydrate the area, and a cool, damp cloth applied two or three times a day will help soothe the burn.

SWALLOWED OBJECTS Dogs are incredibly mouth-oriented creatures, designed to use their jaws and teeth the way people use hands. Dogs explore their world in the same way small children and infants do, by putting everything in their mouths. They stick their pointy or pushed-in noses into everything, and bite, chew and taste to learn about it. Just about anything that doesn't move faster than the dog is fair game. Consequently, they often swallow inedible objects.

Eating non-edible stuff is called pica. Dogs often accidentally swallow pieces of toys, but pica refers to almost an obsessive urge to eat rocks or gulp mouthfuls of dirt, sticks, sand or other nondigestible objects.

Eating non-edible objects can become tempting when the object is flavored or scented and becomes irresistible. Common problem objects include grease-covered items from the kitchen, milky baby bottle nipples, and used tampons or soiled diapers. Most items tend to smell like you—such as worn socks—so keeping these items out of mouth-reach is important.

Some dogs seem to be drawn to dirt, or even want to chew rocks. Wild animals occasionally target soils such as clay that absorb toxins. Parrots in the wild eat mineral-rich dirt to supplement their diet. We don't know if that's behind the urge, but probably the smell plays a role in the attraction, especially if some other critter has urine-marked the area. Dogs may taste the dirt to better understand what the message says.

Whole toys or parts of toys, jewelry, coins, pins, erasers, and paper clips are often swallowed. String, thread (with or without the needle), fishing hooks and lines, Christmas tree tinsel, and yarn are extremely dangerous. And for dogs able to crunch up the object, pieces of wood or bone prove hazardous. Dogs may even eat rocks.

SWALLOWED OBJECTS

SYMPTOMS: Pawing at mouth; choking or gagging; vomiting; diarrhea; swollen stomach; painful abdomen (hunched posture); constipation
FIRST AID: If possible, remove small objects caught in mouth; DON'T PULL STRING ITEMS, which risk killing the dog; see vet for evaluation if object is not removable or if blockage continues
VET CARE: X-rays; endoscopy; surgery to remove object
PREVENTION: Supervise play with toys; keep swallowable objects dot of reach; DON'T GIVE DOG SWALLOWABLE BONES!

Objects small enough may pass through the digestive system and be eliminated with the feces and cause no problems. If the item was swallowed within two hours it's probably still in the stomach. If the object isn't sharp, feed your pet a small meal first. Dogs vomit more easily if the stomach is full. Give your dog one to two teaspoons of 3 percent hydrogen peroxide for every pound he weighs. You can repeat in five minutes if it doesn't work. If he won't vomit, you'll need to see a veterinarian. For sharp objects go to the vet immediately. It could cause as much damage coming back up if the puppy vomits.

After two hours, the object will have passed into the intestines and vomiting won't help. Most objects small enough to pass through the digestive system may be eliminated with the feces and cause no problems. Feed a bulky meal of dry food to cushion stones or other heavy objects, and help them move on out. Food also turns on the digestive juices, which can help soften wads of rawhide treats, so they pass more readily. In most cases as long as it is small enough, objects pass harmlessly through the body and end up on the lawn. Monitor your dog's productivity. Use a disposable Popsicle stick or plastic knife to chop up and search through the droppings for the object.

The exception to allowing small objects pass are swallowed metal objects like coins or batteries. DON'T WAIT, get your dog seen immediately. Stomach acids interact with these metal objects and cause zinc or lead poisoning. String is another dangerous object when swallowed and requires you to seek professional help. But any object, even tiny ones, potentially may lodge in and block the intestinal tract.

Specific signs depend on where the blockage is located. An object caught in the stomach or intestines causes vomiting which may come and go for days or weeks if the blockage is not complete and food can pass around it. Complete blockage is a medical emergency that results in a bloated, painful stomach with sudden, constant vomiting. The dog refuses food, and immediately throws up anything she drinks.

Dogs may paw at their mouth when objects catch between teeth or stick to the palate. If something catches in the throat, the dog typically gags, coughs or even retches in an attempt to move it. Use extreme caution when investigating such cases. A dog upset by the experience may object to your attempts to open her mouth, and you could be bitten.

You could injure your dog by trying to remove the object. String-type articles may be caught between the teeth in the mouth, with the rest swallowed. Never pull on this visible end, because string and thread is often attached to a needle or fishhook that's embedded in tissue further down the digestive tract. Pulling the string at your end could further injure the intestines, and kill the dog.

Intestines propel food using muscle contractions called peristalsis that move through the entire length of the intestine (kind of like an earthworm) to help push the contents through. But when a foreign object like string is caught at one end, the intestine literally "gathers" itself like fabric on a thread, resulting in a kind of accordion formation. The result is sudden severe vomiting and diarrhea, and rapid dehydration. Your veterinarian should evaluate any blockage situation to determine the best course of treatment. Surgery is often necessary to remove the obstruction.

If blockage is not promptly addressed, the resulting damage may become irreparable. Sharp objects may slice or puncture the bowel, and obstruction may interfere with blood flow to the organs and cause bowel tissue to die (see PERITONITIS) which usually kills the victim.

Often, the owner witnesses the dog chewing or swallowing the object. Other times, diagnosis can be based on symptoms. However, X-rays usually are necessary to determine the exact location and size of the blockage, and sometimes to identify the object itself. When the obstruction is caused by a non-metal object which isn't visible on X-rays, barium is used to better define the situation. Barium is given either orally or as an enema to help provide a positive contrast that outlines the foreign object during X-rays.

Once located, the object is surgically removed, and when possible, any internal damage is repaired. If surgery can correct the problem before peritonitis sets in, most dogs fully recover. Should tissue die, the damaged sections of the intestine may be removed and the living portions of bowel reattached; these dogs typically have a good prognosis.

The best course is preventing your dog from swallowing dangerous items. Choose dog-safe toys that can't be chewed into tiny pieces, and supervise object play. Anything a child would put in his mouth is fair game for dogs, especially puppies. Real bones and rawhide chews should only be offered with supervision. Puppy-proof your home by thinking like your dog, so that you won't be caught off guard when your dog eats the rubber bumpers off the door stops.

SWEAT GLANDS

Sweat glands are sac-like structures in the skin that open to the air, and secrete fluid. Dogs have two kinds of sweat glands, the apocrine glands and the eccrine glands.

Apocrine glands are found throughout the body, and empty secretions into the adjacent hair follicles. The scented fluid they produce is thought to play a role in reproduction as a sexual attractant. Eccrine glands are limited to the dog's footpads and nasal pad. They are like human sweat glands that open to the surface and secrete watery fluid as a means of cooling the body.

But sweat glands in dogs are not particularly effective and do little to regulate the pet's temperature. Instead, a dog pants to cool off, lolling her wet tongue out of her mouth and breathing across it to produce an evaporative cooling effect. Dog skin also helps regulate body temperature when blood vessels in the skin dilate to dissipate heat, and constrict to retain warmth. The exception to this rule is the hairless variety of the Chinese Crested breed which, in addition to panting, also sweats.

536

DOG FACTS

TAPEWORMS Tapeworms are ribbon-like flat worms that live in the intestines. There are several varieties, but *Dipylidium caninum* is seen most often in cats and dogs. While tapeworms are rarely a serious health risk, they can pose nutritional problems interfering with food absorption.

Immature worms must spend developmental time inside an intermediary host before being able to infest your dog. The flea serves this purpose. If your dog is infested with fleas, she is also highly likely to have tapeworms. That's why incidence of tapeworms closely parallels the summer months of flea season.

Tapeworm eggs are eaten by the flea larvae, which then develops as the flea itself matures. When a pet nibbles to relieve that itch, she often swallows the flea and infects herself with tapeworm.

The head of the tapeworm, called the scolex or holdfast, is equipped with hooks and suckers that are used to anchor itself to the wall of the small intestine. There is no mouth as such; in fact tapeworms don't even have a digestive system. Instead, nutrients are absorbed through the segmented body.

TAPEWORMS

SYMPTOMS: Ricelike debris or moving segments stuck to dog's anal area or feces
HOME CARE: None
VET CARE: Antitapeworm medication
PREVENTION: Flea control; prevent dogs from eating wild game

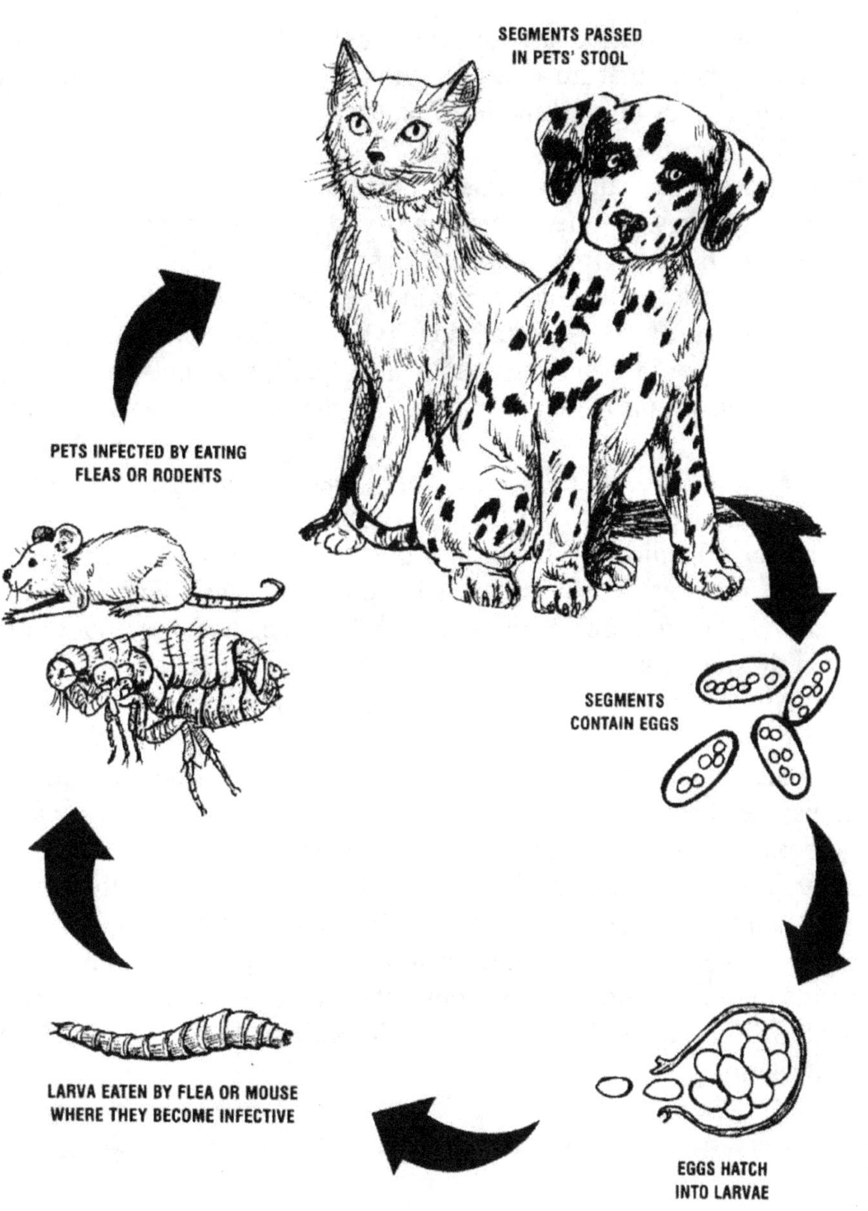

Tapeworm life cycle

Called proglottids, these segments are linked together like a chain. The parasite continuously grows new segments that are added from the neck down. Adult worms continue to add segments as long as they live, sometimes attaining lengths of two feet or more composed of hundreds of segments.

Each proglottid contains both male and female reproductive organs. When mature, the segment produces up to 200 eggs. Segments furthest from the scolex are most mature, and once "ripe" they are shed from the worm's body, and pass in the feces.

Once outside the body, each segment can move independently like tiny inchworms, but when dry they look like grains of rice. Infested dogs typically have segments stuck to the hair surrounding the anal area, or in their bedding. Eventually, the segments dry and rupture, releasing the eggs they contain into the environment. The life cycle is complete in two to four weeks.

Tapeworm eggs are passed and shed so sporadically, that examination of the stool may be inconclusive. It's considered diagnostic to find the segments on the pet.

Tapeworms are rarely a medical problem, and are usually considered an unpleasant annoyance. The moving proglottids may cause irritation to the anal region, which may prompt dogs to excessively lick themselves or "scoot" their rear against the floor or ground.

Without treatment, however, massive tapeworm infestations potentially interfere with digesting food and/or elimination. Puppies may suffer intestinal blockage should too many worms become suspended the length of the intestinal tract.

Also, the hooks of the holdfast can damage the intestinal wall. Diarrhea with mucus and occasionally blood may be signs of tapeworm infestation. Long-term infestation can result in an unkempt, dry-looking coat and generally unhealthy appearance, and reduced energy.

Flea tapeworms are the most common kind of cestodes affecting dogs. However, other species may be contracted if the dog eats wild animals like mice or rabbits.

There are several safe and highly effective treatments for tapeworms, which may be administered either as a pill or injection. Unless constantly exposed to reinfestation by fleas, a one-dose treatment will eliminate the tapeworms. Controlling fleas is the best way to prevent tapeworm infestation.

TEETH The bony growths on the jaw found inside the mouth are called teeth. They are used to capture, kill and prepare food for eating, and as tools for defense.

Almost without exception, puppies are born without teeth. Deciduous teeth, or "milk teeth" begin to appear at about three weeks of age. By six to eight weeks of age, the puppy will have a full set of 28 baby teeth. A puppy's age can be estimated by which teeth have erupted.

The incisors are the first to appear at about two to three weeks of age. Puppies have six incisors on both the top and bottom jaw at the front of the mouth. Four needle-like canines appear at age four weeks, and frame the incisors, one on each side, top and bottom. Premolars and molars begin to grow behind the canines at three to six weeks of age; there are three on the top and three on the bottom on each side. The last molars appear by six to eight weeks of age.

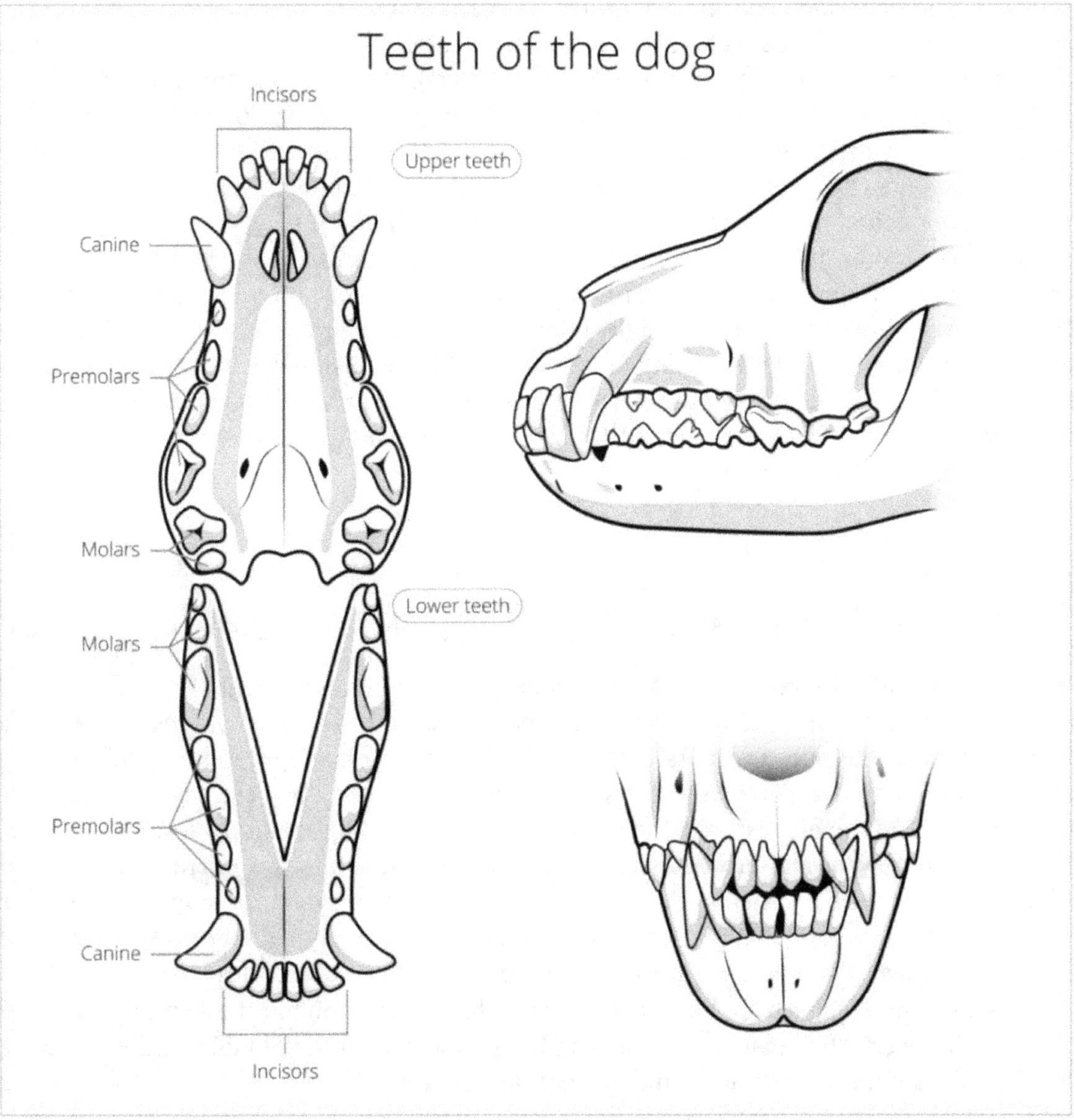

Teeth of the dog

Incisors
Upper teeth
Canine
Premolars
Molars
Lower teeth
Molars
Premolars
Canine
Incisors

At about the same time, permanent teeth begin pushing out the milk teeth. The roots of the baby teeth are absorbed by the body, and in most cases, milk teeth simply fall out. Permanent teeth replace the milk teeth tooth for tooth, but in addition add four premolars and ten molars. There are 42 permanent teeth in place by about seven months of age.

Dogs use their incisors to rip and scrape meat from bone and secondarily as a grooming tool to nibble matter from their fur. Stabbing canine teeth are used to capture and hold objects and prey. The premolars and molars in the rear of the jaw are sharp, triangular teeth that include the "carnassial" teeth characteristic of meat eaters. They work like scissors to shear flesh and crush bone. The flattened molars are designed to crush vegetable foods and bone.

When deciduous teeth don't fall out on time, the dog may appear to have a double set of teeth. Retained baby teeth should be extracted so that permanent teeth will have room to grow. Sometimes, a crowded mouth pushes teeth out of alignment, resulting in difficulty eating or poor dental hygiene (see PERIODONTAL DISEASE).

When the mouth is closed the lower canine teeth are normally situated in front of the upper canines, the upper incisors overlap the lower, the upper premolar points fit into the spaces between lower premolars, and the upper carnassials overlap the lower. Malocclusion refers to the abnormal "bite" or fitting of these teeth. Malocclusion can be normal for certain dog breeds due to differences in the shape of the jaw and mouth. For instance, the flat-faced (brachycephalic) dog breeds like Bulldogs have a normal malocclusion because their lower jaw is longer than the upper.

TEMPERAMENT TESTS

TEMPERAMENT TESTS Temperament testing strives to be a canine crystal ball to identify personality tendencies and predict potential problems. They measure different aspects of temperament such as stability, shyness, aggressiveness, and friendliness, and the pup or dog fails if he exhibits unprovoked aggression, panic without recovery, or strong avoidance. Once tested, puppies or shelter dogs can be better matched with owners. Better matches save dog lives and preserve loving relationships.

A wide variety of test protocols have been developed to assess general temperament, suitability for adoption, suitability as therapy or assistance dogs and for aggression. No test is entirely predictive of behavior in the new home and few if any have been well validated. Tests for puppies between seven and ten weeks of age often include these basics:

- Cradle pup on his back like a baby, place a hand gently on his chest and look directly in his eyes. Pups that accept this handling are considered biddable, while those that resist are more likely to be independent-minded.

- Hold pup suspended under her armpits with hind legs dangling, while looking directly in eyes. Again, those pups that submit are said to have a low score for willfulness, while those that struggle may want to do things their own way.
- Drop keys or tin pan to test him for noise sensitivity.
- See how pup reacts to a stranger entering the room—or to being left alone in the room. Does she run and greet, or cower and cry?

Personality and temperament aren't cast in stone at birth. Nature and nurture work together, making predictive tests even more difficult to measure. Early experience, socialization, development and the consequences of learning will all have an impact on behavior. Many behaviors of personality such as resistance to handling, possessive aggression, territorial vocalization, excessive reactivity and many forms of fear might not emerge until the pet matures. A dog may be born with a slightly anxious temperament but the environment and experience shapes the fear that develops.

Testing for behaviors such as dominance, activity levels in novel situations and fearfulness might therefore have greater predictability after three months of age. The later the test, the more likely you are to get an accurate reading.

Tests such as the AKC Good Citizenship Test and American Temperament Test Society are often used to assess temperament of family pets. It's easier with adult dog because character has formed. Such evaluations might include:

- Accepting a friendly stranger's petting
- Walking on a loose lead including through a crowd
- Basic obedience—sit, down, stay, come when called.
- Reaction to another dog
- Reaction to distraction such as dropped chair or jogger running past

More specific tests might then be added to assess a dog's suitability as a therapy dog, such as how he reacts to wheelchairs, people with canes, or unexpected body postures and movements.

Shelters often use behavior assessments to determine whether a dog can be re-homed. Failure can mean death to the dog. Although emerging evidence supports the premise that shelter dog assessment tests have some predictive value, many of these tests have not been adequately validated.

There is an accurate prediction for separation anxiety, and also has to do with the owner's temperament. Once in the new home the separation anxiety may fade away—or get worse. Even if you know what the dog's doing, it's difficult to predict the way that the owner's going to be able to respond. People are limited by their personalities.

Dogs that repeatedly exhibit aggression when touched or approached in a nonthreatening manner, aggression to other dogs, possessive aggression and fearfulness on the screening tests, are at risk for continuation or reemergence of these problems in the new home. There are also problems inherent in shelter temperament testing including the stress of sheltering on the individual, the duration of sheltering, the age and health of the individual, the unknown predictive value of failed tests and the potential risks to the tester. Such tests work best when used in combination with histories from the dog's original owner.

The ASPCA uses the SAFER assessment program developed by Certified Applied Animal Behaviorist Dr. Emily Weiss, along with the Meet Your Match adoption programs. Mary Burch, Ph.D., a Certified Applied Animal Behaviorist, evaluated existing behavior assessment protocols and helped create the ADOPT shelter protocol, which stands for Assess Dogs on Practical Tasks. Such behavior assessments often rate such things as:

- In-kennel and approach behaviors
- Leash/collar and on-leash behaviors
- Reactions to petting, handling, play and distractions
- Reaction to other animals (e.g., dogs, cats)
- Guarding of food or possessions

Some tests for aggression involve provocation--for instance, using a stuffed boxing glove or Assess-A-Hand (Sternberg protocol) to determine if the dog might bite. A childlike doll or Assess-a-hand may not accurately predict the dog's response. Dogs may willingly attack a fake hand or doll because they know it's fake, but refrain from biting a real child or human hand.

Temperament testing effectively picks up the main tendencies of a dog especially if they're extreme. Whether people are testing properly is also the question. Temperament testing is as good as the tester (see AGGRESSION, FEAR, SEPARATION ANXIETY and SOCIALIZATION).

TEMPERATURE

TEMPERATURE Temperature refers to the body's warmth as measured by a thermometer. The adult dog's normal body temperature ranges from 101 to 102.5 degrees, while a newborn puppy's temperature is considerably lower at 92 to 97 degrees (see PUPPY). A body temperature outside the normal range is an indication of illness.

Temperatures higher than normal are referred to as a fever, and can be a sign of infection related to a wide variety of illnesses, or of heat stroke (see HYPERTHERMIA). A drop in body temperature may indicate shock as a result of trauma, or loss of body heat from extreme cold (see HYPOTHERMIA). Treatment addresses the cause.

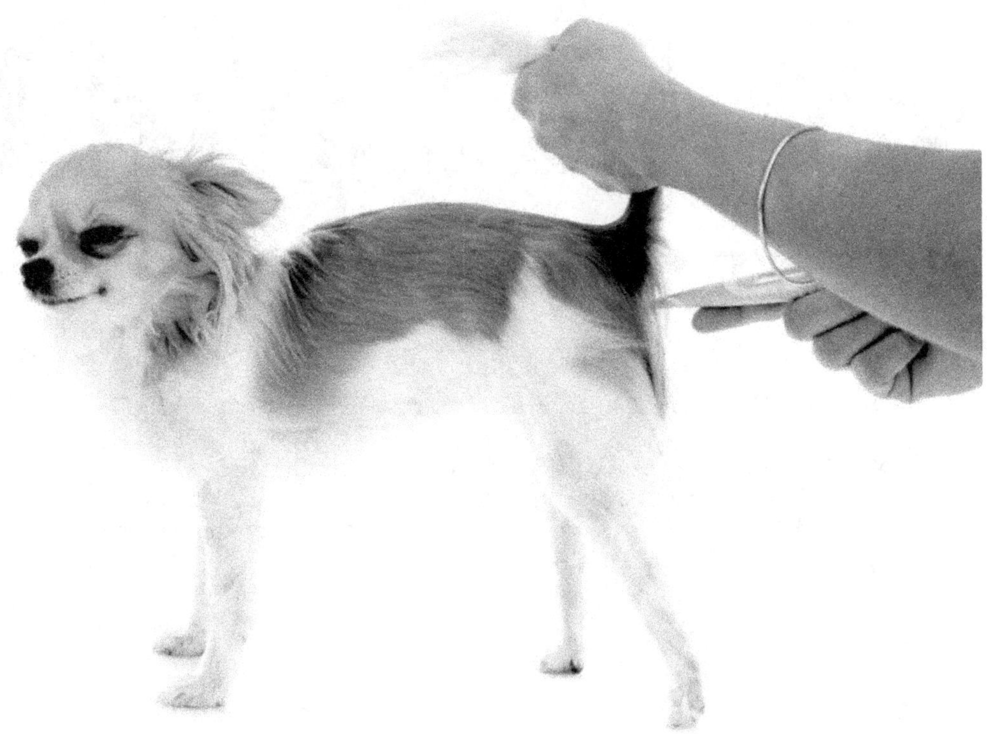

Use a rectal thermometer, either digital or bulb, to take your dog's temperature. Most dogs don't mind the procedure, but if yours protests, be gentle and firm to get the job done (see RESTRAINT). First shake down the thermometer until it reads about 96 degrees. Use baby oil, mineral oil or petroleum jelly to lubricate the tip. Your dog will need to remain still for at least one minute, so allow her to choose a comfortable standing or reclining position.

Use one hand to firmly grasp and lift her tail to expose the anus. Your other hand gently inserts the greased end of the thermometer about one inch into the dog's rectum—do not release the thermometer while taking the temperature. Speak calmly to your dog, so the thermometer will remain in place for the specified time, then remove and wipe clean, and read the temperature. Clean and disinfect the thermometer after each use with alcohol or a comparable disinfectant.

TETANUS

SYMPTOMS: Face and jaw muscle spasms; rigid extension of rear legs; difficulty breathing
HOME CARE: None; EMERGENCY! SEE VET IMMEDIATELY
VET CARE: Tetanus antitoxin injection; antibiotics; fluid therapy; sedatives
PREVENTION: Remain vigilant to wounds and treat promptly; sometimes vaccination as recommended by vet

TETANUS Tetanus is caused by a bacterial neurotoxin called *Clostridium tetani*. Almost all mammals are susceptible to tetanus, which is also referred to as lockjaw. Dogs can be affected, but generally are resistant to the infection.

The bacterium is a common inhabitant of the soil. Also, many animals naturally harbor the bacteria in their intestines without it causing illness. In most cases, the infectious agent is introduced into tissue through a deep puncture wound.

Signs may take only two days to develop following injury, or may take several weeks; generally, illness appears within two weeks. The bacterium grows best in low-oxygen locations, such as a sealed-over flesh wound. As the agent grows, it manufactures a toxin that affects the central nervous system.

The toxicity causes severe muscle spasms particularly of the face and jaw, and rigid extension of the rear legs. These spasms may be triggered by nearly anything—a loud noise, bright light. The dog typically will stiffly extend his tail, wrinkle his forehead (which pushes the ears erect), and his lips will pull back in a grin. The poison also interferes with blood circulation and respiration; about 80 percent of untreated dogs will die, usually of suffocation.

Diagnosis is based on signs, and history of a wound. It is imperative that the wound be thoroughly cleaned of infected tissue to help eliminate the bacterium. Treatment includes tetanus antitoxin, antibiotics, fluid therapy to fight dehydration, and sedatives to control spasms. The sooner signs appear following the injury, the more guarded is the prognosis.

Once treatment is begun, dogs may not show improvement for several days, and it may take six weeks or longer to fully recover. Because most dogs are resistant to tetanus, preventative vaccination is rarely recommended and the disease can be prevented by reducing opportunities for wounds. Dogs that are exposed to livestock, such as herding dogs, may benefit from preventative vaccines.

THREADWORMS

SYMPTOMS: Coughing; watery diarrhea or bloody, mucus-filled diarrhea; cracked, bleeding footpads
HOME CARE: None
VET CARE: Supportive care; fluid therapy; medication to kill the parasite
PREVENTION: None

THREADWORMS Threadworms (*Strongyloides stercoralis*) are tiny, round intestinal parasites that aren't particularly common. The infective larvae penetrate the dog's skin from contact with infected soil, either through the footpads, or through the mouth or esophageal structures when they are swallowed.

From point of contact, larvae enter the dog's bloodstream and are carried to the heart and lungs. To reach the dog's intestines, the worms must be coughed up and swallowed. The mature worms live in the surface tissues of the small intestine, where they produce eggs that hatch into larvae. These larvae are passed in the dog's stool, where they develop further in the soil. The worms either become free-living adults that spend their entire life in the soil, where they mate and reproduce; or they develop into the parasitic form that affects dogs. Only female worms infect dogs, and they are able to reproduce in the dog's body without need of a male worm's fertilization.

Infections are most common in warm climates, and cause more problems in young puppies than adult dogs. Typically, the first signs are coughing prompted by the worms in the lungs. This is followed by large amounts of watery diarrhea, or bloody mucus-filled diarrhea. Dogs may also suffer characteristic changes in their footpads from the penetration of the worm similar to the pododermatitis seen in some cases of hookworms. Diagnosis is based on signs of disease, and by finding the larvae in a stool sample.

The recommended treatment involves supportive care and sometimes fluid therapy to combat dehydration. Thiabendazole, Ivermectin and fenbendazole are common treatments of this parasite.

TICK PARALYSIS

This is a progressive paralysis that most commonly affects dogs, sheep and, rarely, humans. It's caused by a neurotoxin found in the saliva of some ticks (*Dermacentor, Ixodes* and *Amblyomma* species). The disease has a worldwide distribution, but the species responsible have not been identified in all countries.

Usually, the affected dog has a heavy load of ticks; however, it may take only one tick to cause clinical signs. Paralysis usually doesn't develop until ticks have been attached and feeding for about six days.

The dog typically feels no particular discomfort, but over a 48 to 72 hour period, affected dogs become progressively weaker. First signs may be an elevated temperature, sometimes vomiting, an altered bark, or difficulty swallowing.

You may not notice anything is wrong until the dog displays incoordination of the hind legs characterized by an unsteady gait. This progresses to forelimb paralysis. Reflexes are lost, but the dog retains sensation and consciousness as the paralysis worsens. She's able to feel your touch or a needle prick, but can't move or respond. Eventually, the dog is totally immobilized and unable to stand, walk, or even raise her head. If the clinical signs are not arrested, they will lead ultimately to respiratory failure and death.

Diagnosis is based on characteristic signs, as well as the presence of the parasite. Treatment is simple; remove all the ticks, and paralysis will normally disappear within a few hours. Use an approved insecticide and/or mechanically remove all visible ticks. When the signs have progressed to a great degree, antiserum may be necessary to save the dog's life. Prognosis for recovery is usually good, and dogs typically suffer no permanent damage.

TICK PARALYSIS

SYMPTOMS: Ticks on dog; progressive weakness; fever; vomiting; strange-sounding bark; trouble swallowing; incoordination of hind limbs; paralysis; respiratory failure
FIRST AID: Remove ticks immediately; see vet as soon as possible
VET CARE: Same; sometimes antiserum; supportive therapy
PREVENTION: Prevent ticks

Dogs that have suffered a bout of tick paralysis develop only short-term immunity, and can suffer another episode should they again be exposed to a toxic tick bite within as little as two weeks of recovery. Protect your pet by using appropriate tick preventatives.

TICKS Ticks are an extremely common skin parasite of dogs. These spider-relatives have eight legs and live off blood. They typically are gray to brown with oval-shaped leathery or hard flat bodies that inflate as the tick feeds. Ticks come in a vast array of species, and vary from pinhead size to as large as a lima bean when fully engorged.

Ticks that usually afflict dogs spend up to 90 percent of their time off the host. They typically are a three-host parasite; that is, ticks target a different kind of animal during each stage of development. Should a preferred host (like a deer or rat) be unavailable, ticks will feed from what's handy, including cats, dogs or people.

Tick eggs hatch into tiny seed ticks, six-legged larvae that live in vegetation until they can board a passing host animal. Seed ticks feed for several days, then drop off and molt into eight-legged nymphs, which again seek an appropriate host. After another blood meal, nymphs drop off and molt into adults. Adults must again feed before mating. Once fertilized, females drop off the host to lay 1,000 to 4,000 eggs. The entire life cycle can take as long as two years.

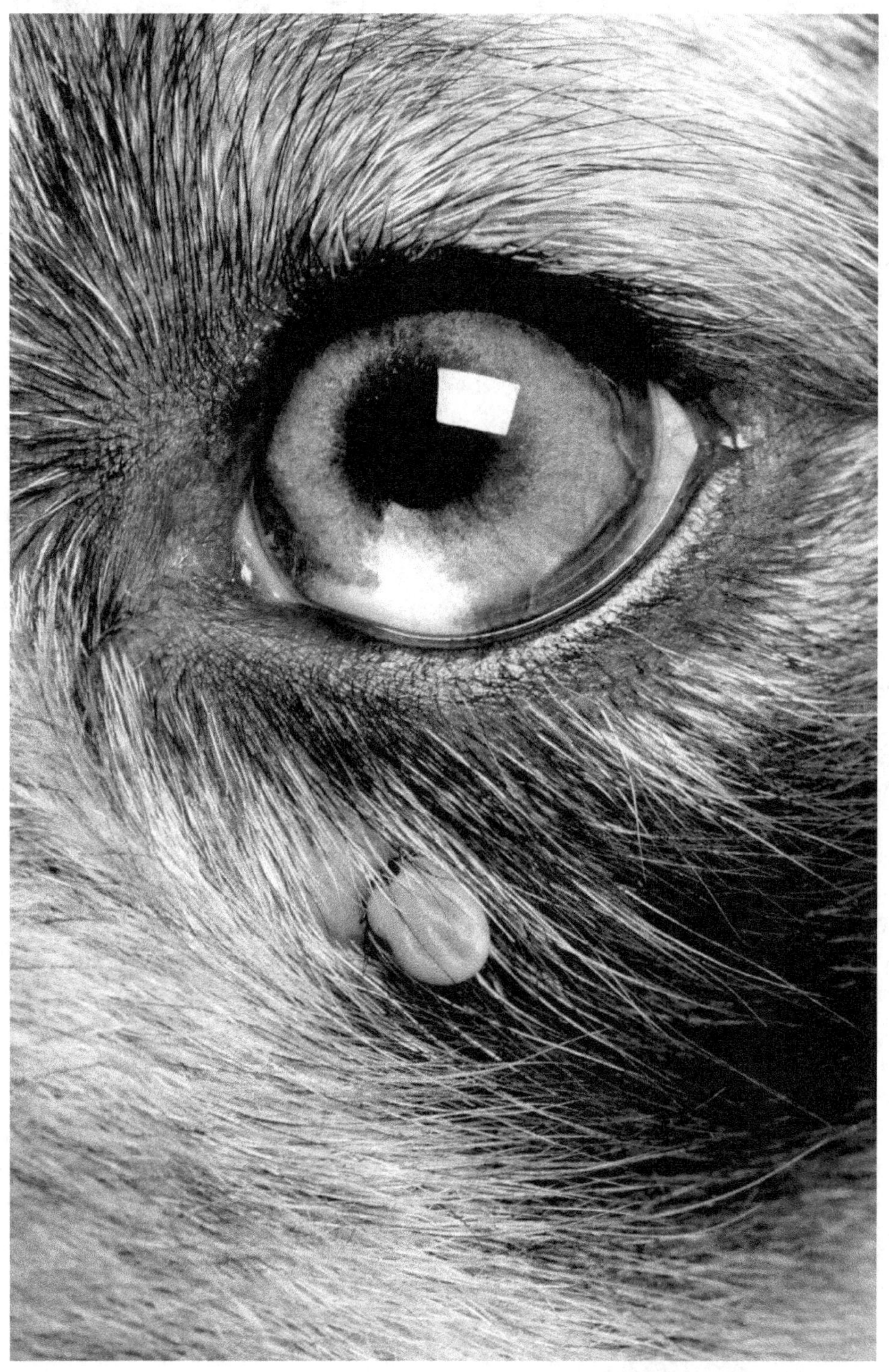

Ticks bury their heads beneath the victim's skin to feed, and can cause infected sores and prompt skin disease (see HOT SPOTS). Massive infections cause anemia. Ticks are also the vectors, or transmitters, of many devastating illnesses that affect dogs or even people (see BABESIOSIS, EHRLICHIOSIS, LYME DISEASE, ROCKY MOUNTAIN SPOTTED FEVER, and TICK PARALYSIS).

TICKS

SYMPTOMS: Pinhead- to lima-bean-size parasites attached to the skin of dog's head, neck, and behind or inside the ears
HOME CARE: Wear gloves or use tweezers to remove ticks; daub alcohol on exit wound
VET CARE: Same as home care
PREVENTION: Tick repellents and insecticides

The best way to avoid tick infestation and potential disease is to use effective tick control. There are tick collars made to kill ticks. A number of canine flea preventative preparations are also effective against ticks. Ticks frequent high grass and vegetation. Inspect your dog after field excursions and remove ticks before they have a chance to attach themselves. Simply combing or brushing your dog will eliminate a number of them from his fur before they have a chance to burrow into place.

Wear gloves to remove ticks from your pet to avoid exposing yourself to a tick-borne disease agent. Ticks are usually found on the head, back of the neck and inside the ears where the dog has trouble reaching to scratch. Use tweezers to grasp the tick right at the skin level, and pull firmly straight out.

TOAD POISONING

SYMPTOMS: Drooling; seizures; sudden death
HOME CARE: EMERGENCY! SEE VET IMMEDIATELY! If help is half hour or more away, flush dog's mouth with water and induce vomiting; provide artificial respiration if necessary
VET CARE: Supportive care; medication to control seizures; fluid therapy to combat shock
PREVENTION: Don't allow dog to play with toads, particularly if poisonous varieties live in your region

TOAD POISONING Toads are a kind of amphibian that live on land. Most toads secrete a nasty-tasting but harmless fluid as a defense, and dogs that play with toads and taste this noxious substance may slobber and drool.

The south is home to a tropical toad (*Bufo marinus*) which secretes a toxin in the fluid. The toxin can affect a dog's heart and circulation, and cause death in as little as fifteen minutes. Signs of toad poisoning vary from mild drooling to seizures and sudden death. If you suspect your dog has had contact with such a toad, get her to your veterinarian immediately. Prognosis depends on the amount of poison the dog absorbs.

If help is more than half an hour away, and your dog is conscious, flush her mouth with running water. Use a turkey baster, the spray nozzle attachment from your sink, or the garden hose, but take care she doesn't inhale the fluid. Also attempt to induce vomiting. Give your dog one to two teaspoons of 3 percent hydrogen peroxide for every pound he weighs. You can repeat in five minutes if it doesn't work, but then rush to the vet clinic. Be aware that you may need to perform artificial respiration.

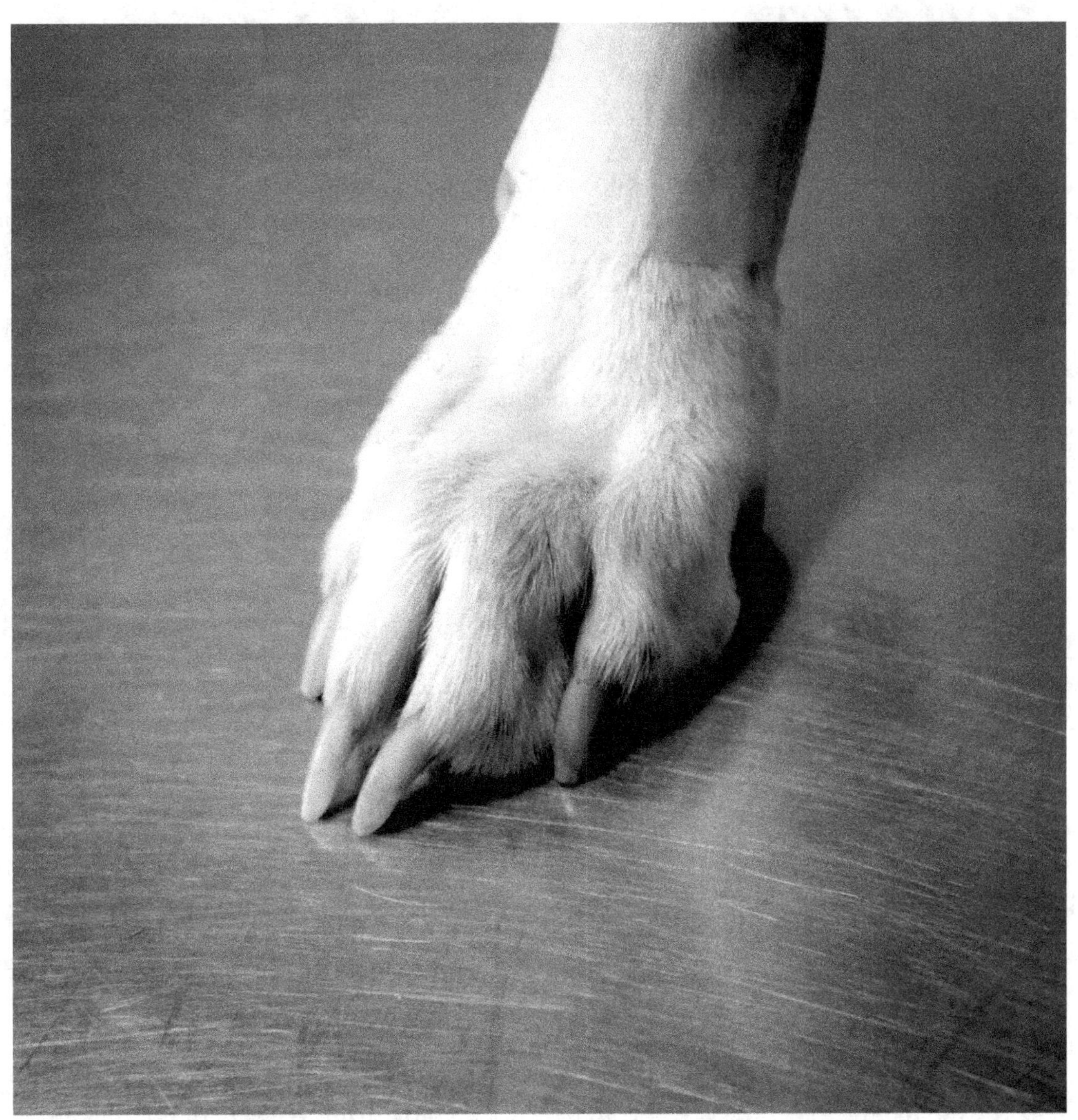

TOENAILS Toe nails, or claws, are found at the ends of each toe. Most dogs have five toes on the front feet, and four on the back. The fifth toe, called a dewclaw, doesn't touch the ground and may be present on either front or hind legs, but often appears on the hind feet of large breed dogs. Dewclaws are sometimes surgically removed by a veterinarian shortly after a puppy is born, to prevent them catching on objects and causing the dog injury. However, the Briard and Great Pyrenees standards call for dewclaws to remain intact.

Dewclaws are thought to be a throwback to an archaic ancestral form, since the extra toes serve no functional purpose.

The claw itself is made of hard, non-living protein that is usually white to clear, and sometimes black. The quick deep inside feeds the rigid structure with a network of blood vessels and nerves. Claws grow from the quick, and in dogs, the nails are rather blunt and wear down through normal activity when they make contact with the ground.

The dog's footpads are very thick and callused, and are the strongest area of the body. Canine claws protect the toes, are used as back scratchers, and serve as tools for digging. Toenails that don't wear down through normal activity may overgrow, split or tear and cause the dog pain and lead to infection. Address your dog's toenail needs in routine grooming (see GROOMING).

TONGUE The tongue contains the sensory organs that provide dogs with their sense of taste. The long mobile organ is rooted in the floor of the mouth. The tongue also acts as a tool for self-grooming, eating and drinking, and as the dog's primary cooling mechanism (see PANTING and TEMPERATURE).

Not everything is known about the dog's sense of taste. We know that a facial nerve is "wired" to the taste buds on the front two-thirds of the tongue only, leaving the remainder somewhat of a mystery. Most of the dog's taste buds are circular structures located on the upper forward surface of the tongue, and in four to six large cup-shaped bumpy papillae at the rear of the tongue.

The majority of canine taste buds respond to sugar, which can get them in trouble (see ANTIFREEZE POISONING and CHOCOLATE). This is most likely a reflection of their omnivorous evolution. Dogs needed to eat seasonal fruits and vegetables to survive, so they evolved a sweet tooth because sweetness is a mechanism in plants that signals optimum ripeness. And like people, dogs are able to detect a kind of "fruity-sweet" flavor that attracts us, and them, to the calorie-rich ripeness of fruits and vegetables.

The second greatest number of canine taste buds respond to acidic tastes, which correspond to sour and bitter in people. However, dogs don't appear to have a specific response to salt. Odors coupled with taste tend to impact what the dog will eat.

TOUCH Touch refers to the sensation produced when contact is made with the skin. The sense of touch arises from countless temperature- and pressure-sensitive nerve endings found in the skin. Touch serves as a protective mechanism that prompts feelings of pleasure or discomfort in response to external stimulation. When something is too hot or too cold, feels good or causes pain, the nerves tell the dog to react appropriately. Direct contact with the skin isn't necessary, because each hair on the dog's body acts like an antenna that feeds sensation down to nerves called mechanoreceptors found near the base of each hair in the skin.

Nerves in the paw pads react to vibration. Sense of touch is most sensitive in the area surrounding the muzzle, which also contains the sensitive whiskers. Temperature is detected by specialized thermoreceptor nerves scattered over the body. Some react to cold while others respond to heat. Dogs even have a special cold receptor on the lips, the purpose for which remains unknown.

Nociceptors are sensitive to pain; some respond to mechanical stimulation like crushing or squeezing, and others are sensitive to temperature extremes (see PAIN).

Touch is also a pleasurable sensation, which is why petting feels so good to both you and your dog. It is this sensation that newborn puppies experience as their mothers wash them. Contact with other creatures provides an emotional link between them, and is also thought to be a component of communication.

TOXOPLASMOSIS Toxoplasmosis is a disease caused by the single cell organism *Toxoplasma gondii*, a parasitic protozoan. Infection with this agent is quite common in people and many animals, but illness is relatively uncommon. Domestic and wild cats are the only animals in which toxoplasmosis can reproduce. Clinical disease in dogs is rare.

The protozoans multiply in the wall of the small intestine and produce egg-like oocysts. Only infected cats are able to pass these immature forms of the organism, which are shed in the cat's stool. Oocysts can survive in moist or shady soil or sand for many months.

The disease is spread when an animal or a person swallows these infective oocysts. Toxoplasmosis can be contracted by ingesting infected animals, eating raw or undercooked meat, or contact with infective soil or cat feces.

Once inside the bird, rodent, dog or person, the protozoan continues to mature, causing pockets of disease throughout the body. In most cases of canine infection, at this point the dog's immune system renders the organism dormant so it causes no illness. If the dog's immune system is suppressed due to other illness, however, the dormant infestation may become active and cause clinical disease.

Signs when they occur include difficulty breathing with coughing, fever, neurological signs, gastrointestinal problems, and/or sudden death. Diagnosis is based on clinical signs, and blood tests showing elevated antibody levels which indicates exposure has taken place. Sometimes, the parasite can be found in body tissues.

Healthy adult humans rarely get sick, even when infected. The most common sign is swollen lymph glands. However, the disease can cause life-threatening illness in immune-suppressed people, and can severely injure or kill unborn babies. YOU CANNOT CONTRACT TOXOPLASMOSIS FROM YOUR DOG; and the chance of contracting toxoplasmosis from a well-cared-for pet cat is extremely low (see TOXOPLASMOSIS in CAT FACTS).

The most common infection source in people in the United States is undercooked or raw meat, especially pork. Protect yourself and your dog by avoiding undercooked or raw meat, and never feed pork to your dog. Prevent your dog from eating wild game, or from drinking from potentially infected mud puddles. Wash your hands after handling raw meat, wear gloves when working in the garden to prevent contracting the agent from the soil, and keep your dog out of the cat box. Prompt disposal of cat feces will virtually eliminate the chance of exposure (see ZOONOSIS).

TOXOPLASMOSIS

SYMPTOMS: Breathing problems; coughing; fever; diarrhea; neurological signs
HOME CARE: None
VET CARE: Rarely needed; supportive therapy; fluid therapy; medication to control diarrhea and respiratory signs
PREVENTION: Prevent dogs from hunting; keep yard clean; prevent snacking from cat litter box

TRAINING

Training is teaching. Dogs have been bred to be highly trainable, and many are eager to learn because it pleases their owners. Dogs are able to learn a wide range of simple to complicated commands, depending on the individual animal, the breed, and on the competence of the trainer.

Learning can be categorized a couple of different ways. **Classical conditioning** forms an association between an outside event, like running the water in the sink, and a reaction, such as a bath. Depending on the reaction, the dog associates the event with a pleasant or unpleasant experience and behaves accordingly. **Operant conditioning** deals with relationships between stimuli, responses, and consequences. The puppy learns that what he does is critical to what happens next. For instance, he receives a treat for a good behavior like pooping outside in the right place.

Dogs behave in certain ways because the action is self-rewarding. It feels good to scratch an itch or go to the bathroom as soon as the urge strikes. Trial and error lessons are the most powerful because it self-trains them when the action (sniffing the cricket) rewards the behavior (the cricket jumps—what fun!). In the same way, Puppies learn that biting Mom-dog's tail prompts a scary GRRRRR! and an end to the game. That's no fun at all. When they play nice, though, they are rewarded with Mom's fun interaction. Effective trainers use these principles to teach dogs to behave appropriately.

Specialized training educates dogs to serve in traditional roles as hunters, herders, and protectors, or as surrogate eyes, ears or extra hands for people requiring such assistance. But all dogs benefit from a basic knowledge of obedience. This helps dogs understand the differences between acceptable and unacceptable behavior, and promotes more suitable canine companions.

Principles of effective training involve positive and negative reinforcement, which basically mean rewarding the dog for doing the right thing, and correcting for inappropriate performance. Most dogs respond enthusiastically to praise—"good boy, King!"—or to treat and toy rewards. Conversely, verbal shaming from the beloved owner—"bad boy!"—or being shut away in a room by himself, is often enough to keep a dog in line.

Punishment in the form of pain has no place in training--ever. Dogs trained in this way may react with extreme shyness or aggression, which can in fact endanger the trainer or others. Dogs that are hit or slapped with objects or hands learn to associate hands with pain rather than petting.

The key to successful training is to figure out what motivates your dog do what he does, and use that to train the response you want. In effect, training fools the dog into believing it was all his idea.

Negative experiences also have their place in training, and can be anything the dog considers unpleasant—being separated from you, or the games stopping are examples. At its best, they interrupt or make the inappropriate behavior undesirable so the dog makes the correction himself.

The word "no!" spoken in a commanding tone, along with clapping your hands, shaking a tin can filled with marbles, hot- tasting or foul-smelling sprays judiciously applied to forbidden objects, or even a tossed toy all work to some degree. When the dog corrects the behavior, reward him with a "good boy, King!"

One of the most effective methods, though, simply waits to catch the dog in the act of doing something RIGHT and then rewarding the behavior. In this way, the dog tries to figure out how to please you, rather than being in fear of punishment for some unknown infraction.

The best training methods use consistency, patience, and positive reinforcement. Commands are linked to short, single-syllable words like "sit" or "come," and correct performance is rewarded with verbal praise or another strong motivator such as a treat or favorite toy. Bad behavior is corrected with "no!" either alone or in combination with a physical interruption (i.e., noisemaker); and when the dog does the right thing, he is immediately rewarded.

Training is best begun during puppyhood, but can be implemented at any age. Short sessions several times a day work better than a single marathon session. You must act confident, or your dog will try to buffalo you and cut corners. Use the dog's own language of erect posture, unflinching eyes and low compelling voice (not high, loud or strident) to assume command so your dog will listen to you and be eager to do your bidding.

Entire books are written on the subject of dog training. However, detailed step-by-step instruction is best received through demonstration in a class in which both owner and dog participate. Classes are often sponsored locally by animal welfare organizations or dog clubs. Ask your veterinarian for a recommendation.

It's not necessary for your dog to be an obedience champion (see TRIALS) to be a wonderful companion; however, it helps, and will promote a more rewarding relationship.

Without exception, all dogs benefit from basic training. At a minimum, your dog should respond to his name, understand and obey the meaning of the word "no," come on command, and accept a leash. This basic education goes beyond having a well-behaved dog; it's a safety issue that protects you both from liability and injury. The dog that understands these basic commands may be prevented from dashing into traffic, or eating a poisonous substance. And leash training not only keeps a dog under the owner's safe control, but gives you both freedom to explore the world beyond your house and property.

Your dog's name should be linked with praise as well as an action command whenever possible. Say, "Good boy, King!" and "King, come!" Conversely, whenever he must be shamed or corrected, do not use his name, but only the word "no" and "shame on you, bad dog." You want your dog to associate his name with only good, positive things.

Dogs should wear a collar with appropriate identification at all times. Use one sized appropriately to your dog; a flat leather or woven nylon collar works well. Avoid electronic/shock, slip and so-called "choke" training styles of collar. Misuse of these training tools risks injury to the dog, may promote behavior problems, and can damage a positive pet relationship. Head halter products and no-pull harnesses offer humane ways to teach dogs without using force.

Train your dog to accept the leash by first simply clipping the leash to the collar to let him get used to the idea. Some pets throw a fit, and others could care less. Give him lots of positive reinforcement for putting up with the contraption. Next, just pick up your end of the leash. Give short tug-release instructions while calling your dog's name, or use his favorite toy or treat to lure him to follow you at the leash's direction. Praise him when he stays by your side.

Use the leash to train your dog to come. Again, use short tug-release instructions as you command "come!" and perhaps tempt him with his favorite toy or treat. Praise him when he responds appropriately. One of the easiest ways to train puppies to come is to run away and have the pup chase after you. Couple the game with the “come!” command, and allow the puppy to catch you, making that (and perhaps another favorite game) a part of the reward.

Use meal times as a training tool as well. If you know the sound of kibble hitting the bowl always brings your dog running, then couple that trigger with the "come" command; reward him with his food. Make sure he knows you think he's the smartest dog in the world, and he'll do his best to prove you right!

Be careful, however, that you never call your dog to come in order to punish him for some infraction. That will undermine all your training. If your dog must be corrected, or you need to perform some unpleasantness upon his person (i.e., trim his toenails), then don't command him to come; simply go get him.

Training sessions should be fun for you both. The one-on-one attention is glorious for your dog, so make the most of each session. Be sure to always end on an up note; you want your dog to remember he did well and was praised for doing well, so finish with an exercise he's already mastered (see HOUSE TRAINING and TRIALS).

TRAVELING

All dogs travel during their lives, if only during an annual trek to the veterinarian's office. But many dogs routinely make trips to the groomer, or a boarding facility, and show dogs travel a great deal.

All dogs should travel in the safety of a confined carrier or restraint even for relatively short trips. Upset tummies and nervous behavior are better controlled in an easily cleaned area. However, large and giant breed dogs may be more difficult to accommodate, and often are better confined in the back seat.

DON'T ALLOW YOUR DOG TO RIDE IN YOUR LAP. Even dogs accustomed to car rides may be startled by something unexpected, leap from an open window, or interfere with control of the car. During a car accident, an unrestrained dog becomes a furry projectile that not only suffers injury itself, but could severely injure others. Your dog could escape the car and become lost when rescuers seek to help you, or conversely, could try to attack and prevent rescuers from offering you aid.

Additionally, don't let your dog hang her head out the window in a moving vehicle. This will prevent eye injuries, as well as keeping your dog inside the car rather than trying to leap out.

Commercial carriers, from elaborate to simple, are available for your dog's comfort. The best are big enough for the adult dog without being cramped; cardboard pet totes available from pet supply stores or the veterinarian's office are fine for short trips. But long trips or repeated outings require better accommodations, so plan on getting a more substantial crate. Bigger dogs benefit from harnesses that can be secured to a seat belt. Grills that screen the rear of the car are also helpful to give a big dog room while keeping her out of your lap.

Airlines, busses and trains that allow pets have various rules regarding fees and pet accommodations. Health certificates signed by your veterinarian are an absolute must—your dog won't be allowed to travel these public transportation systems without one. They're only good for ten days, so call in advance to be sure you're prepared. Solid plastic carriers must be airline approved if you are transporting the dog with cargo. Only a few small animals sized to fit beneath the seat as "carry on" luggage are allowed on certain flights, so call ahead and reserve space if this is your intention. Airline carriers are usually box-shaped hard plastic with a grill opening in one side or the top. Canvas bags or duffle-type carriers with zipper openings are also popular for smaller dogs.

Traveling is often stressful for pets, especially if your dog associates car rides with a visit to the vet. Train your dog to better accept car rides by turning the crate or carrier into a play area or even a bed. Take your dog for short car rides that end at a canine playmate's house, or a park for play (and a healthy treat or two?), so she'll associate the car with good things. In some cases, your veterinarian may prescribe a tranquilizer for you to give to your dog to reduce her anxiety during trips (see CAR SICKNESS).

If your dog is traveling with you for extended periods (particularly across state lines) you are required to carry with you a vaccination and health certificate, and copies of your dog's medical records. Out-of-country travelers should call the local embassy or consulate of the country of destination at least a month in advance to get necessary information on pet travel. Some countries only require health and vaccination certificates, while others may impose a six-month quarantine.

Should you decide to leave your dog at home when you travel, investigate the services of a pet sitter, or boarding kennel. Some states license kennels and inspect them on a regular basis, and pet sitters may also be regulated by various associations. Ask your veterinarian and other pet owners for a recommendation.

TRIALS Trials are competitive events established to test the performance and/or appearance of dogs against an established standard of excellence. There are three basic categories of dog sport competition: dog shows, field trials, and obedience trials. These may be formal "licensed" events which earn participating dogs points or credits toward titles and championships, or they may be informal "fun matches" that offer practice to participating dogs and their handlers.

Dog shows are essentially beauty contests in which registered purebred dogs are judged on conformation, that is, how closely they meet their breed's standard. Dogs are judged on general appearance, size, coat and color, how they move, and even their temperament. Specialty conformation shows are limited to dogs of a single breed or grouping of breed; for instance, the Pekingese Club of America Specialty is for Pekingese only. An all-breed conformation show includes dogs of all breeds. Competition is fierce, with various classes competing in a process of elimination with only the winners advancing to the finals. A separate category, called Junior Showmanship, judges youthful dog handlers aged ten through 16 on their ability to show dogs in conformation trials.

Obedience trials test both the dog and handler on how well they perform pre-established exercises: heel on and off leash, stand for examination, come when called, stay in a sitting and down position, fetching an object, leaping a high jump and broad jump, scent discrimination, etc. While conformation trials require participants to be a recognized breed and intact (able to produce puppies), any dog breed or combination of breed, neutered or intact, may compete in obedience trials. Three levels of progressively difficult competition—Novice, Open, and Utility trials—earn the dog points toward titles, and ultimately championship.

The Canine Good Citizen Program encourages all dog owners to train their dogs in basic obedience. Dogs are tested in a pass/fail system on such things as walking naturally on a loose leash, walking through a crowd, accepting a stranger's approach, and containing themselves during the unexpected, such as a door slamming. Dogs that pass earn a Canine Good Citizen title (CGC).

Tracking trials test the dog's scenting ability. Again, increasingly difficult tests are set up; the dog able to follow the trail by scent and pass the first level earns a Tracking Dog title (TD); passing a more advanced test earns the dog TDX for Tracking Dog Excellent.

Field Trials and Hunting Tests demonstrate the hunting dog's ability to perform those functions for which he was developed. Pointers, retrievers, spaniels, Beagles, Basset Hounds and Dachshunds compete in various events, according to their breed's purpose. Dogs earn the ultimate titles of Field Champion and Master Hunter.

Herding Trials measure these dogs' ability to herd and control livestock. Herding Tests measure a dog's inherent ability and training potential, while the trials themselves earn points toward titles and championships. The ultimate title here is Herding Champion (HCH).

Lure coursing events test the sighthound breeds (Greyhound, Saluki, Afghan Hound) in the same way field trials challenge scent hounds and sporting dog breeds. Dogs are challenged to run down "prey" (in this case, air-filled plastic bags) as they were bred to do. Field Champion (FC) is the ultimate title.

There are a number of other dog sports available as well. Earth dog events test the terrier's ability to "go-to-ground" in tunneling and digging trials. Dogsledding is a favorite of northern breeds such as Siberian Huskies, Alaskan Malamutes and Samoyeds. Weight-pulling events measure a dog's strength; American Pit Bull Terriers and Staffordshire Terriers are standouts in this event. And Agility Trials wed a number of performance skills into an all-round package of dogs able to leap, climb, run, and do all manner of skills over (and under) obstacle courses. For dogs (and owners) with a sense of humor and creative spirit, Canine Free Style may be appealing; here, nearly anything goes as long as dog(s) and handler(s) are choreographed appropriately to the music with props and sometimes costumes.

TUBERCULOSIS

Tuberculosis is a devastating respiratory infection that affects people. It's so named for the characteristic "tubercles" that form in the lungs as a result of the infection.

Human tuberculosis is caused by one of three bacterium: *Mycobacterium tuberculosis* (the primary agent of people), *Mycobacterium bovis* (also affects cows and other livestock) and *Mycobacterium avium* (affects birds), collectively referred to as the *tubercle bacillus. M. tuberculosis* and *M. bovis* can also infect dogs.

For a while it was thought this disease of antiquity was on the decline; however, in recent years the scourge has made a comeback, due to a combination of emerging antibiotic-resistant strains and an increase in human immunodeficiency virus (HIV) infections. Currently, it's estimated that as many as 25,000 new human cases each year are being diagnosed in the United States.

TUBERCULOSIS

SYMPTOMS: Coughing; labored breathing; retching; weight loss; fever; anemia; enlarged lymph nodes; bloody sputum
HOME CARE: None; EXTREMELY CONTAGOUS TO HUMANS. SEE VET IMMEDIATELY!
VET CARE: None; due to human health risk, euthanasia is recommended
PREVENTION: Prevent your dog's exposure to human tuberculosis sufferers

Dogs typically contract the disease by contact with an infected human. In most cases, the infection causes no signs of disease in a dog with a healthy immune system. When the dog does become ill, respiratory signs such as coughing, labored breathing, retching, weight loss, fever, anorexia, and enlargement of the lymph nodes may be seen. The dog may cough up bloody sputum. Such dogs are extremely contagious, and pose a health risk to other dogs and people.

Diagnosis of canine tuberculosis is extremely difficult. Skin testing and blood tests that detect antibodies (both used successfully in people) are not reliable in dogs. Other methods, such as finding the agent in tissue samples (biopsy) are involved and take a long time to accomplish. An X-ray that shows lung changes may be helpful.

Human anti-tuberculosis medications have been used experimentally in infected dogs. However, successful treatment requires weeks to months of therapy, and because of the potential zoonotic risk, therapy is not recommended in dogs. Sadly, dogs confirmed to have tuberculosis are usually euthanized to protect other pets and people. Fortunately, the disease is considered rare in dogs (see ZOONOSIS).

ULCER An ulcer is a slow-to-heal open sore that may be located anywhere on the body. An ulcer can cause progressive tissue damage and loss, particularly if infection becomes involved. Dogs may suffer eye an ulcer from injury or anatomical conditions (see ECTROPION/ENTROPION), on the skin secondary to insect bites or trauma, or due to other problems like lick sores. Any sore that is slow to heal should be addressed by a veterinarian.

ULTRASOUND An ultrasound is a noninvasive diagnostic instrument which employs sound waves to penetrate various structures of the body. These waves pass over or through tissue in various ways depending on its density. The echo-reflection of these waves provides a two-dimensional image that offers veterinarians an accurate picture of the soft areas of the body that X-rays aren't able to discern.

Doppler echocardiography, the newest form, detects how blood flows throughout the heart. In echocardiography, sound waves are bounced off the heart muscle and surrounding tissues, the echoed signals are processed, and this information is then displayed in a visual or auditory format.

Echocardiography offers the capability to put a transducer on the chest, and look at cardiac anatomy and heart function noninvasively and actually look at blood flow within the heart, and identify congenital and acquired abnormalities. About 90 percent of veterinary cardiologists have fairly high- end level machines and do cardiac ultrasound.

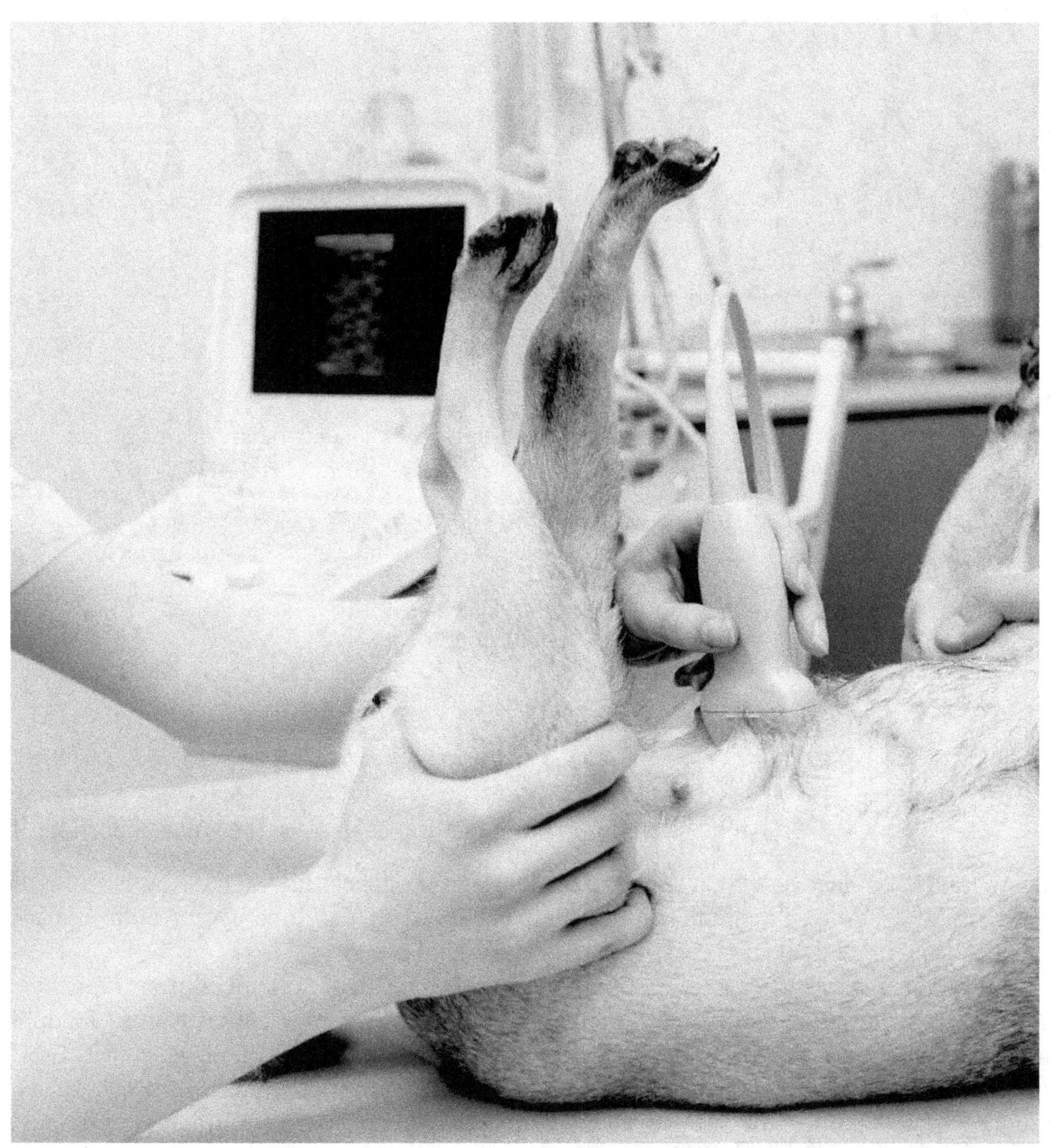

UVEITIS

SYMPTOMS: Change of eye color in one or both eyes; clouding of cornea; rough eye surface; squinting and watering eye; soft eyeball; small pupil that reacts slowly to light
HOME CARE: None
VET CARE: Treat cause if possible; steroids to relieve inflammation; atropine to dilate pupil; medication to buffer pain
PREVENTION: Avoid exposure to systemic illness, parasites, and trauma

UVEITIS Uveitis refers to an inflammation of the iris, the colored portion of the eye, and the ciliary body that supports the lens and produces fluid to the front portion of the eye. The condition is common in dogs, and may affect only one eye or both. Unless diagnosed and treated, the dog may lose her sight in that eye.

When both eyes are affected, the condition is likely a result of systemic illness. Parasites, fungus, and bacterial or viral disease including toxoplasmosis may cause uveitis. Trauma and cancer are other causes, and corneal ulcer often precedes the condition.

Signs of the condition vary depending on the cause. Dogs may squint, suffer watery eyes, clouding of the cornea, or even a change in eye color. Often, the affected eye feels abnormally soft, and the pupil is small and reacts slowly to light (see BLINDNESS, GLAUCOMA and CATARACTS).

Some cases of uveitis are diagnosed with blood tests and evaluation of the fluid within the eye itself. Ultrasound or X-rays may also be required. Treatment depends on the underlying cause; antibiotics, antifungal, and parasite-killing medications address these causes. Treatment almost always involves high doses of anti-inflammatory drugs such as corticosteroids.

VACCINATIONS Vaccinations are medical preventatives, often injections, designed to stimulate the immune system to mount a protective defense against disease. Vaccines essentially program the dog's body to recognize alien substances such as viruses and bacteria as dangerous, and mount an attack to neutralize them.

Vaccinations prompt immunity by exposing the dog to a non-disease-producing form of the foreign agent. Such exposure stimulates the production of protective cells and antibodies designed to seek and destroy pathogens before they cause illness.

Preventative vaccinations are important to protect dogs from life-threatening illnesses. However, even the best vaccine will not provide 100 percent protection. Most vaccines are designed to prevent disease, but some will only reduce the severity of the illness but not keep the dog from getting sick. Your vaccinated dog will still be at risk for disease especially if repeatedly exposed.

Dogs should be vaccinated against those diseases for which they are at risk. Risk factors vary depending on the individual dog's immune competence, exposure, and stress levels (see STRESS).

Very young and very old dogs typically have less effective immune systems, and so are at higher risk for disease. Risk of disease is increased in dogs exposed to other dogs, such as kenneled dogs, show dogs, and dogs being boarded. Dogs in overcrowded conditions such as shelters, and show dogs or working dogs that travel a lot have increased exposure. This also causes higher stress levels which can make a dog more susceptible to illness. And dogs that are allowed to roam, particularly intact animals, have increased exposure to other dogs and disease.

The geographic region in which a dog lives also influences risk, because the incidence for some canine diseases is higher in certain areas than in others. An "only" dog that is a healthy neutered or spayed housedog is probably at lowest risk for exposure to disease.

Due to these many variables, a single vaccination program may not be appropriate for all dogs. Your veterinarian can best design an appropriate regime for your particular pet.

In the past, shots were given every single year as a matter of course, even though no studies had been conducted to show the duration of vaccination protection. Also, puppies and adult dogs were often vaccinated against a wide range of illnesses, even when the risk for getting the disease was slim. Today, veterinarians agree that dogs should be protected against those conditions for which they are at risk.

Most puppies are inoculated with a series of protective shots as maternal protection fades away. A mother dog that has a healthy immune system passes her immunity on to her puppies when they drink the first milk, called colostrum. This passive immunity fades over a few weeks as the babies' own immune system matures and takes over. Unfortunately, this borrowed immunity also interferes with the vaccines. The protective agents in the vaccines are identified as foreign and are attacked and destroyed just like the virus or bacteria would be. That's why a single vaccination given at six weeks of age won't protect puppies from becoming sick.

Your dog's immune system isn't completely mature until about six to eight weeks of age—but Mom's immunity won't stop neutralizing part of the vaccinations until the babies are about fourteen weeks of age; timing is different from puppy to puppy. The window when Mom's immunity has faded and Junior's is finally mature is quite narrow. Therefore, a series of vaccinations are given so that active immunity is stimulated just as maternal protection fades away (see IMMUNITY).

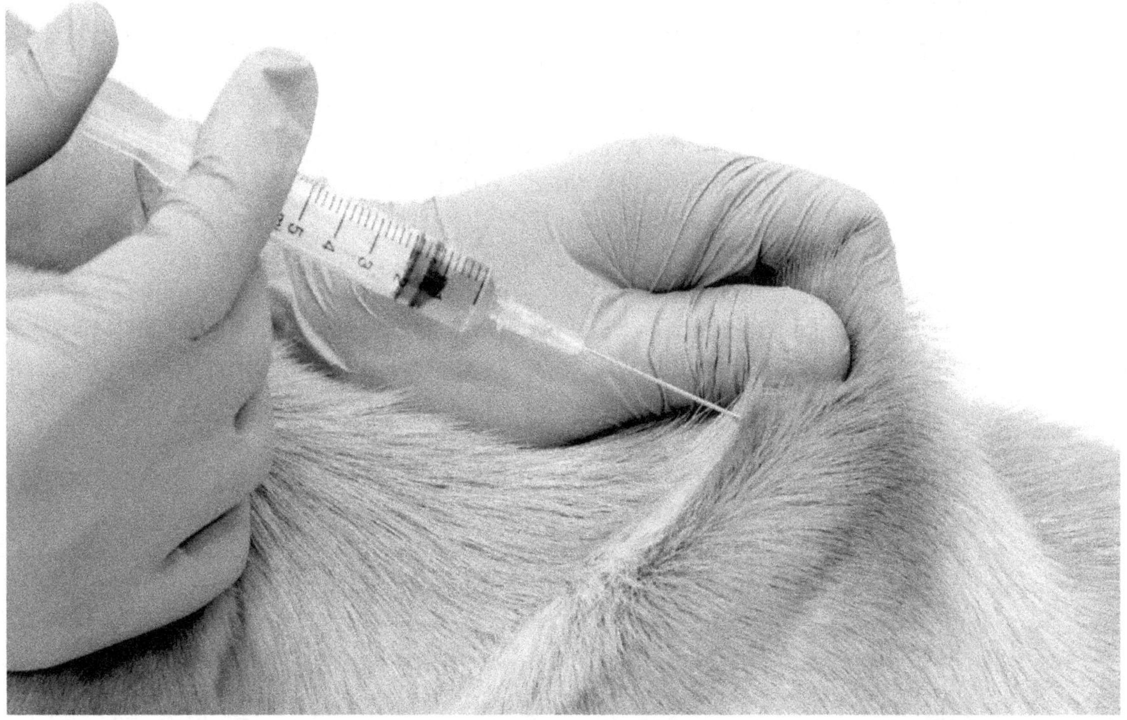

The majority of vaccinations are given by injection beneath the skin. Those for canine parainfluenza virus or kennel cough can be given under the skin, or as drops in the nose to stimulate local protection in cells first exposed to these viruses. Maternal antibodies don't block cell mediated immunity, which means protection can be administered before six weeks of age if the puppy is at risk for exposure. However, the vaccination for kennel cough isn't recommended until nine weeks of age.

Most canine vaccinations are either modified live, or "killed" (inactivated) vaccines. The type of vaccine depends on the infectious agent. For instance, an inactivated vaccine against canine distemper virus isn't effective, so all those used today are modified live vaccines.

Vaccines are modified to reduce or eliminate their ability to cause disease, but when left "alive" they are able to multiply inside the body the way a normal virus would. Modified live vaccines more closely imitate natural infections, so the immune system is better stimulated. They also negate maternal immunity more easily to provide a better and quicker protection for puppies than killed vaccines.

However, some extremely virulent agents like rabies and canine parvovirus may prove difficult to inactivate enough to ensure they won't cause the disease they are trying to prevent. Modified live vaccines can cause problems in pets with suppressed immune systems, or result in birth defects in unborn puppies when the vaccine is given to the dam during pregnancy.

A safer alternative is killed vaccines. They can be given to pregnant dogs, and will not cause disease. They are usually more expensive because they must contain an additive (adjuvant) that stimulates the immune response. While a modified live vaccine may be effective after only one dose, a series of at least two vaccinations is generally required when using killed vaccines to ensure the best protection.

Today, a number of veterinarians also recommend that after the initial puppy shots and first year booster, dogs be re-vaccinated every three years rather than annually. Follow your own veterinarian's recommendation. She'll know best what will work for your individual situation.

The effectiveness of the shots depends on many things: age of the puppy or dog, individual immune competence, exposure risk, and other health problems. In the case of shelter adoptions and of back-door waifs, the puppy may look perfectly healthy but be incubating an illness he was exposed to before you found him. The stress of a visit to the veterinarian may prompt him to come down with something. It's rarely the shot that causes such a problem.

Generally, it is recommended that all dogs receive protection with "core" vaccinations—that is, the most common and dangerous illnesses for which the pet will likely have the greatest risk for exposure. Distemper, parvovirus, hepatitis and rabies are designated "core" vaccinations. "Noncore" vaccinations are recommended for dogs at specific risk for those conditions, such as Lyme disease, kennel cough and leptospirosis.

Your veterinarian determines when to start and how many boosters your pup should receive based on health status and exposure. Usually puppies receive a series of either three or four boosters three weeks apart, starting at either six weeks (6, 9, 12, 16 weeks of age) or starting at nine weeks (9, 12 and 16 weeks). Rabies is given at 16 weeks, and all of the core vaccinations are repeated a year later.

Most of the "core" vaccinations have been shown to provide protection for (on average) about five to seven years. Your puppy as he grows will need to see the vet more frequently anyway if only for well-dog exams. Veterinarians may recommend giving distemper vaccination one year, parvovirus the next, and so on. Usually either an annual or every three years revaccination provides the best insurance on the core vaccines.

The noncore vaccinations are best given more frequently prior to expected exposure. That's because most bacteria-protective vaccines give only about six months protection, which means the leptospirosis, bordetella/kennel cough and Lyme vaccines for your dog are not suited for a three-year protocol. Because rabies is a zoonosis—disease that affects people—local laws dictate how often your dog needs revaccination. That's usually either every year or every three years.

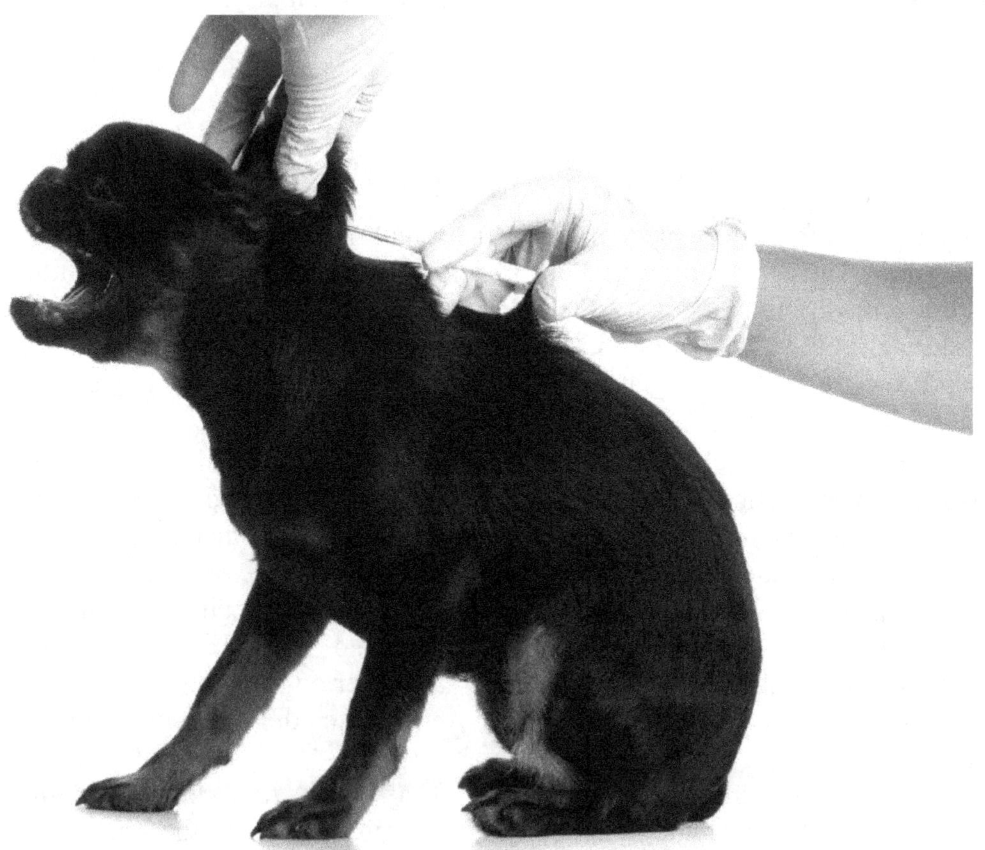

Some puppies and dogs experience a vaccine reaction. Usually the pet acts a bit lethargic for a day or two, and sometimes has a small swollen or sore place at the shot spot. It's a good idea to monitor the site of the injection to make sure any swelling goes away within several days. If it doesn't, a trip back to the vet is in order. Vaccination reactions like lethargy or soreness are much more likely to occur when multiple shots are given at the same time. Ask your veterinarian about spreading the vaccinations out over several visits instead. Rather than the combination shot, for instance, separate inoculations with one or two at a time may be more appropriate.

Occasionally a dog responds adversely to a vaccination. The most serious, called anaphylactic reaction, occurs within ten to 15 minutes following the injection. Signs vary from relatively minor problems like facial swelling or hives, to severe respiratory distress along with vomiting, diarrhea, and collapse. These are emergencies that require immediate veterinary help. If your pet has previously had an allergic reaction to vaccination, medication scan be given prior to vaccinations to prevent or lessen the symptoms of future reactions.

VESTIBULAR SYNDROME

Middle age to senior dogs sometimes suffer from sudden, unexplained balance problems referred to as vestibular syndrome. The pet commonly begins to suffer from dizzy behavior, head tilt, circling, and falling with difficult getting up. Oftentimes the pet's eyes will jerk back and forth from side to side. The head tilt, circling and falling will be in one direction, indicating which inner ear is affected. Usually the dog also vomits and/or refuses to eat, probably due to nausea from the associated signs.

There is no definitive diagnosis, and the signs may be confused with other conditions such as cancer, particularly since most victims are older, senior dogs. The veterinarian makes the presumed diagnosed based on signs, and eliminating other causes, such as inner ear infection, which can be treated and result in resolution of the problems.

When neither an ear infection nor cancer is found, the condition is considered idiopathic (of no known cause). Unfortunately, there is no treatment for idiopathic vestibular syndrome. Most cases, however, gradually get better on their own over a period of a week to a month. The veterinarian may give your dog medications to abate the nausea and dizziness, or possibly fluids if the dog refuses to eat.

In most cases, the signs completely go away and never return. Other times, though, a few of the behaviors linger such as head tilt or circling. When the symptoms persist more than a month without abatement, the veterinarian may recommend further screening tests to look for a tumor.

VESTIBULAR SYNDROME

SYMPTOMS: Dizzy behavior; head tilt; circling; falling; eyes jerking; vomiting; anorexia
HOME CARE: None
VET CARE: Usually goes away without treatment
PREVENTION: None

VOMITING

Vomiting is the forcible expulsion of the stomach's contents up the dog's throat and out of the mouth. Dogs tend to vomit more readily than almost all other animals. When the "vomit center" of the brain is stimulated, the dog begins to salivate and swallow repeatedly. Your dog may seek attention or look anxious. Then, the stomach and abdominal muscles forcibly and repeatedly contract, while at the same time the esophagus relaxes. The dog extends her neck, opens her mouth and makes a strained gagging sound as the stomach empties. When a dog has eaten something she shouldn't, vomiting should usually be induced by the owner or veterinarian (see POISONING).

Most cases of canine vomiting result from gastric irritation due to swallowed grass, eating inedible objects, spoiled or rich food (raiding the garbage, table scraps) or simply eating too much too fast. The most common cause of vomiting in dogs is gluttony. Dogs that gorge their food tend to lose it as quickly as it's swallowed, particularly if they exercise shortly after finishing a meal. This type of vomiting isn't particularly dangerous, but is annoying. Slowing down the rate of consumption will go a long way toward relieving mealtime vomiting. Feed dogs in separate bowls to cut down on "competition" eating, or place a large non-swallowable ball in the dish so the dog is forced to eat around it. Meal-feeding several times a day rather than once will also alleviate overeating. A few dogs vomit when they're excited or fearful (see STRESS, FEAR, and CAR SICKNESS).

Vomiting is different than regurgitation, which is a passive process without strong muscle contractions. Regurgitation can occur minutes to hours after eating, and the expelled material is undigested and may even be tube-shaped like the throat. Occasional regurgitation isn't a cause for concern unless it interferes with nutrition. Chronic regurgitation typically is seen in a young dog that as a result grows very slowly (see MEGAESOPHAGUS).

Vomiting that happens only once or twice isn't a cause for concern as long as the dog acts normal before and after. Resting the digestive tract by withholding food and water for 12 to 24 hours or so will usually resolve the gastric irritation (see ENTERITIS).

You can safely give Pepto-Bismol to manage doggy vomiting. It coats the stomach wall, soothes the upset and the bismuth absorbs bacterial toxins that prompt vomiting. The dose is about ½ to 1 teaspoon per 5 pounds of body weight up to three times a day.

Repeated vomiting, unproductive vomiting, vomiting not associated with eating, and/or the dog acts like she feels bad before or after the event is a cause for alarm. Vomiting can be a sign of canine distemper virus, canine parvovirus, swallowed objects, or liver or kidney disease. If the vomit contains blood or fecal material, if it lasts longer than 24 hours, or if other signs such as diarrhea accompany the vomiting, contact your veterinarian immediately.

VON WILLEBRAND'S DISEASE

Von Willebrand's Disease is an inherited bleeding disorder caused by a defect in the clotting factors of the blood. It has been found in many breeds, but is most common in Doberman Pinschers and German Shepherd Dogs. It's also commonly reported in the Miniature Schnauzer and Golden Retriever.

Most cases are mild, and some even lessen as the dog grows older. Signs include nosebleeds, blood in the stool or urine, bleeding into the joints or beneath the skin, and slow-to-clot wounds that ooze blood for a prolonged period of time (see HEMOPHILIA).

WATER ON THE BRAIN (HYDROCEPHALUS)

Hydrocephalus results with too much spinal fluid is created, causing "water on the brain." This may affect only one side of the brain, or both, and affect the entire ventricular system (hollow structures in the brain that communicate with the spinal cord canal), or only one area of obstruction within the ventricular system.

Overproduction of spinal fluid can cause water on the brain, but this is rare. A tumor in the eye also may cause the disorder. But more often, obstructive hydrocephalus causes spinal fluid to collect due to blockage. Compensatory hydrocephalus results in fluid collecting in areas of the brain that have either been destroyed or failed to develop normally. Both these types can be either present at birth, or acquired later in life.

WATER ON THE BRAIN

SYMPTOMS: Soiling; sleepiness; vocalization; blindness; seizures; over-large dome-shaped head; crossed-eyes; gait abnormalities; coma; abnormal breathing; arch head backwards and extend all four legs
HOME CARE: None
VET CARE: Surgery; medication
PREVENTION: None; avoid breeding dogs known to have a familial history of the condition

The congenital form of hydrocephalus is more likely to occur in small and brachycephalic (flat-faced) dog breeds, such as the Bulldog, Chihuahua, Maltese, Pomeranian, Toy Poodle, Lhasa Apso, Cairn Terrier, Boston Terrier, Pug, and Pekingese. It's an inherited disease in Yorkshire terriers, and normal adult Beagles also have a high incidence of enlarged ventricular systems, but show no signs of disease. The acquired condition can happen in any dog.

Signs of the congenital disease develop before a year of age, and often within a few weeks of birth, but the acquired form can occur at any age. Signs may develop gradually or occur suddenly, and some cases will not show any symptoms at all.

Pressure on the brain from excess water result in behavior changes. Potty accidents may develop in housetrained dogs, for example. Dogs may act sleep, vocalize for no apparent reason, or become extremely excited. The dog may become blind or develop crossed eyes, suffer seizures, or fall into a coma. Odd walking or running gait, or abnormal breathing also can occur, and the dog may arch the body with its head backward while extending all four legs. A large dome-shaped head (due to intracranial swelling) is a common sign.

The veterinarian will want to know of any falls that might have occurred, as well as information about the dog's parentage. Since many of the signs can point to other conditions, a complete physical with blood tests and profiles with urinalysis will be used to rule out trauma, cancer, or infection. A spinal tap and analysis of the fluid, and an electroencephalogram (EEG) may be run. X-rays of the dog's skull, as well as CT-scan and/or MRI provide the final diagnosis.

Severe signs may point to permanent damage in which case surgery and implanting a shunt may be the only option. The shunt drains excess spinal fluid from the brain into the abdomen, where it can be absorbed. Sadly, complications of infection and blockage from tissue or clots are common with shunt placements. When implanted in small puppies, they often require replacement as the dog grows. Hydrocephalus usually results in a shortened life span.

Less severe symptoms may do well with medication that helps reduce the amount of spinal fluid produced. The drug omeprazole (brand name Prilosec) has successfully reduced the production of spinal fluid in dogs by stopping the "pumps" that move the fluid into circulation. Anticonvulsant drugs may also be necessary (see SEIZURES), and steroid medications also may be prescribed.

WART

A wart is a small, horny protrusion of the skin. Canine warts are actually benign tumors of the upper layers of the skin, and are caused by a variety of papillomaviruses.

Warts are much more common in people, who are usually affected on their hands or feet. Geriatric dogs may develop warts anywhere on their body. They're often hidden by fur and don't cause any problem, but should be removed if they become irritated or bleed.

WART

SYMPTOMS: Single to multiple small, horny protrusions of skin; rash in the mouths or eyes of young dogs
HOME CARE: None
VET CARE: Usually goes away without treatment; sometimes surgery when severe
PREVENTION: Avoid contact with dogs suffering the condition

Young dogs may develop a condition called papillomatosis in which warts develop in their mouths, or sometimes on the eyelids, cornea, conjunctiva, or skin in other locations. Clusters of warts typically appear on the gum surfaces or lips. The condition may be spread to another dog by close contact with an infected dog.

Papillomatosis is almost always a transient condition, which cures by itself within a few months. It can be unsightly and uncomfortable for the affected dog, however. If the condition is extreme or is slow to resolve, a veterinarian may intervene with surgery. Cryosurgery (freezing) or electro surgery (cautery, or burning) are options. Once the dog recovers, he's usually immune to the virus and will have no further problem.

WHISKERS Whiskers refer to the thick, wire-like hairs that protrude from the dog's face. Also called vibrissae, whiskers are specialized hairs that are long, supple and thick, or groupings of short stiff bristles.

Whiskers are much more developed in animals that hunt during the night or low-light times. They act as feelers, and are seated deep in the skin where they trigger nerve receptors at the slightest touch.

Dogs have whiskers in four places on each side of the head, and two on the lower jaw. The most obvious are those on each side of the dog's muzzle, where whiskers grow in four rows; they provide information when the dog is sticking his nose in and around objects. Bristles of four or five whiskers above each eye act like extended eyelashes that prompt a protective blink reflex when brushed. A clump of whiskers is located on each cheek, and a smaller one near each corner of the mouth. Finally, the dog has a tuft beneath the chin, which probably serves to keep his head from scraping the ground during tracking behavior, or may even help in food-burying activities (see HAIR).

WHIPWORMS

SYMPTOMS: Diarrhea; vomiting; anemia; weight loss; rough coat
HOME CARE: None
VET CARE: Treatment with medication to kill parasite
PREVENTION: Pick up feces; some heartworm preventatives also protect against whipworms

WHIPWORMS Whipworms (*Trichuris vulpis*) are thin, two to three inch long thread-like intestinal parasite worms that narrow at one end like a whip. All dogs are at risk, but puppies may be more profoundly affected.

Dogs contract the parasite by ingesting eggs found in the soil. Eggs can live for five years in the soil of cold climates. Consequently, whipworms may cause more problems in northern states than in southern climes where the eggs are more readily killed.

The eggs hatch and mature in the dog's large intestine in about 70 to 90 days. The parasite feeds on blood by burrowing into the wall of the intestine. In small numbers, whipworms cause few problems. The female worm produces fewer offspring than many other kinds of intestinal parasites, like roundworms so typically the infestation is light.

Puppies infected with whipworms often are also infected with other parasites, such as hookworms, and the combination can be devastating. A heavy worm load of whipworms may cause diarrhea, vomiting, anemia and weight loss, and such dogs typically have a rough coat or "unthrifty" appearance.

Diagnosis is made by finding eggs during microscopic examination of the stool. But dogs may show clinical signs for several weeks before worm eggs will be shed in the stool. Later, eggs may only be shed intermittently, continuing to make diagnosis difficult.

Effective medications are available, but once whipworms are in the environment, infestations can be hard to contain since dogs are often re-infected from egg-contaminated soil. Treatment for three months or longer may be necessary to totally eliminate the infestation.

Good hygiene is the only way to reduce the chance of your dog contracting whipworms. Pick up the yard after your dog at least weekly, and oftener is much better. Some heartworm preventatives can prevent whipworms as well as some other parasites such as fleas.

WOBBLER'S SYNDROME

More accurately termed cervical spondylopathy, wobbler's syndrome is a malformation and/or misalignment of the lower cervical (neck) vertebrae which results in varying degrees of spinal cord compression. The pressure on the spinal cord causes progressive degeneration of rear-limb function with a resulting "wobbly" gait.

The condition is seen in several breeds of dogs, but most commonly affects Great Danes less than a year old, and Doberman Pinschers older than five. Initial signs are loss of coordination of the rear limbs, along with a peculiar unsteady gait. As the disease progresses, paralysis advances from rear limbs to the forelimbs, with neck movements becoming more and more painful and stiff.

The cause remains a mystery. Experts speculate that genetics, rapid growth and nutrition, alone or in combination, are influencing factors. Because the syndrome may have an inherited basis, dogs diagnosed with wobbler's syndrome should not be bred. Diagnosis is based on signs, breed predisposition, and X-rays.

Your veterinarian may recommend PEMF therapy, which stimulate the electrical and chemical processes in the tissues to relieve inflammation and pain and has shown some benefit in cases of back problems in dogs. Devices may be designed for whole body treatment or targeted areas of the body. Some of these devices have successfully completed efficacy studies and are FDA-approved. Therapeutic products may be available in mats, wraps or other devices from your veterinarian or over the counter (see PULSED ELECTROMAGNETIC FIELD).

Prognosis is guarded, depending on the severity of the condition and age of the dog. Some dogs are helped with corticosteroid therapy, which helps relieve accompanying inflammation. In others, surgical intervention may be necessary to relieve the pressure on the spinal cord, and to stabilize the cervical disks to prevent further damage.

X-RAY X-rays, also called radiographs, are a kind wave-like electromagnetic radiation that's invisible, and is similar to but shorter than visible light.

The unique radiation that's produce can penetrate different body structures in varying degrees, and the result is recorded on photographic film. A negative film image results in areas of the body where radiation is able to fully penetrate. The more waves that pass through, the darker will be the image, while the fewer there are, the lighter the picture on the film.

Empty space allows the greatest penetration, so air-filled spaces like the lungs look black on the film. Fat is next, and is dark gray. Fluid or soft tissue are recorded in varying degrees of medium to light gray. The radiation can't penetrate bone or teeth, which are extremely complex, dense structures; these areas will appear white on the film.

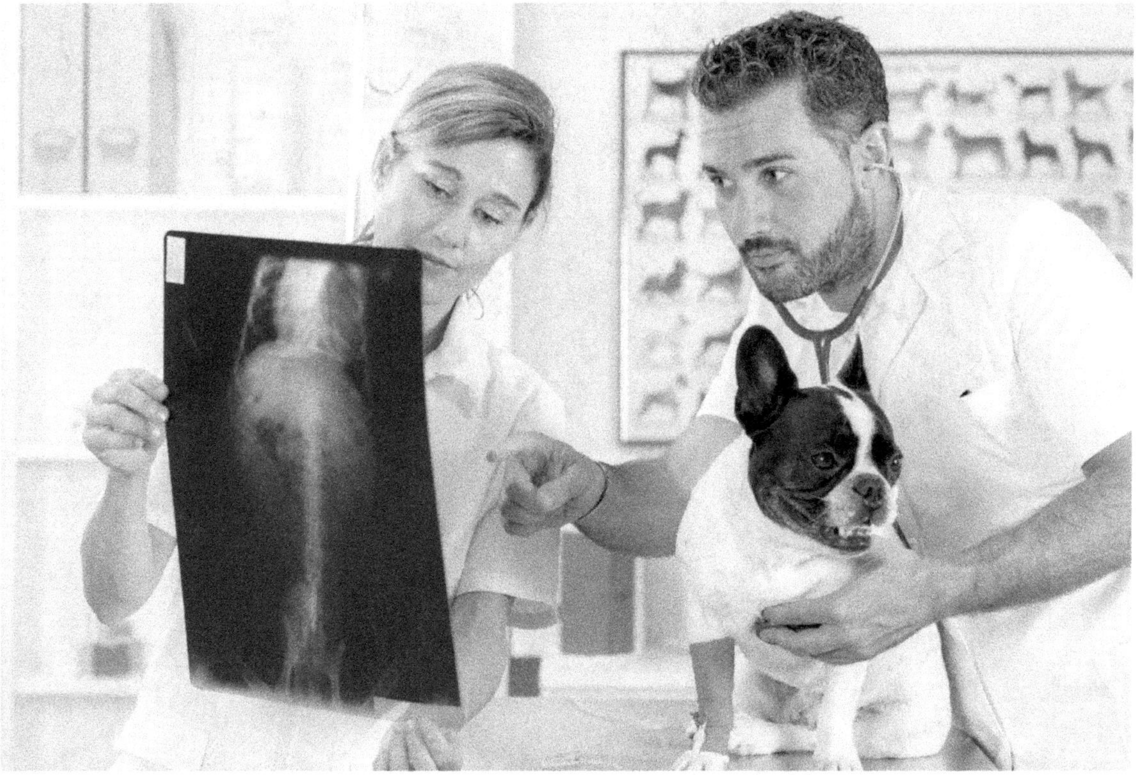

X-rays provide significant diagnostic information in both human and veterinary medicine. Because of radiographs, it's possible to see and diagnose kidney or bladder stones, fractures, and swallowed objects without the need for exploratory surgery. Often, this ensures timely treatment that otherwise might come too late.

Diagnostic X-rays employ a safe radiation level that's carefully regulated. When used therapeutically as a treatment for cancer, radiation is increased to specific levels and targeted to precise areas (see CANCER).

XYLITOL POISONING Xylitol is a naturally-occurring sugar alcohol used for sweetening sugar-free products such chewing gum, candy, toothpaste and baked products. It also comes as a granulated powder. Both forms are highly toxic to dogs. Xylitol ingestion causes a rapid release of insulin in the dog, which in turn results in a sudden decrease in blood glucose levels. Depending on the size of your dog, a single piece of sugar-free gum may cause symptoms that result in death.

The ingested substance may cause vomiting, incoordination, seizures, or even liver failure. Bleeding may develop in the dog's gastrointestinal track or abdomen, as well as dark red specks or splotches on his gums. Usually the symptoms happen quickly, within fifteen to thirty minutes of ingestion, but some kinds of sugar-free gum may not cause symptoms for up to twelve hours.

Diagnosis is based on blood screening tests and urinalysis, as well as coagulation and other tests to screen for bleeding disorders. By the time signs develop, it may be too late for vomiting to do any good. But if you see your dog eat something containing xylitol, induce vomiting immediately and then get to the vet. Give your dog one to two teaspoons of 3 percent hydrogen peroxide for every pound he weighs. You can repeat in five minutes if it doesn't work, but then rush to the vet clinic.

The veterinary treatment consists of supportive care, which may include fluid therapy, and continued blood tests to monitor the progression of the poisoning for at least 24 hours. Dogs suffering from low blood sugar alone tend to recover well. If the dog develops liver damage, the prognosis is guarded.

Protect your dog from xylitol poisoning by knowing the ingredients in your products, and keeping them out of reach. For canine thieves that won't be deterred, be safe and keep xylitol products out of your house altogether.

XYLITOL POISONING

SYMPTOMS: Vomiting; incoordination; drunk behavior; lethargy; seizures; collapse
FIRST AID: EMERGENCY! SEE VET IMMEDIATELY! If you witness the dog ingesting a product with xylitol, induce vomiting immediately and then see the vet.
VET CARE: Supportive care; fluid therapy; monitoring blood and enzyme values
PREVENTION: Keep xylitol-containing products out of dog's reach.

YEAST INFECTION *Candida* is a type of yeast organism that digests sugar and is part of the normal in a dog's mouth, nose, ears, gastrointestinal and genital tracts. This type of yeast sometimes takes over and colonizes damaged tissues especially of immuno-suppressed pets, like geriatric dogs, young pups or those with other underlying diseases. *Malassezia* is another type of yeast that can cause problems for dogs.

A fungal infection called **Candidiasis** develops if an overgrowth of *Candida* occurs. It can affect any age or breed, and may target one area of the body as a local infection (see CYSTITIS, DROOLING and OTITIS). In extreme cases, it can invade the entire body as a systemic infection, often secondary to skin or endocrine disease (see ALLERGY and DIABETES).

Diagnosis is made by examining samples of the affected area. Urinalysis, skin swabs, or biopsies may be conducted. Often, topical medications are apply topically to the affected area, and samples cultured again two weeks post apparent cure to confirm the condition has resolved.

YELLOW SKIN (JAUNDICE) Jaundice refers to the abnormal yellow discoloration of bodily tissues and fluids. In dogs, jaundice is most easily seen in thinly furred or light-colored areas of the body, such as the insides of the ears or whites of the eyes. It is a sign of abnormal liver function, and results from the abnormal deposition of bile pigments throughout the body (see LIVER DISEASE).

ZINC-RESPONSIVE DERMATOSIS This is a skin disorder caused by a deficiency of zinc in the diet. Zinc is required in tiny amounts, and helps promote healthy skin and hair growth.

Alaskan Malamutes, Bull Terriers, Samoyeds and Siberian Huskies may inherit a genetic defect that interferes with the proper absorption of zinc. The condition can be prompted in any dog fed generic foods or other poor quality rations low in zinc, or in dogs whose diets are over-supplemented with minerals, such as calcium.

Signs of zinc-deficiency include thinning of the fur, and a scaly dermatitis especially on the face. The dog's feet also typically develop thick calluses, and crack and bleed. The condition is diagnosed by the signs, and based on the dog's diet history. Correcting the diet to a complete and balanced ration, along with short-term zinc supplementation, will reverse the signs of disease. Most dogs show rapid improvement in as little as one week. Dogs suffering an inherent absorption problem typically require veterinary supervised zinc supplementation for the rest of their lives (see FOOD, FOOD SUPPLEMENTS, NUTRITION, and READING LABELS).

ZINC-RESPONSIVE DERMATITIS

SYMPTOMS: Thinning fur; scaly facial dermatitis; thick footpads that crack and bleed
HOME CARE: Feed complete and balanced diet
VET CARE: Supplement the diet with zinc; sometimes zinc supplement for rest of dog's life
PREVENTION: Feed complete and balanced diet

ZOONOSIS Zoonosis refers to a disease that a person can contract from an animal under ordinary circumstances. Humans are vulnerable to many viral and bacterial diseases, fungus, and parasitic conditions that more commonly affect animals.

Of the 200 plus known zoonosis, only a few are associated with pets. Of these, most cause only transient disease and can be easily treated and resolved, with incidence of such cases remaining low. Still, the potential danger of zoonotic disease mustn't be dismissed, because a few do actually cause severe human illness or even death.

Without exception, the most common zoonosis associated with dogs can be avoided. Routine hygiene and conventional prevention protect your dog and yourself from potential illness (see BRUCELLOSIS, CANINE SCABIES, GIARDIASIS, HOOKWORMS, LEPTOSPIROSIS, PLAGUE, RABIES, RINGWORM, ROUNDWORMS, TAPEWORMS, TOXOPLASMOSIS, and TUBERCULOSIS).

APPENDIX A

DOG ASSOCIATIONS and BREEDS AT A GLANCE

A dog association is a national organization that registers dogs, keeps records of their ancestry in pedigrees, publishes breed standards, sponsors dog shows and events, and determines who will judge them. Kennels are individual establishments that strive to produce the "ideal" dog of a given breed. These dogs then compete in conformation and performance trials sanctioned by the dog association in which that dog is registered. The goal is to determine which dog is closest to the standard of perfection in looks, temperament and/or performance.

Kennels and sometimes individuals hold membership in local or national dog clubs, which in turn are members of one or more dog association. There are several kinds of dog clubs: all-breed clubs, specialty breed clubs (a single breed), and the performance clubs which include obedience, tracking, field trial, hunting test, herding, coonhound, and lure coursing. There are also a number of dog associations. Breed standards may vary from association to association, and not all dog associations recognize the same dog breeds. Be aware that registration does not guarantee the quality of a dog, only that both parents were the same breed. However, registered dogs can prove their quality by earning titles, and dog parents with titles usually produce high-quality puppies. If you are interested in learning more about dog show opportunities for you and your dog, contact one or more of the following organizations.

American Kennel Club (AKC)
http://www.akc.org/

American Rare Breed Association
http://www.arba.org

Australian National Kennel Council
http://ankc.org.au

Canadian Kennel Club
http://www.ckc.ca

Federation Cynologique Internationale
http://www.fci.be/en

Kennel Club of India
http://www.kennelclubofindia.org

Kennel Union of Southern Africa
http://www.kusa.co.za

New Zealand Kennel Club
http://www.nzkc.org.nz

The Kennel Club
http://www.thekennelclub.org.uk

United Kennel Club
http://www.ukcdogs.com

BREEDS AT A GLANCE

Every dog is an individual and generalities may not apply to every dog of a given breed—dogs may be biters or good with kids due to training or circumstances apart from breed tendencies. And dogs may never experience the listed health concerns or may develop others not mentioned. This is a representative list and does not include all recognized breeds.

BREEDS	SIZE	COAT TYPE	COAT CARE	TEMPERAMENT	HEALTH CONCERNS
Affenpinscher	6-8 lb 9-11.5"	medium	medium	likes older kids, smart but resistant to training, likes to dig, usually quiet	Periodontal disease
Afghan Hound	50-70 lb 25-27"	long	high	not good with kids; high activity, quiet, aggressive toward small animals, needs lots of exercise, likes privacy	hip dysplasia, allergies, cataracts, demodicosis, ear infection, hypothyroidism, PRA
Airedale Terrier	45-52 lb 23"	short	low	not good with kids; protective; independent, aggressive, moderate exercise	hip dysplasia, gastritis, skin disease, hypothyroidism, PRA
Akita	80-110lb 24-28"	Short to medium	low	not good with kids, dog aggressive, one person dog	Bloat, PRA, cataracts
Alaskan Malamute	75-85 lb 23-25"	medium	medium	loyal but independent freethinker, needs lots of exercise, likes to howl and bark, dog-aggressive	hypothyroidism, zinc-responsive dermatosis, PRA, bronchitis, hemolytic anemia, cataracts
American Eskimo Dog	25-35 lb 15-18"	long	high	likes older kids, playful, likes to bark, high energy dog needs lots of exercise	none mentioned
American Foxhound	55-75 lb 21-25"	short	low	good watchdog, high energy, needs to hunt, older kids okay	none mentioned
American Staffordshire Terrier	55-70 lb 12-19"	short	low	needs early training, dominant personality, not for homes with kids	Demodicosis, PRA
American Water Spaniel	25-45 lb 15-18"	medium	medium	not good with kids, lots of exercise, suspicious of strangers, possessive of toys, needs firm hand	none mentioned
Australian Cattle Dog	35-45 lb 17-20"	short	low	not good with kids, suspicious of strangers, great watchdog, high energy dog	PRA

				needs work	
Australian Shepherd	45-60 lb 18-23"	medium long	high	enjoys older kids, suspicious of strangers, highly intelligent and trainable, needs lots of exercise	Deafness, PRA, cataracts, Collie Eye
Australian Terrier	10-18 lbs 10-11"	medium	medium	likes older children, not good with small pets	PRA, upper airway disease
Basenji	21-25 lbs 16-17"	short	low	good with kids, energetic, barkless but noisy yodeler, hard to train, moderate exercise	hernias, gastritis, anemia, inflammatory bowel disease, hemolytic anemia, kidney disease, cataracts
Basset Hound	30-55 lbs 14" or less	short	low	moderate exercise, good with older kids, calm, loyal, good natured, easily distracted, tends to be noisy	bladder stones, disk disease, lymphoma, otitis, ectropion or entropion, glaucoma, conjunctivitis, obesity, skin disease, cherry eye, Von Willebrand's Disease, PRA, spine problems
Beagle (two sizes)	18-35 lbs 13" or less or 13-15"	short	low	good with kids, likes to run and bark, extremely friendly, a gentle, happy, and curious dog, good family pet	bladder stones, bronchitis, Cushing's disease, diabetes, obesity, glaucoma, hyperthyroidism, ectropion, cherry eye, cataracts, heart disease, epilepsy, allergy, disk disease, periodontal disease, hemolytic anemia, demodicosis, PRA
Bearded Collie	45-55 lbs 20-22"	long	high	good with kids, needs lots of exercise, will chase cars and kids, smart but stubborn	PRA, possibly Ivermectin sensitivity
Bedlington Terrier	17-23 lbs 15.5-16.5"	short to medium	low to medium	not good with small kids, moderate exercise, stubborn, may be aggressive to other pets especially small animals, likes to bark and dig	PRA, cataracts, copper poisoning, kidney disease
Belgian Malinois	55-80 lbs 22-26"	short	low	protective and affectionate, highly trainable, likes to chase cars, bikes, joggers	none mentioned
Belgian Sheepdog	55-80 lbs 22-26"	long	high	protective and affectionate, highly trainable, likes to chase cars, bikes, joggers	none mentioned
Belgian Tervuren	55-80 lbs 22-26"	long	high	protective and affectionate, highly trainable, likes to chase cars, bikes, joggers	epilepsy
Bernese Mountain Dog	70-100 lbs 23-27.5"	medium	medium	not good with children, stubborn, aloof with strangers, needs lots of exercise	Entropion, PRA
Bichon Frise	7-12 lbs 9-12"	medium to long	high	good with kids, needs light exercise, an active playful and curious dog, sometimes shy, great family pet	runny eyes, cataracts, otitis, skin disease, obesity, tremors, entropion

600 DOG FACTS

Black & Tan Coonhound	70-90 lbs 23-27"	short	low	not good with kids, needs to run and hunt, best in hunting home	PRA
Bloodhound	80-110 lbs 24-26"	short	low	not good with kids, needs to work, best in hunting home	bloat, cherry eye, entropion
Border Collie	38-52 lbs 17-21"	medium	medium to high	good with older kids, highly intelligent and trainable, suspicious of strangers, likes to chase cars, etc., needs a job	PRA, Collie Eye, Ivermectin sensitivity
Border Terrier	11.5-15.5 lbs 9-11"	short	low	affectionate, enjoys kids, likes to dig, a good family dog	none mentioned
Borzoi	55-105 lbs 26-28"	long	high	not good with kids, needs lots of exercise, docile aloof dog loves to run, needs privacy	allergy, bloat, leg fractures, gastritis
Boston Terrier	15 -25 lbs 11-14"	short	low	likes older kids, needs light exercise, playful intelligent, sensitive but sometimes independent, may be aggressive toward smaller pets, likes to bark and dig, good apartment pet	cataracts, PRA, cherry eye, Cushing's disease, demodicosis, respiratory problems, heatstroke, kneecap slipping, mast cell tumor, whelping difficulty. Periodontal disease, corneal ulcers, epilepsy, hydrocephalus
Bouvier des Flandres	65-95 lbs 23.5-27.5"	long	high	easy-going dog, learns slowly, likes known children, chases cars	laryngeal paralysis, bloat, glaucoma
Boxer	55-70 lbs 21-25"	short	low	likes kids, protective, courageous, intelligent, needs moderate exercise	acne, allergy, cancer, cherry eye, Cushing's disease, demodicosis, hyperthyroidism, hypothyroidism, inflammatory bowel disease, periodontal disease, respiratory problems, heatstroke, heart disease, hip dysplasia, spine problems, mast cell tumors, hemangiosarcoma
Briard	55-90 lbs 22-27"	long	high	reserved with strangers, likes older kids, easily trained, needs lots of exercise, likes to chase cars, etc.	none mentioned
Brittany	30-40 lbs 17.5-20.5"	medium	medium	likes kids, needs lots of exercise, friendly, intelligent, wants to please, good with other dogs, good family dog	Hypothyroidism, PRA
Brussels Griffin	8-12 lbs 9-10"	short to medium	low to medium	affectionate, intelligent but stubborn, reserved with	PRA

(rough & smooth coated)				strangers, slow learner, likes to dig and bark	
Bulldog	40-50 lbs 13-15"	short	low	likes kids, needs moderate exercise, gentle, calm, friendly, great family dog, noisy breather (snores, etc.)	bladder stones, demodicosis, hypothyroidism, obesity, respiratory problems, heatstroke, heart disease, cherry eye, entropion, whelping problems, acne, spine problems, disk disease, corneal ulcers
Bullmastiff	100-130 lbs 24-27"	short	low	docile dog, affectionate protector to family, unpredictable with strangers, snores and drools	Bloat, spine problems
Bull Terrier & Miniature Bull Terrier	40-55 lbs 15-22" or 10-20 lbs 10-14"	short	low	likes older kids, playful, gentle, aggressive toward other pets or small children, stubborn, tend to be slow learners	deafness, allergy, obesity, heart problems, hernia, rage syndrome, zinc-responsive dermatosis, kidney disease, demodicosis, eye problems, laryngeal paralysis
Cairn Terrier	13-14 lbs 9.5-10"	medium	medium	not good with kids, moderate exercise, loyal but jealous, dangerous toward smaller pets, likes to bark and dig	allergy, diabetes, obesity, PRA, kidney disease, glaucoma
Canaan Dog	35-55 lbs 18-25"	short	low	territorial dog reserved with strangers, good watchdog	none mentioned
Cavalier King Charles Spaniel	12-18 lbs 11-12"	long	high	loves children (& everyone!), sweet gentle dog, exceptional family/apartment pet	heart disease, cataracts, eye problems
Chesapeake Bay Retriever	55-80 lbs 21-26"	short	low	not good with kids or other dogs, needs lots of exercise, dominant, stubborn, territorial, needs firm hand, barks a lot, best for hunter	bloat, hip dysplasia, entropion, PRA, cataracts, obesity
Chihuahua (smooth or long-coated)	6 lbs or less 6-9"	short or long	low to medium	not good with kids or other pets, light exercise, loyal but jealous, needs lots of attention, tends to yap	demodicosis, fractures, periodontal disease, heart disease, slipped kneecap, epilepsy, hydrocephalus
Chinese Crested	6-10 lbs 11-13"	none to short	low	older kids okay, playful and devoted dog, slow to learn, good house dog	none mentioned
Chinese Shar-Pei	40-55 lbs 18-20"	short	low	aggressive toward other dogs, pets, and children; one-person dog, unpredictable with strangers, very dominant, can be dangerous	allergy, cherry eye, demodicosis, entropion, inflammatory bowel disease, kidney disease, skin problems, hypothyroidism, megaesophagus
Chow Chow	44-70 lbs 17-20"	long	high	not good with kids, moderate exercise, loyal to	hot spots, hip dysplasia, heatstroke, entropion,

DOG FACTS

				one or two people, dog-aggressive, stubborn, independent, can be dangerous	demodicosis, PRA, kidney disease, glaucoma
Clumber Spaniel	55-85 lbs 17-20"	medium	medium	not good with kids, moderate exercise, suspicious of strangers, possessive, easily scent-distracted	obesity, otitis, disk disease, joint problems, entropion
Cocker Spaniel	26-34 lbs 14-15"	long	high	not good with kids, needs moderate exercise, gentle, playful, happy dog, bright but stubborn, hard to housebreak, can be aggressive and tends to bite, needs a firm hand	hernia, slipped kneecap, otitis, allergy, obesity, entropion, ectropion, cataracts, cherry eye, glaucoma, rage syndrome, hypothyroidism, heart disease, allergy, skin disease, periodontal disease, hemolytic anemia, PRA, kidney disease
Collie (rough and smooth)	50-75 lbs 22-26"	short or long	low or high	likes kids, needs lots of exercise, can be high-strung and stubborn, intelligent, affectionate, eager to please	Collie eye anomaly, demodicosis, deafness, lupus erythematosus complex, PRA, cataracts, Ivermectin sensitivity
Curly-Coated Retriever	55-75 lbs 22-25"	medium	high	tolerate kids, needs lots of exercise, independent, stubborn, loves water, best in hunting home	PRA
Dachshund (standard & miniature, longhaired, smooth, or wirehaired)	16-32 lbs 9" or 16 lbs or less 5-6"	short to medium	low to medium	good with kids, moderate exercise, lively, clever, wants to be center of attention, tends to stubbornness	Bladder stones, alopecia, demodicosis, Cushing's disease, disk disease, diabetes, heart disease, hypothyroidism, obesity, PRA, portosystemic shunt
Dalmatian	45-59 lbs 19-23"	short	low	likes older kids, needs lots of exercise, courageous, loyal, needs firm hand, difficult to train, may tend to snap	allergy, demodicosis, diabetes, laryngeal paralysis, hip dysplasia, deafness, allergy, bladder stones, urethral obstruction, spine problems
Dandies Dinmont Terrier	18-24 lbs 8-11"	medium	medium to high	likes kids, stubborn slow to learn, aggressive toward smaller pets, good house dog	none mentioned
Doberman Pinscher	55-90 lbs 24-28"	short	low	older kids okay, needs lots of exercise, bold and loyal, good watchdog, aggressive and independent, very trainable but needs a firm hand, can be dangerous	acne, arthritis, demodicosis, hypothyroidism, liver disease, copper poisoning, wobbler's syndrome, Von Willebrand's Disease, skin problems, gastritis, immune problems, hemophilia, heart disease, joint disease, obesity, diabetes, PRA, bloat, bone cancer, cataracts, kidney disease

English Cocker Spaniel	26-34 lbs 15-17"	medium to long	high	likes kids, needs moderate exercise, friendly, affectionate, sometimes stubborn, good family dog	PRA, glaucoma, cataracts
English Foxhound	50-65 lbs 23"	short	low	good watchdog, high energy, needs to hunt, older kids okay	none mentioned
English Setter	50-70 lbs 24-25"	medium	high	likes kids, needs lots of exercise, stubborn, easily distracted, like to bark, very active, great family dog	Allergy, PRA
English Springer Spaniel	49-55 lbs 19-20"	medium	medium	not good with kids, need lots of exercise and attention, intelligent, easily bored, may snap and bite when surprised	eye disorders, hip dysplasia, skin disease, otitis, PRA, rage syndrome, hemolytic anemia, progressive neurological disorder (weakness)
English Toy Spaniel	8-14 lbs 9-10"	long	high	good with children, affectionate, easily trained, great house pet	none mentioned
Field Spaniel	35-55 lbs 17-18"	medium	high	likes older kids, needs moderate exercise, smart, easily scent-distracted, timid with strangers	otitis, eye infections, PRA
Finnish Spitz	25-35 lbs 15.5-20"	medium	medium	likes older children, cautious of strangers, good watch dog, likes to bark, hard to train, can be dog-aggressive	none mentioned
Flat-Coated Retriever	60-80 lbs 22-24.5"	medium	high	likes kids, needs lots of exercise, has a Golden personality, easily scent-distracted, great family dog	cataracts
Fox Terrier (smooth & wire)	16-18 lbs 15.5"	short	low	independent, smart and friendly, okay with older kids, dangerous for small pets and kids, hard to train, loves to dig and bark	Cataracts, smooth: progressive neurological disorder (weakness) wire: megaesophagus
French Bulldog	28 lbs or less 10-12"	short	low	loves everybody, happy quiet dog, needs light exercise, ideal apartment dog	breathing problems
German Shepherd Dog	60-85 lbs 22-26"	medium	medium	likes kids, needs lots of exercise, highly trainable but firm handling required, intelligent, loyal, affectionate, likes to chase cars, etc., aloof with strangers and may be dog-aggressive	hip dysplasia, gastritis, skin disease, diabetes, megaesophagus, Von Willebrand's Disease, inflammatory bowel disease, malabsorption syndrome, arthritis, hyperthyroidism, hemangiosarcoma, demodicosis, epilepsy, hyperparathyroidism, pannus, lupus, bloat, bone cancer, PRA, heart disease, spine problems, cataracts, anal gland problems

DOG FACTS

German Shorthaired Pointer	45-70 lbs 21-25"	short	low	tolerates kids and other dogs, needs lots of exercise, intelligent, excitable, stubborn, needs to hunt	hip dysplasia, spine problems
German Wirehaired Pointer	50-70 lbs 22-26"	medium	medium	not good with kids, stubborn, suspicious of strangers, needs firm hand, ignores everything for a scent, needs to hunt	none mentioned
Giant Schnauzer	65-95 lbs 23.5-27.5"	medium	medium to high	not good with children, stubborn, dog-aggressive, highly trainable, loyal and courageous, good watchdog	Bloat, PRA
Golden Retriever	55-75 lbs 21.5-24"	medium	high	likes kids, needs lots of exercise, intelligent, eager to please, loyal, gentle, may be pushy for affection	Allergy, epilepsy, hyperthyroidism, hypothyroidism, obesity, hip dysplasia, PRA, cataracts, entropion, heart problems, diabetes, bloat, bone cancer, portosystemic shunt, Von Willebrand's Disease, hot spots, otitis
Gordon Setter	45-80 lbs 23-27"	medium	high	likes kids, wary of strangers, needs lots of exercise, stubborn, easily bored	Bloat, PRA
Great Dane	100-165 lbs 28-32"	short	low	likes kids, needs lots of exercise (and room!), gentle, calm, affectionate, can be dog-aggressive, can be dangerous	acne, bloat, bone cancer, demodicosis, hypothyroidism, megaesophagus, entropion, hip dysplasia, wobbler's syndrome, tumors
Great Pyrenees	85-100 lbs 25-32"	long	high	confident and gentle with family, protective, suspicious of strangers, hard to train, dog-aggressive; needs to work	bloat, bone cancer
Greater Swiss Mountain Dog	125-130 lbs 25-28"	short	low	not good with children, stubborn, aloof with strangers, needs lots of exercise, can be dangerous	Bloat
Greyhound	60-90 lbs 26-28"	short	low	not good with small kids, needs lots of exercise, gentle, sensitive, can be shy, may be aggressive to small pets	Allergy, periodontal disease, PRA, pannus
Harrier	40-55 lbs 19-21"	short	low	outgoing, likes other dogs, a hunter not a pet	not mentioned
Ibizan Hound	45-50 lbs 22.5-27.5"	short	low	quiet reserved dog, friendly but needs privacy, aggressive to smaller pets	none mentioned

				and children, likes to run, slow learner	
Irish Setter	60-70 lbs 25-27"	long	high	likes kids, needs lots of exercise, energetic, excitable, sometimes clownish, needs firm hand, loyal and pushy-affectionate, easily distracted	allergy, bloat, hypothyroidism, skin disease, hip dysplasia, otitis, PRA, entropion, heart disease, epilepsy, megaesophagus, digestive problems, bone cancer
Irish Terrier	25-27 lbs 17-18"	medium	low to medium	likes kids, good watch dog, likes to bark and dig, stubborn	none mentioned
Irish Water Spaniel	45-65 lbs 21-24"	medium	medium	likes kids, needs lots of exercise, clownish personality, curious, stubborn, suspicious of strangers, dog-aggressive, needs firm hand, needs to work	none mentioned
Irish Wolfhound	105-120 lbs 30-32"	medium	medium	needs to run, suspicious of strangers and dog-aggressive, quiet and gentle affectionate dog to those he knows	bloat, hypothyroidism, portosystemic shunt
Italian Greyhound	7-13 lbs 13-15"	short	low	not good with kids, needs light exercise, calm, sometimes timid, likes privacy	fractures, PRA, epilepsy, periodontal disease
Jack Russell Terrier (smooth and wire)	10-16 lbs 12-15"	short	low	high energy clever dog, likes to bark and dig, very affectionate but stubborn, hard to train	progressive neurological disorder (weakness)
Japanese Chin	4-7 lbs 8-9"	long	high	not good with kids, needs light exercise, playful and bright, resists training, easily spoiled	respiratory problems, heatstroke, eye problems, spine problems, heart disease, periodontal disease
Keeshond	35-42 lbs 17-18"	long	high	likes kids and strangers, intelligent and highly trainable, likes to bark	Epilepsy, hyperparathyroidism, kidney disease, diabetes
Kerry Blue Terrier	33-40 lbs 17.5-19.5"	medium	medium	not good with kids, dog aggressive, stubborn , hard to train, intelligent lovable dog	none mentioned
Komondor	80-120 lbs 23.5" or more	long	medium to high	wary of strangers, good watchdog, highly territorial, best as working dog, not a family pet	Bloat
Kuvasz	70-115 lbs 26-30"	medium	medium	not good with kids, aggressive toward strangers and other dogs, protective guard dog, best as a working dog, not pet	Bloat
Labrador Retriever	55-75 lbs 21.5-24.5"	short	low	likes kids, needs lots of exercise, gentle, intelligent,	hip dysplasia, cataracts, PRA, entropion, obesity, epilepsy, oral cancer, hemophilia, otitis, portosystemic shunt,

				loyal, gregarious, demands attention, great family dog	megaesophagus, spine problems, boat, diabetes
Lakeland Terrier	17 lbs 13-15"	medium	medium	likes older kids, quiet slow to learn dog, aggressive toward smaller pets, likes to dig	none mentioned
Lhasa Apso	13-15 lbs 10-11"	long	high	not good with kids, needs moderate exercise, one or two person dog, playful, easily spoiled, slow to train	allergy, eye problems, kidney problems, periodontal disease, epilepsy
Maltese	4-7 lbs 7-8"	long	high	older children okay, quiet smart dog easily trained, affectionate, good house dog	Spine problems, periodontal disease, slipped kneecaps, heart disease, tremors
Manchester Terrier (& Toy)	12-22 lbs 15-17" or 12 lbs or less 8-13"	short	low	devoted but bossy pet, likes older kids, aggressive toward smaller pets, likes to dig	Slipped kneecaps, periodontal disease, Von Willebrand's disease
Mastiff	170-200 lbs 27.5" or more	short	low	likes kids, needs moderate exercise, independent, can be aggressive, loyal, gentle and good natured with firm handling, can be dangerous	bloat, hip dysplasia, bone cancer
Miniature Pinscher	8-10 lbs 10-12.5"	short	low	not good with kids, needs light exercise, independent, bold, big dog in small package (but not a lap dog!), tends to be dog-aggressive	kidney stones, obesity, periodontal disease
Miniature Schnauzer	13-15 lbs 12-14"	medium	medium	good with older kids, moderate exercise, loyal and playful, sensible, likes to bark and dig	allergy, obesity, bladder stones, hypothyroidism, cataracts, liver disease, heart disease, diabetes, acne, pancreatitis, PRA, kidney disease, Von Willebrand's disease
Newfound-land	100-150 lbs 26-28"	long	high	outstanding child's pet, needs lots of exercise, loyal smart dog easily trained, great family dog	bloat, bone cancer, hypothyroidism
Norfolk Terrier	11-12 lbs 9-12"	med	low	not good with young kids, needs moderate exercise, likes to dig, bark, and chase, affectionate and loyal	allergy
Norwegian Elkhound	48-55 lbs 19.5-20.5"	med	med	likes older kids, intelligent and trainable dog, high energy pet not happy confined indoors	hyperparathyroidism, PRA, kidney disease, glaucoma
Norwich Terrier	12 lbs 10" or less	medium	low	not good with kids, needs moderate exercise, similar to Norfolk Terrier	allergy
Old English Sheepdog	60-90 lbs	long	high	likes kids, needs lots of exercise, lovable, loyal,	

	21" or more			easygoing, adopts kids as "part of flock," likes to chase	allergy, cataracts, deafness, demodicosis, diabetes, spine problems
Otter Hound	65-115 lbs 23-27"	medium	medium	boisterous dog, needs lots of exercise, best when given work to do	none mentioned
Papillon	8-10 lbs 8-11"	long	high	not good with kids, needs light exercise, energetic and playful, highly trainable, protective of owner, likes to bark	Fractures, periodontal disease
Pekingese	14 lbs or less 8-9"	long	high	not good with kids, needs light exercise, stubborn, likes to bark, hard to train, best as pet of single person	Entropion, eye problems, respiratory problems, disk disease, slipped kneecap, hernia, difficult whelping, epilepsy, hydrocephalus
Petit Basset Griffon Vendeen	35-45 lbs 13-15"	medium	medium	happy dog, likes kids, easily scent-distracted and hard to train, can be stubborn, good family pet	none mentioned
Pharaoh Hound	45-60 lbs 21-25"	short	low	affectionate playful dog, loves to run, older kids okay, needs privacy and her own space	none mentioned
Pointer	45-75 lbs 23-28"	short	low	tolerant of kids, needs lots of exercise, lives for scent, high energy, friendly, good with other pets	none mentioned
Pomeranian	3-7 lbs 5-7"	long	high	intelligent, affectionate dog, loves kids, good watchdog, excellent house pet, easily spoiled	Hypothyroidism, slipped kneecap, periodontal disease, epilepsy, hydrocephalus
Poodle (Miniature)	15-35 lbs 10-15"	medium to long	high	likes kids, needs moderate exercise, intelligent and highly trainable, good family dog	bronchitis, diabetes, cataract, Cushing's disease, epilepsy, hypothyroidism, hemolytic anemia, glaucoma, PRA, respiratory problems, portosystemic shunt
Poodle (Standard)	50-65 lbs 15" or more	medium to long	high	loves kids, needs lots of exercise, intelligent and highly trainable, excellent family dog	bloat, cataract, epilepsy, Addison's disease, disk disease, kidney disease, Von Willebrand's disease
Poodle (Toy)	7-12 lbs 10" or less	medium to long	high	not good with young kids, needs moderate exercise, playful, sometimes high-strung, intelligent, easily spoiled and sometimes stubborn, can be yappy	bronchitis, glaucoma, cataracts, dry eye, otitis, allergy, heart disease, epilepsy, slipped kneecap, PRA, collapsed trachea, Cushing's, epilepsy, hypothyroidism, whelping problems
Portuguese Water Dog	35-60 lbs 17-23"	medium to long	high	high-spirited dominant dog needs firm direction, not good with kids, a working dog	none mentioned
Pug	14-18 lbs 9-11"	short	low	good with older kids, needs light exercise, sturdy,	bladder stones, demodicosis, periodontal disease, whelping

DOG FACTS

				clever, affectionate, often a one-person dog, slow to learn, good apartment dog	problems, proptosis of eyeball, respiratory problems, gastritis, encephalitis, eye problems, heart disease, cherry eye, heatstroke, slipped kneecaps
Puli	28-35 lbs 16-17"	long	high	not good with kids, excellent watchdog, bonds with one person, dog-aggressive, likes to bark and chase	none mentioned
Rhodesian Ridgeback	65-75 lbs 24-27"	short	low	likes older children, great protector and guard dog, smart dog that needs firm training	Bloat, spine problems
Rottweiler	85-115 lbs 22-27"	short	low	not good with kids, needs lots of exercise, needs firm handling, intelligent, strong, alert, can be dangerous	hip dysplasia, obesity, entropion, joint problems, inflammatory bowel disease, bloat, spinal cord problems
St. Bernard (long and short coated)	120-170 lbs 25" or more	short or long	low to high	likes kids, needs lots of exercise, easygoing, cheerful, loyal and patient, good family dog, snores and drools	bloat, bone cancer, epilepsy, hip dysplasia, joint problems, entropion, ectropion, spine problems, bone cancer
Saluki	40-60 lbs 23-28"	short	low	affectionate but needs her space, loves to run, slow learner, prefers quiet home without kids or other pets	none mentioned
Samoyed	35-55 lbs 19-23.5"	long	high	likes kids, needs moderate exercise, independent, intelligent, needs firm hand or can get into trouble	hip dysplasia, PRA, glaucoma, skin problems, zinc-responsive dermatosis, cataracts, spine problems, kidney disease, portosystemic shunts
Schipperke	12-18 lbs 10-13"	medium	medium	devoted to owners, reserved with strangers, likes to bark	none mentioned
Scottish Deerhound	75-110 lbs 28-32"	medium	medium	not good with kids, requires lots of running room, a loyal devoted companion, aggressive toward other pets	bloat, bone cancer
Scottish Terrier	18-22 lbs 10"	long	medium	not good with kids, needs moderate exercise, independent, loyal to one person, curmudgeon	allergy, deafness, lymphoma, oral tumors, periodontal disease, obesity
Sealyham Terrier	20-24 lbs 10-11"	medium	high	good watch dog, friendly to family, stubborn	none mentioned
Shetland Sheepdog	14-18 lbs 13-16"	long	high	older kids okay, needs moderate exercise, intelligent, eager to please,	PRA, Collie eye , heart disease, epilepsy, deafness, obesity, hypothyroidism, lupus, pancreatitis, Von

				loyal, may be shy, likes to bark and chase	Willebrand's disease, possible Ivermectin sensitivity
Shiba Inu	13.5-16.5"	short	low	independent and affectionate to family, aggressive with strange people or pets, stubborn to train, good apartment dog	none mentioned
Shih Tzu	9-17 lbs 9-10.5"	long	high	not good with kids, needs light exercise, affectionate, playful, can be stubborn, needs lots of attention, easily spoiled	obesity, respiratory problems, periodontal disease, otitis, kidney disease, eye problems
Siberian Husky	35-60 lbs 20-23.5"	medium	medium	friendly, affectionate, needs lots of exercise, very vocal, stubborn and slow to train	cataract, laryngeal paralysis, lupus, Rocky Mountain spotted fever, zinc-responsive dermatosis, glaucoma, bronchitis
Silky Terrier	1-10 lbs 9-10"	long	high	likes older kids, curious and affectionate, aggressive toward smaller pets, likes to bark and dig	Slipped kneecaps
Skye Terrier	20-25 lbs 9.5-10"	long	high	not good with children, affectionate dog cautious with strangers, slow to learn	Copper poisoning
Soft-Coated Wheaten Terrier	30-40 lbs 17-19"	long	high	sensitive, affectionate dog, needs moderate exercise, intelligent, needs slow training	Kidney disease
Staffordshire Bull Terrier	24-38 lbs 14-16"	short	low	affectionate to those he knows, aggressive toward other animals, dominant dog, can be dangerous	Demodicosis, cataracts
Standard Schnauzer	30-45 lbs 17.5-19.5"	medium	medium to high	likes older kids, great watchdog, good family pet	none mentioned
Sussex Spaniel	35-45 lbs 13-15"	medium	high	not good with kids, needs moderate exercise, reserved with strangers, scent-distracted, stubborn, can be noisy (baying), hard to housebreak, needs job to do	otitis, eye problems
Tibetan Spaniel	9-15 lbs 10"	medium	medium	not good with small kids, affectionate and sweet, but suspicious of strangers, stubborn, good watchdog	PRA
Tibetan Terrier	18-30 lbs 14-17"	long	high	loves kids and other pets, happy, friendly dog, great family dog	none mentioned
Vizsla	45-60 lbs 21-24"	short	low	likes kids, needs lots of exercise, playful, happy, sensitive yet stubborn, easily scent-distracted, timid around strangers, needs to hunt	none mentioned

Weimaraner	45-70 lbs 23-27"	short	low	not good with kids, needs lots of exercise, stubborn, independent, best as hunter	hip dysplasia, allergy, tumors, bloat, spine problems
Welsh Corgi (Cardigan)	25-38 lbs 10.5-12.5"	short	low	not good with kids, needs moderate exercise, intelligent, obedient, playful and friendly, big dog in small package	PRA, bladder stones, glaucoma, disc disease, hip dysplasia, obesity
Welsh Corgi (Pembroke)	25-30 lbs 10-12"	short	low	not good with kids, needs moderate exercise, intelligent, obedient, playful and friendly, big dog in small package	PRA, bladder stones, glaucoma, disc disease, hip dysplasia, obesity, kidney disease, Von Willebrand's disease
Welsh Springer Spaniel	35-45 lbs 17-19"	medium	medium	good with older kids, needs moderate exercise, timid of strangers, easily bored, needs a job	cataracts
Welsh Terrier	20 lbs 15-15.5"	medium	medium	not good with children, friendly, dog-aggressive, likes to dig and bark	none mentioned
West Highland White Terrier	15-22 lbs 10-11"	medium	medium	not good with kids, needs moderate exercise, affectionate, loyal to owner	allergy, copper poisoning, liver disease, hernia, glaucoma, heart disease, tremors, cataracts
Whippet	18-30 lbs 18-22"	short	low	likes kids, needs moderate exercise, bright, affectionate, gentle, likes to run	gastritis
Wirehaired Pointing Griffon	50-65 lbs 20-24"	medium	medium	not good with kids, needs lots of exercise, good watchdog, needs firm training, not a housedog, give him a job	none mentioned
Yorkshire Terrier	7 lbs or less 7-9"	long	high	not good with kids, needs light exercise, intelligent, courageous, affectionate, can be stubborn, likes to bark	eye problems, periodontal disease, slipped kneecap, liver disease, PRA, heart disease, spine problems, pancreatitis, portosystemic shunts

APPENDIX B
RESOURCES

ANIMAL WELFARE & INFORMATION SOURCES

American Humane Association
http://www.americanhumane.org

American Society for the Prevention of Cruelty to Animals
https://www.aspca.org

Humane Society of the United States
http://www.humanesociety.org

National Animal Care and Control Association
http://www.nacanet.org

Pet Partners (formerly Delta Society)
https://petpartners.org/

FURTHER READING

Complete Puppy Care by Amy Shojai

ComPETability: Solving Behavior Problems in Your MultiDOG Household by Amy Shojai

ComPETability: Solving Behavior Problems in Your CAT-DOG Household by Amy Shojai

Complete Care for Your Aging Dog by Amy Shojai

The First-Aid Companion for Dogs and Cats by Amy Shojai

612 DOG FACTS

PET SERVICES

Association of Professional Dog Trainers
http://www.APDT.com

Certification Council for Professional Dog Trainers
http://www.ccpdt.org

International Association of Canine Professionals
http://www.canineprofessionals.com

International Boarding and Pet Services Association
http://www.ibpsa.com

National Association of Professional Pet Sitters
http://www.petsitters.org

National Animal Poison Control Center
https://www.aspca.org/pet-care/animal-poison-control

National Association of Dog Obedience Instructors
http://www.nadoi.org

Pet Sitters International
https://www.petsit.com

Spay USA
http://www.spayusa.org

EXPERT RESOURCES

American Animal Hospital Association
https://www.aaha.org/pet_owner

Animal Behavior Society
http://www.animalbehaviorsociety.org/web/index.php

International Association of Animal Behavior Consultants
http://iaabc.org

American Holistic Veterinary Association
http://www.ahvma.org

American Veterinary Chiropractic Association
http://www.animalchiropractic.org

American Veterinary Medical Association
https://www.avma.org/Pages/home.aspx
The International Veterinary Acupuncture Society
https://www.ivas.org

American Board of Veterinary Practitioners
http://www.abvp.com

American Board of Veterinary Toxicology
http://www.abvt.org

American College of Theriogenologists
http://www.theriogenology.org/

American College of Veterinary Anesthesiologists
http://www.acva.org/

American College of Veterinary Behaviorists
http://www.dacvb.org/

American College of Veterinary Clinical Pharmacology
http://www.acvcp.org

American College of Veterinary Dermatology
http://www.acvd.org

American College of Veterinary Emergency and Critical Care
www.acvecc.org

American College of Veterinary Internal Medicine
http://www.acvim.org

American College of Veterinary Microbiologists
http://www.acvm.us

American College of Veterinary Nutrition
www.acvn.org

American College of Veterinary Ophthalmologists
http://www.acvo.org

American College of Veterinary Pathologists
http://www.acvp.org/

American College of Veterinary Preventive Medicine
http://www.acvpm.org

American College of Veterinary Radiology
http://www.acvr.org

American College of Veterinary Surgeons
http://www.acvs.org

American College of Zoological Medicine
http://www.aczm.org/aczmmain.html

American Veterinary Dental College
http://www.AVDC.org

CANINE RESEARCH ORGANIZATIONS AND FOUNDATIONS

AKC Canine Health Foundation
http://www.akcchf.org

Canine Eye Registration Foundation (CERF)
http://www.offa.org/eyes.html

Morris Animal Foundation
http://www.morrisanimalfoundation.org

Orthopedic Foundation for Animals
http://www.ofa.org
(Orthopedic and genetic diseases)

PennHIP
http://www.pennhip.org
(Hip dysplasia)

Veterinary Medical Databases
https://vmdb.org

APPENDIX C

Symptoms at a Glance: The Quick Reference Guide for Home Diagnosis

The following correlates to an alphabetical list of the common signs and symptoms of illness with the troubling condition(s) that each may indicate. To use the chart, look up one or more of the problem signs your dog may be suffering. Then read the corresponding entry topic to learn more about a given disease or condition. This will help you identify what's troubling your dog and learn whether immediate veterinary care is necessary or a home remedy may suffice.

Whenever possible, the appropriate home treatment or first aid is listed in the text entry so that, if possible, you can tend to your dog yourself. However, this chart is only a guide. No book can ever replace the expertise of a veterinarian, who is in the best position to accurately diagnose and treat any troubling illness from which your dog may be suffering.

SIGNS AND SYMPTOMS	DISEASE OR CONDITION
abortion, still-birth	brucellosis
aggression, toward people/other pets	dominance, fear, hyperthyroidism, rabies, rage syndrome
appetite, increased	Cushing's disease, diabetes mellitus, hyperthyroidism, megaesophagus
appetite, loss of (anorexia)	abscess, Addison's disease, anemia, babesiosis, cancer, canine coronavirus, canine distemper virus, canine influenza, dehydration, diabetes, coccidiosis, copper poisoning, ehrlichiosis, enteritis, blastomycosis (fungus), valley fever (fungus), fever, grape toxicity, hyperparathyroidism, hypoparathyroidism, infectious canine hepatitis, insect bites, kennel cough, kidney disease, lead poisoning, leptospirosis, liver disease, lungworms, mastitis, parvovirus, pain, pancreatitis, periodontal disease, peritonitis, prostatitis, pyometra, rabies, Rocky Mountain spotted fever, salmon poisoning, salmonella, stomatitis, swallowed objects
barking, voice changes	laryngeal paralysis, laryngitis, tick paralysis, tumor, water on the brain

blackheads/pimples, on chin and mouth	acne
bleeding	aspirin toxicity, cancer, ehrlichiosis, hemophilia, infectious canine hepatitis, leptospirosis, poison, trauma, heat stroke, blood disorders, Von Willebrand's disease
blood, coughing up	cancer, heartworms, infectious canine hepatitis, poison, tuberculosis
blood, in bitch's milk	mastitis
blood, in stool	aspirin toxicity, cancer, canine parvovirus, coccidiosis, colitis, copper poisoning, histoplasmosis (fungus), hookworms, infectious canine hepatitis, inflammatory bowel disease, liver disease, poison, Rocky Mountain spotted fever, salmon poisoning, salmonella, threadworms, blood disorder, whipworms, kidney disease
blood, in urine	babesiosis, bladder stones, cancer, copper poisoning, cystitis, ehrlichiosis, infectious canine hepatitis, liver disease, poison, Rocky Mountain spotted fever
blood, in vomit	aspirin toxicity, cancer, canine parvovirus, kidney disease, ulcer, NSAIDs poisoning (Tylenol), other poison
bloody nose	cancer, ehrlichiosis, head trauma, hyperthermia, infectious canine hepatitis, poison, Rocky Mountain spotted fever, hemophilia, Von Willebrand's disease
blindness	cataract, epilepsy, glaucoma, poison, progressive retinal atrophy, proptosis of eyeball, PRA, diabetes, liver disease, water on the brain
breathing, choking/gagging	cancer, anaphylaxis, bloat, insect bites, poison, swallowed/inhaled objects, tuberculosis
breathing, gasping, wheezing	anaphylaxis, asthma, collapsed trachea, heartworms, insect bites, laryngeal paralysis, laryngitis, pneumonia, poison, tetanus, heart disease, kennel cough
breathing, labored	anaphylaxis, anemia, asthma, bloat, cancer, canine distemper virus, canine influenza, collapsed trachea, electrical shock, blastomycosis (fungus), heart disease, heartworms, hernia, insect bites, internal bleeding, trauma, lungworms, pneumonia, poison, Rocky Mountain spotted fever, tuberculosis, vaccine or drug reaction
breathing, excessive panting	antifreeze poisoning, asthma, bloat, hyperthermia, hypoparathyroidism, laryngeal paralysis, pain, poison, snake bite
breathing, rapid	anemia, bloat, eclampsia, electrical shock, pneumonia, poison, shock, snake bite
breathing, shallow	bloat, electrical shock, hernia, pain

breathing, stopped	anaphylaxis, drowning, electrical shock, hypothermia, poison, tick paralysis, trauma
bruising	hematoma, hemophilia, poisoning
bumps	abscess, atopy, insect bite, cancer, cuterebra, cyst, warts, papillomatosis, vaccination reaction
chewing, of coat or skin	allergy, canine scabies, insect bite, lice
chewing, grinding teeth	babesiosis, canine distemper virus, epilepsy, lead poisoning, poison, rabies
choking/gagging	bloat, collapsed trachea, flukes, swallowed objects
circling	bloat, Cushing's disease, cryptococcosis (fungus), head trauma, otitis
coat condition, dry	giardiasis, malabsorption syndrome, roundworms, tapeworms, whipworms
coat condition, oily	malabsorption syndrome, seborrhea
coat condition, ricelike debris	tapeworms
coat condition, dandruff	seborrhea, cheyletiellosis
collapse	Addison's disease, anaphylaxis, antifreeze poisoning, babesiosis, bloat, cancer, eclampsia, epilepsy, parvovirus, disk disease, heart disease, heartworms, insect bites, poison, snake bite, xylitol poisoning, water on the brain
constipation	bloat, cancer, lead poisoning, diabetes, kidney disease, swallowed objects
coughing	bronchitis, canine influenza, collapsed trachea, flukes, blastomycosis (fungus), valley fever (fungus), histoplasmosis (fungus), heart disease, heartworms, kennel cough, laryngeal paralysis, laryngitis, lungworms, pneumonia, Rocky Mountain spotted fever, threadworms, tuberculosis
crying, whining, yelping	bladder stones, bloat, car sickness, disk disease, dominance display, fear, fractures, hip dysplasia, pain, insect sting, water on the brain
depression	anemia, canine coronavirus, dehydration, ehrlichiosis, fever, histoplasmosis (fungus), hemophilia, kidney disease, lead poisoning, peritonitis, rabies, salmon poisoning, salmonella, shock, snake bite, stress, Addison's disease, canine parvovirus, abscess, pneumonia, pyometra,

	cancer, hypothyroidism, liver disease, prostatitis
defecation, strained or unproductive	colitis, constipation, inflammatory bowel disease, prostatitis, swallowed object
defecation, large volume	malabsorption syndrome
diarrhea	Addison's disease, changing diet, food allergy, antifreeze poisoning, canine coronavirus, canine distemper virus , canine herpesvirus, canine parvovirus, chocolate poisoning, coccidiosis, colitis, copper poisoning, enteritis, feeding milk, flukes, food allergy, grape/raison toxicity, histoplasmosis (fungus), giardiasis, hookworms, hyperthermia, infectious canine hepatitis, inflammatory bowel disease, lead poisoning, leptospirosis, liver disease, pancreatitis, poison, Rocky Mountain spotted fever, roundworms, salmon poisoning, salmonella, snake bite, swallowed objects, threadworms, whipworms
discharge, from penis	balanoposthitis, candidiasis (fungus), cystitis, prostatitis
discharge, from vagina	candidiasis (fungus), cystitis, imminent birth, pyometra
drinking, difficulty or refusal	cancer, rabies, oral burns, foreign object in mouth, canine parvovirus, tetanus
drinking, increased thirst	antifreeze poisoning, chocolate poisoning, Cushing's disease, diabetes mellitus, hyperparathyroidism, hyperthyroidism, infectious canine hepatitis, kidney disease, leptospirosis, pyometra
drooling	car sickness, chocolate poisoning, eclampsia, foreign body, hyperthermia, insect bites, pain, periodontal disease, poison, rabies, snake bite, toad poisoning, insecticide toxicity, oral burns, stomatitis
drunk, incoordination	antifreeze poisoning, babesiosis, canine distemper virus, carbon monoxide poisoning, Cushing's disease, disk disease, eclampsia, epilepsy, head trauma, hypoparathyroidism, insect bites, otitis, poison, tick paralysis, xylitol poisoning
ears, dark crumbly debris	ear mites, insect bites
ears, discharge and/or odor	otitis
ears, red or raw	allergy, otitis
eyes, change of color	uveitis, corneal ulcer, infectious canine hepatitis
eyes, crossed	water on the brain
eyes, cloudy	cataract, glaucoma, infectious canine hepatitis, keratitis, uveitis

eyes, dilated/nonresponsive pupil	glaucoma
eyes, discharge/runny	canine distemper virus, canine influenza, cherry eye, dry eye, ectropion/entropion, ehrlichiosis, glaucoma, infectious canine hepatitis, Rocky Mountain spotted fever, salmon poisoning, uveitis, ulcer
eyes, glazed/staring	epilepsy, hyperthermia, rabies
eyes, hard	glaucoma, tumor
eyes, out of socket	proptosis of eyeball
eyes, pawing at	cherry eye, dry eye, glaucoma, pain, uveitis, foreign object, ulcer
eyes, rough surface	uveitis
eyes, soft	uveitis
eyes, sores/ulcers	dry eye, ectropion/entropion, keratitis
eyes, squinting	dry eye, ectropion/entropion, glaucoma, infectious canine hepatitis, keratitis, leptospirosis, otitis, pain, ulcer, uveitis, allergies
eyes, swelling	cherry eye, glaucoma, allergic, tumor
eyes, sunken	dehydration
face rubbing	inhalant allergy, hypoparathyroidism, porcupine quills, insect sting, periodontal disease
fading puppies	brucellosis, canine herpesvirus, hypoglycemia
fainting, esp. during exercise	anemia, asthma, bloat, histoplasmosis (fungus), heart disease
flinching	arthritis, disk disease, fear, fractures, hip dysplasia, pain
footpads, thickened/cracked/bleeding/swollen	canine distemper virus, canine demodicosis, hookworms, lupus erythematosus complex, threadworms, zinc-responsive dermatosis
growling, snarling	aggression, dominance, epilepsy, fear, pain, stress
hair loss	allergy, fleas, Cushing's disease, hot spots, hypothyroidism, mange, ringworm, seborrhea, shedding, stress, sun burn, zinc-responsive dermatosis
head tilt	disk disease, cryptococcosis (fungus), head trauma, otitis,

	tumor
hiding	fear, pain, stress, rabies
hunching (painful abdomen/back)	bloat, botulism, brucellosis, cystitis, disk disease, grape/raisin toxicity, infectious canine hepatitis, kidney disease, lead poisoning, leptospirosis, pancreatitis, peritonitis, poison, prostatitis, Rocky Mountain spotted fever, salmonella, swallowed object, trauma, bladder stones/obstruction
hyperactivity, agitation	chocolate poisoning, hyperthyroidism, lead poisoning, other poison, snake bite, insecticide poisoning
itching, all over	flea allergy, food allergy, mange, insect sting, vaccination reaction
itching, of back and tail	fleas
itching, of chest, armpits and feet	inhalant allergy
itching, of chin and face	inhalant allergy, demodicosis
itching, of ears	ear mites, otitis, sun burn, ticks, fly bites
itching, localized	demodicosis, hot spots, insect bites, sun burn
itching, self-mutilation	canine scabies, demodicosis, hot spots, lick dermatitis, obsessive/compulsive disorders
mouth, blue-tinged tongue/gums	asthma, heart disease, pneumonia, respiratory distress, poison
mouth, bright red gums	carbon monoxide poisoning, gingivitis, hyperthermia, leptospirosis, poison, stomatitis
mouth, brown tongue	kidney disease, leptospirosis
mouth, burns	caustic poisons, electrical shock
mouth, difficulty chewing/swallowing	botulism, burns, insect bites, porcupine quills, poison, rabies, tick paralysis, cancer, tetanus, foreign body
mouth, dry/tacky gums	dehydration, kidney disease
mouth, jaw paralysis	abscess, fracture, rabies, tetanus
mouth, loose/broken teeth	gingivitis, periodontal disease, trauma
mouth, pale	anemia, canine coronavirus, coccidiosis, dehydration, eclampsia, fleas, hookworms, hemophilia, shock, trauma, canine parvovirus, hemangiosarcoma
mouth, pawing at	caustic poison, periodontal disease, porcupine quills, swallowed objects, abscess, cancer

mouth, sores/ulcers	kidney disease, poison (caustic)
mouth, stringy saliva	dehydration
mouth, swollen/bleeding	gingivitis, insect bites, periodontal disease, salivary mucoceles, trauma, snake bite
mouth, yellow/brown tooth debris	periodontal disease
odor, anal area	anal glands, flatulence, poor grooming
odor, ammonia breath	kidney disease, dehydration
odor, ammonia urine	bladder stones, cystitis
odor, bad breath	cancer, periodontal disease
odor, of body	cancer, demodicosis, skunk, abscess, dermatitis
odor, from ears	otitis, cancer
odor, mousy	acanthosis nigrans, demodicosis, seborrhea
lethargy or listlessness	anemia, fever, dehydration, grape/raisin toxicity, shock, hypoglycemia
licking, anal region	anal gland problem, constipation, swallowed object
licking, coat or skin	abscess, allergy, fleas, hookworms, insect bites, lice, lick sores, mange
licking, feet	inhalant allergy
licking, genitals	balanoposthitis, bladder stones, brucellosis, estrus, pyometra, trauma, cystitis, labor, mating
limping, lameness	arthritis, demodicosis, cancer, ehrlichiosis, fractures, valley fever (fungus), hemophilia, hip dysplasia, slipping kneecap, Lyme disease, Rocky Mountain spotted fever
loss of consciousness	asthma, antifreeze poisoning, asthma, carbon monoxide poisoning, chocolate poisoning, drowning, electrical shock, hyperthermia, hypothermia, shock, snake bite, trauma, heart disease, dehydration, hypoglycemia
lumps	abscess, allergy, cancer, cuterebra, vaccination reaction
milk, yellow/blood streaked	mastitis
muscle tremors, twitches	chocolate poisoning, dehydration, eclampsia, ehrlichiosis, hyperthermia, hypoparathyroidism, poison, tetanus, insecticide toxicity, epilepsy, brain tumor

nose, bloody	cancer, ehrlichiosis, infectious canine hepatitis, poison, Rocky Mountain spotted fever, shock, trauma, Von Willebrand's disease, hemophilia
nose, discharge/runny	canine distemper virus, canine herpesvirus, canine influenza, ehrlichiosis, infectious canine hepatitis, kennel cough, rhinitis, sinusitis, foreign object, cancer
nose, eroding	lupus erythematosus complex
pacing	bloat, car sickness, Cushing's disease, eclampsia, poison, pain, fear, chocolate toxicity
paddling, with feet	dreaming, seizure (epilepsy), xylitol poisoning
pale: ears, nose toes, tail tip, scrotum	pale: ears, nose toes, tail tip, scrotum
pale: lips, tongue, gums	anemia, babesiosis, eclampsia, electrical shock, fleas, histoplasmosis (fungus), hemophilia, hookworms, poison, shock, snake bite, trauma
paralysis	botulism, disc disease, cancer, trauma, tick paralysis
pulse, too fast	anemia, hyperthermia, shock, heart disease, hyperthyroidism, dehydration
pulse, too slow	hypothermia, poison, heart disease, Addison's disease, dehydration
rolling	submission display, pain, play, poison, head trauma, otitis
salivation	anaphylaxis, car sickness, insect bites, poison, chocolate poisoning, eclampsia, foreign body, hyperthermia, insect bites, pain, periodontal disease, rabies, snake bite, toad poisoning
scooting (on bottom)	allergies, anal gland problems, tapeworms
seizures	antifreeze poisoning, brain tumor, canine distemper virus, canine parvovirus, chocolate poisoning, Cushing's disease, grape/raisin toxicity, electrical shock, epilepsy, low blood sugar, cryptococcosis (fungus), hypoparathyroidism, kidney disease, lead poisoning, liver disease, poison, snake bite, toad poisoning, head trauma
shivering	car sickness, disk disease, electrical shock, fear, fractures, hypothermia, pain, poison, shock, snake bite, eclampsia, insecticide toxicity
skin, blisters/charred	caustic poison, frostbite, sun burn
skin, black (or color change)	chronic dermatitis, acanthosis nigrans, lupus erythematosus complex, mange

skin, greasy	acanthosis nigrans, seborrhea
skin, lumpy/bumpy	cancer, insect bites, vaccination reaction, papillomatosis (warts)
skin, moist sores	candidiasis (fungus), frostbite, hot spots, seborrhea, sun burn
skin, painful	abscess, burns, frostbite, ulcers
skin, pepperlike debris esp. at tail root	fleas
skin, red and peeling	burns, frostbite, lupus erythematosus complex, sun burn
skin, sores/ulcers	burns, candidiasis (fungus), valley fever (fungus), lick sores, lupus erythematosus complex, mange, sun burn, tumor
skin, scabby/crusty	fleas, lice, mange, ringworm, sun burn
skin, scaly/dandruff	lice, mange, seborrhea, zinc-responsive dermatosis
skin, swelling	abscess, anal glands, balanoposthitis, burns, cancer, frostbite, hypothyroidism, tumor
skin, thickened	acanthosis nigrans, canine scabies, hypothyroidism, sunburn, chronic dermatitis
skin, waxy debris	seborrhea
skin, yellow tinge (jaundice)	babesiosis, copper poisoning, leptospirosis, liver disease, hemolytic anemia
sleeping too much	anemia, carbon monoxide poisoning, disk disease, obesity, fever, hypothyroidism, hypoglycemia, pain, stress, water on the brain
sneezing	rhinitis, sinusitis, foreign body, abscessed tooth, lungworms
sores, draining	abscess, anal glands, cancer, cysts, ulcers
sores, slow healing	abscess, cancer, ulcer, lick granuloma
stiffness, of joints	arthritis, cancer, disk disease, fractures, hip dysplasia, Lyme disease
stiffness, paralysis	botulism, disk disease, fractures, cryptococcosis (fungus), poison, snake bite, tick paralysis, tetanus
stiffness, odd gait	

	arthritis, cancer, disk disease, eclampsia, hip dysplasia, poison, tetanus
sterility, loss of libido	brucellosis, prostatitis
swelling, of abdomen (no pain)	copper poisoning, Cushing's disease, heart disease, heartworms, obesity, pregnancy, roundworms
swelling, of abdomen (painful)	bloat, cancer, canine herpesvirus, infectious canine hepatitis, constipation, liver disease, peritonitis, pyometra, swallowed objects, pancreatitis, hemangiosarcoma, urethral obstruction
swelling, of breast	cancer, false pregnancy, mastitis, pregnancy
swelling, of ear flap	hematoma
swelling, of ear tips, nose tail, toes	frostbite
swelling, of face/head	abscess, anaphylaxis, hypothyroidism, infectious canine hepatitis, insect bites, Rocky Mountain spotted fever, salivary mucoceles, snake bite, water on the brain
swelling, of joints	arthritis, ehrlichiosis, Lyme's disease
swelling, of legs	ehrlichiosis, heart disease, heartworms, Rocky Mountain spotted fever, liver disease, cancer
swelling, of lymph nodes	brucellosis, plague, tuberculosis, cancer
swelling, of penis	balanoposthitis, foreign object
swelling, of scrotum	brucellosis, post-neutering
swelling, of skin	abscess, cancer, cuterebra, fracture, hernia, insect bites, hematoma, trauma
temperature, too cold	anemia, dehydration, hypothermia, hypothyroidism, kidney disease, salmon poisoning, shock, snake bite
temperature, fever	abscess, babesiosis, canine coronavirus, eclampsia, ehrlichiosis, valley fever (fungus), histoplasmosis (fungus), heat stroke, canine parvovirus, canine distemper virus, prostatitis, pyometra, seizures, infectious canine hepatitis, leptospirosis, Lyme disease, mastitis, metritis, pancreatitis, peritonitis, plague, pneumonia, Rocky Mountain spotted fever, salmonella, tick paralysis, tuberculosis
urination, blocked	bladder stones, cancer, grape/raisin toxicity
urination, excessive	antifreeze poisoning, chocolate poisoning, Cushing's disease, diabetes mellitus, hyperparathyroidism, hyperthyroidism, kidney disease, leptospirosis, pyometra

urination, frequent/small amounts	bladder stones, cystitis
urination, in odd places	bladder stones, cystitis, diabetes mellitus, kidney disease
urination, straining, splattery stream	bladder stones, cystitis, cancer
urination, with blood	bladder stones, cancer, cystitis, poison, hemophilia, prostatitis, hemolytic anemia, Von Willebrand's disease
vomiting	Addison's disease, eclampsia, kidney disease, inner ear infection, food allergy, anaphylaxis, antifreeze poisoning, botulism, canine coronavirus, canine parvovirus, carbon monoxide poisoning, car sickness, chocolate poisoning, copper poisoning, grape/raisin toxicity, enteritis, hookworms, hyperparathyroidism, hyperthermia, NSAIDs poisoning (Tylenol), insect bites, lead poisoning, leptospirosis, liver disease, megaesophagus, overeating, pancreatitis, other poison, Rocky Mountain spotted fever, salmon poisoning, salmonella, snake bite, swallowed objects, tick paralysis, whipworms
vomiting, unproductive (or prolonged)	bloat, poison
weakness	Addison's disease, anemia, aspirin toxicity, babesiosis, botulism, cancer, canine distemper virus, heart disease, hemophilia, hookworms, hyperthermia, hypoparathyroidism, kidney disease, poison, shock, snake bite, tick paralysis, liver disease, insulin reaction, hypoglycemia, disk disease
weight, unable to maintain	cancer, giardiasis, malabsorption syndrome, megaesophagus, poor nutrition
weight gain	diabetes mellitus, hypothyroidism, obesity
weight loss	anemia, aspirin toxicity, babesiosis, brucellosis, cancer, coccidiosis, copper poisoning, diabetes mellitus, ehrlichiosis, blastomycosis (fungus), valley fever (fungus), histoplasmosis (fungus), heartworms, hookworms, hyperthyroidism, NSAIDs poisoning (Tylenol), kidney disease, liver disease, lungworms, malabsorption syndrome, megaesophagus, malnutrition, pancreatitis, salmon poisoning, tuberculosis, whip worms, heart disease, pain, arthritis, diarrhea, anorexia, roundworms

A

B

C

D

E

F

G

H

I

J

K

L

M

Q

R

S

T

U

V

W

X

Y

Z

ABOUT THE AUTHOR

Amy Shojai is a certified animal behavior consultant, and the award-winning author of more than 30 bestselling pet books that cover furry babies to old fogies, first aid to natural healing, and behavior/training to Chicken Soup-icity. She has been featured as an expert in hundreds of print venues including The Wall Street Journal, The New York Times, Reader's Digest, and Family Circle, as well as television networks such as CNN, and Animal Planet's DOGS 101 and CATS 101. Amy brings her unique pet-centric viewpoint to public appearances. She is also a playwright and co-author of STRAYS, THE MUSICAL and the author of the critically acclaimed September Day pet-centric Suspense Series.

642
DOG FACTS

CPSIA information can be obtained
at www.ICGtesting.com
Printed in the USA
LVHW060936180319
611003LV00021B/554/P

9 781944 423865